NOMMO

NOMMO

An Anthology
of Modern
Black African
and
Black American
Literature

EDITED BY

William H. Robinson
DIRECTOR OF BLACK STUDIES
RHODE ISLAND COLLEGE

The Macmillan Company, New York

The Macmillan Company
866 Third Avenue, New York, New York 10022

Collier-Macmillan Canada, Ltd., Toronto, Ontario

Library of Congress catalog card number: 76-129752

First Printing

ACKNOWLEDGMENTS

Appreciation is expressed to the authors and publishers of the following for permission to reprint from their publications.

"White Power" by Julius Lester. Reprinted from *Look Out, Whitey! Black Power's Gon' Get Your Mama* by Julius Lester. Copyright © 1968 by Julius Lester and used by permission of the publisher, The Dial Press.

"The Coming of the Hoodlum" by Johnny Scott. Reprinted by permission of The World Publishing Company from *From the Ashes: Voices from Watts* edited by Budd Schulberg. An NAL book. Copyright © 1967 by New American Library, Inc.

"Die, Nigger, Die" by H. Rap Brown. Reprinted from *Die, Nigger, Die* by H. Rap Brown. Copyright © 1969 by Lynne Brown and used by permission of the publisher, The Dial Press.

"Blame Me on History" by Bloke Modisane. From the book *Blame Me on History* by Bloke Modisane. Copyright © 1963 by Thames and Hudson. Reprinted by permission of E. P. Dutton & Co., Inc. and Thames and Hudson Ltd.

"Road to Ghana" by Alfred Hutchinson. Copyright © 1960 by Alfred Hutchinson. Reprinted from *Road to Ghana* by Alfred Hutchinson by permission of The John Day Company, Inc., publisher, and Victor Gollancz Ltd.

"America, Their America" by John Pepper Clark. Reprinted from *America, Their America* by John Pepper Clark. Copyright © 1964 by Andre Deutsch Ltd.

"An Act of Prostitution" by James Alan McPherson. Copyright © 1968, 1969 by James Alan McPherson. From *Hue and Cry* by James Alan McPherson, by permission of Atlantic-Little, Brown and Co.

iv

"The Urchin" by Can Themba. Copyright 1967. Reprinted by permission of the estate of Can Themba.

"Rain" by Richard Rive. Copyright © 1964. Reprinted by permission of Richard Rive.

From *The Flagellants* by Carlene Hatcher Polite. Reprinted with the permission of Farrar, Strauss & Giroux, Inc. from *The Flagellants* by Carlene Hatcher Polite, copyright © 1967 by Carlene Polite.

From *Pimp: Story of My Life* by Iceberg Slim. Copyright © 1967 by Holloway House Publishing Company.

"Howard Street" by Nathan C. Heard. Reprinted from *Howard Street* by Nathan C. Heard. Copyright © 1968 by Nathan C. Heard and used by permission of the publisher, The Dial Press.

"Boy!" by Ferdinand Oyono. Reprinted with permission of The Macmillan Company and Heinemann Educational Books Ltd. from *Houseboy* by Ferdinand Oyono. © by Rene Julliard, 1960. Copyright © by The Macmillan Company, 1970.

"No Bride Price" by David Rubadiri. Copyright © 1967 by David Rubadiri. Reprinted by permission of East African Publishing House Ltd.

"The Electronic Nigger" by Ed Bullins. From *Five Plays by Ed Bullins*, copyright © 1968, by Ed Bullins, reprinted by permission of the publisher, The Bobbs-Merrill Company, Inc.

"Madheart" by LeRoi Jones. From *Four Black Revolutionary Plays*, copyright © 1969, by LeRoi Jones, reprinted by permission of the publisher, The Bobbs-Merrill Company, Inc.

"The Rhythm of Violence" by Lewis Nkosi. Reprinted by permission of Lewis Nkosi, c/o International Famous Agency. Copyright © 1964, The Oxford University Press.

From *Libretto for the Republic of Liberia* by Melvin B. Tolson. Copyright © 1953 by Melvin B. Tolson. Reprinted by permission of Twayne Publishers, Inc.

"Who but the Lord," "Still Here," and "Harlem" by Langston Hughes. Copyright 1948 by Alfred A. Knopf, Inc. Reprinted from *The Panther and the Lash*, by Langston Hughes, by permission of the publisher.

"Prime," "The Backlash Blues," "Final Call," and "Little Song on Housing" by Langston Hughes. From *The Panther and the Lash*, by Langston Hughes. Copyright © 1967 by Arna Bontemps and George Houston Bass. Reprinted by permission of Alfred A. Knopf, Inc.

"A Ballad of Remembrance," "Incense of the Lucky Virgin," "Summertime and the Living . . . ," and "Runagate, Runagate" by Robert Hayden. From *Selected Poems*. Copyright © 1966 by Robert Hayden. Reprinted by permission of October House Inc.

From *Selected Poems* by Gwendolyn Brooks.
"Negro Hero," Copyright 1945 by Gwendolyn Brooks Blakely.
"Beverly Hills, Chicago," Copyright 1945 by Gwendolyn Brooks Blakely.
"Truth," Copyright 1949 by Gwendolyn Brooks Blakely.
"The Bean Eaters," Copyright © 1959 by Gwendolyn Brooks.
"The Ballad of Rudolph Reed," Copyright © 1960 by Gwendolyn Brooks Blakely.
"We Real Cool," Copyright © 1959 by Gwendolyn Brooks.
From *In the Mecca* by Gwendolyn Brooks.
"Boy Breaking Glass," Copyright © 1967 by Gwendolyn Brooks Blakely.
Reprinted by permission of Harper & Row, Publishers, Inc.

From *Ivory Tusks* by Samuel Allen: "View from the Corner," "In My Father's House," "A Moment Please," "That's Mighty Fine," and "My Friend." Copyright © 1952 by Samuel Allen. Reprinted by permission of Samuel Allen.

From *Spirits Unchained* by Keorapetse Kgositsile: "To Fanon," "Lumumba Section," "Spirits Unchained," "Brother Malcolm's Echo," and "Mandela's Sermon." Copyright © 1969 by Keorapetse Kgositsile. Reprinted by permission of Broadside Press.

From *Song of Lawino* by Okot p'Bitek. Copyright © 1966 by East African Publishing House. Reprinted by permission of East African Publishing House Ltd.

From *Coups de Pilon* by David Diop. "Listen Comrades" (*Ecoutez camarades*),

"The Renegade" (*Le renegat*), "Africa" (*Afrique*), and "Nigger Tramp" (*Negre clochard*) appear in David Diop's *Coup de Pilon* published in *Presence Africaine*, Paris (1956).

"An Interview with an Architect of Negritude: Césaire" by Ellen Conroy Kennedy. Copyright May, 1968 by *Negro Digest*. Reprinted by permission.

From *Cahier d'un retour au pays natal* by Aimé Césaire. This extract is taken from Aimé Césaire's *Return to My Native Land* (translated by Emile Snyder) published by *Présence Africaine*, Paris (1968).

"A Conversation with Léopold Senghor" by Dr. Rosey E. Pool. Copyright May, 1967 by *Negro Digest*. Reprinted by permission.

"The Defense and Illustration of Negritude" by Léopold Senghor. Reprinted by permission of Léopold Sédar Senghor.

From *Selected Poems* by Léopold Sédar Senghor: "Black Woman," "Ndéssé or Blues," "Spring Song," and "New York." Translated and introduced by John Reed and Clive Wake and published by Oxford University Press. Copyright © Oxford University Press 1964. Reprinted by permission of Atheneum Publishers and Oxford University Press.

"Statement" by LeRoi Jones. Copyright © 1967 by LeRoi Jones. Reprinted from *Journal of Black Poetry*, No. 4, 1967. Used with permission of the author and Ronald Hobbs Literary Agency.

"A Black Criterion" by Clarence Major. Copyright © 1967 by Clarence Major. Reprinted by permission.

"Roots" by Ezekiel Mphahlele. Copyright 1962 by Frederick A. Praeger, Inc. Reprinted by permission of Frederick A. Praeger, Inc. and Faber and Faber Ltd. from *The African Image*.

Excerpt from *The Wretched of the Earth* by Frantz Fanon. Translated from the French by Constance Farrington. Reprinted by permission of Grove Press, Inc. Copyright © 1963 by *Présence Africaine*.

Excerpts from *White Man, Listen!* by Richard Wright. Copyright © 1957 by Richard Wright. Reprinted by permission of Doubleday & Company, Inc.

From *A Man of the People* by Chinua Achebe. Copyright © 1966 by Chinua Achebe. Reprinted from *A Man of the People* by Chinua Achebe by permission of The John Day Company, Inc., publisher, and David Higham Associates, Ltd.

From *The Second Round* by Lenrie Peters. Copyright 1965 by Lenrie Peters. Reprinted by permission of Heinemann Educational Books Ltd.

From *The Beautyful* (*sic*) *Ones Are Not Yet Born* by Ayi Kwei Armah. Copyright © 1968 by Ayi Kwei Armah. Reprinted by permission of the publisher, Houghton Mifflin Company, and Heinemann Educational Books Ltd.

From *The River Between* by James Ngugi. Copyright 1965 by James Ngugi. Reprinted by permission of Heinemann Educational Books Ltd.,

From *Jagua Nana* by Cyprian Ekwensi. Reprinted by permission of Harold Ober Associates Incorporated and David Higham Associates Ltd. Copyright © 1961 by Cyprian Ekwensi. Published by Fawcett Publications, Inc.

From *The Dark Child* by Camara Laye. Reprinted with the permission of Farrar, Strauss & Giroux, Inc. from *The Dark Child* by Camara Laye, copyright 1954 by Camara Laye.

"The Strong Breed" from *The Lion and the Jewel* by Wole Soyinka, published by the Oxford University Press. Copyright 1964 by Wole Soyinka.

From *The Song of a Goat* by John Pepper Clark. Reprinted from *Three Plays* (London: Oxford University Press, 1964), by permission of John Pepper Clark.

"Piano and Drums," and "You Laughed and Laughed and Laughed" by Gabriel Okara. From *Poems from Black Africa*, edited by Langston Hughes. Copyright © 1963 by Langston Hughes. Reprinted by permission of Indiana University Press.

"The Meaning of Africa" by Abioseh Nicol. From *Poems from Black Africa*, edited by Langston Hughes. Copyright © 1963 by Langston Hughes. Reprinted by permission of Indiana University Press.

"The Myth of Non-Violence Versus the Right of Self-Defense" from *Black Man's*

Burden by John Oliver Killens. Copyright © 1965 by John Oliver Killens. Reprinted by permission of Trident Press, division of Simon & Schuster, Inc.

From *Soul on Ice* by Eldridge Cleaver. Copyright © 1968 by Eldridge Cleaver. Used with permission of McGraw-Hill Book Company.

From *The Crisis of the Negro Intellectual* by Harold Cruse. Reprinted by permission of William Morrow and Company, Inc. Coypright © 1967 by Harold Cruse.

"A New Day" by Charles Wright from *The Best Stories by Negro Writers*. Reprinted by permission of Robert Lantz-Candida Donadio Literary Agency, Inc. Copyright © 1967 by Little, Brown and Company, Inc.

"Sinner Man, Where You Gonna Run To?" by Larry Neal. From *Black Fire*, edited by LeRoi Jones and Larry Neal, William Morrow & Co., Inc., New York, N.Y. Copyright © 1968 by LeRoi Jones and Larry Neal. Used with permission of Mr. Neal and Ronald Hobbs Literary Agency.

"Song of Genesis" from *The Nigger Bible* by Robert deCoy. Copyright © 1967 by Holloway House Publishing Company.

From *Free-Lance Pallbearers* by Ishmael Reed. Copyright © 1967 by the author. Reprinted by permission of Doubleday & Company, Inc.

"The Job" by Ben Caldwell. First published in *The Drama Review*, Volume 12, Number 4 (T40), Summer, 1968. Copyright © 1968, *The Drama Review*. Reprinted by permission. All rights reserved.

"The Monster" by Ron Milner. First published in *The Drama Review*, Volume 12, Number 4 (T40), Summer, 1968. © 1968 by *The Drama Review*. Reprinted by permission. All rights reserved.

"Poem for Black Hearts," "Black Art," "W.W.," "The World Is Full of Remarkable Things," and "Black People: This Is Our Destiny" from *Black Magic Poetry 1961–1967*, copyright © 1969, by LeRoi Jones, reprinted by permission of the publisher, The Bobbs-Merrill Company, Inc.

"The New Integrationist," "In the Interest of Black Salvation," "The Wall," "The Traitor," and "No More Marching" from *Black Pride* by Don L. Lee. Copyright 1967 by Don L. Lee. Reprinted by permission of Broadside Press.

"Blackwoman," "A Message All Black People Can Dig," and "A Poem for Negro Intellectuals" from *Don't Cry, Scream* by Don L. Lee. Copyright 1969 by Don L. Lee. Reprinted by permission of Broadside Press.

"At That Moment," "What We Know," from *26 Ways of Looking at a Black Man* by Raymond Patterson. Copyright 1968 by Raymond Patterson. "#1, 3, 19, 23, 31, 37, 40, 85" from *Riot Rimes, U.S.A.* by Raymond Patterson. Copyright 1969 by Raymond Patterson. Universal Publishing and Distributing Corporation.

"nigger" and "to blk/record/buyers" from *Homecoming* by Sonia Sanchez. Reprinted by permission of Broadside Press. Copyright © 1969 by Sonia Sanchez.

"Written for Love of an Ascension—Coltrane" from *Paper Soul* by Carolyn M. Rodgers. Copyright 1968 by Carolyn M. Rodgers. Reprinted by permission of Carolyn Rodgers.

"White" and "Welfare" from *Now See Here, Homes* by Horace Mungin. Copyright 1969 by Horace Mungin, Brothers Distributing Company.

"For Nigareens" and "To a Wite Boy (or an answer for a late question)" from *Black Essence* by Jewel C. Latimore (Johari Amini). Copyright 1968 by Jewel C. Latimore, Third World Press, Chicago.

"For Malcolm, A Year Later" and "It Was a Funky Deal" from *Poems from Prison* by Etheridge Knight. Copyright 1967 by Etheridge Knight. Reprinted by permission of Broadside Press.

"Blues Note" from Bob Kaufman, *Solitudes Crowded with Loneliness*. Copyright © 1965 by Bob Kaufman. Reprinted by permission of New Directions Publishing Corporation.

"Oct. 5th, 1963" from *Golden Sardine* by Bob Kaufman. Copyright © 1967 by Bob Kaufman. Reprinted by permission of City Lights Books.

"The Relation of AMSAC and the American Negro to Africa and Pan-Africanism" by Jaja A. Wachuku from *1962 American Society of African Culture Pan-*

Africanism Reconsidered. © 1962 by American Society of African Culture and Del ware Corporation. Reprinted with permission of The Regents of the University of California.

To Robert Hayden

The complex but enduring relationships between black Africans and Afro-Americans have been and continue to be extensively discussed. Traditionally, these relationships have been studied by ethnological, sociological, political, philosophical, and religious experts, too few of whom have been either African or Afro-American. As a consequence, relatively extensive objective data on black Africans and Afro-Americans is available, but there is little subjective record of their own human emotional experience. With the black man's emergence from the intellectual and artistic oblivion in which tradition has held him, it is important that more be known of the black feelings, black thoughts, and black imaginations that have sustained the African and Afro-American during neglect. The most authentic reflections of a people's humanity—of its intellect and its resolve—are to be found amongst its creations; especially in its literature, where deliberate artistic efforts are made to document ordeals and the feelings they produce. The modern writings of Africans and Afro-Americans are meaningful in that they embody a recognition of two similar yet discrete historical perspectives, a recognition that permits their authors to assess accurately and poignantly the human worth generated by the endurance of frustrating denials.

Avoiding outright political writings by leaders, this book offers aspects of the mosaic of sensibilities known only by black men in Africa and America of the past decade or so. They have absorbed similar oppressions and now travel similar but separate routes toward fulfillments that often seem, in one way or another, contingent upon the actual or surrogated presence of the white man. In the African selections in this book is a literary measure of the impact of modernization on the black African. There is also, in all the selections, a wide sampling of attitudes: from the fears of some Afro-Americans who dread imminent racial obliteration, to accounts of the brutalized life of black South Africans; from the urgings of Afro-Americans who, drawing upon their unique black experiences, would "struggle to redeem and convert a fallen America," to the vexations of modern Africans who anguish over what aspects of modern living they will accept and what aspects of traditional life they will strive to keep intact to sustain their prized "African identity." Such writings have obvious sociological value, recording as much about the proponents of "civilization" as those whom it civilizes; but, simultaneously, many of these writings are clearly beginning to assume value as literature that will endure as literature.

It is regretted that more African writers could not be reached for permission to include their works. The omission of the important and related body of West Indian literature is also regretted.

Thanks are hereby given to many people, including the staff of the Drum and Spear Bookstore in Washington, D.C.; the staff of the Moorland-Spingarn collections at Howard University; my students, black and white; and my editor, D. Anthony English, who endured. Special thanks are offered to my wife for special reasons.

W. H. R.

Contents

Introduction

Backgrounds

On one level, it seems clear that the problems of modern black Africa and Afro-America are totally different; but on a more basic level, it seems equally clear that many of the problems of both peoples have been provoked and greatly shaped, in one way or another, for one end or another, by the aggressively dynamic, potentially domineering presence of the white man. This is not to suggest that black people were leisurely living out uncomplicated, bucolic lives of Edenic simplicity and romantic incorruptibility before the advent of the white man—the black man has his share of shameful vices, weaknesses, and pettinesses. It is rather to indicate something of the massive impact that modern white civilization has obviously had, and still has, on blacks throughout the world, and to indicate black reactions and adjustments to such impact. To be sure, there have been persistent problems of differences between Africans and Africans, Africans and Afro-Americans, Afro-Americans and Afro-Americans. In Africa, for example, there have been profound, often internecine oppositions over such issues as tribal supremacy, regionalism, colonialism, Pan-Africanism, and African Socialism. King Affonso of the sixteenth-century Congo was only one of several African chieftains whose antislavery attempts were frustrated by the greed of his own people; when the almamy (i.e., religious leader) of the eighteenth century Futa Turo in northern Senegal declared that no slaves could pass through his realm en route to foreign sale, black slavers merely worked out another route that bypassed his kingdom and continued to carry slaves to waiting French slave ships. In America blacks have long and sometimes seriously quarreled over such matters as American or African or West Indian identity, regional superiority (Northern born, reared, and educated Negroes asserting notions of cultural superiority over Southern born, reared, and educated Negroes who countered with equally foolish claims of greater affluence, purer "racial" stock), class status, skin color, and other divisive allegiances.

But there is also a history of continuing similarities engendered by religious, educational, political, and cultural contacts to which both modern Afro-America and Africa point on occasion. Backed, at first grudgingly, by white American sponsorship, Negroes blazed Christian missionary paths through various parts of nineteenth-century Africa: William H. Sheppard to the Congo;[1] Reverend Levi Coffin to South Africa;[2] Alexander Crummel to Liberia;[3] the irrepressible Bishop Henry M. Turner to South

1

Africa to ordain African ministers, several of whom exchanged pulpits with their Afro-American divines.

Such exchanges were not always predictable. John Chilembwe (1860–77?–1915) of Nyasaland (now Malawi) came to America in 1897 with the evangelical English fundamentalist, Joseph Booth, and studied at the Virginia Theological Seminary and College at Lynchburg, not very far from Harper's Ferry. While attending college, Chilembwe "probably learned of the Negro's revolutionary heritage and apparently of the abolitionist John Brown and his raid upon Harper's Ferry in 1859." Indeed, George Simeon Mwase (1880?–1962), black African biographer of Chilembwe, points out that at a strategy meeting with fellow rebels, shortly before leading a bloody if shortlived uprising against white colonists in Nyasaland in 1915, Chilembwe exhorted his soldiers with "something about a Mr. John Brown of America, who after losing his hope . . . in regard [sic] slave trading . . . determinate [sic] to strike a blow and lose his own life. . . . John said his case stands the same as that of Mr. John Brown. . . . 'Let us strike a blow and die,' for our blood will surely mean something at last. They all came to the final conclusion of *'Let us strike a blow and die.'* "[4]

Again with white American assistance, the Republic of Liberia was founded and developed by American Negroes such as New York-born, Cambridge-educated Alexander Crummell who spent twenty years there preaching and offering valuable advice to the Americo-Liberian leadership; and Virginia-born Joseph J. Roberts who worked his way up to become the first president of Liberia and later the first president of Liberia College. There were others. Periodically, whenever white hostility seemed overwhelming, there were various "back-to-Africa" agitations. Martin Delany led an exploratory expedition into the Congo seeking acceptable relocation sites for harassed blacks. The results of his inquiry were published under his title of Commissioner to Africa as *The Official Report of the Niger Valley Exploring Party* (1861). His colleague on the trek, West Indian-born but American resident Robert Campbell, wrote his findings as *A Pilgrimage to My Motherland* (1861), concluding that "with as good prospects in America as colored men generally have, I have determined, with my wife and children, to go to Africa to live." From the early twentieth century on, the succession of Pan-African conferences and their proliferating Negro world cultural festivals have served to bring Afro-Americans and Africans back together, to focus on black accomplishments around the world, to remind Afro-Americans of "Mother Africa," and to ponder the viability of blackness in the future.

In literature, South African novelist Peter Abrahams recalled the thrills he knew when he discovered in Johannesburg's Bantu Men's Club a shelf of books written by Afro-Americans: "There was *Up From Slavery;*[5] *Along This Way* by (James) Weldon Johnson; a slim volume called *The Black Christ;*[6] a fat volume called *The New Negro.*[7] I turned the pages of *The New Negro.* These poems and stories were written by Negroes! Something burst deep inside me. The world could never again belong to white people only! Never again!"[8] Abrahams is only one of many African writers who have acknowledged artistic inspiration, influence, and guidance from Afro-American writers. On the other hand, modern Afro-American writers are increasingly proud to refer to things African in their own writings, and they are adopting "African" or "Eastern" names in place of their white-imposed "slave names," e.g., Marvin X. (Marvin Jackmon), Johari Amini (Jewel C. Latimore), Askia Muhammad Toure (Roland Snellings), Malaika Ayo Wangara (Joyce Whitsitt), Abd-al Hakim (Gerald A. McWorter), and others. Afro-Americans have sustained dramaturgical interest in the homeland from the time of the founding of their Shakespeare-producing African Grove Theatre in 1820 in New York, to Willis Richardson and May Miller's *Negro History in Thirteen Plays* (1935), featuring two plays about African heroes, to today's LeRoi Jones in his African-based play, *A Black Mass* (1965). Afro-American novels about Africa have been few. They include Henry F. Downing's pioneering *The American Cavalryman; A Liberian Romance* (1917); George W. Ellis' *The Leopard's Claw* (1917), which ranges from Scotland to West Africa (Sierra Leone) and features African characters incidental to the major activities of white aristocratic Oliver Monchrief and his loves; George Schuyler's slashingly satirical *Slaves Today: A Story of Liberia* (1931), illustrating crass black opportunism. John Davis' compilation of *Africa from the Point of View of American Negro Scholars* (1958), the American Society of African Culture's *Pan-Africanism Reconsidered* (1962), edited by Samuel Allen, and *Apropos of Africa: Sentiments of American Negro Leaders on Africa from the 1800's to the 1900's* (1969), edited by Adelaide C. Hill and Martin Kilson, are a few recent acknowledgments of the long-standing and continuing interest between blacks in Africa and America.

Despite all of these and other modes of similarities, it cannot be denied that the white man and his ways have drastically altered the black man and his ways, especially in the modern world. Indeed, the very identities, psychological, national, and cultural (literary), of the blacks involved have been profoundly shaped by the modern white man. This process has been recorded in veritable libraries of studies, tomes, monographs, ethnological, psychological, sociological, philosophical, and religious expositions. But the humanity, pathos, and humor of all of this is infinitely more revealing, more poignant in the creative literatures of the people involved, namely black writers in modern sub-Saharan Africa and in Afro-America. Before one can appreciate the modern stances of these writers, a word or two on the backgrounds of their white-imposed identities might be helpful.

WHITE-IMPOSED PSYCHOLOGICAL IDENTITIES:

"Brother," asks Toundi Ondua in the novel *Une Vie de Boy* (1960, translated by John Reed, 1966) by the French-speaking author, Ferdinand Oyono, "Brother, what are we? What are we black men who are called Frenchmen?" The widow Chiaku in English-speaking John Munonye's novel, *The Only Son* (1966) finds that her lifelong efforts to rear her only son, Nnanna, in the traditions of their people of a Nigerian village are utterly ignored when he is taken from her by whites who will train him in Christian ways. Like Ondua, Mrs. Chiaku wonders also of the efficacy or even the validity of her tribal identity when such an event can take place with such ease. "What, after all, am I? Am I an American or a Negro? Can I be both? Or is it my duty to cease to be a Negro as soon as possible and be an American?" So ruminates W. E. B. DuBois[9] on behalf of most thinking American Negroes. All such questions of psychological identity are, of course, an inevitable feature of African and Afro-American literature—when one considers the history of the often traumatic realities of many black-white experiences. The stalemated aftermath of such confrontations has not been healthy for either the victimizing whites or, especially, for the victimized blacks. The long endemic extent of the ensuing psychological sickness of the blacks has often been noted. As Frantz Fanon (1924–1961), brilliant Martinique-born, Algeria-based psychiatrist, has explained it:

> The white man wants the world; he wants it for himself alone. He finds himself predestined master of the world. He enslaves it. An acquisitive relation is established between the world and him. But there exist other values that fit only my (i.e., black) forms. Like a magician, I robbed the white man of "a certain world," forever lost to him and his. . . . Somewhere beyond the objective world of farms and banana trees and rubber trees, I had subtly brought the real world into being. Between the world and me a relation of coexistence was established. (p. 128)

> Ontology—once it was finally admitted as leaving experience by the wayside—does not permit us to understand the being of the black man. For not only must the black man be black; he must be black in relation to the white man. . . . Overnight the Negro has been given two frames of references within which he has had to place himself. His metaphysics . . . were wiped out because they were in conflict with a civilization that he did not know and that imposed itself on him. (p. 110)[10]

Given such a context, Fanon argues, most such blacks are wretchedly sick, psychologically speaking, made so and kept so by the very natures of the people involved. Given such an absurd context, Fanon's prescriptions include the ultimate-if-necessary resort to armed and violent revolution, as in his *Toward the African Revolution* (1952–1961; 1967).

"We submit," write black psychiatrists William Grier and Price Cobbs, "that it is necessary for a black man in America to develop a profound distrust of his white fellow citizens and of the nation. . . . If he does not so protect himself he will live a life of such pain and shock as to find life itself unbearable. For his own survival, then, he must develop a cultural paranoia in which every white man is a potential enemy unless proven otherwise."[11] With characteristic arrogance and unnecessary ignorance, many early white Christian missionaries set about discouraging "heathen ways" among potential African converts, not at all aware of the psychological damage they might inflict upon a people who for years had their own involved ontologies that necessarily included accommodation of surges of guilt, repression, compensation, and other psychological agitations. An illustrative example of this is cited by Melville Herskovits who documented an instance of the Paramaribo Negroes of coastal Guiana. These people claim that insanity is tied up with *winti*, African spirits:

These spirits, which are inherited, are thought to come to an individual at about the age of puberty, after which active worship in the form of dancing to drums takes place. Everywhere in the New World, before and after emancipation of the slaves, pressure has been used by European officials to discourage the worship of these pagan deities. This has driven the worship of African gods—in this instance the *winti*—more and more into secret ritual. Yet the forbidden dances do take place. In Paramaribo dancing is permitted several times during the year, and then the adherents of the *winti* worship them openly. But there are some *winti* who drive their followers to more frequent worship with an urgency that cannot be denied; were followers to inhibit the call of the gods to dance and persist in their refusal over an extended period of time, the Negroes say they would go insane. Indeed the *winti* worshippers insist that the insanity found among the Christian Negroes of Paramaribo is due to this cause. It is believed that these persons have inherited spirits, and because their new religion prohibits dancing for them, the resistance to the bidding of the inherited gods robs them of their reason—that is, the spirits which "possess" them drive them mad.[12]

The literature that records and measures the extent of psychological damage induced by domineering whites on hapless blacks in Africa and Afro-America is extensive, with most observers being impressed with the unusual adaptability of the black man.

WHITE-IMPOSED NATIONAL IDENTITIES

Just as their psychological identities have often been distorted by conflicts of their own and white demands, so have blacks in Africa and Afro-America been made to adjust to white-imposed national identities. "When Europe divided up the continent of Africa at the Berlin Conference of 1885, many African peoples were split by the new and often arbitrary boundaries drawn by colonial powers. This resulted in tragic situations where some members of the same tribal group came under one colonial system while other members came under different colonial systems."[13] This can be seen by glancing at two of the various kinds of colonial administrations that were imposed on the Africans.

France, for instance, favored an official policy of assimilationism, by which a colony became an integral, if noncontiguous, part of the mother country, with its population and society made over—to whatever extent possible—in her image. "The aim is to make the African a black Frenchman and to make the colonies not self-governing Dominions but so many departments of France."[14] England, on the other hand, used the administrative device of "indirect rule," which officially sought to employ native institutions that would be supervised by British officials and progressively transformed Africans for the responsibilities of modern life and government. The English desire, said Sir Donald Cameron, "is to make the native a good African, and we shall not achieve this if we destroy all the institutions . . . superimposing upon them what we consider to be better administrative methods." Cameron's paternalism is spelled out as he commends English ambitions at "trying, while we endeavor to purge the native system of its abuses, to graft our higher civilization upon the soundly rooted native stock."[15] In white America, there was the same kind of compulsion to order and define the world, which included defining the identities, intellectual worth, and destinies of imported black slaves. The difficulties in determining what a Negro was in America have led to some elaborate legal rulings. In New Orleans, for example, the anxiety to define blacks brought about the use of terms such as *sacatro* (Negro and griffe); *griffe* (Negro and mulatto); *marabon* (mulatto and griffe); *mulatto* (Negro and white); *os rouge* (Negro and Indian); *tierceron* (mulatto and quadroon); *quadroon* (white and mulatto); *octoroon* (white and quadroon), and others. Perhaps the most ambitious of such undertakings was the creation of an ethnic group never before seen on the face of the earth, an entirely brand new "race"—the American Negro.

WHITE-IMPOSED CULTURAL IDENTITIES

Understandably, adjustment to or rebellion against these imposed identities constitutes sizeable portions of the history of black literature. Recognizing that many whites justified and underscored their charges of the black man's backwardness on the African peoples' lack of a worthy cultural past, blacks began the struggle to achieve education, especially to master the art of writing. With these skills they hoped to present refuting views of themselves and their past. Thus, as exiled critic Ezekiel Mphahlele has said, the very act of writing in Africa "first entered the field of cultural activity as a response to the presence of the white man. It was he, after all, who brought with him formal schooling and presented a challenge by his completely different way of life—and death."[16] Such a statement ignores the literate history of past West African kingdoms and centers of learning such as Timbuktu and Jenna where culture flourished in Arabic, and also ignores the lengthy tradition of literate Swahili on Africa's eastern coast. Applied to English literature of the modern world, however, it is more appropriate.

The educational pattern of early blacks in Africa and Afro-America—administered by and for religious missionaries and/or slavemasters—was similar. For instance, the sponsors of the earliest black South African writers were missionaries in orders such as the station of the Paris Evangelical Mission at Morija (Basutoland—now Lesotho), the London Mission Society, and the Catholic Trappist Mission at Marianhill. In Afro-America when early Negroes were allowed to read and write in the North, it was usually only for specific religious or practical business purposes. John Eliot, "Apostle to the Indians," encouraged such education for blacks as early as 1674: "I will put Bibles and other good and proper books into their hands; will allow them time to read and assure myself that they do not misspend their time. If I can discern any wicked books in their hands, I will take away those pestilential instruments of wickedness."[17] Other religions—the Quakers are conspicuous examples—occasionally encouraged Negroes to read, preferably denominational literature. The Society for the Propagation of the Gospel was a bit more lenient, although not lax, in its program of reading for slaves. With such orientation, blacks who did secure an education were likely to become grateful, pious graduates, articulate enough in various denominations of the Christian religion, but not much informed about their own past cultures, except in negative ways. Such education impressed upon its students that a good character in literature was necessarily a Christian, one struggling to overcome a sense of original sin, and having allegiance to a puritanical code of duty, whose artistic, aesthetic tastes were derived from Europeanized Greek and Latin and European models, and whose best behavior was imitative of European styles. Africa and things African were heathen and evil, in need of redemption and the advanced civilization of the West. Blackness, including black skin, was a badge of divine condemnation. Later, when blacks won access to educational facilities, either segregated or integrated, they set about creating a literature whose history, up to the 1960's, was characterized largely by reactions to the white man's stereotypes. In a century of widespread extremisms, including literary extremisms, Afro-American literature often found itself just as extreme. In the 1960's, however, there began to appear a revolt against this kind of reflex reaction, and a differently oriented black literature appeared.

The Black Rage

Although not all writings by Africans and Afro-Americans wrestled with identity problems as overtly as may have been suggested, most of these authors, either consciously or unconsciously, and despite occasional literary explosions of ostensible race pride, were writing almost exclusively to and for white audiences. Black literature was, for some time, a record of various reactions, all directed toward the white man—quarrels with, refuting assertions against, thinly veiled admirations of the white man. It was not until later, beginning about the 1930's and 1940's, that black writers finally came to grips with the root of the matter—to recognize, assess, and assert their own definitions of their identities. Along the way there were some instances of genuine literary rage at the white-imposed identities, but before the awakening to their own discovery and celebration of their black identities early Negro writers contained, sublimated, or otherwise dealt with their rage in the form of literary acquiescence to the status quo by assuming the literary stances of accommodation, accepting, explicitly or implicitly, the values of white models of religion, morality, education, and culture.

ACCOMMODATION

Generally speaking, the literature of colonialized blacks in Africa and America has progressed in an evolution much like the three-part pattern of oppressed peoples' writings described by Frantz Fanon as (1) assimilationist; (2) pre-revolutionary; and (3) revolutionary. The proportion of one stage or another of this pattern, the rate of progress from one stage to the other, depended much on the kinds of relationships that existed between the dominant whites and the colonized blacks. As, for instance, the regard of white New England puritan employers for their free black laborers differed from the regard of Negroes held by white Southern slavemasters, so the white colonialists' regard differed for Africans in various parts of the continent, in southern Africa (Angola, South West Africa, South Africa, Rhodesia, Mozambique), East and Central Africa (Kenya, Tanzania, Uganda, Malawi, Zambia), French-speaking West Africa (Senegal, Guinea, Ivory Coast, Cameroon), and English-speaking West Africa (Sierra Leone, Ghana, Nigeria). However different the official white regard for blacks in Afro-America or Africa, the overriding fact remained that such regard always had to be contended with by the blacks. It is easy, therefore, to see that during their assimilationist phases of development these writers seem quite similar.

South Africa

The literary genesis of the African Chaka legend—from accommodationism to activism—is an example of the literary pattern for most of the writers here concerned. South African-born Thomas Mofolo (1873?–1948) wrote several missionary-inspired books in his native Sesotho language: *Moeti oa Bochabela* (*The Pilgrim of the East*, serially in the *Leselinyana*, the oldest Sesuto newspaper, 1906); *Pitseng* (*In the Pit*, 1910), but he is remembered for his *Chaka, An Historical Romance*, as it was known in translation from its original Sesuto (1925) into English by F. H. Dutton and W. R. Moule, and published in 1931. Hailed as "the first historical novel in modern African literature—and a masterpiece,"[18] it has been translated into several foreign languages, reprinted in English in 1967, and abridged for children in 1949. Mofolo's treatment of Chaka the Zulu, an actual African warrior king (1787–1828), is under noticeable missionary religious and English literary influences, not at all in the tradition of protest as that word is generally used. His account of Chaka is in keeping with expected Christian reaction to the bloody career of a man who deliberately chose and consistently followed a life of military force, a man of barbarous rise and inevitable downfall; a man who was described by the novelist H. Rider Haggard as "an African Attila who . . . slaughtered more than a million human beings," who with his 100,000 man army possessed by brute force an area of Africa larger than all of modern France. Called by Mofolo as "the originator of all that was evil," Chaka has nevertheless caught the attention of several other later African writers who have since transmuted him into a modern national African hero, in the dead center of meaningful protest. A white author, E. A. Ritter, has written a biographical history that discounts some of Mofolo's accounts of military brutalities in *Shaka Zulu* (1957), whereas imaginative treatments of the warrior chief include a *Shaka* for the theater by South African H. I. E. Dhlomo, and another dramatization by Seydou Badian Couyate, a minister of Mali. Leopold Senghor of Senegal has poeticized Shaka in *Ethiopique*s (1956); he has also been dramatized by Condetto Nenekhaly Camara of Guinea (1967) and by F. M. Mulikita of Gambia in *Shaka the Zulu* (1967) in which the hero defends his brutal ways as harsh but necessary orientation for his emerging people's own good, and where the murder of Shaka by his own brothers is made to appear as treachery of great magnitude.

There were other South African writers who, like Mofolo, found Western white ways appealing enough to illustrate them as verities of Christian experience. Henry M. Ndawo's *U-Hambo luka Gqobaka* (*A Journey To-wards Conversion*, 1909) in the Xhosa language, and John K. Bowke's *U-Ntsikana. Ntsikana: The Story of an African Convert* (1914) in Xhosa and English are examples. Even when South African writers chose to write in English, as in *Mhudi, An Epic of South African Life a Hundred Years Ago* (1930) by Solomon T. Plaatje, "the first South African author to write a novel in English,"[19] it was to imitate English thought and values as well as English literary standards. One finds various vernacular lit-eratures of this assimilationist period in this part of Africa, but as South African-born writer Lewis Nkosi admits, "Vernacular literature is more or less moribund." Given the racial realities of apartheid strictures that censor vernacular literature, it is not surprising that area writers in Eng-lish would be utterly frustrated in their attempts to portray anything other than that which the white authorities approved. Certainly Jahn is correct when, remembering the voluntary exiles of Peter Abrahams, Lewis Nkosi, Ezekiel Mphahlele, Bloke Modisane, Arthur Maimane, and other gifted blacks from the area, he writes "Since the end of the Second World War, the only significant African literature from the south of the con-tinent has been written in English by those who have left the country."[20] These writers are mentioned again in the section on Black Revolts.

East and Central Africa

In East and Central Africa, the literary gleanings are the slimmest of any of the three sub-Saharan areas of Africa under consideration here, largely because the literature in English from this region is so recent. When one includes the works of James Ngugi and Grace A. Ogot (Kenya), Okot p'Bitek and Joseph Burura (Uganda), David Rubadiri, Aubrey Kachingwe, and Legson Kayira (Malawi), Felix Tchicaya U Tam'si (Cen-tral Congo), and Shaaban Roberts (Tanganyika), one has gone far to-ward mentioning the bulk of the more promising writers in English from this area. Unlike South African vernaculars, there is a lively, three-hun-dred-year old tradition of East African vernacular literature in Swahili that still flourishes here, as exemplified in a recent work, *Poems from Kenya; Gnomic Verses in Swahili*, by Ahmad Nassir bin Juma Bhalo, translated and edited by Lyndon Harries (1966), who has also edited *Swahili Poetry* (1962) and *Swahili Prose Texts* (1965). Edgar Wright has gone so far as to point to what he feels is a complicating factor in the development of East African literature: the writers trying to decide which (Swahili or English) would be the better vehicle for literary expression. "Nevertheless, modern writing in the countries of this area is developing mainly in English . . . the growth of radio, television, and all the acces-sories of a Westernized civilization; the desire to find a reading public— all these are reasons for the growth of a literature in English."[21] Some East Africans, including John S. Mbiti of Kenya and Shaaban Roberts of Tanganyika, have written in both Swahili and English. "It is," says critic Gerald Moore, "far too early to arrive at any conclusions about East African literature in English. There just isn't enough of it. And what there is of it is mostly so recent, so completely contemporary that any kind of critical judgement is extremely difficult, since there is absolutely no basis of comparison within the same culture."[22] New as this literature is, it is encouraging to note that its writers include, in addition to Grace Ogot, several other women authors, namely Barbara Kimenye of Uganda, author of two volumes of short stories, *Kalasanda* (1965) and *Kalasanda Revisited* (1966), Rebecca Njau of Kenya, who has several plays and some fiction to her credit, and Charity Waciuma of Kenya, who has written a charming biographical *Daughter of Mumbi* (1969). The works of newcomers are welcome. *A Calabash of Life* (1967) by Khadambi Asalache of Western Kenya, and *Return to the Shadows* (1969) by Uganda's Robert Serumaga are both first novels of some promise. Described as "a village opera," *Orphan* by Uganda's promising Okello Oculi (featuring a central character named Okello) rehearses, in free verse, the miseries afflicted upon his people and their determination to survive. Some of Oculi's literary promise has already been realized in his experimental novel, *Prostitute* (1968). It is interesting to note that these writers are emerging with an almost characteristic sorrow that runs through much of their work, born perhaps of the trauma of civilization, and reflecting a weary kind of sophisticated cynicism at the advent of local political leadership, black or white.

French Africa

It is from French-speaking and English-speaking West Africa that European and American readers will find the greatest, most varied, and most recognizably competent or poor literary performances. It is from these literatures that European and American readers can see more clearly the unfolding of the three-stage pattern of oppressed peoples' writings described by Fanon. During their assimilationist phase, Negro writers of French-speaking Africa seemed convinced of the touted value of white ways, of the promises inherent in their *evolué* status, and of the relative backwardness of African ways. Collaborating with white Frederick Carrère to write *De La Sénégambie française* (Paris, 1855), the mulatto and religious zealot, Paul Holle, made his recently acquired, "racially" motivated views known. An example of the extent to which several early French-speaking mulatto colonials went in fervent dedication to Mother France, and, not at all incidentally, to their own ethnic class, Holle would demand that Senegalese children speak French, preferably by force, because the Muslim and particularly the black respect only force. "Let us have no more talk of toleration and religious freedom . . . we must not forget that we are dealing with races of crude instincts . . . Furthermore, if we reflect that all primitive societies have passed through this stage of government by force, we can accept the propriety of a force applied with intelligence and moderation."[23]

There were other French-speaking Africans who believed themselves to be as French as the French had told them they were in officially proclaimed rights of assimilation during the revolutions of 1789 and 1848. In 1912, however, Ahmadou Dugay Clédor, vice-president of the Senegalese Union for the Propagation of French, attacked the governor-general with charges of racial bigotry, and, although competent in administration of the building of ports and railways, utterly without any real native policy. Claude Wauthier, African specialist, feels that Clédor's attitude, as expressed in two studies, *La Bataille de Guile* (1912) and *De Faidherbe a Coppolani* (1913), marks "the turning point in French colonial policy, when the true policy of assimilation was renounced and a distinction began to be drawn between native officials and French officials."[24] But it is important to remember that Clédor was typically arguing mainly for rights of class and status. Neither he nor many other mulattoes were overly concerned with the improved welfare of pure-blooded natives, black Negroes, or black slaves. The self-interest of these mulattoes is perhaps best seen by glancing at the work of some island-born French-speaking authors of this "mixed blood" classification. Their attitudes are also found in the early literature of other assimilationist-minded French-speaking Africans of the continent. Julian Raimond (1743–1802), an octoroon, was born in Santo Domingo into inherited wealth, which included the market value of thirty-seven black slaves. A veteran of the French battles fought in the American Revolution, Raimond spent much of his life in Paris where he proliferated pamphlets that argued for the rights of mulattoes in the colonies, but he rarely mentioned black Negroes or black slaves, and then only to augment his statistics. Quibbling over the legality of his mulatto status ("I am the legitimate son and grandson of European fathers and landowners of Saint Domingue . . ."[25]), he could cite the virtues of such phrases as "All men are born and remain free and equal in rights," and he could write, on the other hand, ". . . if, unfortunately, there exists, under French rule, a land where slavery is thought necessary for a time, there must be, I say, but two classes in that land, the free and the enslaved, even if it were only to restrain the latter effectively."[26] Raimond meant black slaves, not mulattoes. Auguste Lacaussade (1817–1897) from Reunion Island had the benefits of a wide liberal arts education and a distinguished career as a poet (*Les Salaziennes*, 1839; *Poemes et payages*, 1852) and as translator-secretary for the critic Saint-Beauve. A champion of freedom for all men, Lacaussade once owned slaves, and although his poetry often acclaims the natural beauties of his island home, his heart was clearly in Paris. Victor Séjour (1817–1874) was one of many New Orleans-born Creole poets whose affluence, sometimes valued in terms of the slaves they owned, allowed him to escape the American South and flee to Paris, the city with which most of these Creole poets had always strongly identified, as is evident in their American-published volume of verse, *Les Cenelles* (1845), sometimes loosely called the first anthology of Negro verse in America. Séjour wrote about two dozen melodramatic plays, all in French, that were extremely popular during his time abroad, but with titles such as *La Chute de Sejan*, (1849), *Les Fils de Charles-Quint* (1864), and *Richard III* (1870), not about blacks or New Orleans slaves. Other French-speaking Negroes sustained this tradition of native loyalty to things French through a period of confusions and contradictions, such as the example of Blaise Diagne's becoming undersecretary for the colonies in 1919, the same year he became president of the first Pan-African Congress. "Straddling these apparently contradictory offices, he proclaimed, 'We French natives wish to remain French, since France has given us every liberty.' "[27] Twenty years later, in

1939, a new colonial Frenchman began to emerge, for in the pages of a Parisian review a brilliant poem, *Cahier d'un retour au pays natal,* by Césaire Aime was published. Attracting the attention of the surrealist André Breton, who supplied a preface to the 1947 edition of the poem, *Cahier d'un retour au pays natal* celebrated blackness in ways previously unattempted—but this will be part of the discussion of these writers in the Black Revolt section.

English-Speaking West Africa

Never having had to contend officially with the intimidating *de jure* apartheid of white-dominated southern Africa, with the eventually exposed hypocrisy of French assimilationism, or with the ravaging *de facto* racism of Afro-Americans, English-speaking writers of West Africa were officially encouraged, under British indirect rule, to manifest themselves. Yet their literature reflects their adjustment to the multiple impacts that white civilization had upon them. It is not surprising to find that, however different the influences of French assimilationism were supposed to be from English indirect rule, most English-speaking West African writers, in their assimilationist phase as well as in the modern stage of revolution, differ only in the degree to which they approved of the various manifestations of the white presence in their part of the continent.

Jacobus Elisa Johannes Capitein (1717–1747) may be seen as an exception to the tradition of West African writers that protested slavery. Kidnapped into slavery as a boy, he was sold and passed on to be educated at Halle and the University of Leyden, becoming so enamored of Western ways that he complied in a request to write and publish, in Latin and in Dutch, an elaborate rationalization of slavery: *A Politico-Theological Investigation of Slavery as not Incompatible with Christian Slavery* (1742). Made a chaplain for the Elmina slave castle in his native Ghana, to which he returned in 1742, Capitein was ignored or disrespected by Europeans because of his color and ostracized by his own people for his compromising views on slavery. He died in disillusion.

More representative are the works of two other early West Africans who wrote in English, both of whom, like Capitein, were kidnapped as children and sold into slavery: *Thoughts and Sentiments on the Evil of Slavery,* (London, 1787) by Ottobah Cugoano from Ajumako, Ghana; and *The Interesting Narrative of the Life of Olaudah Equiano, or Gustavus Vassa the African* (London, 1789) by a young black from modern Eastern Nigeria. Although both men remained in England, they vigorously campaigned against the slave trade, using whatever influence they could, Cugoano in letters to King George III and the Prince of Wales; Vassa in speeches and an antislavery petition to the Queen of England.[29] Among those English-educated West Africans who returned to leadership roles in their homelands and wrote on behalf of their people, one finds only variations in the degrees to which they went in their admiration of English and European ways. Although it can be easily misconstrued, there is truth enough in Wauthier's citing of David Kimble's remark that "in the tradition of Africanus Horton, James Brew, Mensah Sarbah, Casely-Hayford, and many others, J. W. deGraft-Johnson wished to preserve the British connection."[30] Educated in medicine at the University of Edinburgh, James Africanus Beale Horton (1838–1888) of Sierra Leone is on record as an open admirer of Western civilization and worked to have his countrymen emulate it. Cambridge-educated Joseph E. Casely-Hayford (1866–1930) has been praised by some as "one of the greatest figures of African nationalism in the Gold Coast,"[31] and damned by others as being "informed by a deep consciousness of his own impotence vis-a-vis the British."[32] Kwamankra, hero of Casely-Hayford's rambling novel, *Ethiopia Unbound* (1911), spends a good deal of his time defending African civilizations and philosophies, but he is impressed by a remark from a white friend who exclaims, "Your friends, by Jove, are a credit to Africa," and, in reflective moments, this thinly veiled autobiographical hero is given to quoting Shakespeare and finding analogies of African events with events from the *Odyssey*. DeGraft-Johnson of Ghana seems to express the feelings of most of these English-speaking West African writers by explaining, "the metropolitan powers that governed Africa in the recent past, notably Britain, France, and Belgium, have to a great measure contributed toward the advance of the African peoples in modern times. In certain cases grave mistakes have been made, but on balance the economic prosperity and social well-being of the Africans have been greatly improved."[33]

Afro-America

Fanon's pattern of literary evolution through the three stages of assimilationist, prerevolutionary, and revolutionary writings is especially vivid in the Afro-American context. The long tradition of the first stage of assimilationist or integrationist literature is heavily emphasized. This emphasis is understandable when it is recognized that most black Americans have long believed in and accepted the stated national, political, and social goals of freedom and equality for all, despite the fact that they recognized that too often such goals were not designed for them, that the white American majority often found itself unwilling to grant but a limited and prespecified contact or relationship with blacks. It was not by the wishes of the Afro-American minority but rather by the social mandate of the white American majority that Negro churches, Negro educational systems, Negro fraternal orders, and Negro housing patterns and employment possibilities have come into being. Predictably, reactions to such white denials, indifference, or outright hostility have galvanized Negroes into all kinds of desperate positions. A few Negroes favored literal separatism and/or "a return to Africa," or a migration to some Haitian or South American refuge. Others sought enclaves in unoccupied areas of various states where they could establish all-black communities and survive as best they could unto themselves. Some Negroes now, professing unbearable despair and frustration, see no escape possible for the Negro whose days, they predict, are numbered before imminent racial genocide breaks out. Some other blacks, who are examined in the Black Revolt section, also demand all-black controlled communities, not to survive in cowering malignant isolation away from the mainstream of activity, but rather to get themselves together and then to generate and diffuse their peculiar spiritual and moral wherewithal that they believe would reinvigorate a moribund country, a civilization described as spiritually dead, morally corrupt, culturally atrophied on fixations on death, to establish a land of living, hope, freedom, spiritualism, and spontaneity. It is worthwhile to glance at the beginnings of the literary evolution that arrived at such positions as are today claimed by these bold, but harried black writers.

· As far back as 1773, blacks petitioned for a return to Africa to be free of the official and unofficial hostility of white Americans. "We are willing to submit to such regulations and laws as may be made relative to us," several Boston Negroes declared in a petition, "until we leave the province, which we determine to do as soon as we can, from our joint labors procure money to transport ourselves to some part of the coast of Africa."[34] Later in the same century, free Negroes in Newport, Rhode Island, outlined their hopes for a return to Africa: "Our earnest desire of returning to Africa and settling there has induced us further to trouble you . . . that a number of men from among ourselves shall be sent to Africa, to see if they can obtain by gift or by purchase of some of the kings, or Chief people, lands proper and sufficient to settle upon. . . ."[35] With some regularity since these times, various Negro groups have tried to lead black Americans to some land—the West Indies, Central America, Africa— where they might develop in their own ways and at their own rates. Almost as persistent as these agitations were the urgings of other Negroes to found all-black communities on American soil. The mass migration of southern Negroes from Mississippi, Louisiana, Alabama, and Georgia to the North and West around 1879 was encouraged by the exhortations of Louisiana's Henry Adams who organized almost 100,000 Negroes for a trek to free Kansas; and Benjamin "Pap" or "Mose" Singleton who actually led several thousands of Negroes northward. Such interest is still active; the number of all-black villages and towns throughout America is uncounted. Robert S. Browne of Fairleigh-Dickinson University has proposed a separate black nation that would be comprised of several Southern states. The Republic of New Africa, based in Detroit, with similar aims, also demands Southern states (Louisiana, Mississippi, Alabama, Georgia, and South Carolina) and, to finance their new nation's birth and initial development, $400,000,000,000 in unpaid back slave wages as reparations.

Despite such movements, however, the predominant concern of Afro-American literature has been most definitely and consistently integrationist-minded. Not even during the Harlem Renaissance of the 1920's and 1930's, when artistic celebration of blackness and Africanness began modestly, was there much emphasis on blacks leaving the country or forming enclaves around the land. The overwhelming preoccupation of most black American writers with integration easily describes the bulk of their literature. Their personal and literary orientation toward what is loosely described as "white values" is evident in recurring motifs that can still be found in their writings today, although today there is a decided struggle for yet unclarified alternative "black" life styles. Although the integrationist-minded writers may have claimed that they did not want integration at the expense of Afro-American cultural denial, some of them repeatedly created characters whose references and aspirations were based on "white values" for their worth. Thus there were and remain cherished motifs of skin color; extensive and preferably Northern, Ivy League, or European education; "proper speech"; "civilized manners"; puritan appreciation of work; praise for the drive for acquisition and visible display of wealth; individualism. Such motifs are perhaps familiar to some readers of the more popular Afro-American literature, but the same designs are also apparent in the lesser known, and less available writings by these authors.

Early Negro writers, as susceptible as anyone else to the fervent religious and legal demands of their times, seemed resigned to an acceptance of the roles predesigned for them by colonials who, often well-meaning enough but woefully ignorant, pointed to free-wheeling Biblical interpretation of the human races and their earthly destinies, or to bigoted judicial renderings of the black man's legal place in a white man's world. Thus Lucy Terry (1730?–1821) "the first American Negro poet" ("Bars Fight," 1746), and Phillis Wheatley (1754?–1784) who published a volume of verse, *Poems on Various Subjects, Religious and Moral* (1773), could both "know their places" when both are said, anecdotally, to have chosen not to sit with whites when invited to dine. Jupiter Hammon (1711–1804?) on broadside verse and in a prose piece, *Address to the Negroes of the State of New York* (composed 1786) could solicit Negro acceptance of the racial status quo of his times.

Other early Negro writers sought to placate their inner rage by submitting their wares to the touted critical objectivity of white establishment cognoscente. Thus, several Negro authors ignored the racial issue to write of "just people," but invariably such people turned out to be "just white people," thinking, talking, and acting like white people. James T. Franklin is an example of such writers. Better known as a poet (*Mid-Day Gleanings*, 1893; *Jessamine*, 1890), he has also published a three-act play, *Retribution* (1890), and a sorry, stilted novelette, *Crimson Altars, or A Minister's Sin* (1895), which treats the sensational matter of a villainous minister who, despite his marriage and three children, freely and openly gloats that he uses his pulpits to seduce trusting young female members of his various congregations. Very few of these works of Franklin's are concerned with Negroes, although *Mid-Day Gleanings* includes five prose selections, one of which, "A Mid-Ocean Story," features a Negro seaman. Several Negro women of the same century produced fiction that also sought to bypass racial realities by avoiding Negro characters: Mrs. A. E. Johnson in her widely-hailed novel, *Clarence and Clorine, or God's Way* (1890), a simplistic account of the rise of poor but steadfastly pious Clarence Burton and his equally virtuous sister to religious and commercial success; Barbara Pope, who published many short stories in the feminist *Waverly Magazine* of the 1890s; Adah Menken (nee Philomene Croi Theodore), praised by ranking English writers including Algernon Swinburne, Charles Dickens, and others, who wrote a single volume of poems, *Infelicia* (1888), one copy of which includes a handwritten commendatory note by Charles Dickens as well as his autograph, but who, "at least a quadroon,"[36] spent a busier, more romantic life as a celebrated European actress.

Mrs. Menken's exploitation of color-conscious whites points to the familiar staple of the color motif that is found in so much Negro literature.

Such an admiration of light skins dates back to the first known novel by an American Negro, *Clotel, or The President's Daughter* (1853) by William Wells Brown. This motif is used in Frank J. Webb's *The Garies and Their Friends* (1857), and in Frances E. W. Harper's *Iola Leroy, or Shadows Uplifted* (1892). In early poetry, too, color consciousness was a factor as, for example, with Albery A. Whitman (1851–1902), a popular and eloquent Methodist preacher who published sermons and at least seven volumes of ambitiously metered poems, including the verse novels, *Not a Man and Yet a Man* (1877) and *Twasinta's Seminoles, or Rape of Florida* (1885), both of which feature octoroons, fair-skinned, raven-haired heroines and handsome heroes of measurably mixed blood. This preoccupation with fair-skinned characters by Negro writers swelled the tradition of "the tragic mulatto," which was nourished by Charles Wadell Chesnutt and his Rena Walden in *The House Behind the Cedars* (1900); Walter White's Mimi Daquin of *Flight* (1926); Jessie Fauset's Angela in *Plum Bun* (1928); and Olivia Cary of *Comedy, American Style* (1933); Nella Larsen's Helga Crane in *Quicksand* (1928); and Clare Kendry of *Passing* (1929). Although there have been some variations on this color theme, happily (the endings of White's Mimi, Mrs. Fauset's Angela, and Miss Larsen's Irene Redfield, for example, are not all that tragic), it has nevertheless remained a favorite concern of Negro writers to this day, as with such recent characters as Hal Bennet's Neva Manning in his *A Wilderness of Vines* (1966) and Eloise McLindon in his *The Black Wine* (1968).

Along with delineations of the difficulties concomitant to the problems, real and imagined, faced by protagonists of passable fair skins, Negro writers have dealt with the range of imposed stereotypes by making much of the virtues of securing a formal education. Indeed, it sometimes seems as though their heroes and heroines believe that such an education will alleviate their problems almost automatically. While John Saunders in *Appointed, An American Novel* (1894) by "Sanda" (W. H. Stowers and W. H. Anderson) has a fair complexion and "regular features," as does, of course, his betrothed, he soon finds that an education does not help him, a University of Michigan graduate in civil engineering, to become anything more than an intellectual assistant bookkeeper and valet to a white friend; nor does another kind of education prevent Saunders from being lynched by a mob of white southerners. Such a novelized account of formal education in early Negro writing is unusual. Abe Overly of Robert L. Waring's book, *As We See It* (1910), is more typical as he finds that a formal education at Oberlin College yields him uncommon rewards that include a wife who incredibly saves $2500 from his after-class janitorial duties salary, and a degree in civil engineering with which he patriotically spurns a lucrative offer from some important but "foreign," "non-American," "wily Japanese" to work instead as a loyal American civil engineer, designing narrow-gauge railroad track to the coastline of Louisiana. Like most protagonists of early Negro literature, the heroes, educated or not, usually speak flawless English. These "correct speaking" Negroes were sometimes unintentionally more amusing than anything else. Madison Washington of Frederick Douglass' four-part short story, "The Heroic Slave," (1853) mastered northern education enough to be able to overthrow and admonish white slavers who had captured him and placed him aboard the *Creole* with, "Mr. Mate, you cannot write the bloody laws of slavery on those restless billows. The ocean, if not the land, is free!" A more extreme example of such affected speech is to be found in the deservedly little-known novelette, *Selene* (1896), by Kenneth Young. In an outburst typical of the language used by other Negro characters in the mercifully brief story, Selene's black lover exclaims, "O, Mockingbird! Why dost thou persist in thy evening guttural song . . . when thou art championed by an angelic songster . . . Away!" On occasion, all or most of these so-called white-oriented motifs were embodied in a single well-educated protagonist who spoke perfect English, thrived on commercially competitive individualism, and, to be sure, had "regular features and a light complexion." The hero of D. I. Imbert's almost obscure novelette, *The Colored Gentleman* (1931) is such a character; West Indian Francis LaFarge, wealthy, "educated in England, admitted to the bar in London," grows weary of his island provincialism, yearns for the challenging competitiveness of the United States, to which he forthwith sails, meeting on shipboard wealthy Juanita LaBlanc of the "clean-cut features, which were of an olive tint," whose face "was oval and her complexion fair." As affluent and well-traveled as Francis, Juanita is the daughter of a Frenchman, a Colonel from New Orleans; but she can recall nothing of her dead mother: "My Mammy told me she was a beauty of the brunette type."

It follows, of course, that in this Negro-written literature, which extolled light-skinned, educated, "proper-speaking" characters, dark-skinned characters would be present, contrastingly, as extensions of the white stereotyped "comic darky," who, ignorant and dependent, forever bumbled over polysyllabics in a Southern Negro dialect. Even when early Negro writers did use a dark-skinned hero, it was not always to indicate "blackness" in the radical meaning of that word today. The blackness of the commercially sensationalized ghetto life of Claude McKay's *Home to Harlem* (1928), whose black Jake Brown is delightedly and animalistically given to a lifetime of such existence, is a conjuring up of what many white readers expected and demanded of books about black urban life: wailing jazz, smoke-filled gambling dens, glorification of primitivism, generous sexuality acted out by eager women and virile black men with throbbing passions and ready razors. Nor did other early black-skinned characters protest as loudly as they now do. Belton Piedmont of Sutton Griggs' *Imperium in Imperio* (1899) is a black hero who is eventually executed by his long-time mulatto friend for refusing to participate in a mad scheme to involve and coordinate all foreign enemies of the United States with trained blacks who will together militarily seize Texas and Louisiana, Louisiana to be ceded to such foreign allies as their reward. Patriotic and loyal to the end, Piedmont insists that his corpse be shrouded in an American flag. Zora, in W. E. B. DuBois' *The Quest of the Silver Fleece* (1911) even as a dark-skinned teenager can be self-consciously proud of her color and her race when she tells her bookish boyfriend, "No, no, they (white people) don't rule; they just thinks they rule. They just got things—heavy, dead things. We black folks got the spirit. We's lighter and cunninger; we fly right through them; we come and go again just as we wants to. Black folks is wonderful." Yet, years later, after she has completed a wide if informal education that included exposure to African history, she can claim her prize collection of books to be Plato's *Republic,* Gorky's *Comrades,* a *Cyclopedia of Agriculture,* Balzac's novels, Spencer's *First Principles,* Tennyson's *Poems.* "This is my university," Zora explained. Lifelong romantic lover of his people that he was, DuBois continued to use dark-skinned protagonists, such as Matthew Townes of *Dark Princess* (1928), and Manuel Mansart of the Black Flame Trilogy: *The Ordeal of Mansart* (1928); *Mansart Builds a School* (1959); and *Worlds of Color* (1961).

But there were louder voices of black rage and protest. Unwilling to emigrate from America with some desperate Negroes, and not anxious, with others, to placate the various impositions of the American white power structure, a well-attended school of Negro writers has hammered out a long and loud tradition of increasingly violent protest literature. It is important to remember, however, that for all of their literary rage, many of these writers were and are still protesting for full acceptance into the mainstream of American life as it is presently structured. In retort to the clamorous protest raised by these writers from DuBois' time to today are those Americans, black and white, who argue that the hard-won achievements of the modern Negro do not warrant a continued black literary rage. Such critics hold that the modern black American is at last gaining his full participatory role in the range of American life. Such persons point to statistics that indicate that Negroes are increasingly securing more high-level governmental positions of power, from the Cabinet appointment of Robert Weaver as the first black Secretary of Housing and Urban Development; to the seating of Thurgood Marshall as an Associate Justice of the United States Supreme Court; to the record number of black members of the 92nd Congress—twelve Democratic members of the House of Representatives and one Republican Senator; to the passage of the Civil Rights Acts of 1957, 1960, 1964, and 1968, and the Voting Rights Act of 1965; to the symbolic (but perhaps prophetically symbolic) nomination of two black men, the Reverend Channing Phillips and Julian Bond, as presidential and vice-presidential candidates of a major political party; and, on another level, to the proliferation of black studies courses and degree programs at the high school, college, and university levels. But, curiously, some of the literature from this school of modern Afro-American writers does not reflect sanguine optimism for the future role of the black American. Indeed, such literature graphs quite a contrary trend of thought as it, citing its own array of statistics, focuses on the seemingly chronic persistence of the stultifying manifestations of "white racism" in religion, education, the armed forces, housing and employment patterns, and in the macabre creations of expendable, intellectually vacuous "Uncle Tom" Negroes. All genres of such black literature depict the persistence of the black rage.

These writers are aware, for instance, of "the existence of concentration camps," already established in various parts of the country, legally sanctioned by Title II of the 1950 McCarran Internal Security Act, and maintained by the federal government. These "detention camps" are described in Charles Allen's *Concentration Camps U.S.A.* (1966), a slim book that sells steadily in black communities across the land. Such writers are mindful, as is Johnny Scott, that the ghettoes still flourish and, even worse, that the conditions that help create them are still at work. Although black ghetto life has long been depicted and studied, there continue to be those writers, black and white, who still treat the sensational symptoms rather than the malignant causes of such life. A few Negro writers of this persuasion include "Iceberg Slim," who has exploited ghetto life in his best-selling, autobiographical *Pimp* (1967), *Trick Baby* (1967), and *Mama Black Widow* (1969); Clarence Farmer, *Soul on Fire* (1969); and Nathan Heard, *Howard Street* (1969).

Incidents of racial tensions and confrontations in the military in America and abroad are common enough so that television actor Hari Rhodes can make quite believable the contemporary events of his novel, *The Chosen Few* (1965), in which black Blood Burrell and his fellow United States Marines are obliged to engage in actual armed battle against some bigoted white citizens of Jacksonville, Florida, to retrieve the mangled body of their lynched Marine buddy. In the political sphere, John A. Williams' *The Man Who Cried I Am* (1967) narrates the international activities of American Negro writer Max Reddick who stumbles—too late—upon the discovery of white America's "ultimate solution" designed for uncommonly ambitious blacks. Half-playfully with Mr. Carpentier in his play, *The Electronic Nigger* (1969), but soberly serious elsewhere, Ed Bullins, a powerful new black playwright, has feared that the days of the American Negro are numbered, with the advent of tractable, inexpensive, if mechanical automation. Prompted by both historical and personal repetitions of white hypocrisy and white betrayals, H. "Rap" Brown also senses imminent doom for American Negroes whose deaths he would make partially meaningful by retaliatory violence. Given to understand the openly admitted greedy motivations of American capitalists as explained by Julius Lester's "White Power," or to know the flagrant bigotry of our judicial court system, as in MacPherson's "Act of Prostitution," it is easy, at least for black Americans, to understand that there must be the uncompromising determination of poet Robert Hayden's freedom-bound slave in "Runagate," or the grim meanness of Miss Brooks' *Bronzeville Blacks;* that some modern blacks display the near-psychotic symbiotic verbal abuse of Miss Polite's Jimson and Ideal, intellectual blacks hoisted on their own petards, in the aptly named novel, *The Flagellants;* defensive rituals, as in Jones' *Mad Heart.* Even as empathetic, life-loving, and gentle a man as the late Langston Hughes could appreciate the value of the Black Panthers. Los Angeles-based Ron Karenga, leader of a Black Power organization called US, has summed up the attitudes of this school of modern black writers: "The year 1969 will be the year for reconstruction; 1970 will be the year of separation; 1971 will be the year of the guerrillas—of defense rather than development."

If such Afro-American writers focus mercilessly on the manifold evils of racism as evidence to justify their rage and fears of imminent racial genocide, it is, perhaps, an understandable extremism, to remind readers of the possibilities, if not the probabilities, of imperfect man as he comes painfully to grips with the unrealized dimensions of the American Dream, easily one of the most ambitious, most optimistic social schemes imagined by real, ordinary, and most various man. In Africa, the concerns with white concocted injustices are different, and generally are of less intensity. The exception is, of course, white-controlled southern Africa, where, because as in Afro-America, there is also an expressive dominant white power structure, the blacks' literature—Nkosi's *Rhythm of Violence*, Richard Rive's *Rain*—could easily be adapted to Afro-American contexts. But, as illustrated with modern East- and West-African literatures, it is irresponsibly simplistic to present a body of writing that sees the world as divided into white villains and black saints. With black men in power in the independent French-speaking and English-speaking West African states, African writers know very well that white men have no inherent monopoly on worldwide afflictions of broadcast evils. Indeed, such writers, with a new and terrible sense of their mission in life as authors, may share the sentiments of Nigerian Wole Soyinka, who recently addressed a Stockholm gathering of African writers:

> My concern in this talk is primarily with the non-South African writer and why, before very long, he may begin to envy the South African the bleak immensities of his problems. For the South African has still the right to hope, and this prospect of a future yet uncompromised by failure on his own part, in his own right, is something which has lately ceased to exist for other African writers. . . .
>
> For the situation in Africa today is the same as in the rest of the world; it is not one of the tragedies which come of isolated human failures, but the very collapse of humanity. Nevertheless the African writer has done nothing to vindicate his existence, nothing to indicate that he is even aware that this awful collapse has taken place. For he has been generally without vision.[37]

In Afro-America there has also been much discussion about the role of the black writer in reshaping American ends, but to mention African and Afro-American ideas of the writers' responsibilities is to move into an entirely new area of concern, the realm of black revolutionary literature.

New Black Revolts

Reacting to the stereotypes imposed by whites, African and Afro-American writers struggled argumentatively to counter with attempts to show basic similarities—psychological, national, and cultural—between themselves and white persons. Such extended efforts were mostly directed toward white audiences, many of whom remained unconvinced, as evidenced by white publishers' preferences for Negro-written sensational novels and poems. The indulgence of some white publishers for badly written but sensational novels by Negroes has had its damaging effects all around. Gullible white readers were grossly misled into believing these books, while other, more knowledgeable white readers, perhaps in the name of expansive "understanding," readily forgave the black writers' obvious lack of literary skills. Seeing the success of these writers, younger potential Negro writers simply continued the tradition, still alive, so that today there are a good number of badly written books by Negroes. As long as Negro writers argued, in whatever competence, from the posture of trying to emphasize black and white peoples' similarities, their literature was predesigned to become variations of propaganda attempting to offset white propaganda. Not until black writers began to deal with the root matters of identity, of who *they* felt themselves to be, ethnically and artistically, and not until they began to write realistically of their own people, would these writers begin to recognize an untapped potential for a whole new literature. In view of the real pressures involved, such a recognition would be no simple undertaking. Such writers first had to slough off white-imposed identities and honestly reclaim, assess, and celebrate their own definitions of their black and African selves.

NEW BLACK IDENTITIES

The claims that the African, wherever in the world, was completely made over by virtue of his contacts with the white man are patently untrue; there was the important matter of psychological and cultural pride that would somehow persist: in Africa there was the matter of Negritude; in Afro-America there was the matter of Blackness, or "Soul." Widely discussed issues emanating from West Africa and the West Indies, and from Afro-American, ghetto-identified intellectuals, Negritude and/or Soul have attracted attention from around the world for many reasons, not the least of which is the rare and happy fact that both of these assertions of black personality are, whatever else, one fundamental basis on which most concerned black and white observers can agree. For Negritude and Soul both proudly sing that there is indeed a decided difference between the white man and the black man. Having agreed on this difference, however, the same black and white observers have found aspects of the agreement on which to disagree. Although most blacks understand perfectly that the two terms are practically interchangeable, Afro-American "Soul" has never received the elaborate philosophical, poetic, and even political explication that Negritude has, especially from Leopold Senghor, president of French-speaking Senegal. Opinions and findings of Negritude by white critics have ranged from an easy equation of such differences as prima facie evidence of black inferiority and white superiority; to the sanguinity of Janheinz Jahn who says in *Muntu* (1958, 1961) and elsewhere that only Negritude can reinvigorate a badly worn out Western civilization which has become a vast, dried up, mechanical wasteland of a culture; to the suspicions of Jean Paul Sartre in his *Orphee Noir* (1948), where he assumes a political Negritude to be presently in a dialectical process, to be ignored after the synthesis of African national independence; to the convictions of Lilyan Kesteloot, who feels that Negritude will endure as long as black men remain consciously black men.

The late distinguished Africanist, Melville Herskovits, pondered long over certain recurring literary patterns he found in his extensive study of West African oral literature. Finally he asked, "Can we find an explanation for the absence of the tragic theme?"[38] The next year, Sheik Anta Diop provided an answer of sorts in his comprehensive work, *The Cultural Unity of Negro Africa* (1959), which points out specific contrasts between African and European life styles, and supplies references to which exponents of Negritude and Soul would likely heartily subscribe:

> The Meridional cradle, confined to the African continent in particular, is characterized by the matriarchal family, the creation of the territorial state, in contrast to the Aryan city-state, the emancipation of women in domestic life, exenophilia, cosmopolitanism, a sort of collectivism having as corollary a tranquility going so far as unconcern for tomorrow, a material solidarity of right for each individual, which makes moral or material misery unknown to the present day . . . In the moral domain, it shows an ideal of peace, justice, of goodness and an optimism which eliminates all notion of guilt or original sin . . . The types of literature most favored are the novel, tales, fables and comedy.

> The northern cradle, confined to Greece and Rome, is characterized by the patriarchal family, by the city-state . . . The particular character of these city-states, outside of which a man was an outlaw, developed an internal patriotism, as well as xenophobia. Individualism, moral and material solitude, a disgust for existence . . . are attributes of this cradle. An idea of war, violence, crime and conquests, inherited from nomadic life, with as consequence a feeling of original sin, which causes pessimistic religious or metaphysical systems to be built, is the special attribute of this cradle . . . The literary style par excellence is tragedy or drama.[39]

Something similar to Diop's findings has long been expressed by Africans throughout the world. Arabian Amr ben Bahr, grandson of a Negro slave known as Al-Jahiz, is said to have been the founder of the classical Arabian prose style and one of the greatest scholars of the ninth century. In one of his works, *Kitab al-Sudan wa l'-Bidan* (*The Superiority in Glory of the Black Race over the White*), he stated, "Negroes are distinguished amongst other people by their natural gift for rhythmic dancing and are the best artists on the drum, all of this without any special training. They are also great singers."[40] "We are almost a nation of dancers, musicians, and poets," reported Gustavus Vassa in his autobiography, *The Interesting Narrative of the Life of Olaudah Equiano or Gustavus Vassa the African* (1789).[41] Dragged from his knees while at prayer in a white church, St. George's in Philadelphia, and told that he and his fellow black worshippers could not pray there, Richard Allen decided to form his own denomination of Methodism. He may have been referring to "special qualities" of Negroes when he wrote in 1793, "I was confident that there was no religious sect or denomination that would suit the capacity of the colored people as well as the Methodist; . . . Sure I am that reading sermons will never prove so beneficial to the colored people as spiritual or extempore preaching. . . ."[42]

There was certainly a distinctiveness to the works of some Harlem Renaissance writers of the 1920's and 1930's who began to express a newly found sense of their blackness, their African roots, whether or not, as Langston Hughes has reported, it was called Negritude or Soul or whatever. It was black. Countee Cullen wrote in "Harlem Wine," "This is a wine that must flow on/ Not caring how or where,/ So it has ways to flow upon/ Where song is in the air." Jamaican-born Claude McKay remembered in "The Tropics in New York" that back home there were "Bananas ripe and green, and ginger roots,/ Cocoa in pods and alligator pears,/ And tangerines and mangoes and grape fruit,/ Fit for the highest prize at parish fairs." In "The Negro Speaks of Rivers," Langston Hughes responded to remembered glimpses of his racial past: "I've known rivers . . ./ I bathed in the Euphrates when dawns were young/I built my hut near the Congo and it lulled me to sleep,/ I looked upon the Nile and raised the pyramids above it." Waring Cuney reminded the needlessly shamed Afro-American domestic of her African black beauty: "If she could dance/ Naked,/ Under palm trees/ And see her image in the river/ She would know." The reverberations of these pulsating new sounds were heard and amplified across the sea in Haiti by Jean-Price-Mars; in Paris by black French colonials studying abroad: Étienne Léro and Réne Ménil in their 1932 founded journal, *Legitime Defense;* and later by Léopold Senghor from Senegal; Léon Damas from French Guiana; Aimé Césaire from the island of Martinique, all of whom founded *L'Etudiant Noir* in 1934. With the concept and use of "Negritude" so powerfully wrought in Césaire's ground-breaking *Cahier d'un retour au pays natal* in 1939, an explosive international consciousness of blackness quickly began to develop.

The momentum of this movement, in all of its exhortations of the uniqueness, promises of blackness, did not arise without its critics. The late Richard Wright, for instance, could bring his worldwide experiences to bear on his conclusion that what blacks were extolling as perception, insights, and behavioral patterns peculiar to themselves were really no more than the predictably defensive, self-conscious mutterings of any oppressed people viewing from "the frog perspective" those in the world who were regarded as better off than they; that such "special feelings" are shared by similarly oppressed Asians and Africans and Afro-Americans: "We are dealing here with values evoked by social systems or colonial regimes which make men feel that they are dominated by powers stronger than they are." Ezekiel Mphahlele, long-time critic of Negritude, points to the romanticized abstract exaggerations of the concept that would tend to balance, for only a short while, sheer fantasy rather than produce an art that would empirically treat verifiable realities. Lewis Nkosi has also said as much, calling Negritude as practiced by French African writers "a poetry of gesticulating rhetoric" and he goes on to say that his reactions to such writings are "widely shared in the English-speaking writing circles, and the widening gap between the two schools is disturbing. Nigerian and Ghanaian writers (as well as South African ones) tend to dismiss offhand the writing by French Africans as mawkish and romantic; the French Africans, on the other hand, regard the English-speaking Africans as superficially educated and sadly ill-equipped to engage in intellectual gymnastics with them."[43] The efficacy of the surrogated presence of former English and French colonial rulers is still evident.

In Afro-America there has not been such extensive expository debate over the matter of "Soul," the notion that blacks are naturally endowed with inimitable physical graces, psychological and spiritual attitudes, mastery of rhythms and song, and uncommon durability. One finds, now and again, a writer who does not wish to be accepted as a Negro writer at all, for example, Willard Motley (*Knock on Any Door,* 1947; *We Fished All Night,* 1951), and Frank Yerby, the best-selling creator of more than two dozen commercially successful costume romances. Usually one finds Afro-American writers concerned with only the positive aspects of these "soulful" traits. W. E. B. DuBois has claimed, "the Negro people as a race have a contribution to make to civilization and humanity which no other race can make." He continues:

> This race has the greatest gifts of the Gods, laughter. It dances and sings; it is humble; it longs to learn; it loves men; it loves women. It is frankly, baldly, deliciously human in an artificial and hypocritical land. If you will hear men laugh, go to Guinea, "Black Bottom," "Niggertown," Harlem. If you want to feel humor too exquisite and subtle for translation, sit invisibly among a gang of Negro workers. The white world has its gibes and cruel caricatures . . . but to the black world alone belongs the delicious chuckle.[44]

Alain Locke, Rhodes Scholar, beloved educator, and knowing critic, saw, even as he guided the Harlem Renaissance into being, that "the American Negro race" was a deliberate artificiality, but, things being what they are, it is turning out that this "race" may be one of the very few meaningful realities in this country of persistent illusions:

> Social prejudice, which was meant to hamper the Negro . . . has turned out to be a great spiritual discipline and a cultural blessing in disguise. For it has developed in the Negro a peculiar folk solidarity, preserved its peculiar folk-values and intensified their modes of expression; so that now they stand out in the rather colorless amalgam of the general population as the most colorful and distinctive spiritual things in American life.[45]

With or without such prestigious definitions of black American life styles, with which some of them are directly familiar, many modern black writers are asserting their personal definitions of their personally defined identities in personal ways. Unlike the narrator of Ralph Ellison's novel, *Invisible Man,* who gropes through various adventures for an identity of which he finally is not confident, black youths of today, according to poet-critic Larry Neal, already "know who we are, and we are not invisible, *at least not to each other.*" Appealing to just this acknowledgement of their black and visible selves, such writers turn away from traditional American literary reality that has ignored or distorted their black existence. Fully aware that they are not and, for various reasons, never will be white, these writers assume they are giving legitimizing voice to hitherto unheard and unappreciated history, birth, loves, hates, lives and deaths of the black American, especially (and often romantically) the black ghetto mother, father, and family. Often these writers become self-appointed, dogmatic mouthpieces for, rather than accommodating voices of, the black masses. Because they are loud and raucous, sensational and exploitative in the name of their black identity, such writers attract most attention. There are other less obtrusive, more disciplined black writers who, while not as confident of their identities as some of their less disciplined writing fraternity, do manage to find value and meaning in honest examination of their black experiences.

The great thing here, however, is that, various notions of the black identity aside, no longer is the black American writer deferring as much as in the past to the approbations of conventionally white norms of reality, experience, and literature. It is no exaggeration to view this development as anything short of an American cultural and literary revolution.

LITERARY DIRECTIONS IN MODERN AFRICA

Even in the excellent study of militant African and Afro-American writings by the perceptive and knowing critic, Mercer Cook of Howard University, there are noticeable differences in the intensities of the two literatures. "In the main, statements by the Africans seem to me less extreme and violent than many by West Indians and North American Negroes."[46] The same kind of relative lack of intensity is also found in other, not necessarily militant, literature of the Africans. Generally, the abiding concern of modern Africans is to ponder the kind of role they will play in the future of the world, as independent, responsible, necessarily involved, free black Africans. For instance, how much artistic and cultural reverence for their lengthy historic past will be psychologically, culturally, and practically helpful in this new world? How much of this reverence might impede successful negotiations with a modern, sophisticated, competitive world? Such concerns are clearly of great importance to modern Africans because their answers involve the difficult business of possibly reshaping their prized African personality. Their mixed feelings about the matter, their sometimes divided allegiances to the old world and the new, and their literary directions can be seen in their descriptions of modern life in the traditional village and modern life in the new African cities.

Like writers everywhere in a changing world, African writers have also felt and recorded the impact of civilization on traditional rural life and on the accelerations of urban living. But there have been marked differences between African and other literary accounts of the dynamics of such change. For the Africans, the land, especially of the village ("to which the Africans are mystically bound," as one native writer would have it)[47] has meant dramatically more, psychologically, religiously, politically, economically, and socially, than it has for most other peoples. To the extent that a number of important exceptions can be found to his statements, Kenyan-born John S. Mbiti is generalizing freely about "the African," but his remarks, so understood, have their special value in offering poignant insights into the values of the village as a rapidly disappearing African way of life. Describing the network of the profoundly important traditional kinship system as including all relatives, dead, living, and not yet born, Mbiti continues with regard to the importance of the African "extended family":

In traditional life, the individual does not and cannot exist alone except corporately. He owes his existence to other people, including those of past generations . . . Whatever happens to the individual happens to the whole group, and whatever happens to the whole group happens to the individuals. The individual can say: "I am, because we are; and since we are, therefore I am." This is a cardinal point in the understanding of the African view of man.[48]

Aspects of other important roles played by the traditional village are repeated features of all genres of modern African literature, especially with its major writers, such as Amos Tutuola and Chinua Achebe in the novel and John Pepper Clark and Wole Soyinka in the drama. Beginning with *The Palm-Wine Drinkard* (1952) and continuing through *My Life in the Bush of Ghosts* (1954), *Simbi and the Satyr of the Dark Jungles* (1955), *The Brave African Huntress* (1958), and *The Feather Woman* (1962), Tutuola has laid all of his locales in rural Nigeria, drawing from the mosaic of his Yoruba tribal background for plots. Chinua Achebe bases two of his novels—*Things Fall Apart* (1958) and *Arrow of God* (1964)—in village settings, and while his *No Longer at Ease* (1960) takes place in the city of Lagos, Nigeria, its plot depends almost entirely upon the intrusion of the enduring and pervasive potency of a village-founded prejudice about caste, as the London-trained protagonist discovers to his woe when he falls in love with a girl, however well-trained a nurse, from the wrong caste. Even in Chinua Achebe's city-based *A Man of the People* (1966), there are pivotal motifs of rural backgrounds. As with Tutuola, John Pepper Clark in *Three Plays: Song of a Goat; The Masquerade; The Raft* (1964) and *Ozidi* (1966) lays his actions in villages. As does Tutuola, Wole Soyinka explores his Yoruba tribal past for its legacy of myths, legends, customs, and ontology chiefly to show the universality of mankind's foibles and his tendencies toward easy escape from reality by erecting idealized pasts. This is repeatedly apparent in all but the second and fourth of his *Five Plays: A Dance of the Forests; The Lion and the Jewel; The Swamp Dwellers; The Trials of Brother Jethro; The Strong Breed* (1964); and in *The Road* (1965) and *Kongi's Harvest* (1967). Preoccupied with a passion to show the folly or evil of human hypocrisy, Soyinka, a brilliant craftsman and satirist, can sometimes seem, in his searching focus on the guilts of most people, as zealous as a celibate monk convinced utterly of universal sin. It is hard to find a single guilt-free personage, historical, spiritual, symbolic, or human, among the more than forty characters (some roles doubled by several of the two dozen or so actors) in *A Dance of the Forests*. About to celebrate the gathering of the tribes, several counselors decided to invite some of their "illustrious ancestors," but the two who show up, Dead Man and Dead Woman, are hardly illustrious. In the presence of a clever interrogator, several human characters are made to reveal their hidden guilts, both in their present roles and in the archetypal historical roles that they also play. Professor of *The Road* is an extremely complex man, called "mad" by other characters in the play, but in the foreground of his mosaic of mystical, religious, and psychological aspects is his preoccupation with guilt. Although Soyinka is concerned usually with more than the exigencies of human guilt, such a consciousness is the favorite device in his universal drama, as can be seen in *The Strong Breed.*

Amos Tutuola and others may be charged with deliberately choosing the pastoral simplicities of African village or traditional life, thus making it easier for them to invest such locales with their wonted fantasizing, fable characters who move at their creators' will through events of the writers' imaginative and sometimes capricious choosing. Other African writers may be charged with exploiting rural settings for other forms of escapism. Increasingly in modern Africa, there are those who feel that, if it is to become meaningfully durable, African literature must take a more realistic look at the present. Mbella Sonne Dipoko has declared that African literature is more than a literature of revolt and dialogue and compromise. "It is also something else. It is the alienation of the citizen from the city he built with passion and his words of love . . . The literary movement of *Negritude* was only a sublimation of a social dream: the desire of the people for a happier city. It was this dream which some African poets interpreted in terms of the past, instead of in a vision of the present and the future. They started by presenting black Africa and traditional values as the antithesis of white Europe and industrialization. We have seen that this did not last."[49] Certainly no such charge may be leveled at Soyinka, Achebe, Clark, Camara Laye, "Mongo Beti" (Alexandre Biyidi), and other modern major African writers, whose works depict believable settings and complex characters who confront or are confronted by recognizably real situations.

Soberly probing their roles as responsible writers, such modern African writers recognize, with Tanzania's Julius Nyerere, that the Africa of today is faced, not so much with the philosophical speculation of "To change or not to change," but with the pressingly realistic dictum of "Change or be changed." Such change is seen nowhere more interestingly than in the literature that presents African adjustments to the life in the modern African cities. The facts of African urbanization are undeniable: "Although eight out of ten Africans still live in rural areas, they are moving to urban centers faster than any other people on earth . . . Between 1950 and 1960—a mere ten years—the number of Africans living in cities increased by 69 per cent."[50] In a 1965 study of West African urbanization, it was shown that in that area there was a population of about sixty-seven million, over half of whom were concentrated in the approaches to and environs of cities in Nigeria, Ghana, Liberia, and Sierra Leone.[51]

Yet, as was true in Achebe's novels, *No Longer at Ease* and *A Man of the People,* the formative influences of village or traditional ways are still variously manifested even in the emerging city-based literature. With the rural newcomer acting upon the developing cities and these burgeoning metropolises acting simultaneously on the newly urbanized African, neither the modern African personality nor the modern African city has yet been completed. The literary accounts of such reciprocity make for singularly interesting reading. It should be noted here that "the city" in African literature is often a European or American city: London, to Gustavus Vassa; Paris, to the Negritude poets and to Cheik Hamidou Kane, as in his *Ambiguous Adventure* (1969); and Princeton and New York City (especially Harlem) to John P. Clark in his critical reminiscence, *America, Their America* (1969). But the modern African city is becoming increasingly important in recent literature: there is Sophiatown of Bloke Modisane's autobiographical *Blame Me on History*, his classic short story, "The Dignity of Begging," and Lewis Nkosi's story of callous brutality, "Potgeiter's Castle"; Lagos, Nigeria, of Cyprian Ekwensi's *Jagua Nana* and *People of the City;* Conakry, Guinea, of Camara Laye's *The Dark Child;* Dar es Salaam in J. A. K. Leslie's *Survey of Dar es Salaam* (1963); the Ghanaian city of Kansawora in Ayi Kwei Armah's *The Beautyful* [sic] *Ones Are Not Yet Born* (1968); Sharpeville, South Africa, to CredoVusa' mazulu Mutwa's *My People, My Africa* (1969) and Richard Rive's *Emergency* (1964). On the surface, themes used in some of this urban-based literature are the predictable ones: they view the sprawling, congested, fast-paced, commercially exploitable city living with ambivalence, ennui, bitter-sweet nostalgia for the old village ways; they behold the emergence of the powerful individual whose worth has often been proven by rugged, conniving, dangerous, even murderous competition; they document the process whereby accelerated living corrodes, hardens, and finally shatters old family and tribal ties.

To be sure, some ambitious writers have tried to capitalize on facile exploitation of the obvious themes expected from such city-based literature. In the sensationalized *Shadow of Wealth* (1966) by Ghana's prolific Asare Konadu (*Wizard of Asamang* and *Come Back, Dora*, 1966; *A Woman in Her Prime*, 1967), we encounter the melodramatic unfoldings of a once wretchedly poor village boy, Joseph Frimpong. He goes to the city and rises to become the powerful and affluent Managing Director of Ghana Tematro Corporation, spicing the tedium of contending with a wife and eleven children by supporting choice women, including Alice Boayke, a beguiling divorcée who leaves her two children back in her native village to seek opportunities in the city, where she is gradually overwhelmed into scandalous city behavior. But major African writers do more than this with such themes, which is why, beneath the surface of their themes of both city- and village-based works, there are themes of meaningful protest. In both areas, these writers are really lodging revolts against the impositions clamped on them by outside forces. In both areas, major writers see themselves not so much as craftsmen somewhat removed from the action of adjusting to the realities of the past and present but as "word warriors." Henri Krea of Algeria explains it: "Le poésie et la revolution sont la même chose." On an American lecture tour in 1969, during the heat of the Nigerian-Biafran civil war, Nigerian author Chinua Achebe told a University of Texas audience the same thing: "I think there is a myth about creativity being something apart from life. There are forms of creativity which suit different moments. . . . It is impossible to write anything in Africa without some kind of commitment, some kind of message, some kind of protest. Even those novels that look like very gentle recreations of the past were a kind of protest. They were saying, in effect, politely saying that we had a past."[52] And while the writers of independent Africa may not have the same intensity of identity problems or quite the same political goals as their Afro-American brethren, there are in both literatures of today those writers who insist on the functional, revolutionizing role of literature.

AFRO-AMERICAN LITERARY REVOLTS

Given "the historically relentless persistence of pervasive white American racism"—as some black rhetoricians would have it—many modern Afro-American writers have long recognized that the range of choices for black life styles has always been and will likely remain confiningly small. Thus, much in the New Black Revolt literature is as old as the history of American racial confrontations. There have been historical distributions of emphases given to one choice of life style or another, but the actual choices—from despair, resignation, assimilationism, emigrationism—have Afro-American precedents. Lately, however, some modern black writers have begun to convince themselves that they are beginning to fashion viable new revolts. There are those, of course, who would become, with whatever force necessary, almost contiguous parts of the present system. But such writers, vociferous as they can be, are to be distinguished from other modern black writers who proclaim that they do not want to function in the system as it is presently structured, who claim that they are going "to turn this country around," destroying the old materialistic, individualistic America and substituting a more spiritual, communal, humanitarian order. Seeing themselves in the vanguard of social revolution as critically needed but racially denied potential leaders who would revitalize a land described as morally bankrupt and culturally suicidal, such writers point to the fact of their "racial" endurance and survival of a history of protracted racial persecutions as evidence enough of their qualifications as new leaders for a badly needed new America. "We are not a minority," they assert, "but the chosen few."

Positing that they differ from white men on more accounts than skin complexion, they are concerned with a host of revolutionary undertakings, not the least of which is wrenching the black man free from his dangerously long dependence upon "white values." The black poet must destroy the white criterion's hold on the black mind, states Clarence Major, "because seeing the world through white eyes from a black soul causes death."[53] Quoting black poet Don L. Lee, critic-poet-fiction-writer Larry Neal points out, "Black artists are culture stabilizers; bringing back old values, and introducing new ones."[54] The black poet's role, announces LeRoi Jones (Imamu Amiri Baraka), "is the destruction of America . . . to contribute as much as possible to that. But now I realize that the Black poet ought also try to provide a 'post american form,' even as simple vision for his people. We must, in the present, be missionaries of Blackness, of consciousness."[55] John Killens is even more specific in his description of the uniqueness and special potential of these "missionaries": "The Black writer's ship is not a *Ship of Fools*. His mood is not 'Stop the world, I want to get off.' He wants to ride this old world, kick over all the old dungheaped corrals, tame this Wild West crazy beast, like the champeen bronco-buster he certainly is. He wants to bring sanity to this madhouse, even if he has to bring the building down first. Black writers are singing of love; healthy love, requited love."[56] "Brothers, sisters,/ come on back, get back/ back to what we were—still is—/ get back," urges Don L. Lee. Among the most promising black poetic sisters is Sonia Sanchez who helps clarify the intended role of the revolutionary black woman in support of her black man; "to all sisters":/" hurt./ u worried abt a/ little hurting./ man/ hurt/ ain't the bag u/ shd be in./ loving is/ the bag, man./ there ain't no MAN like a black man./ he puts it where it is/ and makes u/ turn in/ side out."[57]

Understandably, the movement has its share of confusions and contradictions. For instance, on the one hand, members urge repudiation and destruction of "white Western life styles, especially white sexual inhibitions," and presumably such members would substitute a black humanism that would be frank, honest, earthy, spontaneous, and uninhibited. But, at least in the instance of *The Black Woman's Role in the Revolution*, the authors, "sisters of the B.C.D.," a collaboration of black authors, the dicta are fairly conventional, almost puritanical, as the authors lay down party line rules and regulations about what the black revolutionary woman should do about her hair and make-up ("be natural"); drinking alcohol ("unhealthy habit; no drinking in public . . . one of the worst smelling things in this world is an alcohol breath"); smoking cigarettes ("bad for your health"); wearing pants ("we have no business in them . . . they look terrible, horrible, repulsive . . .").[58] Where they are clear-minded, however, they make their greatest impressions. Unlike many of their American Negro predecessors who, anxious to flatter the white literary establishment, utilized traditional aesthetics, rhythms, content, forms, language, syntax, spellings, an increasing number of these new black writers today are busily creating an expanding body of literature that is pointedly defined by its own world of black references. This literature is drawn from their own acceptance and celebration of their black identity, their own black martyred heroes (Malcolm X, Martin Luther King, Jr., Medgar Evers), and from their own black musicians who are using musical instruments to produce something more than fixed, written protractions of interesting tonalities (Sun Ra, Pharaoh Saunders, John Coltrane, Ray Charles, James Brown); their own black poets (Gwendolyn Brooks, Langston Hughes, LeRoi Jones, Marvin X). Unlike earlier Negro writers, many of these black writers are asserting (sometimes to a point close to rank chauvinism) pride in the color and looks and movements and laughter and talk and dance and song of black men, black women, black children. And these writers present their feelings deliberately in often defiant uses of "Ghettoese", a language that, used knowingly, has a vocabulary, a grammar, a syntax, and spelling derived from fusion of Southern Negro dialect and city argot. It matters not in the slightest to these writers that some readers may find their work "marred" by obscenities or affected speech, or that it is thought to be so much "pop poetry." The less gifted of such writers, having nothing but empty rhetoric to express nothing, do try to animate their bayings with indiscriminate repetitions of all the foul words they have ever heard. Such bayings are easily recognized, however, by today's alert black readers, and are quickly dismissed for the drivel that they are. The talented of these writers, on the other hand, know and demonstrate when "an obscenity" or an unusual spelling is legitimate, organic, functional, and dramatic. Certainly swear words were not needed at all to vivify one of the most powerful books of our times, *The Autobiography of Malcolm X*, written by Alex Haley. In six years of acquaintance with Malcolm X, Haley reports that he heard Malcolm swear only once, and then to say "hell." On the other hand, for all of its use of language that has been traditionally deemed vulgar, deCoy's *Nigger Bible* means to be something more than sensationalized heresy, something more than an obscenely anthropomorphic version of the Genesis story. Indeed, it may be argued that deCoy's work is a rare dramatization of the biblical Genesis passage which says, "And God said, 'Let us make man in our image, after our likeness. . . .' And God created man in his own image, in the image of God created he him; male and female created he them. And God blessed them and God said unto them, 'Be fruitful, and multiply . . .'" The ghetto observers in Don L. Lee's poem, *Wall of Respect*, are most sincere when, expressing their pride and admiration for the black heroes painted on the wall before them, they exclaim, in their own hyperbole, "ain't the motherfucka layen there?" "French," replied French-born, French-speaking Jeanne d'Arc naturally enough to her English captors who asked her in which language her vision of Christ spoke to her. Black readers of Don L. Lee's spelling understand that there is an intended world of difference between a "blk woman" who is thereby "together" and a "whi—te woman" who is thereby not "together." Readers recognize that Jewel Latimore's "For Nigareens" is attitudinally needed now; such readers recognize that Sonia Sanchez' poem, "to all sisters," (p. 30) need not be about sex at all; such black readers see that, beneath his frequent exhibitionist screechings, LeRoi Jones is, in his own black way, a gentle man, a pious man, a moralist. What seems important to these black writers is that their black readers do indeed understand and react to their works. It has some importance, too, that younger white readers around the world are also beginning to understand and react.

While there is a good deal of ritualistic symbolic violence in the works of several of these writers, there is also, as may have been anticipated, actual literal violence depicted on occasion. In the quite ridiculous book-length, comic-strip novel, *The Black Commandoes* by Julian Moreau (Atlanta 1967), Denis Jackson avenges the murder of his Louisiana childhood friend by growing up to become "a millionaire several times over," and, with an I.Q. of "well over two hundred," serves as a recruiter for the Black Commandoes, who vengefully participate in rampages of killings, including seventy-one Ku Klux Klansmen in Mississippi, the hatchet assassination of Governor Malice of Louisiana, and the destruction of half the Los Angeles Police force, in an attack on the entire Chicago Mafia, and in the humbling of the President of the United States, escaping, whenever necessary, in a black flying saucer. Dan Freeman in

Sam Greenlee's slickly written *The Spook Who Sat by the Door* (1969), resigns from five years of valuable Uncle Tomming with the C.I.A. to organize a well-trained, nationwide network of black paramilitary Freedom Fighters whose first assault is on Chicago, Illinois. Whereas such pieces of violence may seem to be nothing more than so much sensationalized amusement to some white readers, aware of the white population majority and military monopoly, these works represent a kind of desperate, therapeutic escapism for harried black readers. Other black writers would suggest less violent methods of reform: Harold Cruse, for instance, would have the Afro-American intellectual elite contribute to an American cultural, political revolution by coming to grips with the reasons it is completely ignored by white American thinkers and social scientists.

As major African writers make so much more of themes from African village and city life than do other African writers, so major Afro-American writers have distinguished themselves from lesser authors in their measurably more powerful treatments of black American life. Being responsible craftsmen, they present believable characters in a believable manner. Ralph Ellison's invisible man is not really invisible to anyone except white people, such as the "tall blond man" encountered in the prologue of *Invisible Man* (1952). When the nameless protagonist puts on dark glasses, he is thereby mistaken by a Harlem woman as Rhinehart, her lover; but she remembers that Rhinehart always wore a hat; adding a hat to his dark glasses, the hero is mistaken as a belligerent by his favorite bartender; later he is thought to be a numbers man; buying knob-toed shoes he is mistaken as an adulterer, a Harlem storefront church minister. Some white policemen mistake him also, but, like the "tall blond man," they insist that he be what they expect him to be; the various Harlem characters at least recognize that he is *not* Rhinehart. Several, if not most, of Richard Wright's heroes are not necessarily blacks or even Americans in that they do not want various things because white people have them. Bigger Thomas of Wright's powerful *Native Son* (1940) does not want to fly airplanes simply because white people fly them. Cross Damon in *The Outsider* (1953) is not at all concerned with the skin color of black Joe Thomas or his white landlord, Mr. Herndon, or the white Communist leader, Gil, all of whom he bludgeons to death. The nameless black giant of the Wright short story, "Big Black Good Man," a merchant marine, docks in Copenhagen, buys whiskey and the services of a local prostitute, and on a return trip awards the frightened, racist hotel clerk a gift of six shirts; but such transactions are carried on in every dock in the world by all kinds of merchant marines. The hero of "The Man Who Lived Underground" dramatizes a human, not necessarily a black or Negro or American or Yugoslavian, compulsion for some kind of comprehensible psychological reality, even a reality that depends upon lies. Bigger Thomas wants to know how it feels to be Bigger Thomas, man. Cross Damon (as Charles Webb or Addison Jordan or Lionel Lane) deceives himself into believing that simply by killing people who once knew him by one or another of these names he could achieve and sustain a Godlike freedom. Much has already been made of James Baldwin's reputed self-loathing (which might easily be a personal rather than a racial indictment), and of some of his characters who strive, not for an individualism or even a humanity, but the cathartic approbation of white people. When, for instance, Rufus Scott in *Another Country* (1962) leaps to his death from the George Washington Bridge, he does so after grinding psychological pressures have shattered him, a sensitive musician, into the fragments of a man, reduced to making something of a living as a male prostitute, unable to contain the shock of white rejection. Several heroes from Chester Himes' works are also black men who are defeated by their inability to sustain survival relationships with domineering whites who demand that such relationships dramatize their own notions of racial superiority: Charles Taylor of *The Third Generation* (1954), Bob Jones of *If He Hollers Let Him Go* (1945), Lee Gordon of *Lonely Crusade* (1947), and the frustrated novelist Jessie Robinson of *The Primitive* (1956) (which Himes called his best work). In these and the works of other major Afro-American writers are reflected the serious regard for the craft of writing, consciously controlled uses of the components of the poem, the story, the play, and the novel. This kind of writing will endure the explosive bursts of topical rage. Wright, Ellison, Baldwin, Himes, Ann Petry, and others will be read for some time.

This glance at the array of selected modern African and Afro-American writers may seem to indicate a gamut of thematic differences, ranging in Afro-America from increasingly loud protest for mainstream acceptance, to desperate depictions of near fantasies of violent racial confrontations, to a determined artistic effort to assume the vanguard for social and moral reform; in Africa, topics range from languorous, poeticized reminiscences of African antiquity or the traditional ways of the African village, to facile exploitation of city-based topics. One can also see, however, that with most writers the ordeal of color, common to both groups, has exacted a heavy toll. One might also see how, with the major writers from both groups, these same themes can be transmuted into meaningful literature that will endure for numerous reasons. The fact of the matter is that in both Africa and Afro-America there was indeed the profound shock of black and white encounter; there were uncounted losses for both peoples. That was in the historic yesterday. But however many, however brutal the black losses, black hope has survived. That hope is a matter of today. What directions are chartered for this black hope is the stuff of these selections.

NOTES

1. William H. Sheppard, *Pioneers to the Congo* (n.d., n.p.).
2. Levi Coffin, *Observations of Persons and Things in South Africa, 1900–1905* (Philadelphia, 1905).
3. Alexander Crummell, *Africa and America* (Springfield, Mass., 1891).
4. Robert I. Rotberg, ed., *George Simeon Mwase, Strike a Blow and Die* (Cambridge, 1967), p. 36.
5. Booker T. Washington (1901).
6. Countee Cullen (1929).

7. Alain Locke (1925).
8. Peter Abrahams, *Tell Freedom: Memories from Africa* (1954, 1969), p. 226.
9. Cited in Edwin S. Redkey, *Black Exodus: Black Nationalist and Back-to-Africa Movements, 1890–1910* (New Haven, 1969), p. 10 n.
10. Frantz Fanon, *Black Skins, White Masks* (New York, 1967; trans. by Charles L. Markham), p. 128.
11. William Grier and Price Cobbs, *Black Rage* (New York, 1969), p. 149.
12. Frances S. Herskovits, ed. Melville J. Herskovits, "Freudian Mechanism in Negro Psychology," *The New World Negro* (Bloomington, 1969), p. 149.
13. John S. Mbiti, *African Religions and Philosophy* (New York, 1969), p. 102.
14. T. Walter Wallbank, *Documents on Modern Africa* (Princeton, 1964), p. 49.
15. Ibid., p. 45.
16. Ellis A. Komey and Ezekiem Mphahlele, eds. *Modern African Stories* (London, 1964), p. 9.
17. Lorenzo J. Greene, *The Negro in Colonial New England: 1620–1776* (New York, 1942), pp. 237–238.
18. Janheinz Jahn, *A History of Neo-African Literature* (New York, 1968), p. 101.
19. Ibid., p. 105.
20. Ibid., p. 100.
21. Edgar Wright, "East and Central Africa," *Journal of Commonwealth Literature*, 2 (December, 1966): 17.
22. Gerald Moore, "Literature and Environment in East Africa," *East African Cultural Heritage* (1966): 116.
23. In Robert W. July, *The Origins of Modern African Thought* (New York, 1967), p. 172.
24. Claude Wauthier, *The Literature and Thought of Modern Africa* (New York, 1967), p. 202.
25. In Mercer Cook, *Five French Negro Authors* (Washington, 1943), p. 17.
26. Ibid., p. 6.
27. Judith I. Gleason, *This Africa. Novels by West Africans in English and French* (Evanston, 1965), p. 13.
28. Paul Edwards, ed. *Thoughts on the Evil of Slavery by Ottobah Cugoano* (London, 1969), pp. xix–xxiii.
29. Gustavus Vassa, *The Interesting Narrative of the Life of Olaudah Equiano, or Gustavus Vassa, the African* (London, 1787), p. 236.
30. In Wauthier, p. 200 n.
31. Ibid., p. 102.
32. Aryee Quaye Armah, "Pan-Africanism and the White Man's Burden," *Harvard Journal of Negro Affairs* 1 no. 2 (December 1965): 34.
33. J. C. deGraft-Johnson, *African Glory* (New York, 1954), p. 189.
34. Herbert Aptheker, *A Documentary History of the Negro People in The United States* (New York, 1951), p. 8.
35. Anthony Taylor, *Proceedings of the African Union Society in Newport, Rhode Island*, 1787 (unpublished manuscript).
36. Arna Bontemps and Jack Conroy, *Anyplace But Here* (New York, 1966), p. 123.
37. Wole Soyinka, "The Writer in a Modern African State," *The Writer in Modern Africa*, ed. by Par Wastberg (New York, 1969), p. 16.
38. Frances S. Herskovits and Melville J. Herskovits, *Dahomean Narrative* (Evanston, 1958), p. 5.
39. Cheik Anta Diop, *The Cultural Unity of Negro Africa* (Paris, 1962, as translated by *Presence Africaine*), pp. 195–196.

40. Cited in J. A. Rogers, *World's Great Men of Color* (New York, 1947), p. 91.
41. Vassa, *Narrative of Life of Olaudah Equiano*, p. 5.
42. Richard Allen, *The Life, Experience and Gospel Labors of the Rt. Reverend Richard Allen* (Philadelphia, 1838), p. 18.
43. Lewis Nkosi, "Contemporary African Prose and Poetry," *Handbook of African Affairs*, ed. by Helen Kitchen (New York, 1964), p. 265.
44. W. E. B. DuBois, *Dusk of Dawn* (New York, 1940), p. 8.
45. Alain Locke, "The Negro in American Culture," *Anthology of American Negro Literature*, ed. by Sylvestre Watkins, (New York, 1944), p. 157.
46. Mercer Cook and Stephen Henderson, *The Militant Black Writer in Africa and The United States* (Madison, 1969), p. 56.
47. Mbiti, *African Religions and Philosophy*, p. 219.
48. Ibid., p. 108.
49. Mbello Sonne Dipoko, "Cultural Diplomacy in African Writing," *The Writer in Modern Africa* (New York, 1969), pp. 50 and 68.
50. Leon E. Clarke, ed., *From Tribe to Town* (New York, 1969), p. 4.
51. Ruth P. Simms, *Urbanization in West Africa* (Evanston, 1969), p. xii.
52. Bernth Lindfors, "Achebe on Commitment and African Writers," *Africa Reports* 3 (March, 1970): 17–18.
53. Clarence Major, "A Black Criteria," *The Journal of Black Poetry* (Spring 1967): 15.
54. Larry P. Neal, "The Black Arts Movement," *The Drama Review* XII no. 4 (Summer 1968): 29–30.
55. LeRoi Jones, "Statement," *The Journal of Black Poetry* (Spring 1967): 14.
56. John Killens, "The Writer and Black Liberation," *Black America* ed. by Pat Romero (Washington, 1969): 271.
57. Sonia Sanchez, *Homecoming* (Detroit, 1969), p. 22.
58. Sisters of the B.C.D., *Black Woman's Role in the Revolution* (Newark, 1969), *passim*.

The Black Rage

ESSAYS

"White Power"

■ Julius Lester

The essence of power in America is fantastically simple: money. An official of U.S. Steel has bluntly stated, "We're not in business to make steel. . . . We're in business to make money." The rights of people in America have always been subordinated to this end. Blacks have always known it. Whites were bribed to look the other way. (The white union member sells himself every year for higher wages.) Slavery existed so that white people could make money, and the rhetoric was found to justify that. Blacks were freed because slavery threatened the North's ability to make money, and they were reenslaved when the white folks worked out how they could *all* make money again. In each instance, the rhetoric was found to justify the act.

America's attitude and treatment of the black man is extended around the world, and it is called foreign policy. This is occasionally admitted, as when President Johnson went to the Far East in the fall of 1966 and told a group of American soldiers at Camp Stanley, Korea, "Don't forget, there are only two hundred million of us in a world of three billion. They want what we've got and we're not going to give it to them."

The war in Vietnam is the most glaring example at present of the "American way of life." The rhetoric says that the U.S. is fighting to ensure Vietnam for the Vietnamese. (It would seem that the simplest way to do this would be to get out and let the Vietnamese have it.) On August 4, 1953, President Eisenhower told a conference of U.S. governors in Seattle, Washington: "Now let us assume that we lost Indochina. . . . The tin and tungsten that we so greatly value from that area would cease coming. . . . So when the United States votes 400 million dollars to help that war, we are not voting a give-away program. We are voting for the cheapest way that we can to prevent the occurrence of something that would be of a most terrible significance to the United States of America, our security, our power and ability to get certain things we need from the riches of the Indochinese territory and from Southeast Asia."[1]

[1] Felix Greene, *Vietnam, Vietnam* (Palo Alto: Fulton Publishing Company, 1966), p. 26.

On April 4, 1954, *U.S. News & World Report* ran an article, "Why U.S. Risks War for Indochina: It's the Key to Control of All Asia." The core of the article was in this statement: "One of the world's richest areas is open to the winner in Indochina. That's behind the growing U.S. concern . . . tin, rubber, rice, key strategic raw materials are what the war is really about. The U.S. sees it as a place to hold—at any cost."

The reality had not changed when Henry Cabot Lodge, then ambassador to South Vietnam, spoke before the Middlesex Club of Cambridge on February 28, 1965. "Geographically, Vietnam stands at the hub of a vast area of the world—Southeast Asia—an area with a population of 249 million persons. . . . He who holds or has influence in Vietnam can affect the future of the Philippines and Formosa to the east, Thailand and Burma with their huge rice surpluses to the west, and Malaysia and Indonesia with their rubber, ore and tin to the south. . . . Vietnam thus does not exist in a geographical vacuum—from it large storehouses of wealth and population can be influenced and—undermined."[2]

President Johnson tells us, in solemn tones, that he wants peace, that we will have peace as soon as the North Vietnamese stop interfering in the affairs of South Vietnam. Perhaps the best reply to this comes from a French Catholic magazine, *Frères du Monde*, published by the Franciscan order. "We hold no necessary grudge against the USA, but we say 'no' to a system which nourishes itself by means of war, which orients itself toward war and profits handsomely from it. It is imperative that the responsibility for all this be clearly fixed. . . ."

Peace is irrelevant to White Power, if not downright dangerous. Eisenhower can, of course, pour on the rhetoric when he's not talking to the emissaries of W.P. "Every gun that is made, every warship launched, every rocket fired signifies, in the final sense, a theft from those who hunger and are not fed, those who are cold and not clothed. We pay for a single fighter plane with a half-million bushels of wheat. We pay for a single destroyer with new homes that could have housed more than 8,000 people." This is most definitely true, but Eisenhower has been unequivocal in his support of the war in Vietnam. The reality remains the words of another General, Curtis Le May: "Tell the Vietnamese they've got to draw in their horns and stop aggression or we're going to bomb them back into the Stone Age."

Let's take a closer look at White Power by examining the budget that was projected for 1967. The total cost of Johnson's budget was 172 billion dollars. Of this amount 76.8 billion dollars was to be used for national defense. It is here that the control of the U.S. by White Power is most strikingly exemplified. According to John M. Swomley, Jr., since World War II the Defense Department has "built itself into the biggest business of the entire world."[3] In 1954 the economic holdings of the Defense Department came to 200 billion dollars, four times the value of all the plants and equipment in all U.S. manufacturing corporations. The Defense Department owns and controls land greater than the areas

---

[2] *Ibid.*, p. 127.
[3] "Economic Power of the Pentagon," *Economic Notes* (June 1964).

of Rhode Island, Massachusetts, Connecticut, Vermont, New Hampshire, Delaware, Maryland and New Jersey put together. This land includes not only air-force bases, army camps, nuclear-testing grounds, missile sites, but huge tracts whose use nobody but the Defense Department knows.[4] With a budget of 76.8 billion dollars the Defense Department is the biggest employer, contractor, purchaser, owner, and spender in this country. Thus, it is no accident that retired generals invariably become heads of huge corporations and heads of corporations become Secretaries of Defense. It is inevitable that war becomes good business. Defense Department contracts go to all the major businesses in the country. This is hailed as a stimulus to the economy. Unemployment is cut, not only by increasing the draft, but by the jobs created by the need for war supplies. It is amusing when the Department of Labor announces that Negro unemployment is dropping. Of course it is. Black unemployment drops as the number of blacks inducted into the armed forces rises.

With the Defense Department controlling so much money, it is inevitable that it and government become the target of business. This 76-billion-dollar defense appropriation was the largest single item in the 1967 national budget. Next were welfare and social programs, with 57.8 billion dollars. This, of course, is the "rhetoric"—the war on poverty, welfare, etc. When one looks at where Johnson planned to get the funds for his 172-billion-dollar budget, it is apparent that the 57 billion dollars for welfare and social programs is nothing more than an insult.

The government's budget for 1967 was to be financed by 73.2 billion dollars from personal taxes, 28.4 billion dollars in workers' and employers' payroll taxes, 13.7 billion dollars from the buying public in excise taxes. This came to 115.3 billion dollars that would come from the consumer. Johnson was only to collect 33.9 billion dollars from corporation taxes. This was less than half the amount that would be collected from personal-income taxes. Yet, with business making larger profits than at any time in history, why wasn't business paying more taxes on these profits?

The answer is simple. Tax laws are written so that the rich won't have to pay taxes. The rich create foundations because foundations are tax-exempt. Why have the rich suddenly become so interested in art? Why are paintings selling for such fantastic prices today? They are tax-exempt investments.

Oilmen have it particularly easy. In 1965, the Drive News Service of New Orleans reported that "Investors in the oil business reap huge profits —tax free . . . by special privilege tax bonanzas one oil man was required to pay no taxes from 1958–1961, though his total net income was $9,419,000. Take another case: one oil and gas operator who had sold $50 million worth of oil in the last 12 years, whose income in the years 1958–1960 was in excess of $5,500,000, yet this man has paid NO TAXES SINCE 1929. Or take for instance one oil company listed in a Treasury Department study. This company made profits of nearly $66 million in a six year period—yet, they ended up the six years not only

[4] *Ibid.* (August 1964).

paying no taxes, net, but getting a $425,000 tax refund on previously paid taxes . . . one wealthy industrialist, worth $85 million told the *Wall Street Journal:* 'When a fellow is in my income tax bracket, he automatically goes into the oil business. This is a legal way to escape confiscation of earnings.' " Do not be confused by rhetoric. "Confiscation of earnings" means taxes.

Business is the residence of White Power. Government is only the anteroom, the lobby. It is from there that the orders are carried out, but they are made elsewhere.

A clear example of the love affair between government and business can be seen in U.S. intervention in the Dominican Republic. We were solemnly informed that the Dominican Republic was in danger of being taken over by Communists, etc., etc., etc. Whenever Communism is brought into the picture, interpret that to mean, American business is in danger.

The Dominican Republic was about to have elections and it looked as if Juan Bosch was going to be returned to power. His political philosophy was simple: Privately owned business was detrimental to the people. Therefore it either had to be taken away from the owners or severely regulated by government. This was enough for the U.S., and off went the Marines. Jack Minnis, formerly of SNCC, researched the reasons for their going. They are as follows:

The Aluminum Company of America, which is controlled by the Mellon family of Pittsburgh, owns mines in the Dominican Republic from which it gets about one million tons of aluminum ore a year.

The South Porto Rico Sugar Corporation owns 300,000 acres of sugar land in the Dominican Republic. Its board of directors interlocks with the Rockefeller Chase Manhattan Bank and with Corn Products, Inc. (makers of Karo and other corn-syrup products). One of the largest exports to the U.S. from the Dominican Republic is corn.

The United Fruit Company owns 2,300 acres of banana cultivation in the Dominican Republic.

It is also interesting to note at what point business and government really become indivisible. Ellsworth Bunker, then the U.S. ambassador to the Organization of American States and now ambassador to South Vietnam, is a director of the National Sugar Refining Corporation. (And the U.S. does not get any sugar from Europe.)

Most interesting of all is the fact that President Johnson sent McGeorge Bundy (now of Black Power fame) as his special emissary to look the Dominican situation over. McGeorge had proper incentive, as the Bundy family owns a large fish-packing company in the Dominican Republic, Gorton's of Gloucester, Inc.

This is the crystal-clear reality of White Power, be it exemplified in Vietnam, South Africa, the Dominican Republic, or Harlem. The white folks own everything and everybody. It's up to us to see that they don't keep it.

Malcolm X spoke to this when he returned from his trip to Mecca and Africa: "Almost every one of the African and Asian countries that has gotten independence has devised some kind of socialistic system, and this is no accident. This is another reason why I say that you and I here in America—who are looking for a job, who are looking for better housing, looking for a better education—before you start trying to be incorporated or integrated, or disintegrated into this capitalistic system, should look over there and find out what the people who have gotten their freedom are adopting to provide themselves with better housing and better education and better food and better clothing.

"None of them are adopting the capitalistic system because they realize they can't. You can't operate a capitalistic system unless you are vulturistic; you have to have someone else's blood to suck to be a capitalist. You show me a capitalist, I'll show you a bloodsucker. He cannot be anything but a bloodsucker, if he's going to be a capitalist. He's got to get it from somewhere other than himself, and that's where he gets it—from somewhere or someone other than himself. So, when we look at the African continent, when we look at the trouble that's going on between East and West, we find that the nations in Africa are developing socialistic systems to solve their problems. . . ."[5]

Malcolm X did not reach the point of advocating socialism, but he did urge all blacks to "find out what they [Africans] are using to get rid of poverty and all the other characteristics of a rundown society." It is not clear to many in "the movement" that the answer is socialism of some sort. One of the saving graces of "the movement" and of SNCC, in particular, has been its unwillingness to dogmatically align itself with any doctrine. (Each individual in SNCC is like a separate political party and any attempt by others to force rigid doctrine on the organization is firmly resisted.) However, there is agreement with Malcolm that justice, equality, and freedom are inconsistent with the principles of this country. Capitalism is congenitally unable to allow black men to be free.

Black Power recognizes this and sets itself in opposition to the system. Stokely Carmichael said in an address at Berkeley, in October of 1966, "Even if I were to believe the lies of Johnson, if I were to believe his lies that we're fighting to give democracy to the people in Vietnam, as a black man living in this country, I wouldn't fight to give this to anybody. We have to use our bodies and our minds in the only way that we see fit. We must begin, like the philosopher Camus, to come alive by saying NO! . . . and we have to say no to many, many things in this country. This country is a nation of thieves. It has stolen everything it has, beginning with black people. . . . This country cannot justify its existence any longer."

Black Power is not a move to have the power of this country, as it is presently organized, more evenly distributed. The system makes that impossible. It is a move to destroy power as it now exists. "I do not want to be a part of the American pie," Stokely told the Berkeley crowd. "The American pie means raping South Africa, beating Viet Nam, beating South America, raping the Philippines, raping every country you've been in. I don't want any of your blood money. I don't want it. We have grown up and we are the generation that has found this country to be a world power,

[5] George Breitman, ed., *Malcolm X Speaks* (New York: Grove Press, Inc., 1965), p. 73.

that has found this country to be the wealthiest country in the world. We must question how she got her wealth. That's what we're questioning. And whether or not we want this country to continue being the wealthiest country in the world at the price of raping everybody across the world. And because black people are saying we do not now want to become a part of you, we are called reverse racists. Ain't that a gas!"

Few of SNCC's friends or critics understand what is happening. It is sad to hear Bayard Rustin say, as he did that October, "I told them . . . that you cannot bring the dynamics of protest and sit-ins into politics, that absolution is absolutely necessary in sit-ins, but that intelligent compromise is absolutely essential in politics. You buy and sell in politics. You have to." But, Bayard, we know that. That's the American way of life and that's why we're not in politics and want no part of the American way.

White Power is formidable. It controls local, national, and international events. It elects city councilmen, legislators, senators, and Presidents. It controls wages and prices. It controls the press, radio, and television. It controls life and death. Its one concern is profit and the perpetuation of the conditions that allow for maximum profit. It is no accident that foreign heads of state who visit America stop first in New York to visit with David Rockefeller, then proceed to Washington to see the President. They know what White Power is and that LBJ is simply its spokesman.

"Give me your wretched, your poor," begins a much-loved American poem. Yes, give them to me and I will keep them wretched and poor, but will perform the miracle of making them think that they are affluent and well. Yes, give them to me and I will make them think that there has never been a nation of people more fortunate. Yes, give them to me and I will hide their wrinkles with cosmetics, drown their cries with delicacies, and cover their weaknesses with exotic fabrics.

There is no wind that blows that is not moist with the blood of black people. There is no wind that blows that does not carry the smell of napalmed flesh. There is no drop of water that comes from our faucets that has not known the putrefaction of a black, brown, or yellow body.

America has done well. The "wretched of the earth" are the blood in her veins. Blacks in South Africa are paid thirty cents an hour so that the wives and daughters of American white men can ring their necks with jewels. The cotton pickers of Mississippi get thirty cents an hour so that the sons of American white men may go to Harvard to continue the tradition of their illustrious parents. Whites are given the right of life, liberty, and the pursuit of happiness because it is profitable. Blacks are told to be satisfied with the promise of that right. This, too, is profitable. The Vietnamese are told to relinquish what is theirs or die, because it is profitable. Nazi Germany, the graveyard of six million Jews, is rebuilt and rearmed, because it is profitable. White Power knows only one kind of friend: he who allows himself to be turned into profit. White Power has only one enemy: he who refuses.

Black Power is more than proud to be an enemy of White Power.

from The Coming of the Hoodlum

■ Johnny Scott

What was Watts like?

The year the Hoodlum (we can forget that name, he was no hoodlum, but his friends were, even though they shared his feelings, what made him different?) was elected president of the student body at his junior high school many things happened: inter-school council meetings were held, speeches given, a girl found raped in a classroom during a lunch break, the accent given to good oral hygiene, a seventh-grade girl stabbing her math teacher seventeen times with a butcher-knife because he called her "stupid." But he survived, as the class dwindled in number from 750 to 550, but on the day of graduation this was said:

> Lives of great men all remind us
> We can make our lives sublime;
> And, departing, leave behind us
> Footprints on the sands of Time.

I *apologize*, Mr. Longfellow.

> Leave Markham knowing you left
> Far more than mere footprints,
> Leave Markham knowing you helped
> Begin a brighter future for us all.

From seventh grade to ninth grade, from 750 to 550, from small children to wide-eyed adolescents. But, three days later, they had all matured: 250 were left, the "largest incoming class in Jordan's history," or so it went according to the head counselor: the following years would see larger classes, to be sure, more babies were born each year, illegitimacy and wedlock both strove to rise higher even as people married younger and lives broke up faster. Had the Hoodlum changed in this time?

Yes. He had learned to feel. He had learned that there was no love in this world. He had learned, three years later, as 97 men and women walked across an auditorium stage to receive diplomas, that of the forgotten and the fallen, of those empty 153 "other" diplomas that were not given, there could be no crying. They had not asked for remorse. Even now, they sat in the audience, among the spectators, silent when the speeches were given, laughing when the clowns tripped over their gowns, crying as a brother finally made it, gone when it was over: gone as surely as Death leaves when faced with an attitude of toughness. For the Hoodlum had grown a shell of toughness, that resisted both the hate of the streets, and the love that he tried, wanted, to release. It would have been futile for him to relate these emotions.

At one time, like most of his friends, the Hoodlum hated school, hated Jordan High especially for what it had done to him: *nothing.* That was the reason for all hatred toward the school: his class read no better than sixth-graders and this showed in its average gradepoint: 1.8, the equal of the bottom fifth of the intellectual cracker barrel. His hatred did not last long, a break came, the big break in his life—accepted into Harvard College, the acme of the East, the springboard of Presidents and businessmen; most of all, the place from which decent homes came: *homes* like they didn't exist in his world. Had he been a brilliant student to be admitted? Not if his grades were looked at—3.03. Had he exceptionally high college board scores? Not especially—1096. What had he done in school to earn entrance into a Harvard class which claimed an average I.Q. of 128, was selective enough to pick 1,200 people from over 6,000 applicants from the best schools and training institutes in the world?

Nothing, nothing except survive those years of his childhood. Nothing, nothing except remember what those years were, except make it his purpose to somehow do something about it. Nothing, nothing save start out on a career that soon would see him thrown into an even graver crisis: to decide between one's environment, one's home, and the atmosphere of Academia.

It is very simple. Have a sister and have her an unwed mother. Close your eyes, blush with secret shame, hide the secret, live on as though nothing happened. Bury that scar with the other scars. And then, at an airport, pose for pictures as the first Negro to enter Harvard with her and your other sisters. With teachers that did not know her but looked away when looked to for answers why: the pictures were taken, the plane took off, and you sat on the plane remembering the past: "I'm surprised you aren't going to Pomona or Whittier College, or somewhere like that! You could have been something but you talked too much. You could have done something with your life. *I thought you were different from the rest!*"

But you got off that plane. With two suitcases, a shaving kit, an open-flight back home for Christmas, and the determination to be something you had only seen in books. A man in love with his dreams. Was it any wonder, then, that the Hoodlum found it so easy to read Herman Hesse's *Steppenwolf*?

His eyes opened again and he was in Boston. He was in Harvard Square, in the Old Commons, the day bright and the opening of school still three days off. Thoughts reeled in of childhood and growing up. The sight of Mama waving good-bye. My sisters laughing. Irvin's crooked grin concealing his devilish heart. Mr. Anderson and Mrs. Trotter, former high school teachers and friends. Both of them, standing there beneath the plane, so small and yet, so BIG. Watts was just as big as they were. Where was everybody? But then, he wasn't lost. He was in Harvard Square, away from ties he had always hated. He had begun to wonder why he was here, who he was, most of all, why Harvard had let someone with the mark of the ghetto, with the sign of the outcast, into its ivied walls. It was as though Cain had slipped unawares into the Garden of Eden again, but this was a Cain that did not know what his crime was, nor where he was, but only that he did not belong here: neither Harvard, nor Watts would ever be personal worlds for him, and yet they were, because he lived within them.

Now there had been those along the way who sought to look after him. People like Christopher Wadsworth, Senior Advisor at Harvard, and Dr. Dana Cotton, member of the Admissions staff. To him, all of eighteen years old, much of what he saw and felt inspired fear: fear as the voices of the past came into his ears, voices that had predicted failure along the route toward self, voices that never stopped singing in his ear: the voices of the Serpent, the man who wore so much clothing until his body could not be seen and yet who, with but a single question, three words, could disrupt all of his life. *Who are you?* The fear was not of Harvard, but of Watts: a much stronger force than books. He could sit down in dining halls, he could talk with any of a number of people, he could try to study. And then, his sister's face floated across the pages. Here, and then gone. But he could not articulate. He only stammered before the judges, his advisors, these kindly men who sat in on him when he came to them for help: for a help that could not be named, a help that welled up from the bottom of his being, a need that had been there for so long until it was becoming painfully obvious that there could be no life inside of that world. No life was in education if that life had to be shared with the voices of a dead past—a past of Death, whose presence never failed to make itself felt. A presence so overpowering as to draw tears when he sat in his room, isolated, and played the muted trumpet of Miles Davis, played "It Never Entered My Mind," and then turned his gaze outward, into Harvard Yard, into tradition, and history, into all that he had ever read of as a young child striving to find values in life: and could not see because he was blind.

Hello, Mr. Wadsworth, I understand you want to see me?

Yes, I do. How are things here at Harvard for you?

Oh. They're all right, I guess.

Like the way they've been treating you here?

Yes. Everything's all right, I guess. It's an all right place. It hasn't done anything wrong to me I can think of.

Guess it's kind of different from Watts, eh?

Yes. It's a little different from Watts.

How's that?

Well, it ain't anything you can put your finger on. It's like, well, it's like this is a new life, a different place, with different people. It's the kind of thing I expected (seeing surprise on his face), so I don't feel out of place in the sense of running into prejudice.

But then, conversations always ran through those currents for him: he sought to express the difference. It would have been easy to say that he *felt* two different people within him, but he was afraid that someone might overhear and call him crazy. For expressing fears. But this wasn't the simple case, it went much deeper, much further, than an alienation from Harvard society.

Ghettoes are built within the mind, and in one part of the Hoodlum's mind he was *black*, which meant apart from all that is white and stands for white, which meant the faces and opinions of his former friends, those that now were in Watts, behind him and yet in front of him, in front of his face as he sat and talked with Wadsworth: while there was its opposite, that part which had seen the humanity of all men because it had seen the humanity within itself, and known that love could be if only men dedicated their minds to liberation. But to express this was difficult. He would slow down in his speech, some of his Cambridge comrades noticed an overly drawn-out drawl, while at the same time injecting a hatred of white society, a hatred that carried itself into his living quarters. There, walking in late at night from drunken sprees, he found his two white roommates listening to Bach, Mozart.

What is this Mozart *shit?* he would holler, and then, striding to the record player, place atop it jazz albums that were freedom songs: the songs of protest, that spoke out against all the injustices, that were in themselves reflective of the black position, of the position of Watts and black life as it had to reach out for breath in an all-white, and all-dominated superstructure largely unknown to it. A super-society that was predicated upon a foundation of books, of knowledge: the same books that had fed the Hoodlum's soul at night when he was a child. His mind would roll back: there was Dale and Jack and J. C., finally reading *Baldwin* after I've been through King Arthur and so much more of other things until it's almost pitiful. But then, he would be glad at the same time, glad to see the hunger for truth in the faces of others. He had begun to wonder to himself about the possibility of communication amongst peers. That Christmas of 1964, he sat in an old garage in Watts, talking with some of his former childmates, deep in the depth of Harvard and what Veritas might mean for Us.

That's right! They have got so much to read, to see, to understand! IT'S LIKE THEY GOT THE POWER AND THEY DON'T REALLY KNOW IT BUT AS LONG AS WE SIT HERE TALKING ABOUT IT INSTEAD OF GETTING UP AND DOING SOMETHING WE GONNA ALWAYS BE ON THE BOTTOM, FELLAS! Yes, he had styled himself a revolutionary. He had majored in African History, would sortie and frequent with the foreign exchange-students. Much of what they said and much of their humor he couldn't understand. But he could sense their own feeling of desolation in this great community, a sense of aloneness that was very much within him, too, and as homing devices are attracted to one another, he came to know of those customs. But he was also a Negro, a fact he couldn't, didn't, escape from: he did sort out other Negroes on the campus and together they formed a group which centered its interests, aspirations, on a black culture: the scene was established for a black dialogue, meetings were called in which other Negroes of the freshman class discussed racial sorespots on the Cantabrigian scene. Then, though no resolutions were ever reached, they always ended the meetings with firm declarations on the strength of black peoples, of their right to survive, of their pride in themselves as future leaders, and on the beauty of the black woman, a beauty that could not be mared in its sensuality— not even by the stated four-hundred-year rape of Prospero.

That was a year of many changes. From revolutionary, the Hoodlum went to mystic. His religion had become one of Godhood, though it concerned no Christian God. He found himself in his room again many nights, questioning his belief in life. Am I a Muslim? Can I, do I, I know that in *some* ways I hate white people, but then there are some that are all right! I can't be a Muslim! But that doesn't make me an Uncle Tom! It was a term that had come to be feared, as many people were becoming aware of the yet-carpetbagging ghost of Uncle Tom stealing in and out of the nights with caches of cash while whites walked away smiling, thinking communication had been established with *comprehensible* Negroes. But nothing is so reprehensible as an Uncle Tom, or the smug face of the white collar that tells of working for everything he's ever gotten in life. As if life wasn't a struggle in the ghetto, but rather, a mere question of survival! What was the difference? What had Harvard become that he thought like this? He lay on his bed into the waking hours, looking at the sun flood the room, the bed, the body, his mind: standing up, he would shiver with the first cold, and then, smile almost ritualistically. To think that I can be here anyway, be here and be mad and be free! Walking into the Co-Op, he bought records, books, gloves, paper, pencil, letterheads, anything he could buy: he charged it willfully, beyond his allowance, wanted to break himself completely, knew that destruction loomed just ahead but rushed on pell-mell.

There was a continued interest in his plans, his future, his life. Many worked with him. Not much was said in those meetings of what impressions were being made. The talk centered around Harvard, Watts, clothes, studies, anything, in fact, but who was talking to who. And why, in the first place! It should have seemed natural to believe that sincerity surrounded every meeting, that this sincerity provoke a concern in his wishes. But the Hoodlum would not have sensed this, nor would he have responded. His world was too clouded, too filled with the spectres of his world, *that* world which now included Harvard as well as Watts, which began to space time and memories: so that there were times when he was afraid of going home, afraid of going there and finding that he wanted Cambridge instead. The exact fear he had when first arriving of wanting Watts more than he wanted Cambridge. The Hoodlum *knew* that he was changing, in name and form as well as in belief. The Hoodlum was dying, he was fighting, kicking, yes, but he was also dying. And this is why he was so sad. No one is happy, not very happy, when a part of them dies, when a fragment of the past begins to recede into the mists.

To be sure, he had encountered prejudice. But it was a subtle kind unknown even to its perpetrator. He had gone to the B'nai B'rith House at Harvard, for example, for a party given there one evening by the Hillel Foundation. The place was packed. Of the group he was with, there were six altogether, four whites and two Negroes, not much in the way of overt attention was paid. But then, as our Hoodlum stood away from even this group, in a corner, watching the people, hearing the sounds of the party, listening to the wonderment in his own eyes, a small, bespectacled Caucasian fellow strode up to him and, there, from the top of a drink, asked, "Do you feel a little uncomfortable here, if you don't mind my asking?"

"Only if you feel uncomfortable." To know that he did not know that I would not know until the morrow that the B'nai B'rith was a Jewish Foundation. Or that Jews had suffering in common with *us* Negroes, and that they, too, were meeting injustice in the present world.

There were questions that could not be so easily answered, though: What does *your* father do for a living? No, he wasn't a Civil Service employee. Then, he was not unemployed. He could not answer that question. He did not know the answer. My father is a laborer. The hardest kind of worker, because to hustle in the streets, knock someone in the head and take their money, run away, that would be so much easier a way to survive. Always in fear of capture. If it wasn't the police who were after you, it was your wife: Why don't you go out and get a job? Oh, I suppose there ain't any work that's *good enough* for you? Things that prep school kids would not understand, had not been raised to understand, might not ever understand. Why were black men so concerned about being black men? Why did they insist on making things so difficult to explain, making civil rights the perpetual subject of discussion—Watts was forever on the lips of white boys, wanting to know what it was like. Is it really that bad? Have you ever seen anyone shot? Is there really police brutality? Have you ever been shot at?

They had never seen the lonely unlit streets of Watts. Had never been afraid at night, typing or reading, of the animal sounds. Look out the window and see the dog packs roaming the streets of the projects, knock over and then forage through garbage cans, no one chasing them away but only watching. Green beast eyes glowing in the night, out of the night, and the moon, the moon's pale light, above your head as you gazed back into those eyes, into their unthinking depths, and heard the low guttural growls of the beast. He feared dogs, a feeling quite unlike even his closest friends on that campus, in that world. Negroes from middle-class backgrounds who had attended prep schools and achieved glowing records. Negroes from South Side Chicago housing projects who taught him how to light matches against the wind. Harvard Negroes, who believed in themselves and looked on life, all of life, as part of the game. The Education Game: to play it you have to seem it, have to become so much a part of the accepted stereotyped portraiture of the aspiring Negro that you finally become accepted. But acceptance was not really this feeling. It would have been as easy to accept the dog packs. Thoughts of Harvard, of the long-haired, well-groomed dogs that strode, romped through the Freshman Yard—friendly dogs, *cared for* by their owners. Could it be that in the dog packs, in Watts, he saw himself and his friends? So close to fighting over garbage, the garbage that life lumped out to you, in trash cans called haunted schoolyards and wind-swept playgrounds: where the only sound was the continual grating of the rings, the iron rings, suspended by chains, swinging back and forth over the sandpit, the housing projects silhouetted in the gray stormy weather against the horizon—one's face turned toward the projects above the buildings into the grayness of God's Heaven. Where little kids fought over games, spilled blood, and ran in gangs while inside those buildings, locked away from sight of the world, fought the owners of the children: to have the love of a child.

But what did they say whenever faced with this Hoodlum? Of course, thoughts arose concerning his maturity: what is a man that he tells of youth and youth's own fears, of dogs and people and the hardships, the tragedies. Not as if he were singing a song, but because he simply believed that he had lived this way and that in this survival, he had a particular influence which had to be realized sooner or later. There was fear of a growing rift in that Cambridge. Because he feared the eyes of man, the Hoodlum withdrew, regardless of their interest in his story. Tragedy had withdrawn as it only knew how: the universal had been tapped, no matter how slightly or unseemingly, in the lives of all who had grown to know him, and within that human shell another life was being born: I stepped forth, aware that a man can create a ghetto within the confines of his own mind. Stake out the preposed borderlines of blackness and whiteness: move at that instant into the outside world, itself both black and white, a world of externals and appearances: become two people, black and white, not Good and Evil. Learn to immerse oneself into the plights, the stories, of other people because you can tap the extent of sorrow in the lives of all you meet. Tell Negroes to beware of their blackness: it may be but another white man's values. Tell whites of how books, of how *Bleak House*, can become real, the fog a part of your nostrils: your sister pregnant and your mind totally detached from this reality: that you moved intermittently between Harvard and Watts, afraid of committing yourself to one or the other completely. No one could tell me anything. I knew what the answers were. There was only one question that had everyone confused.

It was the middle of the school year. It was the beginning of spring. Christmas was over and so, too, was much of the light-hearted air that had atmospherized Harvard Yard during its opening three months. Now, education had set in and our Hoodlum raised himself from his bed to look out of the window, to take stock of that change in the air, and then, to walk out of the door into the crisp thirty-degree weather before quickly retiring to his room. Damn, it's colder than hell out there! he would mutter —though, of course, the winter had been much colder. He was simply looking for an excuse not to go to class and this coldness was the best excuse he could find. Of course, it would soon be warm, but that did not matter. His bookshelf would always be there, big and with each day's trip to the Harvard Bookstore growing bigger (though we must remember that these book-buying excursions took place in the late afternoon when it had grown commensurately warmer). There was no thought in his mind of attending classes. Was he an ingrate, or a rebel, or a reactionary, some radical, perhaps, if it might not be asking too much, could he well have been simply involved in finding out what life was all about, or is that too simple? If he was a product of the slums, then of what slums, and what sort of product was he?

Did his eyes see Harvard: the Yard and the Yale Game behind, the counseling sessions over with, his position in the movement of things firmly established? No, not really that kind of world. It was too artificial, too involved with the processes of trying to make a better living when all he wanted was to simply let time pass by. He didn't know who Norman Mailer was, though *The Naked and the Dead* was out. Nor had he read James Joyce. *Finnegans Wake:* what was that? Or if one knew who Samuel Beckett and the race-screaming LeRoi Jones (who could sink down into the limpid surfaces of reality and come out with some pretty valid

insights into the nature of homosexuality, which scares most college kids)
were—then it was just as easy to assume a literary superiority, a greater
racial awareness. He was not that involved, in other words, with the world
situation at large. You had on your hands a kid who was genuinely
wrapped up in trying to make meaning out of a wrecked life instead of
scrapping all remembrances of it completely, then having the courage to
admit this rejection consciously to himself, and then moving on to re-
structure a new world. Nothing unusual at all.

He was on academic probation—make up your grades or flunk out.
Only nine out of that class of twelve hundred flunked out. A lot of others
took leaves of absence to study themselves, and there were the perpetual
Radcliffe cases: those unnamed medical leaves of absence so that some
girl could have her illegitimate baby in peace. A world that was, in retrospect, quite similar to Watts. And yet, because of its tremendous freedom,
there were the canoe rides on the Concord River where cold was the name
of the air and pretty was the color of the fish, a great deal more warming.
Most of the time life back home was cold. Parents here were people you
could see and appreciate. Made you wonder why white kids would rebel.
If you had the chance, you surely wouldn't walk out on a million-dollar
inheritance.

The shocking realization was that this was me, JOHNIE, who had grown
up in Watts and had seen policemen literally crack skulls open while
women fell to their knees crying like babies at seeing their babies carried
off to jail, who had seen his father's house burn to the ground, who had
almost become inured to death and blood and tears. Too much of it spoils
the novelty. My own morality was not based on a Western system of good
and evil, traceable to Plato and Hesiod, Jesus and St. Augustine. Rather,
it was a social and cultural orientation to the slums—in which evil was
taken for granted and upon it erected a value system of happiness and
terror. I knew that I was not alone. My friends, all of us who have been
nursed on this world, live according to this system of values. This was
something neither Chris Wadsworth, nor Dr. Cotton, nor anyone else in
that entire place would have gathered, no farther than seeing a bit of the
sun just before it sinks into the sea, and then, until the next day, is lost.
They only saw the moon, good people for all that they were, showing
human characteristics of love and warmth and sincerity in their work
that make definite impressions but which could not at that time be extended into this many-surfaced world.

Some might run the risk of calling it all a dreamworld and they would
be wrong, as wrong as those who would call the Hoodlum a racist when all
he was, in truth, was a bearer of the imprint from that world. He was
beyond even looking back upon his world and calling it sordid, brutal,
with a frankness that at times had left him overwhelmed, typical advertising adjectives of revealing books. No, this for him was a dynamism
that time and again cost him, cost him friendships and relationships that
might have offered a way out of this reality into another: an escape. And
he would have been glad for a hand toward escape, though now, when
Harvard is superimposed over Watts, though the Hoodlum is placed above
my own reflection in the mirror, I suppose there truthfully could have

been no escape. Harvard had become a ghostyard, empty. There were animal sounds in the air. The snow had become brown and slushy. Snow was not pretty, it acted as an obstruction. In his way of travel, in my way, and everyone else's. People were laughing and looking real because they tasted joy denied to me. A man can flunk out of school for many reasons.

On June 7, 1965, exactly nine months later, I returned to Watts. This time it was for keeps, if anything in life can be applied that label. But the Hoodlum was fired, fire: he believed in God. He had believed in the possibility of all men finally coming together, in truth, he had dedicated himself to some personal ministering of his own to the needs of his friends and companions, with whom he had shared the living experience, Watts. There, within that jet, the mind's eyes traveled both back and forth in time, seeing Harvard before arriving that September 21, 1964, and leaving that June day, seeing Christmas and seeing Jordan High, seeing all that he was. Most of all, understanding that things would have to be different from here on out. Something had happened, he did not know what. But there was one thing that had to be true: he was more than a year older, he had done a lot more than party late at night, or lose his virginity, or take Chinese Philosophy. He had changed. Back home.

The last thing he remembered reading in the Harvard *Crimson* was that applications this year for those 1,200 spots had risen to 6,500. To be sure, there would be more Negroes. It has been getting like that all across the country. But then, that was progress. This, 1965, would be the year, His year: his resolution. And in August of that year, Watts and all of Los Angeles would burn before he began understanding why life was so much dearer than death.

from Die, Nigger, Die

■ H. "Rap" Brown

My first contact with white america was marked by her violence, for when a white doctor pulled me from between my mother's legs and slapped my wet ass, I, as every other negro in america, reacted to this man-in-flicted pain with a cry. A cry that america has never allowed to cease; a cry that gets louder and more intense with age; a cry that can only be heard and understood by others who live behind the color curtain. A cry? Or was it a scream? Whatever it was, we accepted it.

I had been born in "america, the land of the free." To insure my country's freedom, my father was somewhere fighting, for this was a year of the second war to end all wars—World War II. This was October 4, 1943, and victory was in the air. The world would now be safe for democracy.

But who would insure my freedom? Who would make democracy safe for Black people? America recognized long ago what negroes now examine in disbelief: every Black birth in america is political. With each new birth comes a potential challenge to the existing order. Each new generation brings forth untested militancy. America's ruling class now experiences what Herod must have at the birth of "Christ": "Go and search . . . and when ye have found him, bring me word again, that I may come and worship him also." America doesn't know which Black birth is going to be the birth that will overthrow this country.

The threat to america, however, does not exist in negro america, but rather as a result of negro america. If one examines the structure of this country closely he will note that there are three basic categories: they are white america, negro america, and Black america. The threat to the existing structure comes from Black america, which exists in contradiction to both white and negro america. It is the evolution of these contradictions that has given rise to the present revolutionary conditions. Revolution is indeed inevitable, and, as the cycle of change closes around america's racist environment, the issue of color becomes more pertinent.

Color is the first thing Black people in america become aware of. You are born into a world that has given color meaning and color becomes the single most determining factor of your existence. Color determines where you live, how you live and, under certain circumstances, if you will live. Color determines your friends, your education, your mother's and father's jobs, where you play, what you play and, more importantly, what you think of yourself.

In and of itself, color has no meaning. But the white world has given it meaning—political, social, economic, historical, physiological and philosophical. Once color has been given meaning, an order is thereby established. If you are born Black in america, you are the last of that order. As kids we learned the formula for the structure of american society:

If you're white,
You're all right.
If you're brown,
Stick around.
But if you're black,
Get back, get back.

Because of the importance assigned to color, negroes choose only to legitimatize two americas: white and negro. When one examines the way in which these two americas are structured, it is obvious that the similarities between them are greater than the differences. The differences exist only in the external control of each and their internal order, which, in turn, create value contradictions. In other words, whites control both white america and negro america for the benefit of whites. And because of this kind of external control by whites in their own self-interest, negroes who structures their communities after those of whites are forced to enforce values of whites. They attempt to explain away their lack of control by saying that they are just members of the larger community of "americans."

A monologue is perpetually expounded by white america which is echoed by negroes afflicted with white patriotism.

> *white america:*
>   Think white or I'll kill you.
>   And if you think too white, I'll kill you.
> *negro america:*
>   Think white or I'll kill you.
>   And if you think too white "the man" will kill you.
>   So think colored.
>   Imitate the white man,
>   but not to perfection in front of him.

As Julian Moreau says in his novel, *Black Commandoes:*

> Attitudes necessary for survival were vigorously pounded into the wooly heads of black boys and girls by their loving mothers. The boys were reared to be Negroes, not men. A Negro might survive a while, but a black "man" didn't live very long. . . . A black boy aiming to reach "manhood" rather than "Negro-hood" rarely lived that long.

For 400 years the internal contradictions and inconsistencies of white america have been dealt with through its institutions. In regard to race or color, these contradictions have always been on a national, never a local or individual level. Whites as individuals have always loved to be thought of as superior. They have always known that if they could justify and make their actions legal, either through their religion, their courts or their history (educational system), then it would be unnecessary to actually rectify them because the negro would accept their interpretation. White america's most difficult problem thus becomes how to justify and not rectify national inconsistencies. If white nationalism is disguised as history or religion, then it is irrefutable. White nationalism divides history into two parts, B.C. and A.D.—before the white man's religion and after it. And "progress," of course, is considered to have taken place only after the white man's religion came into being. The implication is evident: God is on the white man's side, for white Jesus was the "son" of God.

White america has used religion and history to its advantage. Thus, the North never really differed from the South for they both taught the same history. Catholics never differed from other religions for they taught from the same text. Republicans are no different from Democrats, as Democrats are no different from Dixiecrats. As for liberals, Fanon says they are "as much the enemy of oppressed people and Freedom as the self-avowed enemy, because it is impossible to be both a member of the oppressor class and a friend of the oppressed." So we can see that for white america the only real contradictions are those that arise from the Thirteenth, Fourteenth and Fifteenth Amendments of her Constitution. These contradictions give rise to negro america.

Most Black persons of my time were born into negro america. The first thing you learn is that you are different from whites. The next thing you learn is that you are different from each other. You are born into a world of double standards where color is of paramount importance. In your community a color pattern exists which is closely akin to the white man's, and likewise reinforced from both ends of the spectrum. Light-skinned negroes believe they are superior and darker negroes allow them to operate on that belief. Because of the wide color range which exists in negro america, an internal color colony has been created. Dark negroes are taught that they are inferior not only to whites but to lighter-skinned negroes. And lighter-skinned negroes assume a superior attitude.

Negro america is set up the same as white america. The lighter skinned a negro, the more significant a role he can play. (It has always been the one who looked white who made it in negro america. This was the man with the position, the influence, this was the man who usually got the white man's best job.) In between light negro america and Black negro america (in terms of color), there is a special category of people, who are assigned the name of red niggers. These are the people who are light enough to go into light negro america, but do not have caucasian characteristics. They don't have straight hair or white features. So they can go either way, depending on them. They can operate in Black negro america or at the outer fringes of light negro america. Race prejudice in america becomes color prejudice in negro america. That which is cultural prejudice by whites against Blacks becomes class prejudice in negro america. To distinguish themselves, negroes assign class distinctions. Here we find the instituting and substituting of parallel values. Negroes assume that what is good for white america is good for negro america.

Negroes are always confined to what can be called the "shit regiment." I first became acquainted with the shit regiment in the cub scouts. In every parade, we always marched behind the horses, which meant that we always had to march in horsehit. All the way through life there are shit regiments in the negro community and negroes adhere to them. As a matter of fact, negroes will protect these regiments. The debate was never whether or not we had to march, but whether or not the whites were going to put machines down there to wash the horsehit away before we marched in it. There was never any discussion as to whether or not we should march behind the horses. Uh-uh. Everybody accepted that. They just wanted the horsehit washed out of the way before we came through. White america's largest shit regiment is negro america.

Given that negroes are a colonized people, the most important phase of colonization is the sub-cultural phase. In negro america, negroes relate only to negroes of the same educational background. Dr. So-and-So talks only to Dr. So-and-So and the brother on the block better not act like he thinks he can go up to Dr. So-and-So and talk to him man-to-man. To Dr. So-and-So, the brother on the block is nothing but a nigger who's holding the race back. Dr. So-and-So goes to the Episcopal Church, the Presbyterian or the Catholic Church. The brother on the block goes to the Baptist Church, the Holy Rollers or the Sanctified Church. And the Methodist Church is in between the two. It ain't as niggerish as the Baptist Church, but it's not as high class as the Episcopal Church. As negroes become more "white-educated," the transition in religion begins. All of a sudden, it's beneath them to go to church and shout and get happy. That's not dignified. As they get more "educated," their religion gets more like the white man's religion as if their heaven will be segregated too. "Education" even extends down to the naming of the children. The more "educated" the negro becomes, the more European names he picks for his children. Michele, Simone, Hubert, Whitney. All of a sudden, Sam and Bertha Lee ain't good enough anymore. In other words, values are assigned to names. Names must now be more than functional.

The poor negro doesn't aspire to be white, he just wants to make it into negro america. So he works hard all his life and finally rents a little house and puts some furniture in it which he keeps covered with plastic so it won't get dirty. And he gets mad if anybody sits on it, because he's trying to imitate negro america. Once he gets into negro america, he learns of so-called middle-class values, white values. Then he wants to get into white america.

When he tries to enter white america, he is rejected. The doors are shut. Even if he has a big job in some white firm, if he's one of those "only" negroes, he still finds out that he's Black when it's quitting time. The white workers go their way and leave him to go his. They're nice and friendly on the job and all buddy-buddy, but that doesn't go outside the office. They don't want their friends thinking that they're nigger lovers. So this sets up a reaction in the negro. He gets frustrated and tries to live a contradiction and that's why when the rebellions start, he's all for them. He doesn't have the courage to admit it to the white man. When the white folks he works with ask him what he thinks about "the riot," he says it's hurting the cause and all sorts of bull like that. But that night after work, he breaks records getting home to watch it on t.v., cheering like a muthafucka the whole time. Take the Washington, D.C., rebellion, for instance. They arrested something like 3,000 people and when they booked 'em, they found out that the great majority of them worked for the government. Had jobs, making money, still these were the dudes who were out in the street. In Detroit it was the same thing. It wasn't only the unemployed brother. It was the one who was bringing home $110 every Friday. It was the one who had a Thunderbird, and some clean vines. He was the one who had tried to enter white america and had found that no matter what he did, he was still a nigger to the white man.

Those Black people who remain in the Black community, however, remain a viable force. They don't have the frustrations that exist in negro america. In Black america the bonds are tighter. The fight is for freedom, not whiteness.

Negroes have always been treated like wild, caged animals by the white man, and have always felt the passions of caged animals (because they were living in cages), but they would always act civilized with whites, that is, what white people told them was civilized. But inside this "civilized" negro was an undying hate. This hate, however, could only be released in negro america. If it was ever released in white america, it would prove to white people that negroes were savages. That hate became a self-hate. So to preserve their sanity, their humanity and their white civilization, negroes had to hate themselves. And when they hated, they distinguished between those who were most like white people and those who were Black. And they hated Black people and poor negroes. (Poor negroes are those Black people with the values of negro america, but not the means.)

It is clear that the revolution will not come from negro america but from Black america, and Black america is growing. Black america is important because it is here that you will find the self-imposed exiles from both white and negro america. Black america has always offered Blacks human freedoms—a humanism uncommon to white and negro america. Some enter Black america because negro america rejects darker-skinned negroes, and, of course, if a person is rejected by negro america, he is automatically rejected by white america. Other people enter Black america because of some experience they had in their childhood. Still others, because of something they may have read that was written by someone in Black america. Black america has existed ever since the first slave despised the injustice that was done to him and did not seek to accommodate himself to that injustice. Thus, there have always been people who could articulate these injustices and could discuss what the response to these injustices should be. It is self-evident that people always rebel against oppression and there has been one continuous rebellion in Black america since the first slave got here.

from Blame Me on History

■ Bloke Modisane (South Africa)

My mind recoiled with anger and a little with fear, I had not realised the scope of the destruction; it was a wasteland, like a canvas by Salvador Dali, with all the despairing posture of mass desolation, then it began to look picturesque as a slum would to the tourist; there seemed to be a pattern, a design, in the arrangement of the destruction: the bulldozed walls, the bricks, the sand, the door and window-frames, the deserted dustbins, the skeletons of motor-cars, of propped-up trolley carts, a promiscuous assortment of discarded possessions; and rising like tombstones or desert cactus among the desolation were the structures of outdoor lavatories and the rebellious isolated houses which stood defiant against the authority of the bulldozers; these structures were the proud indestructible soul of Sophiatown, defiant erections among the ruins, an undying symbol for those who loved Sophiatown, and those who feared it.

The house of Dr Xuma had always been the model for my landed security. There was a tiny plot in Gold Street next to the Diggers Hall, opposite the house of Mr Dondolo and the shebeen, 'The Battleship,' which I had hoped to purchase after becoming a doctor and on which I would construct my palace; but that dream has been annihilated, it is languishing among the ruins like black South African dreams, yet behind me stood the house of Dr Xuma, bold and majestic, like the man inside it, the man Ma-Willie wanted me to emulate.

After the funeral service, when even the relations had returned to their homes, Ma-Willie and I had a long talk; she spoke with gentleness and care, almost feeling her way around the very words.

"The wayside corn does not grow," Ma-Willie said, in Pedi, a northern Sotho dialect. "Things will be heavy now; to be a doctor, I would have liked to have been able to bear the burden."

"Yes, 'me, I hear you," I said. "I want to look for work, I want to be the one to look after you."

"When my strength is tired it'll be time for you to work," she said, "but first, you must go to school."

"School is for children," I said, "I am a man, I must work and look after you and the children."

"I will work," she said, firmly, "you will go to school."

"Where is the money to come from?"

"We'll see," she said, "God is living."

To be a doctor like Dr Xuma would be to be respected, to live in a big house with separate bedrooms, a room for sitting, another for eating, and a room to be alone, for reading or thinking, to shut out South Africa and not be black; a house in which children would not be sent out if someone wanted to take a bath, we would not have to undress in the dark or under the blankets. Dr William Modisane, I love the sound of the title, the respectability and the security it would have given our family and eased the handicap of being black in South Africa. Money and social position would have compensated for this, maybe even bought us acceptance; I was not particularly concerned with the groans of suffering humanity, was not dedicated to wiping out malnutrition, malaria, or dysentery, I had no pretensions to such a morality, I wanted solely, desperately, none of these things—only to pull my family up from the mud level of black poverty.

Ma-Willie and I had always pointed with pride to Dr Xuma, the African doctor who had studied in America, Glasgow and London; he had success, wealth, position and respect, and my mother was suddenly seized by the vision of a Dr Xuma in the family.

"You will be a doctor," she said, determined.

She turned our home into a shebeen, worked fourteen hours a day brewing and pressing home brews called skokiaan and barberton, and from the proceeds she educated me to high school level and the two girls to primary school level. They dropped out because they could not visualise the immediate benefit of education; but the value of it had been indelibly impressed into my mind.

Moralists and reformists, like Dr Xuma, whose existence did not depend on shebeens spoke out publicly against the medical dangers of these concoctions, but prohibition anywhere places a premium upon the restricted commodity, and thus the churches, the welfare department, the cause-followers fastened on the campaign to stamp out the traffic, focusing on altruistic motives like: the health of the Native, the destitute family of the addict bread-winner; but the police departments, which put up half-hearted banner campaigns, were more realistic than the correctionists who overlooked the human factor; the Africans, like everybody else, wanted to, and would drink, whether it was or was not prohibited.

To the police departments shebeens were a source of unlimited funds, the tariffs for liquor offences were worked out with careful attention, reasonably steep but not calculated to discourage or inconvenience the budget of shebeen queens. The liquor squad was made up of "reasonable men" always willing and prepared to listen to the pleas of the shebeen queens, to make accommodating adjustments. My mother always paid, and I often wondered why she had not taken out an insurance policy against this hazard.

Life in a shebeen exposed me to a rude introduction to the South African police, they made me realise the brutal, dominant presence of the white man in South Africa. I saw my mother insulted, sworn at and bundled into the kwela-kwela, the police wagon, so often it began to seem —and I perhaps accepted it—as a way of life, the life of being black. Listening to the young constables screaming obscenities at Ma-Willie emphasised the fact that we were black, and because my mother was black she was despised and humiliated, called "kafir meid" and "swart hell." I was helpless in the coffin of my skin and began to resent the black of my skin, it offered no protection to my mother from the delinquency of the police constables who saw only the mask representative of a despised race; but Ma-Willie was not black, she was my mother, and if I had been white the whiteness of my skin would have protected her honour. I wished I was white.

Every night was Saturday night, house full, in the charge office of Newlands Police Station, new arrivals waiting to be charged were sardined in the yard immediately behind the office; a continual buzz flowing from the shebeen queens, the drunks, Pass offenders, thieves and all sorts, in a conspiracy of voices, making arrangements, sending out messages, to relations, to friends, about funds, fines.

Tell my wife.

Mother.

Friends.

Ten shillings.

It was always the same, the same voices, the same desperation, the same pleas, and throughout all this I waited outside the police station, waiting for my mother to be charged, fined and released, waiting to escort her home. The police clerks behind the desk were pedantically methodic in their job, and sitting out there with nothing to do I would find leisure in timing the changes of working relays. The offenders were shouted into the charge office.

"Stand against the wall," the police clerk said. "Shake up, this isn't a bed."

"Silence, you devil," the other shouted. "You, you with the black face, shut your stink mouth."

The offenders pushed against each other into a straight line against the wall. The clerk placed the pad in front of him, arranging two carbons between the pages, selected an indelible pencil, sharpened the lead and generally prepared himself for the session.

"Right," he said. "Name? God, these bloody names. Guilty or not guilty?"

"Guilty, my crown."

"Two pounds."

"My wife is bring it, my baas."

"Lock him up."

"Is coming, my baas," he said, "the money."

"Silence. Next. Name? God. Guilty or not guilty? Eight pounds. Good, stand one side."

And so it went on for two hours the clerk working like a robot, questions and instructions rattling away almost as if by reflex action, and at the end of that time the offenders would be ordered off into the yard.

"Hey, Ephraim, open a window," the clerk shouted at the attendant African police boy. "This place stinks."

For the next half-hour the clerks would stretch, smoke and drink coffee and chat together; Ephraim would be fingering the roller and inking the pad.

"Ephraim, tell me," the clerk said, "what is it about you people that smells so bad?"

"Don't know, baas."

"Like shit."

"Yes, baas."

"Bring those stink pots out."

When all the offenders had been charged, there would be another break, then those with funds paid the admission-of-guilt fines and took their turn at being finger-printed by Ephraim; this done they wait against the wall whilst the receipts are being written out, then the names are called out against the receipts and the offenders start hurrying out through the door where the women find their escorts waiting. This would be around one-thirty and I would consider myself lucky if Ma-Willie was in this early batch.

My mother accepted her life, and, I suppose, so did the other shebeen queens; they chose this life and accommodated the hazards, my mother wanted a better life for her children, a kind of insurance against poverty by trying to give me a prestige profession, and if necessary would go to jail whilst doing it. And in our curious society going to jail carried very little social stigma, it was rather a social institution, something to be expected; it was Harry Bloom who wrote: more Africans go to prison than to school.

On the way from the police station Ma-Willie and I would make interminable stops delivering messages from people inside.

The responsibility mounted upon me by the death of my father transformed my entire life, exposed a print of living which appalled me; I became a part of shebeen life and the spectacle of so many drunken people behaving like children horrified me: women breaking into crying fits, men quarrelling and fighting over a trifle, people staggering into drunken sprawls, getting sick and lying in their own vomit was too much for my young and puritanical mind. I loathed the sight, the smell and the taste of liquor, until I imagined myself behaving shamelessly, being unable to realise the weight of the shame.

I observed them before that first drink; when they arrived they were normal, almost as noble as my father, I could not help thinking that any one of them could have been my father, then gradually the similarity would wash away and the man would corrode into a something I could only despise; and yet at that moment of drunkenness they were boldly happy in their stupid argumentative state, singing and dancing, whistling and shouting, unbottled by the drink, existing on another level.

Even against my impulses an admiration for them sneaked through my prejudices, they became less formidable as they became less like a family figure, were human in a free sense, almost approachable; but it had always to be after that drink, before which I could see only the sadness in their eyes, the nervousness in the fingers clutching the scale of skokiaan which was rushed down into their system; to drink was to get drunk, there seemed to be a compulsion to get drunk, it was in the manner they drank the skokiaan, in the way they paused almost to feel the drink taking effect. It seemed there was something in their lives which they detested, wanted to destroy almost; I felt that for them getting drunk was a purposeful destruction of the pain of their lives, a drowning of themselves in this orgiastic expenditure. They were breaking out, escaping from themselves in the very noise which was part of it and of themselves.

Noise was among the pet hates of shebeen queens, for it, too, was an intoxicant; people got drunk with it, and when they were dizzy with it they fought and injured each other; it was also the pied piper which attracted the police and gave the shebeen a bad name, but the noise was that part of drinking that laughter is to joy, and if they had to make a noise then there must be a provision made against police intrusion. So I was trained to be the watch dog capable of spotting a policeman fifty yards away; but the element of risk was a strong potential, the liquor squad was changed much too frequently, and the blank periods before I could recognize the new squad were dangerous to my mother.

By seven o'clock every night I would go on duty and over the week-ends remained on my post until after midnight when the last of the boisterously happy men staggered into the night which would give life to another day, to another night from which they would return to obliterate it from their consciousness. I would go to bed for three hours and be on the post again at three whilst Ma-Willie pressed the brew, and ninety minutes later I would cuddle into my bedding which I made on two long benches placed together; I hated sleeping on the floor and it was uncomfortable sleeping in a foetal position on the bench.

The schedule was unchanging and on top of this were the school hours, the masses of homework done by candlelight with my eyes blearing out; but school was exciting, and history was stimulating. I learned of the rise and fall of man, the dark ages of his soul which he survived, and then his proudest hour, the renaissance of culture, man's most productive age.

I could not resist the glorious history of ancient Greece, the civilisation which was to influence one section of the world and to subjugate and dominate the other; I was excited by the architecture, the philosophy, the drama, and the concept of democracy and government, which provoked a comparison with South Africa, a constitutional democracy; I was aroused by the gallant history of Rome, the Gallic wars of Caesar, the conquests of the world's first fighting machine, the culture which produced Leonardo da Vinci, Michelangelo and others; we were taught that the cultures of Greece and Rome have left their standard on the whole world, that even in South Africa the architecture of the Colosseum, the Johannesburg white cinema, was by influence an example of Roman architecture; but we were not allowed into the galleries to see even copies of the art masters, and all I knew about the "Mona Lisa" was that it was a painting of a smiling woman.

What the history books and the teacher did not point out was that this civilisation initiated and institutionalised the degradation of the human spirit, that it was maintained and sustained by slave labour; tyranny has still to be officially included among the legacies of the civilisation that was Rome.

South African history was amusing, we sat motionless, angelically attentive, whilst the history teacher recounted—as documented—the wars of the Boers against the "savage and barbaric black hordes" for the dark interior of Africa; the ancestral heroes of our fathers, the great chiefs which our parents told stories about, were in a class described as bloodthirsty animal brutes; Tshaka, the brilliant general who welded the Mnguni tribelets into a unified and powerful Zulu nation, the greatest war machine in South African history, was described as a psychopath. A group of us confronted our teacher.

"My lessons come from the history books," he said, "and if you want to pass exams you must reproduce the history lesson, straight from the book if you like."

"What's the truth?" I said.

"That you must learn for yourself," he said. "This is only a historical phase, the situation may be reversed tomorrow and the history may have to be rewritten."

"How did it happen?" I said. "Why?"

"Your history lessons may answer that."

The question has not been fully answered, but the history revealed that truth may have a double morality standard; the white man petitioned history to argue his cause and state his case, to represent the truth as he saw it; he invoked the aid and the blessing of God in subjugating the black man and dispossessing him of the land. It was impossible to understand history, it showed a truth I could not accept, so I learned my history of South Africa like a parrot, I reproduced the adjectives describing African chiefs, and for external examinations I added a few of my own adjectives to flatter the white examiners.

"Which adjectives did you use?" I asked classmates, after writing the examinations. "I described Dingane as malicious, venomous, ferociously inhuman, beastly, godless; I should get a good mark."

from Road to Ghana

■ Alfred Hutchinson (South Africa)

I

I was wide awake. Something was happening. I leaned forward on the bench to catch every word. Mr. Maisels, Q.C., hitched his gown and his baritone filled the court. Mr. Pirow, Q.C., his bushy brows bristling, sawed with his high-pitched, hoarse voice.

"If our application is not granted," Mr. Pirow said, "we will withdraw the indictment and re-indict all the accused."

Jack Hodgson at my side nudged me. I turned to him.

"Hutch, anything on you which you wouldn't like the police to get hold of?"

I had a snap of Hazel in my wallet. She was white but I didn't think it mattered.

"Nothing."

The drama was heightening. I felt the pressure of the accused behind me as they leaned forward too.

"If our application is not granted, we will have to deal with the whole argument of the defence, and, quite frankly, we are not in a position to do so and we are not prepared to do so."

Mr. Justice Rumpff: ". . . the Attorney-General appeared not fully to have considered treason in peace-time without the use of violence or rebellion."

Mr. Trengrove was beginning to reply to the defence argument. Mr. Pirow rose. Mr. Trengrove sat down.

"I am afraid that my hopes that my application for certain amendments to the charge would shorten the proceedings have not been realised. In the name of the Attorney-General I withdraw the indictment."

"Court adjourned."

For a moment there was stillness. Then the gasp found words. We began to troop out of the court and I worried about the snap in my wallet because we were going to meet the police who would re-arrest us.

We stood outside the court waiting to be re-arrested. The usual policemen were there but they did nothing. We knotted into groups. I tried to attach myself to various groups but the groups broke up and re-formed. It was the same question and the same answer: nobody knew. We were free perhaps; perhaps we were not.

I turned to the "Old Synagogue" court with its cupolas and minarets and the Stars of David. I looked at the group of Europeans standing at the bus stop nearby. They stared back at the band of black and white "treason suspects."

"Hutch, what's happening?" said Pat Molaoa. "What's taking place?"

"That's what I'm asking."

The police did not come. In my agitation I found myself beside Ruth

First whose article I had not written. She didn't seem to mind at all. Time passed and the knots began to shred away slowly. I joined the head-shaking people making their way to the Anglican Mission in Proes Street, shaking my head as I went.

I looked back. There was no one on the pavement outside the old synagogue. The police had also left.

We knotted again in the garden of the Anglican Mission as we ate lunch under a jacaranda-tinted sky. Father Mark Nye, the women who had volunteered to cook our lunches, the many friends, asked the same question: was it over?

And two-year-old David Nye came round again offering us cigarettes. "Take one. Take one." And Bruce, his pup, waddled at his heels.

Father Nye made a short speech. It had been good meeting us, he said. Good knowing us. And it was strange to think that we would no longer come to the Mission for lunch. But it was good that the charge had been withdrawn.

And Professor Z. K. Matthews spoke on our behalf and thanked Father Nye for his hospitality, the lady volunteers for their wonderful spirit. And thanked everybody who in one way or another had helped us through the long months, with special thanks, of course, to the Treason Trials Defence Fund.

Joe Slovo, one of the white "treason suspects" and a lawyer by profession, stood on a bench and announced that there would be a party at his house that night to celebrate the occasion. We cheered.

And then we gathered under a tree. And we sang *Nkosi Sikelela i-Afrika:* God Bless Africa. I noticed as we sang that Lilian Ngoyi was crying, singing and the tears falling on the ground. And I looked up into the jacaranda sky.

Mayibuye i-Afrika: May Africa come back.

The "treason bus" shook as it crawled the forty-odd miles from Pretoria to Johannesburg past the familiar scenes. The second "treason bus" shook as it crawled behind. And I tried to feel that I was no longer Accused No. 7; that I had left that number painted on the bench in court.

The bus hummed with the dramatic end of the trial. Were we really free; free after two years? There was much head-shaking in the bus as if in doubt. I turned to my friend, Duma Nokwe, sitting at my side, his big head tilted to one side and his child-like face in repose. He would know. He was an advocate.

"Boy, what's this all about?" I said.

"Boy, it's confusing," he said tiredly. "Legally we are free just now—until a new indictment is framed."

"I'm a simple, blunt man," Joe Matlou was telling someone at the back of the bus. "And when you talk to me, you must remember that you're talking to no ordinary native!"

"Joe again," said Duma with a smile.

"Sing chaps! *Izokunyathela i-Afrika!*" Walter Sisulu shouted above the hum of the bus.

The song rose with its bursts of warnings, cautionings against terrible hurt. Africa will trample you underfoot, Verwoerd. Africa will hurt you. The hurt that the African elephant visits on its foe. We had sung that song for Malan. Then he resigned. We had sung it for Strijdom. Then he died. And now that Verwoerd was Prime Minister, we sang it for him too. Verwoerd beware! We had sung it during the Defiance Campaign as we broke laws and went to prison. We had sung it during the Treason Trial, and now that the trial was over we still sang it.

"We're celebrating, chaps! The moment we get to town! Who's with me?"

Robert Resha, the fat and comfortable "star" of the trial that had ended, was organising a curtain-raiser before the party at Joe Slovo's that night.

"It's fantastic, Boy," Duma was saying.

"It's unbelievable," I said, groping for words. "Two years—and then just like that—like a child smashing a toy."

Duma was looking at the familiar landscape: the swelling veld and *randjies* (ridges). We had come a long way together, I thought, looking at him. He and I and Henri-Gordon "Squire" Makgothi. From the schools where we had been teaching into prison during the Defiance Campaign. And into the Treason Trial which had just ended.

"Boy, we must go and see Squire," Duma said, turning from the veld and *randjies*.

"I was thinking of him, too."

"Squire" had contracted tuberculosis during the trial and was at a chest hospital. The Crown had discharged him—as if having T.B. absolved treason.

In an hour's time I should be seeing Hazel. Perhaps she already knew that I was free; that the trial she had waited so long to end was over. And then I would leave for Ghana. In the shaking, crawling bus, Ghana was very far away, far away and without urgency.

A legal argument was raging in the bus. In many ways all of us had become "lawyers" after two years in court. Joe Matlou was reminding someone about his bluntness and simplicity. And I remembered how at the beginning of the trial his interference with the excited police had both fascinated and frightened me.

"*Afrika! Afrika! Mayibuye!* In the women's time!" Lilian Ngoyi's voice rose above the hum and the bus hushed. "*Diyatshiswa!* The passes are being burnt!" And Lilian Ngoyi burst into the song.

They are being burnt—the passes. In the Orange Free State the women are burning the passes issued to them. Lukhele is there and Mandela and Tambo and Nokwe to defend them. These were the Congress lawyers— and there were many besides: black and white. It was a song after Lilian's heart—the aggressive feminist. A fighter herself, she loved the fighting women. She had taken liberties with the Congress slogan, "Freedom in our lifetime," and changed it to "Freedom in the women's time."

And I remembered that Lilian had been crying not long ago, singing and crying under the jacaranda sky.

Moses Kotane was telling someone about the Zimbabwe ruins, carefully outlining the theories about their origins. And it seemed strange that in the crawling, shaking bus, full of legal questions and doubts and song, he should be talking about the ancient ruins.

"We built them, of course," he said finally. "It is not surprising that the ruling class should deny us the credit for them."

And the bus sang and argued and laughed all the way back to Johannesburg. And I caught a No. 10 bus to Parktown and to Hazel.

"Man, you're free! Do you realise, you're free!" said Hazel. I had feared that she would cry, but she was a very durable person. "It's absolutely wonderful. And now we can go to Ghana without deserting the trial."

Hazel had waited a long time for this to happen. She had lost some weight in the past months. In many ways the two years had been harder for her than for me. I had sat and listened to court. Had caught a train at six in the morning and travelled by bus the eighty-odd miles. But I was doing "something." With her it had been waiting. And she had tried hard to ward off the poverty of the two workless years.

"Yes, free. I can hardly believe it . . ." The painted number still seemed to be behind me on the bench.

"But it's true! It's there!" She pointed to the *Star* I had brought. "You're free, man! Free."

"I can't feel it. Perhaps I've forgotten what it is like. It's still uncertain. No one seems to know what the position really is. Perhaps there'll be a new indictment."

"It's been a long time."

"It has."

And it was as if the whole weight of the two years was pressing on me, blinding me with their anxieties and uncertainties.

"And the end was rather undignified. The court practically scuttled after Pirow's bombshell. And Lilian cried," I said.

"It has been a long time."

The past few months had been terrible. In fact all the time we had known each other had been fraught with terrors and frustrations. But in the last month everything had piled up into a near screech of agony. The police were trailing us. Hazel had been arrested at my home and I had returned to Johannesburg alone. We had tried to stop seeing each other— for a while at least. It was now too dangerous. A lawyer friend had said it was not safe even during the day with open doors. The police would frame us under the Immorality Act. I saw policemen all round. And once a very obvious African detective followed me to Hazel's house.

The Special Branch had been round Hazel's neighbourhood with her photograph, questioning people. They had visited her and interrogated her. They said that they had been instructed to make a report on her to the Ministry of the Interior. In South Africa, the Special Branch men told her, white people, and especially white women, did not mix with non-whites. Perhaps they thought she did not know as she was from England. It was strange, they said, that she mixed freely with "communists" and "traitors" and had been present at protest meetings and rallies. What were her politics? She had no party politics. She was not interested. It was strange that the people she knew, Michael Harmel for one, were "communists," and that she was teaching at a "communist" school—the Central Indian High School. The Special Branch men had gone away, leaving behind their names and telephone numbers in case she wanted to "make an official statement." They were going to make their report and recommendations to the Minister. They did not say what the report and recommendations would be.

Rows of cars lined Mendelssohn Road outside the home of Joe Slovo and his wife Ruth First. Sounds of jubilation rose and spilt into the road. Inside about two hundred people of all races and colours were milling. Nearly all the ninety ex-accused persons were present and most of the sixty-one who had been discharged earlier in the trial. And then there were Congress men and women, members of the Liberal Party and the Institute of Race Relations.

Some of the defence lawyers were present. Mr. Maisels stood in a corner chatting in his baritone—"Mayisela" the Africans were calling him in adoption. Mr. Fischer standing beside his wife was as red and cherubic as ever. Mr. Coaker, Mr. Kentridge, Mr. Nicholas, Mr. Welsh. . . . Out of his gown Mr. Nicholas looked a trifle shy and like a school-boy.

A white policeman had once said, speaking of Mr. Berrange, that he would sooner buy his discharge than face him in the witness box. I looked for him but could not see him.

Robert Resha had once said in a joke that even if we were hanged we had been defended. Brains, grit, patience, work, love—had all gone into our defence over the long months of the trial.

I found myself beside my friend and mentor and hostess—Ruth First. She was on the warpath at once. "Hutch, about that article—I want it. Write it, man." It was the life: Ruth and *Fighting Talk* and articles and apologies. I left Ruth, Hazel at my side, rubbing against the people as a cat rubs against familiar satisfying things.

And I found Michael Harmel, a white friend, for the party ritual: the mutual back slapping; and we withdrew into a corner. We had once written a play together—"2005"—based on the Freedom Charter that had formed a cornerstone of the Treason Trial. But the only remaining copy of that work was with the Special Branch and we did not know how to get it back.

And then, wandering, squirming, and dodging through the chatting and dancing people, I came upon Issy Hayman, who had once run a cycle and watch-repair shop. He had given me two unclaimed watches but they had both been stolen from me. And he said, as he always did, that I reminded him of a character from Gorki.

And I let my essential kindness rest on Hazel's head. And I knew it was safe. I let my fierce possessiveness and protectiveness lie. It was safe. Someone called me Othello, and I did not mind. It was as it should be. It was the life.

"We will miss these good people," Hazel said.

It was a victory for democracy, the speakers said. Even if the Crown drew up a new indictment, the withdrawal of the old one was a victory: a victory for the democratic forces in the country. For those who wanted to see a free and just South Africa for all its peoples.

Izokunyathela i-Afrika—Africa will trample you underfoot—destroy you

—crush you. The African elephant visiting destruction on its foe. . . .

A white chap jumped in through the window. And then another and yet another. One of them sprang on a table and, gesticulating and grimacing and squealing, swung his camera around the gathering. I pushed Hazel away from my side. Flash bulbs exploded in quick succession. He squealed and grimaced, pushing back the hair from his eyes.

Then a body of armed white police barged through the door. They pushed and shouldered their way into us. Big brawny men with cold eyes and tight lips. And I was tinglingly aware of the pistols at their hips.

"Don't push me, man!" Fred Carneson was saying, "Don't push me!"

"Friends," said Joe Slovo standing on a chair, "I ask you to be calm. The police are here in the course of their duty."

The police said that they were on a routine liquor check, to see that the law forbidding "white" liquor to non-whites was not being broken.

It was South Africa.

V

October 22nd, 1958. My case was coming on at 2 p.m. at the Native Commissioner's Court in Fordsburg. I wandered to the Central Indian High School and as I passed one of the classrooms Moosajee leaned out of the window.

"Something terrible's happened. Hazel's deported."

The sun seemed to go out for a moment.

"Don't joke like that, man!"

"*Nkos'phezulu* (God above)!"

African fashion Moosajee put his forefinger between his lips and pointed it to the sky.

Children hung disconsolately in the corridors and they did not even greet me as I passed. The other teachers were at the end of the corridor which served as the staff room. Even the imperturbable Diza Putini was upset. Hazel handed me an official-looking letter and I knew that Moosajee had spoken the truth.

I steadied my fingers. It was from the Department of the Interior. The Honourable Minister of the Interior was considering her removal from the Union, it stated, and went on to quote sections of the Immigrants Act of 1913. Any representations she wished to make had to reach the Department within fourteen days.

"That's all right," I said to my surprise. "They can go to hell."

Something was throbbing towards a climax, a crisis. The climax could not be far away. I was suddenly light with recklessness. They could do what they liked. They could never take Hazel away from me.

"I must leave soon. I don't want to be locked up like Mrs. Hooper," said Hazel smiling wrily.

The Special Branch had made their recommendations and this letter was the result. But the Minister of the Interior had not acted rashly this time. Mrs. Mary Louisa Hooper, a staunch American friend of the African National Congress, had been arrested and hustled into the Johannesburg

Fort Prison. She had successfully sued the Minister of the Interior for damages.

Hazel walked out of the staff room and I followed her into the corridor.

"It's still Blantyre. Nothing changes in the arrangements. I'll leave at the end of the month and that will give you time to get away."

"If I get off, I'll leave tonight," I said.

Tennyson Makiwane, a young "treason suspect" and a reporter for *New Age,* barged into the staff room. He had come for Hazel's story. A few days ago it had been mine.

"Hey boy, the Special Branch is fighting," he said, making notes. "I was also nabbed yesterday for failing to produce a pass. It cost me a precious quid. Peter Nthite's in the cooler. He socked a white cop."

Tennyson was young and loved slang and the dramatic. Peter Nthite, another "treason suspect," had a very short temper.

"They can go to hell," I said.

"Boy, the women are fighting. Honest, they'll burn the bloody passes like in Wynberg and Zeerust."

The struggle against the issue of passes to women had suddenly flared up. Hundreds of African women had trooped into the city from the locations, were demonstrating and being arrested. A few days ago all had been quiet. Now the jails were rapidly filling.

"When's your case?" said Tennyson.

"At two—in the Native Commissioner's Court."

On the way to the Congress Offices, about half a mile from the school, I was on the brink of telling Tennyson my secret. But I checked myself.

Bezuidenhout Street outside the Old Pass Office, where Halberg had taken me, was fevered like overheated dry grass. Hundreds of African women were demonstrating with African abandon. The street milled with black and white uniformed police, the whites armed with guns and the Africans with sticks and assegais. Shouts and songs rose fast and furiously. Huge *kwela-kwelas* (riot lorries) idled as the women clambered into them. The women inside poked their thumbs through the mesh in the Congress salute.

Mayibuye i-Afrika! May Africa come back!

I caught sight of the Special Branch—Sharp, Halberg, Tabete, Solomon Dunga. They had seen us and Sharp was already making an entry in his notebook. I wondered if Halberg would be in court to give evidence or whether he would send the Chief Pass Officer.

"Boy, this place is full of dogs," Tennyson said, walking on.

The Congress Offices were further along Bezuidenhout Street. But it would have been foolhardiness to walk through the demonstrating women and the excited policemen, many of whom were reinforcements rushed into Johannesburg. And for myself I only wanted to finish with the case I had and leave immediately.

The Congress Offices, in the basement of Macosa House, were bustling with activity. Women decked in the black, yellow and green colours of Congress went in and out shouting slogans. Detectives were posted at various points outside the offices and it would have been unsafe for Tennyson and me to go into the midst of the women. Our bail conditions forbade participation in meetings or gatherings except of a purely religious or social nature. We mounted the steps to Walter Sisulu's office.

"Hutch, you look first class," said Walter lifting his eyes from something he was writing. "The arrests are doing you good."

"The women are doing it," I said and greeted Duma, who was immersed in a law report.

Sounds of the demonstrating women surged into the tiny office on the third floor—bursts of whoops and songs.

"Very good," said Walter, listening to the sounds. "First class."

Walter could be arrested and charged with treason a hundred times. It would never change him. He had led the first batch of defiers during the Defiance Campaign of 1952. He had been arrested with nineteen others, while holding the office of Secretary General of the African National Congress, and convicted for "statutory" communism. The terrible weight of the treason trial did not seem to affect him. He had faith. The struggle was a religion. And during the past weeks he had been frantic with worry because, although some women had been issued with passes, nothing had been happening. The shouts of the women were now like music to him.

"Now the Special Branch will have something to worry about!" he said, returning to his writing.

Lilian Ngoyi barged into the office wearing traditional Xhosa costume and Congress colours.

"*Mayibuye!* In the women's time! My sons, the women are teaching Verwoerd a lesson—He has struck a rock. Where are the men?"

Lilian, though debarred by the bail conditions, hovered dangerously close to the demonstrating women whom she would otherwise have been leading. She was the President of the Women's League of the A.N.C. In the next moment she was out of the office again.

"I wish I could get Halberg in the box," said Duma, who was still preparing my defence. "I know he'll send somebody else."

Duma Nokwe was the first African advocate in the Transvaal. Under the Group Areas Act he and Ismail Mahomed, an Indian advocate, were barred from having chambers in His Majesty's Buildings—the legal centre —despite the protests of the Bar Council. Duma humorously described himself as a "roving advocate."

The aging prosecutor looks at the clock and then at the magistrate. The magistrate glances at the clock, straightens the papers in front of him and looks at the prosecutor. The prosecutor stabs the first name on his list and keeps the pencil pinned on it. He calls the name in an aged voice. The young African interpreter shouts in the direction of the door. An African prisoner stumbles forward, running his eyes round the court and the interpreter beckons him into the box. The interpreter breaks into the patter of swearing-in the prisoner in Zulu and raises the prisoner's arm.

Interpreter: *Ithi: Nkos' ngisize!*—Say: God help me.
Prisoner: God help me.

Prosecutor: Failure to pay poll tax for five years.
Magistrate: *Skuldig of onskuldig*—Guilty or not guilty?
Interpreter: The *Nkosi* (his honour) says do you accept the case?
Prisoner: Yes, I accept it. But . . .
Interpreter: *Skuldig, Edelagbaar*—Guilty, your Worship.

The prisoner mutters an explanation to the interpreter. The interpreter silences him with a gesture of the hand. In the tribal court the accused first "agrees" to the case and then defends.

Magistrate: Have you anything to say?
Prisoner: Yes, *Nkosi*. I worked for *Oubaas* (old master) Klaas. *Oubaas* got very ill and *Oubaas* died. The farm was taken by *Kleinbaas* (young master) Piet. I worked for *Kleinbaas* for many years. *Kleinbaas* sold the farm to *Baas* Jan of Klipgat and . . .

The prosecutor glances at the clock, at the prisoner and the magistrate. He stabs his pencil impatiently at the name.

Interpreter: Not all that. The *Nkosi* does not want to hear all that.
Magistrate: Two months—six pounds. Pay up the arrears.

The prosecutor's pencil stabs the next name. The interpreter shouts to the door. A prisoner comes in. The interpreter breaks into the patter of swearing-in. The prisoner raises his arm: God help me.

Prosecutor: Failure to produce a pass on demand.
Magistrate: Guilty or not guilty?
Interpreter: Do you accept the case?
Prisoner: No, I don't accept the case.
Prosecutor: You did not produce your pass on demand.
Prisoner: *Nkosi*, I was not going far from home. My pass is at home, *Nkosi*. I was just crossing the street. I can fetch it, *Nkosi*.
Magistrate: You must always have your pass with you. Two weeks— one pound.

The magistrate again writes something on the paper in front of him. The prosecutor stabs the next name. The interpreter shouts. A prisoner trots in. The patter begins. Help me, God. The magistrate waits. The prosecutor glances at the clock. The interpreter is bored.
No pass. *Skuldig, Edelagbaar*—Guilty, your worship. Three months— ten pounds. The pencil stabs. God help me. Poll tax. *Skuldig*—guilty. Two months—six pounds. Pass. *Skuldig*. God help me. Five prisoners. Ten prisoners. Fifteen prisoners. The prosecutor glances at the clock. The magistrate mops his face. The interpreter abbreviates the patter. I look at the clock and wonder if my case will be heard. A prisoner walks in. The interpreter breaks into the patter, stops halfway and looks quizzically at the prisoner

Interpreter: The prisoner speaks Afrikaans, your Worship.

The interpreter slouches on the stool beside the box, runs his eyes round the court, glances at the clock, and winds his gold watch.

Prosecutor: Failure to produce a pass and to pay tax for three years.
Magistrate: *Is jy skuldig of onskuldig?* Are you guilty or not guilty?
Prisoner: *Onskuldig, Edelagbaar*—Not guilty, your Worship.
Magistrate: What's your name?
Prisoner: Pieter Swarts, *Edelagbaar*.
Prosecutor: *Waar's jou pas?* Where's your pass?
Prisoner: I don't carry one, *Edelagbaar*.
Prosecutor: You don't carry one—what are you?
Prisoner: *Kleurling*—Coloured, *Edelagbaar*.
Prosecutor: Where's your identification card?
Prisoner: I don't have one, *Edelagbaar*.
Magistrate: Did you go for classification?
Prisoner: No, *Edelagbaar*.
Prosecutor: Because you know you are a native. What's your native name?
 You're no Pieter Swarts. You don't even speak Afrikaans properly.
Magistrate: Get a pass. No nonsense. You know you must have a pass.
 Three months—ten pounds.

I am sweating. I am no different from the prisoner. My Afrikaans is no better. I didn't even try to be "classified."
 The prosecutor's pencil stabs away down the list. My hopes that my case will be heard today are sinking. It is past three o'clock. The young white policeman gapes at the sight of an African advocate sitting at the prosecutor's table. Another prisoner is in the box and he also speaks Afrikaans, "Coloured" Afrikaans, however. But he is darker than the man who got three months.

Magistrate: Where's your identification card?
Prisoner: I went for classification, your Worship. They said I was a
 native.
Prosecutor: Then you are a native.
Prisoner: No, your Worship. I'm a Buys.

I am jerked alive. I can hardly believe. History has it that Buys, a renegade white man, left a tribe of half-caste children. I look at the prisoner again. Nothing of the white man remains. Like me.

Magistrate: Have you appealed against your classification?
Prisoner: Yes, your Worship. But Pretoria says I'm a native.
Prosecutor: Then you *are* one.
Prisoner: I'm not a native, your Worship. I'm Buys' grandchild.
Magistrate: There's nothing I can do. The Classification Board says you
 are a native. I give you fourteen days to get your matters in order.

Prisoner: The police will arrest me again, *Edelagbaar*. Give me a note, *Edelagbaar*.
Magistrate: I can't do that.
Prisoner: *Dankie, Edelagbaar*—Thank you, your Worship.

The magistrate looks at the prosecutor and then at the clock. He mops his face. He thinks they can adjourn for a short while. The young white policeman jumps to attention, his hand touching the holster of the gun on his hip. *Staan in die Hof!* Rise in Court!

I remain sitting at the back of the court. I am afraid to look at my brother George at my side. My nose is tingling with tears and my stomach is heavy with helplessness. Duma at the prosecutor's table shrugs off the young white policeman.

"Boy, the Magistrate's Courts make me sick, but this is worse," says Duma, shaking his head at the Native Commissioner's Court. "George," he says, turning to my brother, "as a witness you'll have to be outside the court after this."

Tabete, of the Special Branch, tiptoes into the court and sits on a bench at the back. The white policeman shakes his head and gapes. The magistrate arranges the papers in front of him and glances at the clock behind me.

"P.P.D. Nokwe instructed by Shullamath Muller appearing for the accused," says Duma and sits down.

The prosecutor rises tiredly to his feet and looks at the clock and then at the magistrate.

Prosecutor: The accused is charged with having no documents and with failure to pay tax since 1944—that is, fourteen years. The Chief Pass Officer Johannesburg will give evidence in this case.

Erasmus, the Chief Pass Officer, bows to the magistrate and gives his name. He turns his bulbous forehead to me. I look at him steadily.

Magistrate: In which language will you speak?
I: English, your Worship.
Prosecutor: *U is die Hoof Pasbeampte Johannesbrug*—You are the Chief Pass Officer, Johannesburg?
Erasmus: *Korrek, Edelagbaar*—Correct, your Worship.
Prosecutor: Can you tell the court for how long?
Erasmus: Twenty-two years, your Worship.
Prosecutor: In the course of your duties you have met many natives?
Erasmus: Thousands of natives.
Prosecutor: In your opinion, what is the accused?
Erasmus: A native.
Prosecutor: Tell the court what happened on Friday, 17th October, 1958.
Erasmus: The accused was brought to me at the Pass Office by Detective Sergeant Halberg of the Special Branch and I charged him for failure to produce a pass and failure to pay tax since 1944.
Prosecutor: Thank you.

Nokwe: Mr. Erasmus, I will direct my questions in English and you may give your answers in Afrikaans. Your Worship, my Afrikaans is not outstanding.

Erasmus: It's immaterial to me. English or Afrikaans, it's the same to me.

Nokwe: Thank you, Mr. Erasmus. Mr. Erasmus, you do not claim to be an expert on race—it is a very difficult subject.

Erasmus: I have had long experience with natives.

Nokwe: Will you please answer my question.

Erasmus: No.

Nokwe: No what?

Erasmus: I do not claim to be an expert.

Nokwe: You are liable to make mistakes about the race of a person.

Erasmus: I can tell a native when I see one.

Nokwe: But people sometimes appear to belong to one race and yet in fact belong to another.

Erasmus: Yes, that is so.

Nokwe: So when you say a person belongs to one race, you are merely expressing your opinion.

Erasmus: Yes.

Nokwe: Your opinion could be wrong, of course.

Erasmus: Yes.

Nokwe: Thank you, Mr. Erasmus.

Prosecutor: What is your name?

I: Alfred Hutchinson.

Prosecutor: Are you sure you do not have a native name? What are you —what race are you?

I: Coloured.

Prosecutor: Are you sure? What is your native surname? Answer the question!

I: My name is Alfred Hutchinson.

Prosecutor: What race is your mother?

I: African.

Prosecutor: And your mother's father and grandfather?

I: African.

Prosecutor: Native. What language do you speak in your home?

I: Swazi and English.

Prosecutor: No Afrikaans?

I: No.

The prosecutor sits down stiffly. And I wish I could sit down too. Duma rises to his feet.

Nokwe: With due respect, your Worship, I do not see that there is a case to meet.

Prosecutor: Your Worship, I fail to see what my learned friend means when he says there is no case to meet. The accused is a native and the law lays down that all natives over the age of sixteen have to carry passes. It is for him to prove that he is *not* a native.

Magistrate: The court will adjourn for a few minutes. Court adjourn.

Duma stands talking to the prosecutor and I wander out of the box. It is approaching four o'clock and I despair that my case will come to an end that day. The magistrate returns.

Magistrate: There *is* a case to meet.
Nokwe: As your Worship pleases. What is your name?
I: Alfred Hutchinson, your Honour.
Nokwe: How old are you?
I: Thirty-four years.
Nokwe: What race are you?
I: Coloured, your Honour.
Nokwe: Have you ever regarded yourself as other than Coloured?
I: No, your Honour.
Nokwe: Could you tell the court about your parentage.
I: My father is Coloured. My mother is African.
Nokwe: And your father's parents?
I: My grandfather was a European and my grandmother was an African.

My helplessness mounts. I look at Duma and wonder how *he* could persecute me also.

Nokwe: What are your qualifications?
I: Bachelor of Arts and University Education Diploma.
Nokwe: What is your profession?
I: Teacher.
Nokwe: Tell the court what you were doing in 1944.
I: I was at St. Peter's Secondary School, Rosettenville.
Nokwe: When did you leave St. Peter's?
I: In 1945.
Nokwe: Then what did you do?
I: I went to Fort Hare University College in 1946.
Nokwe: Up to what year?
I: Up to 1948. And again in 1950 for U.E.D.
Nokwe: What did you do in 1953?
I: I attempted law at the University of the Witwatersrand but did not write the examination.
Nokwe: And in 1955?
I: I again attempted law and again abandoned studies.
Nokwe: What are you doing now?
I: I am in the High Treason Trial.
Nokwe: Thank you.

The prosecutor rises wearily to his feet. The court will adjourn any time now.

Prosecutor: You say your grandfather was a European; what was his name?
I: George Hutchinson.
Prosecutor: What nationality was he?

I: English.
Prosecutor: How do you know?
I: I know. I remember him.

How can I tell them that I remember sitting on his knee eating bis-
cuits from his store at "Naboth's Vineyard", disturbed and fascinated by
his sand-coloured eyes? How can I tell them of "Jojo the old Scot" as
the Africans called him; Jojo who had fought against the Zulus at the
Battle of Isandhlwana; Jojo the pioneer of Kimberley and Barberton,
who knew Rhodes and Sir James Fitzpatrick and the great hunter Selous?
Jojo who claimed lineage with the John Hutchinson who had signed
Charles I's death warrant and was later imprisoned in the Tower of
London on a charge of treason . . .?

Prosecutor: When did he die?
I: 1930.
Prosecutor: You went to St. Peter's—a native school.
I: There were Indians and Coloureds too.
Prosecutor: But it was predominantly a native school.
I: Yes.
Prosecutor: You know that under the Population Registration Act you
    have to be classified?
I: Yes.
Prosecutor: Did you go for classification?
I: No.
Prosecutor: Why not?
I: I did not think it was urgent. Besides I did not have the time.
Prosecutor: Why not?
I: Because I have been in the treason trial since 1956 and in court
    almost every day.
Prosecutor: But there have been numerous adjournments, why didn't
    you go then?
I: I was assisting at the Central Indian High School.
Prosecutor: There were school holidays. You didn't go for classification
    because you know you are a native.

George is called into court. The African interpreter rouses himself and
shouts to the door. Erasmus mops his bulbous forehead. The prosecutor
glances at the clock. Duma rises to his feet. George comes into the
court, his shoulders hunched.

Nokwe: Mr. Erasmus, will you kindly take a look at the accused and
    at the witness—look at the nose and the mouth. What would you
    say about them?
Erasmus: I would say they are related.
Nokwe: Closely related?
Erasmus: Yes—brothers, I would say.
Nokwe: Thank you, Mr. Erasmus. That completes my examination of
    the witness for the Crown, your Worship.
Magistrate: Thank you, Mr. Erasmus.

Erasmus bows to the magistrate and smiles worriedly as he stumbles out of court. Duma turns to George, who is rubbing his hands slowly.

Nokwe: What is your name?
George: George Hutchinson.
Nokwe: How old are you?
George: Thirty-two.
Nokwe: What is your race?
George: Coloured.
Nokwe: Have you ever regarded yourself as other than Coloured?
George: No.
Nokwe: Do you know the accused?
George: He is my brother.
Nokwe: By the same father and mother?
George: Yes.
Nokwe: What is your father?
George: Coloured.

I think of my father and my uncle, who both won the D.C.M. during the First World War—my father nick-named the "Flaming brazier" for his terrible short temper. What had they fought for, I wonder.

Nokwe: Your father's father?
George: European.
Nokwe: Where were you when the accused was arrested?
George: I was with him in his car.
Nokwe: What happened?
George: Sergeant Halberg and other members of the Special Branch surrounded the car. Sergeant Halberg asked for our passes.
Nokwe: And then what happened?
George: I showed him a document from the police at Hector spruit saying I am a Coloured.
Nokwe: And then?
George: They let me go and arrested my brother.
Nokwe: Did your brother say anything?
George: He told them he was a Coloured.
Nokwe: Do you have the document with you?
George: Yes.
Nokwe: Please show it to the Court.

The prosecutor rises crampedly to his feet while George looks for the document.

Prosecutor: Your Worship, I protest strongly against my learned friend's action of wanting to hand in material which is clearly inadmissible evidence. The policeman in question had no right to make such a declaration and furthermore he was merely stating his opinion that the person is Coloured.
Nokwe: Your Worship, with due respect I fail to appreciate my learned

friend's anxiety to exclude the police document. It was issued by a competent officer of the South African Police Force who happens to know the family of the accused and that the witness is a Coloured and awaiting his identity card in terms of the Population Registration Act.

Magistrate: Let me see the document.

The young policeman strides with the document to the magistrate, who takes a glance at it and at the clock.

Magistrate: The document is in order.

Prosecutor: As your Worship pleases. You say that your grandfather was a European; how do you know?

George: I remember him as a child.

Prosecutor: When did he die?

George: 1930.

Prosecutor: What is your mother?

George: African.

Prosecutor: Your grandmothers?

George: Africans.

Prosecutor: Where did you go to school?

George: Nelspruit Indian and Coloured School, and Khaiso Secondary School.

Prosecutor: Khaiso is a native school, is it not?

George: Africans, Indians and Coloureds attended it.

Prosecutor: But it is a native school?

George: Yes.

Prosecutor: I have no further questions, your Worship.

The prosecutor glances at the clock as he picks up his notes from the table. I am very tired and envy the interpreter slouched on the stool below me.

Prosecutor: Your Worship, the accused has admitted that his mother, his father's mother—and goodness knows what else—are natives. His grandfather may have been a European but his blood has been swamped by the black flood. The accused has therefore a preponderance of native blood which precludes him from being a member of the Coloured race. Further, the accused went to St. Peter's—a native school. The accused has failed to prove to the court that he is *not* a native, an onus which rests on him. I therefore ask your Worship to find him guilty of failing to produce a reference book as all natives of sixteen years and over are required by law to do.

My grandfather, Chief Matsamo, guarded the eastern approaches of Swaziland whither the banished witches and wizards were sent. In his early reign he sent *impis* to raid the neighbouring tribes. He had over fifty wives. And when I was a baby my mother went to present me to the royal kraal and Matsamo, then in his dotage, gave me milk out of the royal calabash and thanked his daughter for giving him a boy "who would write letters" for him.

Nokwe: The onus of proof does not rest on the accused. It is a duty which the Crown is bound to discharge. It is not the duty of my client to prove that he is a Coloured. But it is the duty of the Crown to prove that he is *not* a Coloured and this the Crown has failed to do. In a number of cases the lower courts have fallen into this error of placing the onus on the accused and it was with this in mind that the learned judge, Mr Justice Rumpff, reminded the courts of the duty which the Crown has to perform.

Duma cites a case and reads the judgement which is in Afrikaans. And I picture Judge Rumpff, the presiding judge of the treason trial, as he sat in court with tremendous intellect in his eyes. The young policeman shakes his head and gapes. Even the interpreter sits up and the magistrate almost imperceptibly nods agreement.

Nokwe: Your Worship, the Crown has failed dismally to do its duty as required by law. Both the accused and the witness have given the court a truthful account of their parentage. They have not tried—as often happens in cases of this nature—to conceal the fact that they are descended from Africans. My learned friend has spoken of a preponderance of native blood in their veins. I submit, however, that the accused is in fact more directly descended from Europeans. He has regarded himself as a Coloured and is such until the Crown proves otherwise. Your Worship, I apply therefore for the discharge of my client.

Duma sits down and taps the table with his fingers. The prosecutor looks at the clock, the interpreter at his watch. The magistrate writes on for a while.

Magistrate: I have listened to the arguments of the prosecution and the defence, and to the statements made by the accused and the witness for the defence. The Crown has failed to establish that the accused is a native and I therefore find him not guilty. (The magistrate turns to me.) See that you get your identity card.

I bowed. I was free. It was 4:30 p.m. The train was at 6:45. There was no time to fetch my luggage. I was leaving for Ghana. I would get the permit to travel through Portuguese territory at Salisbury. I wanted no tomorrow.

from America, Their America

■ John Pepper Clark (Nigeria)

A strange satellite was orbiting very low over the United States, so furiously low that millions of Americans milling from New York City to the village of Anaktuvule Pass in Alaska could see without the help of telescopes out in Cape Canaveral and California the burning body whirling above their heads. Looking very much like a huge helicopter ablaze with characters too weird to decipher by witch-catchers like the Central Intelligence Agency and Federal Bureau of Intelligence, the strange foreign body in the air, showering out sparks and streamers in the wake of its own storm, in a matter of one flash and swirl had left the entire sky over the sub-continent running and awash with a scarlet so terrible to the eyes that some called it blood and others fire.

Those old enough to remember thought it a thousand times more real and menacing than any hoax of a Martian raid Orson Welles had let loose, and on every lip was again that cry of disbelief and despair raised by all Americans when the first sputnik shot into space. Only now it carried the keen edge of the grave. Parents and children fought one another for safety of their shelter, pastors and executive directors shut out members of their flock and staff, schoolchildren milled into the streets before teachers could put lessons into practice, and the football game as well as baseball broke up in the bowl, with rattles, cans of beer and bags, capsules and canisters of lunch beating a scaring tattoo that an ever-on-the-alert militia and reserve corps could not answer. Only the scaremonger gangs of press and politicians kept well in character. What is Washington doing? they beat their breasts. Are the peace-loving people of America going to be strafed to death before the Administration does something? This sure is a Communist plot! Let's hop over and seize this here Cuba before Castro bombs us out! It's not just classified pictures of the US that that man Kruschev wants—why, look at that thing up above there! And you can be sure it carries H-bombs to blow up New York City, Washington DC, and Chicago! And what are we, the most powerful people on earth today, doing but standing around and listening to all that hogwash from the UN—a house fully occupied by black brats and commies?

On this occasion however the Administration was not waiting to be prodded; indeed it was already much ahead of the fastest running and fastest talking messenger of evil omen. Click, went the button to Omaha, whether from the President direct or from the Pentagon, always in alliance with Big Business, nobody it seemed might live to tell. But there for the cowards and the courageous to see with one catch of breath were squadrons of the Strategic Air Command long since air-borne and chasing the strange phenomenon for all their worth. It was like robins flying after an enchanter-owl. "Will they catch up with him? Can they gun him down without harm to millions of Americans below?" The TV news-casters speculated soulfully. "But first," they broke off together "shall we pause for a message—oh, yes, our sponsors have not for one moment lost faith in the will of the American people to overcome all their enemies."

At this point exactly, sounds of sirens, as if all of New York were already flooding with the blood or fire scarlet in the skies, came with one crashing crescendo over the high and low suds of the soap showing in the washing-machine, both of which hordes of housewives, stuck and clinging to their TV sets as a last resort, would very much want to buy at the end of the invasion; and then the siren-sounds drowned every-thing in that madhouse, on fire and out of sight.

And I bobbed out also, from stream of sleep and dream on the couch in my sitting-room and study, to hear the telephone ringing away outside my door in the third entry of Princeton's Graduate College. Someone, puffing down the steps, had already picked the receiver up, calling out briefly: "JP, it's for you again!" I turned over on my side with one grunt after another, for my temples were hammering as hard as if they would split.

"Are you up?" Israel who had been my guest came up to where I lay thrashing still half asleep.

"Ungh," I grunted more.

"That call is for you," he shook me.

"OK, take it for me, will you?"

"Of course, yes." I heard him run down the steps with the fly-lightness of his figure, and then his quick, raucous voice as he asked for who it was that wanted me that early Monday morning.

"It's a Mrs. Somebody," he came back to tell me. "Says she is secretary to a Professor Patterson."

"What does she want?" I shifted position to ease the pain I felt in my every part.

"Don't know," Israel said, "but I can tell you she didn't hide her South-ern accent."

"Hell." I cursed aloud.

I scrambled out from under my wrapper, and staggered out in my pa-jamas into the stairway to take the call in person, half a flight down.

"Hello," I announced myself.

"Is that Mr. Clark?"

"Yes."

"When do you wake up?"

"Let's not go into that; now what is it you want?"

"I don't want anything of you; it is Professor Patterson, the Director of the Woodrow Wilson School, who wants you to see him."

"Professor Patterson—the Director of the Woodrow Wilson School of Public and International Affairs?" I repeated after her.

"Yes, that's right."

"When?"

"I cannot tell you. But are you free all today?"

"In the morning, yes."

"Well, I'll find out from Professor Patterson when he can see you. He is at a meeting now."

"And you have no idea what he wants me for?"

"No, Mr. Clark, I have told you I do not know what the Professor wants to see you for. But I'll ring later and tell you the hour of appointment."

"Thanks a lot."

I hung up the receiver and stumbled up, straight back into bed. Israel had already finished his toilet, and closing the door behind him, looked at me with the anxious eye of the qualified doctor that he was, not of the quacks and powerful performers whose power and antics drove him out of the profession into the yet more sterile one of political study, but of a doctor still able to panic on behalf of a patient because he is a fellow creature in pain and needing personal help and care. I pulled my coverlet up over my face, and before he could find out what the matter was with me, the telephone bell went again and he ran out to take it.

"That woman again," he returned immediately to report, "and she wants you in person she says."

So I pottered again, this time into deeper mystery and a growing sense of anger.

"Yes, Mr. Clark, can you come over at nine tomorrow? Professor Patterson will be in the office to see you then."

"So early?"

"Why, don't you have classes as early as that?"

"No, I don't."

"Are you saying you cannot get up that early to attend classes?"

"Well, I happen not to have early classes."

"You will have to come, anyway. The Director will be in his office between nine and eleven o'clock in the morning, and you'd better make sure you report there on time."

"Well, about ten then."

"What's that you say?"

"I said would ten-thirty to eleven suit the Professor?"

"Now you are calling the hour, but I'll find out from him and let you know. But try on your part, and call us."

"Thank you." After which I hugged the wall back into my room and bed. Israel, guessing that I wanted to rest more and be alone, lugged his bag of books to his shoulders and tramped out to the Firestone Library, a mile on the other side of the campus. I think I must have drowsed more with the dying of his footsteps down the steps and out on the walk through the inner court. When I woke up again with my body more relaxed and my senses beginning to focus, the smell of food was all about the place and I felt uncommonly hungry for breakfast, which I do not normally take. The hour bells of Princeton's many towers, always discordant and never agreeing among themselves, began then their staggered tolling, and looking at my watch, I saw it was long past noon. It now dawned upon me I had been up more than once before, and suddenly nightmare and the day's actual business each fell into place.

That terrible nightmare came actually as a repeat of my experience of

America during the Cuban Crisis six months or more before. Then in Princeton the continuous tearing past overhead of jet-bombers and the horrid noise of other aircraft taking off from military bases close by and returning again from missions known only to those who had profits to gain from plunging the world into war, would not let one sleep. Nor would the mammoth parade by TV stations, whether signing on or off, of all the armed forces and armament at the instant call and command of the American people should that scoundrel Castro and his new-found uncle Nikita Kruschev be mad enough to refuse moving out those missiles aimed at the heart of the United States.

"Will you really go to war?" I had asked the Colonel who I must add, grew almost youthful in those terrible days of tension when every true American male expected to be called up as if service like that would again save anybody.

"Yes." He made no bones about the matter. "The Russians have played with us for too long. Now that we mean business, we hope for their own good they take us seriously."

"How are we for fall-out shelter?"

"Oh, very good," the Colonel disclosed. "The Firestone Library can take the entire student body and faculty members and their families, and quite a good number of town people to boot."

I thought of heavy walls crashing and damming up gates to the underground shelter before the few left after the blast had time to scurry like rats inside their holes, and of rubble and tumbled down structures sealing up and burying people alive like miners marooned in shafts and caves steaming hot and perhaps flooding up as well. And then all in a flash I recalled the stories and reports that a top-secret brain-computing machine stationed on the campus actually dictated to America's fleet of polaris and other nuclear submarines where and when they must deploy themselves and fan-out undersea in their long, deep dives to provide for America and her Free World a constant invisible bulwark. In the event of war therefore Princeton offered the Russians a palpable hit, either directly or as part of the devastation that would be New York or Philadelphia.

"Well, is that all the protection one can expect?" I laughed to cover up the cry in my throat.

"That's very good protection for anybody," the Colonel said. "There are millions not so provided for." Which was true. Not that the millions thought much about the matter for themselves, anyway. There was the jolly fellow I shared drinks with at the Peacock Inn the night the Cuba quarantine was declared.

"What do you think of it all?" I asked.

"Me?" he spread out his arms. "Kennedy is Irish and I am Irish. So what's there to say? Anything he does is good enough for me. I fought in Africa in the last War, and I guess I am not too old to strap my boots on once more." Such are the loyalties at work for the great American cause.

"And you have no plans to fly Parvin Fellows home?"

"No," the Colonel ruled. "They will have to take things as they come— with everybody, I'm afraid."

"I think I better book myself a seat home on the next plane," I said flippantly. And getting back into my room, I slept fitfully through that vision of America I had just dreamed a second time.

Odd, wasn't it? Recalling my imminent interview with the Director of the Woodrow Wilson School, an interview still carrying for me some air of mystery, I rang up his secretary to apologize for not calling much earlier and also to find out whether or not she had herself called as we seemed to have agreed and not got me. Professor Patterson's secretary was out for lunch, some neutral voice told me, but I could call again in an hour if I so wished. That suited me fine, for I could then have lunch myself. Because service in both the breakfast-room and Procter Hall was over already, and not having any stomach to fall across town for a meal, I made for the machine-room on the basement floor, and got myself some chocolate milk and cakes in real American fashion in praise of which I had written this little song:

> A dime
> in the slot,
> And anything
> from coke to coffee
> Spews down your throat,
> from crackers to candy,
> Breaks against the enamel
> wear of your teeth,
> (And as TV minstrels
> will have it ahead
> Of the Congo
> and Guernica) tobacco
> Enough to plant
> another Garden:
> Now, old Moses
> for whom, they say,
> Mannas fell in the desert,
> did he push a button as this,
> and who knows at what price?

Professor Patterson's secretary was back in her seat when I rang the Woodrow Wilson School later. I began with trying to say how sorry and ashamed I was that I overslept and failed to call her back earlier in the day to confirm the hour of appointment, but she seemed either too busy working to listen or was just not interested in long explanations and excuses.

"Mr. Clark, you failed to call me back. Now, why didn't you? That's gross disrespect, the like of which has not been seen here before, a student telling the professor when he would be pleased to present himself for an interview. Anyway, Professor Patterson has now directed that you turn up unfailingly at nine tomorrow morning," she spouted over me without stop.

"Excuse me," I began.

"Now, Mr. Clark, there is nothing to excuse. I think you fully understand all I have said."

"Well, we shall see," I said mysteriously and placed back the receiver on her, for she had started spouting again.

That was how things had been in the few days past. Returning from a brief trip up to Canada the week before, I had joined the rest of the Parvin group for our second pilgrimage to Washington. It had turned out a most tiresome affair. Arriving a little after eight in the evening by train, we had each been claimed and whisked off by host families, all prosperous sons of Princeton. I got billeted with my Nigerian colleague at the William Wrights, real estate people. They were most kind to us, although living out in Virginia, from where Mr. Wright had to drive us into town every morning on his way to work, I half expected any moment to be called "nigger" to my face, and given the necessary works therefrom. On the one occasion our host could not take us direct to where the long day's journey began for us into night, we hopped a bus into town. That seemed to send a shock of silence from aft to stern of the vehicle, accompanied by a spontaneous shying and shooing away movement and a shaking out of dress on the part of other riders, all of them whites, naturally. But that is another story entirely.

What did happen to me however was the merciless drill and systematic brainwashing that formed the Parvin lot ad nauseam all the session, but more blatantly in the course of those Washington pilgrimages. A two-hour visit to a "23 million jobs" school exhibition at the patio of the Department of Agriculture building, and briefings at the hands of AID programme officials lasting more than three hours in the State Department took up all the morning. Then "individual interviews with appropriate State Department area officers" followed hot after a late lunch in the cafeteria there, a large classified affair. And taking the rest of the day was a visit to the Housing and Home Finance Agency, where a representative of Dr. Weaver, who is a Negro conspicuously heading a full government department, told the silliest trash about housing and urban renewal feats, as if he did not know that everybody there knew what cheating and removal and uprooting of those already poor and blighted went under guise of that well-meaning operation called urban renewal.

We had a buffet supper that evening at the palatial home of the Hon. Mr. and Mrs. Andrew Berding, way out in the posh suburb of the capital. The Hon. Mr. Berding had served in the Eisenhower administration as Assistant Secretary of State for Public Affairs, but now, more or less retired from public affairs, engaged himself completely with writing and lecturing. Very urbane and warm, he told us anecdotes late into the night which made my eyes flood with laughing. Although it was dark and we could not inspect the garden and admire its flowers and general layout, I passed a most pleasant and delightful time in the porch with Mrs. Berding, talking flowers, how to breed new kinds, from the rose, red and white, to the hydrangea, dogwood, azalia and tulip, all beginning to blossom and shout out the arrival of spring, after a sharp, long winter, the severest within living memory. And as a grand finale underscoring the perfect union and bliss that was "the Berdings," husband and wife played us their favourite pieces, one on a musical saw, the other accompanying on the piano.

"Oh, how beautifully you play together!" a female guest there gushed "Your timing is just great."

"It ought to be; we've been at it for more than thirty years together," Mrs. Berding, eyes a bit glassy now, said briefly. I thought she was going to cry. Altogether theirs was a performance most charming and soothing. In fact, when a friend's wife drove in from somewhere in the city centre to collect me home at about midnight, it seemed churlish to tear myself away from a party showing no signs of breaking up for the night.

"He now moves with the millionaires," my friend reported to her husband.

"Well, why didn't you tell them about us poor struggling students and family from Nigeria? We need money, you know," he said. "One can't go on rushing from one job to another a whole day for much longer. It's giddy and maddening."

"You are telling me," I slumped into a seat. "I have always wondered how you carry it off in addition to studying full time." It had been a long slogging day, and another was already then hard on its heels.

That day, a Friday, began with a call at the head offices of the US Chamber of Commerce. There we heard from a smug spokesman of the Chamber a dreary lecture "on the role of business in US political process and society," a talk with a most exasperating tone, marked by the man's straight-faced declaration that it was good for big business to organize but bad for workers to have trade unions which was denying the individual his right to find employment. Happily, his were claims soon offset by those put forward by the rough-hewed Dickensian character who addressed the Parvin group on the "role of labour in the political process of the nation, the general outlook on technological change, automation and retraining of displaced workers." It was a fine contrast in the debating styles of two formidable proponents of the American way of life which, both were equally emphatic in stating, secured its firm foundation on the rock of private property and ownership arising from free enterprise that no Communist or Socialist lever could displace or topple over with talks about ownership of means of production and a fairer distribution of national wealth.

Break for lunch came like a fresh burst of air into the stuffy room each spokesman for America was bent on making the place for me. It was more so as Mimi and Eldon Crowell had come over and collected Dan Passent and me to have lunch with them at Washington's club for top lawyers, of which Eldon was a member. For us two Parvins, that really was a break-through of sun and sunshine in a sky oppressive with clouds.

In the afternoon, piloted by a gentleman from the Foreign Student Service Council, the group, striving very much to remain together, toured the American Indian Hall at the Smithsonian Institution of Natural History, and went desultorily on from there to the National Archives. It was here that I realized for the first time that Lincoln's famous emancipation proclamation actually was directed solely at and effective only in the Union-occupied South, so that for a chaotic interval during which self-righteous Northern States searched their hearts and factories and farms, white masters and black slaves did not know for sure on what side of the line they stood. Washington, much steamier than Lagos, was teeming that Friday with wide-eyed, young and old pilgrims visiting from distant states the shrines of George Washington and Abraham Lincoln. And moving among these crowds looking so lost among the relics and replicas of their ghost past, and having my grey retired public-servant pilot close by my side, since all others had either deserted or simply passed out, I felt rather like Dante being shown by Virgil through the various regions of punishment and pleasure in the underworld.

This then provided the backdrop against which the petty drama of my last days at Princeton, and indeed in the United States, was enacted to the exclusion of an outside audience and body of independent adjudgers and critics.

I did not turn up at nine on Tuesday morning at the offices of the Director of Princeton University's Woodrow Wilson School of Public and International Affairs. Later in the day, someone, I think it was that overbearing secretary again, called to say I had a most urgent and important letter to collect from my pigeon-hole at the School. I was not around but went over immediately to take delivery as soon as I was told of it. "Dear Mr. Clark," it directed without much ado, "Will you please arrange with Mrs. Sangston a meeting with me on Wednesday, April 24, to discuss the question of whether your fellowship should be continued beyond May 1." And appended at the bottom was the personal seal and signature of Professor Patterson, the Director.

My first reactions prompted that I simply ignore the note, for what it was worth. I was due to go down with the rest of the Parvin crowd at the latest on May 13. Indeed, Colonel Van de Velde, our ubiquitous stage manager and more, already appeared genuinely to be losing sleep and weight over the failure of some of us to submit to him the plan and itinerary for our individual round-country tour of the United States in fulfilment of the last part of the Parvin bargain before going our different ways home.

I rather looked forward to that advisory session with the Colonel. When I went to Cornell University at Ithaca in Northern New York State and to Canada across the border, he had proved most useful, not only in making funds available, but especially in the plotting out of routes. There, with a map spread out over the litter on his desk, he charted out for me on each occasion the course of my trip, down to the last detail of execution. Old soldiers never die, I said silently to myself in honest admiration. And in my mind's eye I tried to picture the man just as he must have looked in camp, as well as on the field in occupied France. All this was a scene I looked forward very much to seeing him re-live in however obscure an operation.

Meanwhile, I thought I should first make sure of my booking on a boat sailing for the Far East and India from San Francisco on the West Coast on June 23. Confirmation came at last from the Cunard Shipping Line in New York. So I began working out where and what I would like to see more of the United States. The deep South for me was a top issue. I said that would be the first place I would go if I was going to tour the country at all. The Colonel however would not hear of it, offering a stout and sincere resistance which won my praise and thanks not a little. A Rhodesian Parvin had gone South in the last year in company of two white friends, and for all the segregation and discrimination he had suffered before at home, he came back a deeply hurt man, having in addition helped to spoil a pleasant holiday for his friends. Now, that fellow, though a journalist like me, was a most charming and accommodating guy. I got the tip all right.

"I still want to go down South and see things for myself," I insisted.

"Well, you brought some native costumes with you, didn't you?" The Colonel sought a new line of action.

"And what may those be?" I asked.

"Don't get me wrong," he said wanly. "All I mean is whether you have your Nigerian dress with you."

"Like which?" I teased him.

"Well, I had in mind those colourful flowing robes—now, what do you call them? Africans around here and in New York and Washington wear them pretty often."

"You mean the agbada and sokoto?"

"Say that again," he urged, removing his leg off the arm of his chair. "Yes, I think, if you insist on going South, now those are the things you should wear all the time. With your tribal marks showing in addition, they ought to convince everybody you are no American Negro."

"I don't have any such clothes, not even at home in Nigeria," I explained.

"Really?" the Colonel expressed surprise.

"Honestly," I assured him. "We have lots of dresses in Nigeria, depending on where you come from, although the Yoruba agbada has fast become the adopted style with many, especially the Easterners. I know of friends in the Foreign Service who have worn European dress all their lives, but on getting posted abroad, ran off to the market to have that kind of Nigerian dress prominent in their wardrobes."

"Isn't that what they call projecting the African Personality?" the Colonel asked humorously. "That's the first thing I thought you would do coming over here. Your friend from Nigeria is simply delightful in his gorgeous costumes. At parties he makes quite a splash in them."

"Yes," I agreed. "He adopted them back home."

"Aren't you a strange one? A nationalist and fighter like you, without your national costume! I think you ought to borrow some from your friend before thinking of going South."

"Not to carry out a masquerade," I frowned. "If I cannot go anywhere I want to in this country without fear of harm or harassment, then I don't see where all your talk about freedom and equality leads us."

"Well, I confess it is a great shame things are like this in the US. Still, we are trying. I'm only trying to be honest with you. There's no point in having to run off South with your temper as it is. You will only get hurt badly, and then we shall be called to give account. You ought to go to the New England States, or go to the Mid-West and see the Grand Canyon, the Salt Desert and national parks out in the Northwest—they are all splendid sights. And of course you must go to California, the climate is just like yours, only with the steam off. Now this is the tour I should be planning had I the good fortune to be in your shoes."

That was the last friendly talk I had with the Director of the Parvin Programme at Princeton, and it came before our journey of torment to

Washington. After that, like an incensed manipulator of lights in the theatre, he began switching all the lights off around me on the stage, just when I was preparing to take the cue for the formal finishing act, and then make a quiet if not graceful bow-out.

I called on Professor Patterson at his offices at eleven on Wednesday morning. Mrs. Sangston, his secretary, gave me to understand that the Director was at that moment engaged with one or two other professors, and in the meantime would I please take a seat and wait my turn. After some ten minutes, Professor Patterson came out with his visitors, bade them good morning, and then turning my way, waved me into his office.

I recognized him immediately as the gentleman who had laughed quite a lot and very easily at a small house party Professor Livermore and his wife had held for us Parvin Fellows in the home of two lady friends of his right at the beginning of session. I had not met him since, as he too pointed out, as he explained the nature of the painful duty others had advised him to perform by me that morning. Hands in his pockets, when he was not blowing his nose (the effect of a slight cold, he apologized) the Professor, quite small, especially for an American, paced in the small space between his chair and the wall behind, looking out every now and again through the window at the street immediately outside and the John Foster Dulles Annexe to the Firestone Library showing just beyond. It seemed to take him some time coming to the point. I tried in that interval to explain on my side why there had been the apparent wrangling over fixing this appointment. The trouble was that I allowed myself to be drawn into a quarrel with a secretary who I thought was most rude.

"Oh, that's all right," the Professor dismissed that episode. "She has been doing that job for almost thirty years, and nobody has found her wanting before. But to come to the subject of our meeting this morning," he stayed my protest, "you got my letter, I hope."

"Oh, yes," I said. "I am rather puzzled by it. The programme is over except for the round-trip portion of it. So I don't see how the need arises for an extension of my fellowship. Are those for the others under review as well?"

"Well, that's the problem," the Professor stated. "The programme this year is as you say all but ended, and everybody preparing for his journey to wherever he pleases in the US before returning to his own country and job. Now the question is, Mr. Clark, whether you have personally gained anything from coming here to Princeton and the United States as a whole."

"I don't follow what you mean."

"Let's put it this way then," the Professor sat back in his seat. "I hear from the Director of the Parvin Programme that you have not been attending classes, and others in the group have been making full use of courses available here at Princeton."

"I have sat in the classes I thought useful."

"And which are these?"

"I took a course in International Politics—"

"That was the first term, and Professor Sprout reports that you dropped out in the last weeks."

I recalled those classes in International Politics, a discipline not so new now but still doing all in its power to appear logical and scientific, vying in that process with all the natural sciences, especially physics, including nuclear physics at that, in finding a formula for every action of a politician who happened to be prime minister or president, as if politicians even more so than other human beings acted according to fixed patterns of behaviour that the pet theories of professors could track down. Professor Sprout, always in a spruce suit and behind dark glasses, was something of a pioneer in the field. As a matter of fact, he and his wife had brought out at that time a new compendious volume on the subject, a work that modesty never quite allowed him to include in the fat reading list he drew up for members of the class. These consisted mainly of serious-minded young men undergoing this rigorous training in preparation for their teaching assignments later in life. But others were men who had already seen action in the public service of the United States, ranging from a rather panicky and talkative diplomat, who had served in Cuba and other missions in Latin America, to a stocky, solid, silent vice-admiral or officer not much farther down the ladder. "Do you think Krushchev can defend Castro all the way from Moscow?" I had said to him during the Cuba debâcle.

"Well, I am not at all happy and sure about our own logistics," he had told me.

It was in this class I had first met Israel Rosenfield, a brilliant MD now turned candidate for the PhD in politics. Nobody could understand such a change. On the other hand, with his scientific training and a mind exceptionally sharp, he seemed to understand all pretensions and professions there gathered, and because he could not keep to himself the diagnosis for which he personally very much wanted a cure, he got into no end of trouble. "Oh, that young man," the Colonel on our way from Ford's Mahwah had admitted hearing of him, "he fights every problem. Quite like you!" And there were several things needing proof from life, as day in day out in the large classroom down on the basement floor at the Woodrow Wilson Building, one saw the world chopped up and quartered into two polar camps, one the free world, the other the Communist bloc, each lurking like savages or beasts of prey in the dark to eat up the other unto the last. Boxes, circles, arrows, or genealogical trees formed the favourite and familiar symbols and audio-visual devices and aids endlessly chalked up on the blackboard to catalogue and analyse national ideologies, international groupings and alliances, and the emergence and direction of new blocs on the world scene, stressing how ineffective these were without a striking nuclear stockpile like that possessed by the Americans and the Russians. One camp, it seemed, had more of a dynamic philosophy to live by vis-à-vis the worn-out Christian beliefs peddled by the other. But these were sentiments and surmises quickly wiped off the board. "One never knows if the FBI chaps are around," the professor used to warn them as he made sure of a clean slate on the wall.

One pet subject of those classes was that of the famous Games Theory. Put in crude layman terms, it goes like this. Suppose two roads were open to two opposing groups of soldiers, and one camp had to use one of these roads at all costs. Which should its commanding officer choose since the enemy has both under strict watch? Either way, and by a toss-up, says the game theorist! In other words, a complete abandonment of a calculated and reasoned-out choice, and reliance in a blind plunge, since the enemy knows already anyway all the plans possible. Haphazard as it may sound to the simple ear, the top strategists and policy-makers of the great powers seem to have taken for quite some time now many a decisive move, fraught with dangers for millions, by simply playing this game, so like a blind-man's buff to the novitiate. And the absolute virtue of the top-secret, super-guarded computer on the campus, I was told, lay in its powers to dictate the hazard at the peril of the enemy. For example, the perpetual stationing of America's nuclear striking submarines deep in the Atlantic and elsewhere. Or to cite a more down-to-earth, work-a-day instance. How should America react if it came to the hearing of the President and the public that one US citizen was bumped off in Moscow? Now, the expected and safe answer can always be got by a diligent application of the master mind to the game—to satisfy conditions varying from a street brawl to the planting of missiles in a sphere belonging to another; or so the lectures suggested.

"Dr. Van de Velde himself expressed surprise that I stuck it that long, almost to end of term," I offered an excuse. "The whole course had little to do with events happening in actual life. And as a journalist that's all I deal with."

"That may be so," Professor Patterson conceded. "But could you tell me what other things you have done since coming here and which you have found of benefit?"

"Well, I have been attending a course on the Development of American Literature—" I began.

"Professor Thorpe says he has not seen you for some time," he cut in quietly.

"I have been absent for a couple of times," I defended myself like the real schoolboy and truant they had made me out to be. "Yes, I missed classes only two or three times, and on those occasions I had good reasons to—in fact the professor himself permitted me, for example, when I was going to give a reading at Adelphi College." Incidentally, that was a performance I heard later was broadcast by the Voice of America and beamed all over Africa, without their first seeking my permission or making any payment since.

"Well, apart from the Parvin seminar compulsory for the group but which I hear you missed going to quite a number of times, you cannot really pin down any particular course you have done. The professor who takes the Comparative Politics course for which you registered says he doesn't even remember your face. It is evident therefore Princeton has had nothing to offer you."

At that stage of the interview, I thought I might as well have a really straight talk about it, since it became then pretty obvious that the Colonel had taken great care and pains to compile his case. I reviewed for the benefit of the professor the attempts the Colonel and I had made together to find me a suitable course to pursue at Princeton for that one year and special programme I was there. In the Politics Department we had found no opening of practical value, nor had Professor Downer's English School, except for Professor Thorpe's classes held later in the session and several miles out in his home on the outskirts of Princeton. Philosophy, psychology, economics, architecture, and all the other fields of study like engineering and the physical sciences, for which the place is justly famous, I had shown no nose or training for. So at one point it was suggested that I should go and attend undergraduate classes on creative something or the other.

"Professor Patterson, had I come for a second degree," I began, "I should know what to do and how to set about it. A Parvin Fellowship is hardly the way to that."

"That's right." The professor punctuated me.

"Well, I wouldn't try to dispute the charge about those courses, except perhaps to state that even if I regarded myself as a regular student, that should not remove my right to skip classes and pay for it at exams."

"That's the British system, isn't it?"

"But I wouldn't say I have wasted my time coming here," I tried to assure him.

"How have you used it?"

"Well, beside attending those classes they are good enough to concede me, I have done a couple of plays and written a number of poems since coming here."

"Couldn't you have done that elsewhere other than coming here?"

"Yes, one of the plays, perhaps, but not the poems which mostly are out of my US experience."

"So you could easily have locked yourself up in a New York hotel and done the same thing. We have not given you a sabbatical, have we?" he asked. There was a sudden twinkle to his eyes.

"Well, I suppose that's a legitimate charge, but I should have thought the Parvin Fellowship was to allow me room for development here in Princeton."

"That may be so, but the fact is that you have shown disdain for everything Princetonian and American. That has been the impression of everybody here who has expressed an opinion about you."

"Disdain how?"

"You see, we don't mind people talking politics and socialism here. That's not the point at all. This is a healthy community. You may not find all that you want here. Your colleagues however, seem to have, as have thousands of others. So do you think it is of benefit to you and us that your fellowship continues?"

"Is there anything left of it but the round-trip?"

"That's exactly the point," the professor underlined it for me to see. "You have spent much of your time out of here travelling while others stayed in and studied. Now it is their turn to go out."

"That's fair enough."

"Well, what do you think we should do with you?"

"What does a guest do when the host shows him the setting sun?"

"Well, we don't want any bad feelings, but it is the opinion of all that, since you have shown nothing but disdain for Princeton and the US, there could be no point in continuing the association further."

"Thank you," I said, rising to go which brought the professor also to his feet, hands in his pockets again. "And how soon am I expected to leave here?" I asked.

"That would be for Dr Van de Velde to work out. But I suppose as soon as he can straighten out things with the Graduate School people."

"One point I should like cleared. Does this end here in Princeton? I mean, can I continue with any activities I have outside of here?"

"The point, well, is this. Once your association with Princeton terminates, the College, I think, will write accordingly to the Immigration Authorities to state they are no longer sponsoring you for the visa you may be holding, and in that case, I gather, there is nothing left for you but to leave the US immediately. But I should ask Dr Van de Velde about that."

"I see." I said goodbye.

The Colonel had the administrative details of my departure already well in hand, when I brushed past his breathless secretary, who, it goes without saying, knew everything. Surprisingly, and even beyond my own expectation and the promise I had given the other Parvin people, who at this point wanted to take all sorts of steps impossible for their kind, I appeared most collected and calm for my last interview with the old Colonel. This seemed to unsettle him, for he literally jumped at me when, taking the liberties of a valedictory speech, I expressed surprise and a sense of injustice that the private and recruit had not been warned earlier in the campaign of his shortcomings. That would have offered the rascal a fair chance of either choosing to fall into line or quitting at the outset. Instead the company commander, showing no real sign of offence or concern at any time, had left him unreprimanded, only to have him courtmartialled at the point of general and final discharge, booting him out in ignominy at the last minute.

"Don't you teach me how to do my duties, you whippersnapper!" the Colonel lunged dangerously at me. I could see from the corner of my eye his secretary start out of her seat. "I'll throw you out of here now on your neck if you try any more of your cheek here."

"Well, you certainly have thrown me out on a limb already," I said sweetly.

"You have been a delinquent student, a disgrace to the College and your country. You were brought here as a journalist and an ambassador, but what have you done with all the opportunities placed at your disposal here?"

Still maintaining a sweetness and calm foreign to me, I asked whether the occasional absence from classes made one a delinquent student, especially where grades were not taken and no examinations were sat for to tell the best parrot. I also made it clear that at no time did I regard myself as representing anybody or any country, and therefore whatever disgraceful acts I had done must be visited on me alone as a free and willing agent of myself alone.

"Well, we have law and order here, and let me tell you, young man, I have seen more life and been to better places than you. We must have law and order; society cannot afford to go on with persons like you."

"Any society should be able to afford a maverick," I said softly.

"No, that will corrupt other citizens who are regular in their conduct," ruled the Colonel.

"Isn't it because they are so regular that you get the mavericks?" I asked slyly.

"Now, don't try your cleverness on me. I can't argue with you." The Colonel drew the line.

Later, with him reclined and rocking every now and again in his chair, having first wiped off the specks of foam that had sprouted about the corners of his mouth, the Colonel listened soberly to my complaints about the abruptness of my leaving, why on earth this had happened to me at that point of my life, and what it was I was then supposed to be going back to when I left Princeton in disgrace and such haste.

"You have your newspaper job to go back to, haven't you?" the Colonel reflected.

"No, I resigned that, I told you, before coming over here."

"Of course, you can always pick up a job when you return home," he stood firm.

"Well, that's one of the mis-assumptions by people, especially of our programme; that once you have come over for some course of study or in-service training, then you become overnight an expert for every problem in your underdeveloped country. Unless you were already in the top positions that matter, like our own General from Somalia, for example, you cannot jump the junior post you were serving in to go and direct others because you have been at Princeton, and personally, I don't see any job I can go into now without a whole board sitting over it first. You'll agree these things take time."

"Well, you are a poet and playwright, aren't you?" he said with a mischievous cutting edge he could not succeed in containing inside its sheath.

"Now it's you saying so," I laughed.

The following day, in the midst of my packing and awkward explanations to curious colleagues at the Graduate College, I received this letter from the Colonel, written in his own masculine hand. It minced no words. "Mr Clark, you will receive, within the next few days, $100 (stipend for May) plus $25 (help for sending your heavy luggage home) plus $100 (for expenses incidental to your travel home). A total of $225.

"Whenever your heavy (sea) baggage is ready, let Mrs Krulisch know and she will call the freight forwarder Harbourt, so he can make arrangements with you—

R. W. V."

"Well, there goes your $700 travelling money, and all because you won't shut your bloody trap," someone said, handing the ejection note round the small group of friends not quite decided among themselves whether I should be pressed on to stay or be seen take off immediately as I already proposed to do.

"It's so mean of them."

"I told you Princeton is a lousy place."

"The Parvin Fellows ought to rise as a body and threaten them with going off with JP if they don't behave more sensibly."

"There you are asking too much—$700 is no small money to forego."

"Mr Parvin himself I hear is coming from California to a farewell party of theirs next week. Now, that's the man to tell how they are administering the programme he finances."

"Perhaps the Graduate College should do something before then."

"This treatment of JP, rude as he is, is a negation of all that programme stands for."

All this, so genuinely sympathetic and indignant, was highly interesting and explosive stuff to come from my close circle of student friends, many of them Americans. But to have hoped that they or the Parvin Fellows would rise to a man and upturn by force or persuasion what the Princeton authorities had already decreed would have been like expecting America's six million unemployeds and bums, not mentioning the twenty million Negro people burdened by their colour and history, actually forming a large portion of these "superfluous people," as a TV commentator called those of the lower depths of America, to march in their tattered and starved hordes and columns upon Wall Street or Capitol Hill.

For that would be revolution indeed, and revolution of any type for the American is a state and ideal already completely and permanently achieved at home by their founding and fighting fathers several centuries back; and today, it is an objective the Central Intelligence Agency may carry out in dictator-ridden Latin-American republics and Socialist-minded Afro-Asian developing states on behalf of Big Business, the powerful lobby with its hand on the steering-wheel of the diplomacy and foreign policy in Washington. The rub however, as its former Chief Allen Dulles put it with great bite and aplomb before a very amused Princeton audience, could well be that the Central Intelligence Agency might be effecting a coup in some Middle East country while the head of it is being entertained in Washington as an honoured guest by the President and Congress!

In a set-up like that, it is no wonder the American student is so well-contained and content inside his coarse tights and emblazoned jerseys. To pile up grades, he chews hard at studies just as he does at his sweet gums and ice-cream. Games at their best are the pre-occupation of the giant breed, cheered on equally by special athletics scholarships and a colourful thumping college brass band and chorus of acrobatic co-eds. On weekends he will drive as far as the next state or beyond to reach his date who he may take out to the cinema, fondle and kiss good night at the parental or girl dormitory gates. But he may not slip out of that habit into the sloppy one of wanting to go to bed with her when they are not decently engaged and married. And the horror was great, if as happened often, the foreign students from Africa or even Europe expressed disappointment back in the hall of residence at the lack of accessibility of the American College girl who is so coy and sex-scared. Only at Princeton's highly hierarchied set-up, falling into ranks of colour, wealth, education, and age, you could never quite tell whether your American colleague was horrified at your desires because you happened to be of another colour or country!

At Princeton's Graduate College, for example, students, I found, were more or less satisfied, indeed were excited to the point of actually shouting yodels, by the mere presence in their midst of guests coming in from girls' colleges like Bryn Mawr. "Mixers" they call such meetings. Procter Hall often provided the setting for the idyllic picture of innocent mating and coupling. There with tall candles lit on brass stands on the breavy boards, boys and girls would sit and dine late of a Saturday night, sipping sherry and swapping know-how on the latest gadgets, car models, and smart ideas in astronomy or sociology. Those flickering candles, a wit once said unkindly, were to ensure that hosts did not see their guests too close in the face, for these often were most plain if not straight ugly!

Incidentally, woman-lover as I am, I too could not help noticing the determined manner most American girls, especially the college ones, set about making themselves look unattractive and in fact much like the males who, paradoxically, are a most good-looking people. But the American young female, in her court shoes and knee-high hose, when she is in a brief skirt and shorts and not in those ill-mended, rough-and-tumble tights, and with hair down or bobbed over a face, often chubby and irregular in feature, with perhaps a nose too stubby or veering to the crinkly or crooked, provided for me a constant object for sobering reflection far away from the over-painted synthetic models on parade on celluloid. My shock of discovery perhaps was equaled only by that expressed by a New York tube-rider during the newspaper black-out. There was then no wide double sheet for anybody to cover their face. My, the tube-rider had told *Newsweek*, who would have guessed New Yorkers were so ugly! I did not venture to go that far, except to express my silent gnawing hunger because—

> The mannequins
>   in the windows,
> Sure sirens
>   calling without
> Discrimination
>   down the streets,
> Do not make up for me
>   the Marilyn Monroes
> I miss among the smart coffee

Strange indeed that that extraordinary creation and destruction by Hollywood, long gone beyond the pale of death as they put it, but who in life was even farther away from my kind behind a more damning barrier of colour, and perhaps, celebrity, should have formed for me the heart of that hunger for beauty and love, shouted everywhere by America but which she really cannot satisfy. I made a humble wreath to her name that I strung out like this:

> Wellbeing is a bed
> Of rubber foam that
> Possessed, rocks as

Asleep. And not just
The body, but spirits
Sink with sirens. Pain
Is the pin or thorn,
That a foundling around,
Stabs us to waking. Which is
Hard to endure. Thus
Hands softer than
Down, fairer than
Flower, held both to heart,
And flaked all with ash.

At Cornell University, however, where boys and girls compete on equal terms on the same campus, I once walked into a scene in one of the women's halls of residence, just at that time of signing in before lights are out, that I found most affectionate and touching. There in the gloaming of the hall, on a windy, snow-clad night, each boy returning to the larger world open outside the gates was an Orpheus, and each girl being commandeered away by the hall-warden was an Eurydice! After that, I did not exactly mind my own date repeating her mother's lesson to me that New York was not Ithaca, and it would therefore be difficult to continue our mixed dating there.

Grades, dates, and games therefore form the healthy preoccupation of the American student. Protests and demonstrations are adolescent manifestations to be expected among the growing student bodies in the emergent and unstable societies of Africa, Asia, and South America. It matters very little that the Debating Union at Oxford or Cambridge and lately the campaign for Nuclear Disarmament spawns in Britain products that go direct to Westminster. American society, so fluid, they say, in many things, is however too set for that. In fact, for students to engage together in such pastimes in the United States would be to expose themselves to the charge of engaging in un-American activities. The fault therefore lies in their set-up, not in themselves for being dumb and undemonstrative about events outside. Their one failing perhaps may be ignorance of trends and events happening abroad but which the press, TV and radio guardians do not think fit and proper to project and register on their conscious.

There was that controversy we had at Princeton over what foreign papers the Graduate College should retain in its common-room. Many of us from abroad voted for a continuation of our subscription to *The Times* of London, our argument being that not even the *New York Times* in all its amplitude quite carried all the important news items those of us from Latin-America, Europe, Asia, and Africa were pretty certain of reading a day after in the air-freighted edition of *The Times* of London. I took a bet with the Colonel, by the way, that story by story, and not just by linage, his bible *The New York Times* was nowhere near the ambling matron of the British Press in the coverage of foreign news. Neither of us won the wager as we never got down to the brass tacks of taking a comparative count. The row at the Graduate College raged on for days, and notice-boards got plastered several times over with disputatious personal letters and committee notes in wild approval or protest against retaining the services of Aunt Fleet Street. Symptomatic of all was one rebuff roundly delivered by an irate American graduate student: "What do you want to read that red paper for? You must all be Commies!" But wrong labels and false accusations like this all really go back to the great ignorance and self-absorption of Americans as a prosperous self-sufficient people long safe behind the Atlantic and the Pacific and the walls of protective beliefs, tariffs and slogans they have raised about their freely acquired property.

Bars of sororities and fraternities, behind which American students safely operate, when not rioting and derailing trains to no purpose except that the sap of spring runs wild in their blue veins, as at Princeton, are not raised for aliens and the uninitiated; nor did I go out of my way to seek an opening and passage. But Professor Tumins of Princeton's Sociology Department once told us a story at the Parvin Seminar that could well be indicative of the attitude of mind of the typical member of these closed shops and clubs that the American student has made a special preserve. Apparently, there arose a diplomatic and political need among Princeton's exclusive student eating-clubs to have some black faces in their midst. This started a lot of arguing within the cabals and cliques. For which of the African students, in the absence of American Negro youths, were they to invite? Few as they were, they certainly could not all be invited? So a quota system, very traditional with the place, had to be worked out among the various clubs. And what criteria did they agree to apply to their African guests? First of these was that they must show a decent sense of dress—when the hosts themselves are so scruffily turned out! After that, I did not care to hear out the rest of the list.

In my last week of scuttling from Princeton with a few feckless hands trying hard to effect a salvage of some sort, there were inevitably precious possessions and objects I tried very hard to clutch at and rescue, possessions and objects that proved most disconcertingly scarce to recollect in that period of crisis. Surprisingly, the one thing I missed in the US and which I still regret very much was the break-up of my ties with a couple of Negroes out in their comfortable ghettoes and lone posts. I visited my folks of St John's Street, as I came to call them, quite frequently for a time.

The man had been a Captain in the Army during the War but now he was quite contented with being an attendant by day in some Women's Club in Princeton. His wife worked at night as companion and watch for an old invalid widow or spinster with a lot of money. Together they made a jolly, bustling couple with their jobs, home, and children, the first of which had long since begun earning his own keep. The man used to say to me: "Look at your friend who went to College, and to Princeton at that, how much dollar do you think he makes in a week with all his education? Of course, I regret not going to college or continuing with my commission, but look here, my wife and I here comb up quite a bit between us. Which is more than you can say for some people with all their libraries and airs."

It was hard arguing this when examples abounded everywhere, depicting the ugly and unbelievable phenomenon in the American firmament of opportunity and plenty which makes many a cleaner and porter, with his odd shifts and spare-time jobs (called moonlighting), as well off as, if not better than graduate teachers and trained technicians. So although college, they say, is America's best friend, why shouldn't there be drop-outs, and at a very heavy rate too among the Negroes, when the unskilled and uneducated can perfectly well afford to marry the girls of their dreams, and both spouses can settle happily ever after in the regular home plus the automobile that are their combined dreams? The only snag is that the unskilled man might perhaps be more exposed to the dangers of settling down in a rut or getting rattled about in shallow grooves, whereas his compatriots with developed brains and skills may make a better fight of it, against automation, perhaps, and so move up the social scale with a fair degree of acceleration. Yes, this probably was so, agreed my St John's folks, and it certainly has been one of the cruel factors that have kept the black man down and out in America for so long. "But things will sure change," they cheered themselves. "Why, look at you here drinking with us when President Goheen wants you over at the college to dine with him."

My other couple, much older and more by themselves, have a thirteen-acre home on a hill some miles outside of Princeton. From there on a clear-skied day the visitor can see New Brunswick some twenty-five miles away. Not having children of their own, and constantly harassed now by land speculators and city planners making designs on their estate, my friends have turned their property into a trust. It was their hope when their large swimming pool was complete, to license the place as a community and holiday centre for the Negroes, just as the Jews and others do for their people. To this end, they actually invited me and other Parvins, that is, the coloured ones only, to dinner one night, so that each of us in turn, being so highly spoken of in Princeton, could bring over to the opening of the centre envoys and other influential people from our countries. Only their presence and sponsorship, they said, could convince the blacks of Princeton that it was time they all got together. Corporate action, the secret of big business corporations like RCA, all very vulnerable if only the black people of the earth will boycott them for exploiting them, was what a centre like theirs would strive to foster in the heart of members. And could all of us there help?

It was a pity they seemed not to know of the wary habits of diplomats, Africans not excepted. And it was so painful that I never saw them again before being chucked out of the country of their birth and beleaguerment. It seemed a simple and straight natural relation could not exist for long between my American Negro friends and myself without their wanting me to do something or another to help them. And not really being in a position to help myself, I found it a better policy keeping away, although this too was an unnatural and impossible position. In such circumstances, I often found it more congenial and convenient, while in New York, to walk on Harlem's 125th Street, to skirt Times Square, and to meander among the alleys of Greenwich Village, where for all their pimps, prostitutes, dope-peddlers, and promiscuous clients in homosexual pubs, you knew what exactly you were being solicited for, what the risks and price were, and what was more, your own capability, leaving no tender feelings of loyalty and other susceptibilities trampled behind.

But moving to neutral, commercial ground and refusing to get engaged and involved in the affairs of my embattled friends only served to isolate me more, making me most lonely when in the thick of that human mart where Broadway becomes Times Square. After one such fruitless night of seeking for lasting warm contact, I gave, while waiting for my bus connection at the Port Authority Bus Terminal, the following wail and yawn like a lost dog baying the moon—

Day fell here:
Like a drift of dead leaves,
Day fell facewise among the blocks,
And suddenly! down the overgrown plots,
The great tall figures, all sterile
And faceless before, are in woods
Of a festal night conifer-like trees
Ablossom with fruit. All
Who earlier in the fall
Milled here to pluck or pick at a price
The apple or peach, have forced
Thro' the harvest, bitten by
Bugs, have followed nuts
Home to rabbit-holes,
To nest up among boles.
How stripped of sensations now the stalls
All stand—even like a strip-teaser
Without breast or hair!
    Two figures,
Fugitive from light, go kicking
Their shadows down steps belching up
The corner. Just then, as if in affectionate
Recognition, a wake of wrappings,
Fingers have fondled, tongues
Have sucked to stumps, blow
Them kisses with the gum-wetness
Of a wind limping also to bed.
    And I am
As the bum washed up on
The street, where markets are full
To fiesta, lesser by far than the scarecrow
Left over a farm, long after
Elephant trumpet and
      chorus of locust.

So acute grew the emptiness in me during my last days of shunting between Princeton and New York, while there appeared a flooding everywhere, that the final offerings Princeton had for my kind even swept me back to that place. It was like a dog returning to its place of vomit, more so as I had no stomach really for the fare. This was a fourfold feeling. First there was a farewell dinner given to the Colonel and other close faculty members by the Parvin Fellows, minus the Yugoslavian, who refused to do anything which would deplete his funds any more. The one thing I recall of it is Barbara, the Colonel's wife, trying frantically to draw my attention to the fact without actually telling me directly that only that day, very memorable everywhere for the use of police dogs, electric cattle prods, and high-pressured firehoses on young men and women Negro demonstrators down South, those of them so "liberal" in Princeton had gathered together and wired a righteously indignant message to President Kennedy in Washington to please do something to save the good name of the United States.

Another dinner, an official return affair for the group, was graced by Mr. Albert Parvin himself. Flying in all the way from California, there was our benefactor in real flesh and blood, no longer some remote ghost donor like those foundations and trusts but remaining for us an unshakeable legend. An American of straight Armenian stock, he moved in a sprightly way among us in his silk suit in Princeton's famous Lowrie House, and he was full of high hopes that each of us there was at last well prepared, certified and properly diplomaed to return home and spread the good American word abroad.

In between times, the Colonel took the group out sightseeing in New York City. In the course of it we watched the Stock Exchange in action, a real market of an affair except that it was all men and no women and wares, and we also, as the highlight of the day made the ascension of the Empire State Building, the most impressive address in all America, as the ad runs. Sandwiched between those engagements was a lunch date we had at Princeton House with a Vice-President of the Esso cartel, a proud Princetonian. Answering hushed queries as we ate, he summarily dismissed all talks about the existence of monopolies and of their ever ganging up against governments of countries in which they operate. Rather, he preferred to dwell on the huge benefits and blessings that accrue to the natives from Persia to Peru in the form of house projects and other such vital amenities that they could never have had were things left in the ineffectual, grabbing hands of their puppet dictators. And returning to home grounds, he spoke of how corporations like his are really the trust of the people, operating only and solely in the interest and welfare of the general public. Listening to him, I had some idea of how a famous Senator, now dead, must have sounded atop Capitol Hill as he grandly declared that there could never be any conflict of interest in his promoting in Congress the cause of an oil holding of which he happened to be the proud possessor.

My other final engagement was with an old friend and expert from the State Department in Washington. I think he too was an old Princetonian, although his mission that day had a more serious purpose than just social. It was to ascertain from participants themselves whether or not they had found the Parvin programme a useful experience. And to this end he fed me at my interview with him with questions like these: So did I think an examination at the end of the course would be the one way of finding out who had gained from it? But that wouldn't be fair, would it, with members of a group as different in background and outlook as are your General and that young prisons chap from your own country? And there is the difficulty of language, as with the man from South Korea. But isn't the real difficulty the fact that Princeton has not all the faculties to meet the needs of a group like this? For example, it has no School of Journalism like

Columbia, not that those of you who are journalists, a majority in the group, really need any other training. But the agriculturist in the group has had to go to Rutgers, away in New Brunswick hasn't he? And coming to you personally, do you put politics to use in the course of your creative writing? I never felt so prompted in all my life.

One last concrete thing I clutched at was the idea of paying my way on that very round-trip tour of the United States that the Colonel and his governing colleagues at Princeton were so determined on denying me. This the Greyhound Bus people assured and guaranteed me for a ticket as low as $99. So out I whipped those Esso sectional maps of America already packed away in the heavy luggage I had long made secure for its sea voyage home. With help and advice from friends, in place of the Colonel, retired now for ever as far as I was concerned, I mapped a route down South through Washington to Houston in Texas and New Orleans in the brothers Long's Louisiana; on from there (if I was still alive and sound of limb after the colour barriers and bombs of places like Birmingham!) past the deserts and sprawls of New Mexico, and Arizona to the Grand Canyons of Colorado, sheer as the Niagara Falls that I had already seen, and so to Chicago on the Great Lakes, striking West from there on the Golden Route to California and the Orient beyond.

From each of these places I made up my mind I would send affectionate postcards to the Colonel and his wife. That, someone said, should be real cute, although he wondered if the recipients would not consider it so cheeky that they might continue with their apparent pursuit of me out of the United States. But tempting as the whole prospect undoubtedly was, I told myself it was after all not really worth the trouble. New York and Washington DC formed for me the great lounge and hall of the American mansion with Princeton as the holy recess and study. After being received and fêted and then eventually shown the door, it would be superfluous of me, if not exactly prowling and loitering, to insist on seeing the walks and gardens that owners of the house call places like California, the kitchen and incinerator that are spots like Chicago and Pittsburgh, and the water-closet and cellars that go by the name of the Deep South. So why not return home, which is where no one rejects you, and perhaps make a few stopovers in England and Europe, instead of using up time and money, which was running out anyway, in hanging around hosts now turned hostile?

And so it was one Wednesday night in May I found myself on the midnight flight from New York's Idlewild Airport (as it was then) to London.

"Oh, do come back soon, JP!" Ruth and Sam, Cat and Israel, real Americans who had taken me in and would not let me go, all called out to me. But I was past the Customs barrier now, and all I could mumble back was: "Yes, I do hope so!"

STORIES

An Act of Prostitution

■ James Alan McPherson

When he saw the woman the lawyer put down his pencil and legal pad and took out his pipe.

"Well," he said. "How do you want to play it?"

"I wanna get outta here," the whore said. "Just get me outta here."

"Now get some sense," said the lawyer, puffing on the pipe to draw in the flame from the long wooden match he had taken from his vest pocket. "You ain't got a snowball's chance in hell."

"I just want out," she said.

"You'll catch hell in there," he said, pointing with the stem of his pipe to the door which separated them from the main courtroom. "Why don't you just get some sense and take a few days on the city."

"I can't go up there again," she said. "Those dike matrons in Parkville hate my guts because I'm wise to them. They told me last time they'd really give it to me if I came back. I can't do no time up there again."

"Listen," said the lawyer, pointing the stem of his pipe at her this time, "you ain't got a choice. Either you cop a plea or I don't take the case."

"*You* listen, you two-bit Jew shyster." The whore raised her voice, pointing her very chubby finger at the lawyer. "*You* ain't got no choice. The judge told you to be my lawyer and you got to do it. I ain't no dummy, you know that?"

"Yeah," said the lawyer. "You're a real smarty. That's why you're out on the streets in all that snow and ice. You're a real smarty all right."

"You chickenshit," she said. "I don't want you on my case anyway, but I ain't got no choice. If you was any good, you wouldn't be working the sweatboxes in this court. I ain't no dummy."

"You're a real smarty," said the lawyer. He looked her up and down: a huge woman, pathetically blonde, big-boned and absurd in a skirt sloppily crafted to be mini. Her knees were ruddy and the flesh below them was thick and white and flabby. There was no indication of age about her. Like most whores, she looked at the same time young but then old, possibly as old as her profession. Sometimes they were very old but seemed to have stopped aging at a certain point so that ranking them chronologically, as the lawyer was trying to do, came hard. He put his pipe on the table, on top of the police affidavit, and stared at her. She sat across the room, near the door in a straight chair, her flesh oozing over its sides. He watched her pull her miniskirt down over the upper part of her thigh, modestly, but with the same hard, cold look she had when she came in the room. "You're a real smarty," he commented, drawing on his pipe and exhaling the smoke into the room.

The fat woman in her miniskirt still glared at him. "Screw you, Yid!" she said through her teeth. "Screw your fat mama and your chubby sister with hair under her arms. Screw your brother and your father and I hope they should go crazy playing with themselves in pay toilets."

The lawyer was about to reply when the door to the consultation room opened and another man came into the small place. "Hell, Jimmy," he said to the lawyer, pretending to ignore the woman, "I got a problem here."

"Yeah?" said Jimmy.

The other man walked over to the brown desk, leaned closer to Jimmy so that the woman could not hear and lowered his voice. "I got this kid," he said. "A nice I-talian boy that grabbed this Cadillac outta a parking lot. Now he only done it twice before and I think the Judge might go easy if he got in a good mood before the kid goes on, this being Monday morning and all."

"So?" said Jimmy.

"So I was thinking," the other lawyer said, again lowering his voice and leaning much closer and making a sly motion with his head to indicate the whore on the chair across the room. "So I was thinking. The Judge knows Philomena over there. She's here almost every month and she's always good for a laugh. So I was thinking, this being Monday morning and all and with a cage-load of nigger drunks out there, why not put her on first, give the old man a good laugh and then put my I-talian boy on. I know he'd get a better deal that way."

"What's in it for me?" said Jimmy, rapping the ashes from his pipe into an ashtray.

"Look, I done *you* favors before. Remember that Chinaman? Remember the tip I gave you?"

Jimmy considered while he stuffed tobacco from a can into his pipe. He lit the pipe with several matches from his vest pocket and considered some more. "I don't mind, Ralph," he said. "But if she goes first the Judge'll get a good laugh and then he'll throw the book at her."

"*What the hell, Jimmy?*" said Ralph. He glanced over at the whore who was eying them hatefully. "Look, buddy," he went on, "you know who that is? Fatso Philomena Brown. She's up here almost every month. Old Bloom knows her. I tell you, she's good for a laugh. That's all. Besides, she's married to a nigger anyway."

"Well," said Jimmy. "So far she ain't done herself much good with me. She's a real smarty. She thinks I'm a Jew."

"There you go," said Ralph. "Come on, Jimmy. I ain't got much time before the Clerk calls my kid up. What you say?"

Jimmy looked over at his client, the many pounds of her rolled in great logs of meat under her knees and around her belly. She was still sneering. "O.K." He turned his head back to Ralph. "O.K., I'll do it."

"Now look," said Ralph, "this is how we'll do. When they call me up I'll tell the Clerk I need more time with my kid for consultation. And since you follow me on the docket you'll get on pretty soon, at least before I will. Then after everybody's had a good laugh, I'll bring my I-talian on."

"Isn't *she* Italian?" asked Jimmy, indicating the whore with a slight movement of his pipe.

"Yeah. But she's married to a nigger."

"O.K.," said Jimmy, "we'll do it."

"What's that?" said the whore, who had been trying to listen all this time. "What are you two kikes whispering about anyway? What the hell's going on?"

"Shut up," said Jimmy, the stem of his pipe clamped far back in his mouth so that he could not say it as loud as he wanted. Ralph winked at him and left the room. "Now listen," he said to Philomena Brown, getting up from his desk and walking over to where she still sat against the wall. "If you got a story, you better tell me quick because we're going out there soon and I want you to know I ain't telling no lies for you."

"I don't want you on my case anyway, kike," said Philomena Brown.

"It ain't what *you* want. It's what the old man out there says you gotta do. Now if you got a story let's have it *now*."

"I'm a file clerk. I was just looking for work."

"Like *hell!* Don't give *me* that shit. When was the last time you had your shots?"

"I ain't never had none," said Mrs. Brown.

Now they could hear the Clerk, beyond the door, calling the Italian boy into court. They would have to go out in a few minutes. "Forget the story," he told her. "Just pull your dress down some and wipe some of that shit off your eyes. You look like hell."

"I don't want you on the case, Moses," said Mrs. Brown.

"Well you got me," said Jimmy. "You got me whether you want me or not." Jimmy paused, put his pipe in his coat pocket, and then said: "And my name is *Mr. Mulligan!*"

The woman did not say anything more. She settled her weight in the chair and made it creak.

"Now let's get in there," said Jimmy.

II

The Judge was in his Monday morning mood. He was very ready to be angry at almost anyone. He glared at the Court Clerk as the bald, seemingly consumptive man called out the names of six defendants who had defaulted. He glared at the group of drunks and addicts who huddled against the steel net of the prisoners' cage, gazing toward the open courtroom as if expecting mercy from the rows of concerned parties and spectators who sat in the hot place. Judge Bloom looked as though he wanted very badly to spit. There would be no mercy this Monday morning and the prisoners all knew it.

"*Willie Smith!* Willie Smith! Come into Court!" the Clerk barked.

Willie Smith slowly shuffled out of the prisoners' cage and up to the dirty stone wall, which kept all but his head and neck and shoulders concealed from the people in the musty courtroom.

From the bench the Judge looked down at the hungover Smith.

"You know, I ain't never seen him sitting down in that chair," Jimmy said to one of the old men who came to court to see the daily procession, filling up the second row of benches, directly behind those reserved for court-appointed lawyers. There were at least twelve of these old men, looking almost semi-professional in faded gray or blue or black suits with shiny knees and elbows. They liked to come and watch the fun. "Watch old Bloom give it to this nigger," the same old man leaned over and said into Jimmy Mulligan's ear. Jimmy nodded without looking back at him. And after a few seconds he wiped his ear with his hand, also without looking back.

The Clerk read the charges: Drunkenness, Loitering, Disorderly Conduct.

"You want a lawyer, Willie?" the Judge asked him. Judge Bloom was now walking back and forth behind his bench, his arms gravely folded behind his back, his belly very close to pregnancy beneath his black robe. "The Supreme Court says I have to give you a lawyer. You want one?"

"No sir," the hung-over Smith said, very obsequiously.

"Well, what's your trouble?"

"Nothing."

"You haven't missed a Monday here in months."

"Yes sir."

"All that money you spend on booze, how do you take care of your family?"

Smith moved his head and shoulders behind the wall in a gesture that might have been a shuffle.

"When was the last time you gave something to your wife?"

"Last Friday."

"You're a liar. Your wife's been on the City for years."

"I help," said Smith, quickly.

"You help, all right. You help her raise her belly and her income every year."

The old men in the second row snickered and the Judge eyed them in a threatening way. They began to stifle their chuckles. Willie Smith smiled.

"If she has one more kid she'll be making more than me," the Judge observed. But he was not saying it to Smith. He was looking at the old men.

Then he looked down at the now bashful, smiling Willie Smith. "You want some time to sleep it off or you want to pay?"

"I'll take the time."

"How much you want, Willie?"

"I don't care."

"You want to be out for the weekend, I guess."

Smith smiled again.

"Give him five days," the Judge said to the Clerk. The Clerk wrote in his papers and then said in a hurried voice: "Defendant Willie Smith, you have been found guilty by this court of being drunk in a public place, of loitering while in this condition, and of disorderly conduct. This court sentences you to five days in the House of Correction at Bridgeview and one month's suspended sentence. You have, however, the right to appeal in which case the suspended sentence will not be allowed and the sentence will then be thirty-five days in the House of Correction."

"You want to appeal, Willie?"

"Naw sir."

"See you next week," said the Judge.

"Thank you," said Willie Smith.

A black fellow in a very neatly pressed Army uniform came on next. He stood immaculate and proud and clean-shaven with his cap tucked under his left arm while the charges were read. The prosecutor was a hard-faced black police detective, tieless, very long-haired in a short-sleeved white shirt with wet armpits. The detective was tough but very nervous. He looked at his notes while the Clerk read the charges. The Judge, bald and wrinkled and drooping in the face, still paced behind his bench, his nose twitching from time to time, his arms locked behind the back. The soldier was charged with assault and battery with a dangerous weapon on a police officer; he remained standing erect and silent, looking off into the space behind the Judge until his lawyer, a plump, greasy black man in his late fifties, had heard the charge and motioned for him to sit. Then he placed himself beside his lawyer and put his cap squarely in front of him on the table.

The big-bellied black detective managed to get the police officer's name, rank and duties from him, occasionally glancing over at the table where the defendant and his lawyer sat, both hard-faced and cold. He shuffled through his notes, paused, looked up at the Judge, and then said to the white officer: "Now, Officer Bergin, would you tell the Court in your own words what happened?"

The white policeman put his hands together in a prayer-like gesture on the stand. He looked at the defendant whose face was set and whose eyes were fixed on the officer's hands. "We was on duty on the night of July twenty-seventh driving around the Lafayette Street area when we got a call to proceed to the Lafayette Street subway station because there was a crowd gathering there and they thought it might be a riot. We proceeded there, Officer Biglow and me, and when we got there sure enough there was a crowd of colored people running up and down the street and making noise and carrying on. We didn't pull our guns because they been telling us all summer not to do that. We got out of the car and proceeded to join the other officers there in forming a line so's to disperse the crowd. Then we spotted that fellow in the crowd."

"Who do you mean?"

"That fellow over there." Officer Bergin pointed to the defendant at the table. "That soldier, Irving Williams."

"Go on," said the black detective, not turning to look at the defendant.

"Well, he had on this red costume and a cape, and he was wearing this big red turban. He was also carrying a big black shield right outta Tarzan and he had that big long cane waving it around in the air."

"Where is that cane now?"

"We took it off him later. That's it over there."

The black detective moved over to his own table and picked up a long brown leather cane. He pressed a small button beneath its handle and then drew out from the interior of the cane a thin, silver-white rapier, three feet long.

"Is this the same cane?"

"Yes sir," the white officer said.

"Go on, Officer."

"Well, he was waving it around in the air and he had a whole lot of these colored people behind him and it looked to me that he was gonna charge the police line. So me and Tommy left the line and went in to grab him before he could start something big. That crowd was getting mean. They looked like they was gonna try something big pretty soon."

"Never mind," said the Judge. He had stopped walking now and stood at the edge of his elevated platform, just over the shoulder of the officer in the witness box. "Never mind what you thought, just get on with it."

"Yes sir." The officer pressed his hands together much tighter. "Well, Tommy and me, we tried to grab him and he swung the cane at me. Caught me right in the face here." He pointed his finger to a large red and black mark under his left eye. "So then we hadda use force to subdue him.

"What did you do, Officer?" the black detective asked.

"We hadda use the sticks. I hit him over the head once or twice, but not hard. I don't remember. Then Tommy grabbed his arms and we hustled him over to the car before these other colored people with him tried to grab us."

"Did he resist arrest?"

"Yeah. He kicked and fought us and called us lewd and lascivious names. We hadda handcuff him in the car. Then we took him down to the station and booked him for assault and battery.

"Your witness," said the black detective without turning around to face the other lawyer. He sat down at his own table and wiped his forehead and hands with a crumpled white handkerchief. He still looked very nervous but not as tough.

"May it please the Court," the defendant's black lawyer said slowly, standing and facing the pacing Judge. "I move . . ." And then he stopped because he saw that the Judge's small eyes were looking over his head, toward the back of the courtroom. The lawyer turned around and looked, and saw that everyone else in the room had also turned their heads to the back of the room. Standing against the back walls and along the left side of the room were twenty-five or so stern-faced, cold-eyed black men, all in African dashikies, all wearing brightly colored hats, and all staring at the Judge and the black detective. Philomena Brown and Jimmy Mulligan, sitting on the first bench, turned to look too, and the whore smiled but the lawyer said, "Oh hell," aloud. The men, all big, all bearded and tight-lipped, now locked hands and formed a solid wall of flesh around almost three-quarters of the courtroom. The Judge looked at the defendant and saw that he was smiling. Then he looked at the defendant's lawyer, who still stood before the Judge's bench, his head down, his shoulders pulled up towards his head. The Judge began to pace again. The courtroom was very quiet. The old men filling the second rows on both sides of the room leaned forward and exchanged glances with each other up and down the row. "Oh hell," Jimmy Mulligan said again.

Then the Judge stopped walking. "Get on with it," he told the defendant's lawyer. "There's justice to be done here."

The lawyer, whose face was now very greasy and wet, looked up at the officer, still standing in the witness box, but with one hand now at his right side, next to his gun.

"Officer Bergin," said the black lawyer. "I'm not clear about something. Did the defendant strike you *before* you asked him for the cane or *after* you attempted to take it from him?"

"Before. It was before. Yes sir."

"You *did* ask him for the cane, then?"

"Yes sir. I asked him to turn it over."

"And what did he do?"

"He hit me."

"But if he hit you before you asked for the cane, then it must be true that you asked him for the cane *after* he had hit you. Is that right?"

"Yes sir."

"In other words, after he had struck you in the face you were still polite enough to keep your hands off him and ask for the weapon."

"Yes sir. That's what I did."

"In other words, he hit you twice. Once, *before* you requested the cane and once *after* you requested it."

The officer paused. "No sir," he said quickly. "He only hit me once."

"And when was that again?"

"I thought it was before I asked for the cane but I don't know now."

"But you did ask for the cane before he hit you?"

"Yeah." The officer's hands were in prayer again.

"Now, Officer Bergin, did he hit you *because* you asked for the cane or did he hit you in the process of giving it to you?"

"He just hauled off and hit me with it."

"He made no effort to hand it over?"

"No, no sir. He hit me."

"In other words, he struck you the moment you got close enough for him to swing. He did not hit you as you were taking the cane from him?"

The officer paused again. Then he said: "No sir," He touched his face again, then put his right hand down to the area near his gun again. "I asked him for the cane and he hauled off and hit me in the face."

"Officer, are you telling this court that you did not get hit until you tried to take the cane away from this soldier, this Vietnam veteran, or that he saw you coming and immediately began to swing the cane?"

"He swung on me."

"Officer Bergin, did he swing on you, or did the cane accidentally hit you while you were trying to take it from him?"

"All I know is that he *hit me*." The officer was sweating now.

"Then you don't know just when he hit you, before or after you tried to take the cane from him, do you?"

The black detective got up and said in a very soft voice: "I object."

The black lawyer for the defendant looked over at him contemptuously. The black detective dropped his eyes and tightened his belt, and sat down again.

"That's all right," the oily lawyer said. Then he looked at the officer again. "One other thing," he said. "Was the knife still inside the cane or drawn when he hit you?"

"We didn't know about the knife till later at the station.

"Do you think that a blow from the cane by itself could kill you?"

"Object!" said the detective. But again his voice was low.

"*Jivetime Uncle Tom motherfucker!*" someone said from the back of the room. "Shave that Afro off your head!"

The Judge's eyes moved quickly over the men in the rear, surveying their faces and catching what was in all their eyes. But he did not say anything.

"The prosecution rests," the black detective said. He sounded very tired.

"The defense calls the defendant, Irving Williams," said the black lawyer.

Williams took the stand and waited, head high, eyes cool, mouth tight, militarily, for the Clerk to swear him in. He looked always toward the back of the room.

"Now Mr. Williams," his lawyer began, "tell this court in your own words the events of the night of July twenty-seventh of this year."

"I had been to a costume party." William's voice was slow and deliberate and resonant. The entire courtroom was tense and quiet. The old men stared, stiff and erect, at Irving Williams from their second-row benches. Philomena Brown settled her flesh down next to her lawyer, who tried to edge away from touching her fat arm with his own. The tight-lipped Judge Bloom had reassumed the pacing behind his bench.

"I was on leave from the base," Williams went on, "and I was coming from the party when I saw this group of kids throwing rocks. Being in the military and being just out of Vietnam, I tried to stop them. One of the kids had that cane and I took it from him. The shield belongs to me. I got it in Taiwan last year on R and R. I was trying to break up the crowd with my shield when this honkie cop begins to beat me over the head with his club. Police brutality. I tried to tell . . ."

"That's enough," the Judge said. "That's all I want to hear." He eyed the black men in the back of the room. "This case isn't for my court. Take it upstairs."

"If Your Honor pleases," the black lawyer began.

"I don't," said the Judge. "I've heard enough. Mr. Clerk, make out the papers. Send it upstairs to Cabot."

"This court has jurisdiction to hear this case," the lawyer said. He was very close to being angry. "This man is in the service. He has to ship out in a few weeks. We want a hearing today."

"Not in my court you don't get it. Upstairs, and that's *it!*"

Now the blacks in the back of the room began to berate the detective. "Jivetime cat! Handkerchief-head flunky! Uncle Tom motherfucker!" they called. "We'll get *you*, baby!"

"Get them out of here," the Judge told the policeman named Bergin. "Get them the hell out!" Bergin did not move. "Get them the hell out!"

At that moment Irving Williams, with his lawyer behind him, walked out of the courtroom. And the twenty-five bearded black men followed them. The black detective remained sitting at the counsel table until the Clerk asked him to make way for counsel on the next case. The detective got up slowly, gathered his few papers, tightened his belt again and moved over, his head held down, to a seat on the right side of the courtroom.

"Philomena Brown!" the Clerk called. "Philomena Brown! Come into Court!"

The fat whore got up from beside Jimmy Mulligan and walked heavily over to the counsel table and lowered herself into one of the chairs. Her lawyer was talking to Ralph, the Italian boy's counsel.

"Do a good job, Jimmy, please," Ralph said. "Old Bloom is gonna be awful mean now."

"Yeah," said Jimmy. "I got to really work on him."

One of the old men on the second row leaned over the back of the bench and said to Jimmy: "Ain't that the one that's married to a nigger?"

"That's her," said Jimmy.

"She's gonna catch hell. Make sure they give her hell."

"Yeah," said Jimmy. "I don't see how I'm gonna be able to try this with a straight face."

"Do a good job for me, please, Jimmy," said Ralph. "The kid's name is Angelico. Ain't that a beautiful name? He ain't a bad kid."

"Don't you worry, I'll do it." Then Jimmy moved over to the table next to his client.

The defendant and the arresting officer were sworn in. The arresting officer acted for the state as prosecutor and its only witness. He had to refer to his notes from time to time while the Judge paced behind his bench, his head down, ponderous and impatient. Then Philomena Brown got in the witness box and rested her great weight against its sides. She glared at the Judge, at the Clerk, at the officer in the box on the other side, at Jimmy Mulligan, at the old men smiling up and down the second row, and at everyone in the courtroom. Then she rested her eyes on the officer.

"Well," the officer read from his notes. "It was around one-thirty A.M. on the night of July twenty-eighth. I was working the night duty around the combat zone. I come across the defendant there soliciting cars. I had seen the defendant there soliciting cars on previous occasions in the same vicinity. I had then on previous occasions warned the defendant there about such activities. But she kept on doing it. On that night I come across the defendant soliciting a car full of colored gentlemen. She was standing on the curb with her arm leaning up against the door of the car and talking with these two colored gentlemen. As I came up they drove off. I then arrested her, after informing her of her rights, for being a common streetwalker and a public nuisance. And that's all I got to say."

Counsel for the whore waived cross-examination of the officer and proceeded to examine her.

"What's your name?"

"Mrs. Philomena Brown."

"Speak louder so the Court can hear you, Mrs. Brown."

She narrowed her eyes at the lawyer.

"What is your religion, Mrs. Brown?"

"I am a Roman Catholic. Roman Catholic born."

"Are you presently married?"

"Yeah."

"What is your husband's name?"

"Rudolph Leroy Brown, Jr."

The old men in the second row were beginning to snicker and the Judge lowered his eyes to them. Jimmy Mulligan smiled.

"Does your husband support you?"

"Yeah. We get along all right."

"Do *you* work, Mrs. Brown?"

"Yeah. That's how I make my living."

"What do you do for a living?"

"I'm a file clerk."

"Are you working now?"

"No. I lost my job last month on account of a bad leg I got. I couldn't move outta bed."

The men in the second row were grinning and others in the audience joined them in muffled guffaws and snickerings.

"What were you doing on Beaver Avenue on the night of July twenty-eighth?"

"I was looking for a job."

Now the entire court was laughing and the Judge glared out at them from behind his bench as he paced, his arms clasped behind his back.

"Will you please tell this court, Mrs. Brown, how you intended to find a job at that hour?"

"These two guys in a car told me they knew where I could find some work."

"As a file clerk?"

"Yeah. What the hell else do you think?"

There was here a roar of laughter from the court, and when the Judge visibly twitched the corners of his usually severe mouth, Philomena Brown saw it and began to laugh too.

"Order! Order!" the Clerk shouted above the roar. But he was laughing.

Jimmy Mulligan bit his lip. "Now, Mrs. Brown, I want you to tell me the truth. Have you ever been arrested before for prostitution?"

"Hell no!" she fired back. "They had me in here a coupla times but it was all a fluke. They never got nothing on me. I was framed, right from the start."

"How old are you, Mrs. Brown?"

"Nineteen."

Now the Judge stopped pacing and stood next to his chair. His face was dubious: very close and very far away from smiling. The old men in the second row saw this and stopped laughing, awaiting a cue from him.

"That's enough of this," said the Judge. "I know you. You've been up here seven times already this year and it's still summer. I'm going to throw the book at you." He moved over to the left end of the platform and leaned down to where a husky, muscular woman Probation Officer was standing. She had very short hair and looked grim. She had not laughed with the others. "Let me see her record," said the Judge. The manly Probation Officer handed it up to him and then they talked together in whispers for a few minutes.

"All right, *Mrs. Brown*," said the Judge, moving over to the right side of the platform near the defendant's box and pointing his finger at her. "You're still on probation from the last time you were up here. I'm tired of this."

"I don't wanna go back up there, Your Honor," the whore said. "They hate me up there."

"You're going back. That's it! You got six months on the State. Maybe while you're there you can learn how to be a file clerk so you can look for work during the day."

Now everyone laughed again.

"Plus you get a one-year suspended sentence on probation."

The woman hung her head with the gravity of this punishment.

"Maybe you can even learn a *good* profession while you're up there. Who knows? Maybe you could be a ballerina dancer."

The courtroom roared with laughter. The Judge could not control himself now.

"And another thing," he said. "When you get out, keep off the streets. You're obstructing traffic."

Such was the spontaneity of laughter from the entire courtroom after the remark that the lawyer Jimmy Mulligan had to wipe the tears from his eyes with his finger and the short-haired Probation Officer smiled, and even Philomena Brown had to laugh at this, her final moment of glory. The Judge's teeth showed through his own broad grin, and Ralph, sitting beside his Italian, a very pretty boy with clean, blue eyes, patted him on the back enthusiastically between uncontrollable bursts of laughter.

For five minutes after the smiling Probation Office led the fat whore in a miniskirt out of the courtroom, there was the sound of muffled laughter and occasional sniffles and movements in the seats. Then they settled down again and the Judge resumed his pacings and the Court Clerk, very slyly wiping his eyes with his sleeve, said in a very loud voice: "Angelico Carbone! Angelico Carbone! Come into Court!"

The Urchin

■ Can Themba (South Africa)

One sling of the braces would not keep up on the shoulder, just like one worm of pale-green mucus kept crawling down the chestnut lip and would suddenly dart back like a timid creature. But Macala wore his long pants (surely someone's—someone older's—castaway three-quarter jeans) with a defiant pride just ready to assault the rest of the known world. Other boys his ten-year age only had short pants.

He looked up and down from Mafuta's Chinaman store along Victoria Road, Sophiatown, and he thought of how his day ought to begin. Mafuta's was no good: he kept two too-ferocious dogs in his shop, and fairly authenticated rumour had it that he also kept a gun that made a terrible noise. But the vistas up and down Victoria Road offered infinite possibilities for a man. To the left, there were queues on queues of half-frightened, half-foolish people who simply asked to be teased. Then Moosa's store with all those fruity, sweety things in the window: but they said Moosa trained at night with irons. Opposite, across Millar Street, there was a Chink butcher, but his counter was fenced off with wire, and Ooh! those cruel knives and hatchets. There must be a lot of money there for it to be protected so formidably. And, next to the butcher, the Bicycle Shop with its blaring juke-box: *Too roo roo roo tu! Too roo roo roo tu-tu!* Where a passer-by girl would suddenly break into a dance step, seductive beyond her years.

All like that, up to Chang's, and from there just the denuded places the Demolition Squad had left in Sophiatown.

To the right, Macala stared at Benghali House. The only double-storey building in the whole of Sophiatown. In front of it all sorts of pedlars met: sweet-potato sellers, maize sellers, and sweet-reed sellers, African pimpled squash sellers, shoe-lace sellers—all be-damned whether or not the shopkeeper alone held a licence to sell anything.

Macala's eyes glittered as he saw the Ma-Ndebele women squatting in their timeless patience behind their huge dishes of maize-cobs, dried *morogo* peanut cubes, wild fruits like *marula, mahlatswa*—things the urban African never sees on trees these days.

To Macala, these women with their quaint and beaded necks and legs that made them look like colourful pythons, were the fairest game.

He stepped off the veranda of Mafuta's shop, off the pavement, and sauntered swaggeringly towards those placid women in front of Benghali House. He was well aware that the street-corner loungers, enormous liars all of them, were watching him, thinking that the slightest move of Macala promised excitement and trouble.

He stopped in front of a Ndebele woman transfixed to her white dish,

This story was one of the eight prize-winning stories in a contest organized by the South African Centre of the International Pen Club and open to writers of all races in South Africa. (Note By Ezekiel Mphahlele, Editor.)

114

as if one with it, as if trade meant just being there at the strategic place and time: no bawling, no bartering, no bargaining.

"Dis—how much?" and that to Macala was English with a vengeance. She looked up at him with large baffled eyes, but before she spoke, Macala lifted his foot and trod on the edge of the dish, sending its contents churning out of it into the dust of Victoria Road's pavement. He shrieked with delight as he ran off.

What she hurled at him in virulent Ndebele may have been curses, prayers, lamentations. But to Macala it was reward enough, the kind of thing that proves the superiority of the townsman to these odd creatures from the country. And the passing generation's men and women shook their heads and muttered gloomily: "The children of today, the children of today . . ."

His momentum took him to the vegetable vendor just opposite Mafuta's. In fluid career, he seized the handle of the cart and whirled it round and up for the devil of it. Potatoes, onions, pumpkins, cabbages went swirling into the air and plump tomatoes squashed on the macadam. The khaki-coated vendor stood aghast a second before he broke into imprecations that shuddered even the sordid Sophiatown atmosphere. But Macala was away on his mischievous way.

He had passed the "Fish and Chips" too fast for another tilt, and met his pals on the corner of Tucker and Victoria: Dipapang, Jungle and Boy-Boy. Together, they should have been "Our Gang" but their organization was not tight enough for that.

Boy-Boy's was the brain that germinated most of the junior devilry of the team, but he did not quite have Macala's impetuous courage of execution. He looked like a social worker's explanation of 'conditions in the slums': thin to malnourished, delinquent, undisciplined, dedicated to a future gallows. Yet his father was an important man and his mother a teacher. Jungle qualified by the ease with which he could talk of using a knife. In real big-tsotsi fashion. Dipapang initiated nothing, thought nothing, was nothing, but always so willing to join in, try and finish anything the others cared to start.

"Heit, Macacix!" called Boy-Boy. "It's how there?"

Macala suddenly felt in the mood for the jargon of the townships. The near-animal, amorphous, quick-shifting lingo that alarms farm-boys and drives cops to all branches of suspicion. But it marks the city slicker who can cope with all its vagaries.

"It's couvert under the corzet," Macala replied, bobbing his head this way and that to the rhythm.

"Hai, man, bigshot, you must be the reely-reely outlaw in this town," Boy-Boy parried and lunged.

"Naw," Macala feinted, "dis town, Softtown's too small for me. I'll take Western and Corrie and Maclera and London, and smash them into a mashed potato."

Boy-Boy fell for it. "Whew!" he whistled, "don't say you'll crowd me out!"

Macala took him by the throat and went in for the kill. "Didn't I tell you, buster, to keep out of my country, or else . . ."

He proceeded to carry out the menacing 'or else' by choking Boy-Boy and slowly tripping him over a leg he had slipped behind him until they rolled over as Boy-Boy fell, and tumbled into the gutter.

Boy-Boy gasped: "Ah give up, boss, da country's yours."

The mock battle was over and everybody laughed . . . except Jungle. He was reputed to be "serious" and that meant of the homicidal type. He sat there on the pavement drain with his mournful face, sharpening gratingly on the concrete his 3-Star jack-knife which from some hazy movie memory he called his "gurkha." As the laughter trailed off, he suddenly drawled: "Have you guys heard that Mpedi was arrested yesterday?"

They stared at him in genuine stupefaction. Then Boy-Boy said: "Yerrrr! How'd it happen, Jungle?"

But Jungle was not one for elaborating a story. Very unsatisfactorily, he said: "Waal, he was drinking at de English Lady's joint . . . and . . . and dey got him."

"You mean he didn't shoot it out? You mean dey took him just like dat? But I bet ya dey couldn't put handcuffs on Mpedi!" But Macala was very unhappy about the tame way the idol of the township was arrested.

Boy-Boy it was who made a story of it. "Yerrr! But there is an outee."[1] He rose from the pavement and stood before the fascinated gaze of his pals. He stuck his thumbs into his belt and swayed his hips as he strutted up and down before them. Then he mimicked the bull-brained fearlessness of Mpedi, the mirror and form of almost all young Sophiatown, the clattering terror of men, and the perennial exasperation of the police station across the road.

"Ya! Da room was full—full to da door. Clevers, bigshots, boozers, bamboos, coat-hangers, hole-diggers, and bullets, blondes, figure 8's and capital I's, wash-planks and two-ton trucks. Da boys were in de stack and da dames were game. . . .

"Then Bura Mpedi stepped in, his eyes blood-red. The house went dead-still. Ag, man, Bura Mpedi, man. He stood there and looked left . . . and looked right. . . . His man was not there. He stepped in some more. The house was dead. He grabbed a beer from the nearest table and slugged it from the bottle. Who would talk?" Boy-Boy's upper lip curled up on one side in utter contempt, "Heh, who would talk!"

Macala and his pals were caught in Boy-Boy's electric pause. Even Jungle was aroused by this dramatic display of township bullycraft.

Boy-Boy's histrionics continued: "Yerrrre! a drunk girl came from under a table, and tried Mpedi for a drink. "Au, Bura Mpedi, give me a beer." Bura Mpedi put a boot on her shoulder and pushed her back under da table. Hai, man, hai man, dat outee is coward-cool, man. And he hates cherry coat-hangers. But dat night his eyes were going all over looking for Mahlalela. Yeffies! If he'd caught Mahlalela dat night . . . !"

Lifted by the wide-eyed admiration of his pals, Boy-Boy went on to surpass himself. He flung out his right arm recklessly, and declared:

[1] Outlaw, used with a sense of pride.

"But dat's nutting yet! You should have seen Bura Mpedi when dey sent four lean cops to come and take him. Payroll robbery, Booysens . . . one thousand pound! Assault with G.B.H.,² Newlands . . . three men down and out! Housebreakin' 'n *Thatha*³ . . . Lower Houghton!

"Dey came, man dey came. Four cops, two had guns, two had small inches.⁴ Dey surrounded da joint in Gibson Street, and dey called out to him to give up. Dey didn't know Mpedi with moonwash in his brains and a human intestine round his waist. He drew his point-three-five and his forty-five, and he came out shooting: Twah! Rwah! Rwah! Da two cops with small inches ducked into a shebeen near by and ordered themselves a ha' nip brandy. One with da gun ran down Gibson Street for reinforces. Da last cop took a corner and decided to shoot it out with Mpedi. But da bullets came so fast he never got a chance to poke out a shot.

"Hee-e-e, I tell you Mpedi was da outee." Then, still carried forward by the vibrance of his enthusiasm, Boy-Boy rounded off his dramatization by backing away slowly as he fired off imaginary guns, and barked: "Twah! Twah! Twah!"

But the elation that had swelled up in Macala was now shot through with envy. "How come," he grumbled, "da cops got him so easy now?" Yet what really worried him was that he knew how far he was beneath the fabulous Mpedi; that even in his own weight division, he could not make such an awe-inspiring impression. He was not even as good an actor as Boy-Boy to recount and represent the exploits of the almighties. He looked at Boy-Boy bitterly and told himself: I'll beat his brains out if he gets smart with me.

It was Jungle who wrenched him out of his sour reverie. "Boys, I think we should go finish off da Berliners," Jungle said, prosaically.

A flash of fear leapt into Boy-Boy's eyes, for he knew this meant war. Macala was himself a bit scared, but seeing the fear in Boy-Boy, he screwed his heart through a hole too small for it.

And Jungle's "gurkha" went on scraping the pavement concrete, *screech-screech! screech-screech!*

"Come ahn, let's go," Macala suddenly decided.

They swaggered along Victoria Road, filling it from pavement to pavement as if they were a posse. Silent. Full of purpose. Deliberately grim. Boys and girls scampered for cover. Grown-ups stepped discreetly out of their way. Only the bigger tsotsis watched them with pride, and shouted encouragements like: *Da men who rule da town! Tomorrow's outees!*

On the corner of Meyer Street, they broke up a ring of young dicers and forced them to join up. Along the way they collected non-schoolgoing loafers who lounged against shop walls; blue-jeaned youngsters who twisted the arms of school-girls in rough love; odd-job boys who ran errands for shopkeepers; truants, pick-pockets, little thugs, within their age limit—the lot.

² "Grievous Bodily Harm."
³ Taking away, theft.
⁴ Batons.

By the time they turned into Edith Street, they were a miniature army of hell-bent ruffians. Macala led them and felt the strange thrill of the force behind him. He chose Edith Street because it rose into a rocky hill with plenty of stones for ammunition, and dropped suddenly into that part of Sophiatown they called *Berlin,* where the walls were smeared with crude swastikas.

Macala split his men into two groups. Those with thick, bronze buckle belts were to go under Jungle through a cut in the row of houses precariously perched on huge boulders.

The excitement chopped Macala's breath into collops as he gave out his instructions. "You boys get dem from de back. You start de war. When dey come running up Edward Road, dey'll meet us. Use dat butcher of yours, Uncle Jungle."

Jungle gave one of his rare smiles, and his men took position.

Macala and his group, first placing a sentinel on the hill-top, slowly clambered down the rocks and waited for Jungle to get around.

Though going into the den of the enemy, Jungle did not find it difficult to rout them. There was a biggish group of them playing dice in the usual ring, and when he swooped upon them, they instinctively thought it was the police and dashed up Edward Road, sticks and buckle belts raining on their heads.

Jungle himself had chosen a heftily-built fellow and was stabbing at him as he ran. Boy-Boy was later to describe it graphically: "Yerre! Dat guy just wouldn't fall. Jungle had him—zip! But he ran on. Jungle caught him again in the neck—zip! He stumbled and trotted on his hands and feet. Jungle got him in the buttock—zip! But, yerrr! He just wouldn't fall!"

Before the Berliners could rally and make a stand, they had run into Macala's stone-throwing division. Though very one-sided, the fight became fierce. The Berliners were now fighting, and because they were trapped and because they had to fight with their bare hands most of the time, they became young devils from the playgrounds of Hell.

Stones and all sorts of other missiles were hurled in all directions. Knives were brandished and plunged, big-buckled belts were swung in whistling arcs, arms were flailed in the centre of the imbroglio with desperate savagery. Women screamed, shops closed, traffic diverted itself. Now and then, a blood-bespattered boy would stagger off the street to a side wall just to sit down and watch. Too done in to flee.

Then suddenly came the shrill warning cry, *"Arrara! Arrarayii!"* The action stopped almost as abruptly as those ancient films which froze in mid-motion and transfixed the movement into a photograph. And just as suddenly after, they scattered all pell-mell. When the police van came round the corner, it was impossible to decide which flee-ers to pursue. For, now, everybody was running up and down and off the streets. The scores of small boys, ordinary pedestrians who had just alighted upon the scene, Fah-fee runners with full-blown cheeks a-chumping the incriminating tickets of their illicit lottery; everybody was running. In Sophiatown, you do not stop to explain to the police that you had nothing to do with it; or that you knew some of the culprits and could help the police.

The mobile squad were satisfied with merely clearing the street.

Breathless and bruised, Macala found himself at the open commonage called Maccauvlei, adjacent to Waterval Hospital, which served as the waste dumps to the city, and "golf course" to those Africans who went in for the sport of leisure. Macala knew that most of his gang would sooner or later find their way there. He sat on a mound of ash, gasping heavily.

By the time Boy-Boy had arrived there, he had regained his breath, and was pitching chalky, burnt-out pebbles rather pointlessly. Jungle came, for once, apparently, in his seventh heaven. Dipapang, too, grinned happily though his shirt had been torn down and hung like a hula. A few other stragglers from the Black Caps joined them, and then came the News. News that oddly took the shape of "They say."

"Dey say," announced one urchin, "dat one of de Berliners is dead."

Stultifying fright seized them all. Some small boy simply broke out crying. Macala had trouble with a choking clod in his throat.

"Dey say," came in another boy, "de Berliners are going to call in de Big Berliners."

"Agh," grunted Macala in contempt, "we'll go'n tell Bura Shark."

"Dey say de cops're going to round us all up tonight."

Despite all their bravado, all their big-shot stances and their blistering contempt for cops and the law, there is one thing that this knighthood really fears, and it was expressed by a crackling of interjections from each according to his own lights:

"Six lashes and reformatory!"

"De cane and off to a farm!"

"Cuts with a light cane and no fine!"

Someone elaborated the procedure by filling in the gory details: "Dey say, two huge cops hold you down over a big bench an' you got nothin' on. You can't move. Now, maybe de magistrate he said: "Six cuts." Dat's nothin'. If you cry, for every one you get two. An' dose cops who give de lashes, dey train for you, dey pick up weightlifting for you, dey grip a grip all day for you. Den when de other cops got you on de bench, an' you can't move, an' you don't want to cry, de lashing cop he takes de cane, he swishes it over his head, one-two-three, whish! De tattoo jumps up on your buttocks.

"Dey say, he den goes to sit down, light a sigareete, and talks with de other cops. Den he comes again. One of de cops holding you turns your head so you can see de lashing cop coming. He swishes de cane, one-two-three, whish! 'Nother tattoo comes up, dis time with blood. Red blood from your buttocks. He goes for 'nother puff at his cigarette, or maybe he looks for his tea dis time.

"He comes again. Dis time he sneezes his nose on your buttocks, and makes jokes how black buttocks is tough. He swishes the cane, one-two-three, whish! If you don't cry, maybe you get your six lashes straight. But if you cry, only just *Maye Babo*—oh-ho-ho! . . .

"An' dey say, sometimes after you get lashes, six days, two weeks you can't sit in de bus, you give your seat to de aunties. Hai, dat cane dey keep in de salt water when nobody get lashes!"

By that time the horror of the prospect had seeped through every delinquent soul. It was Macala who spoke first.

He said determinedly: "Me, I'm not going home tonight."

But Boy-Boy did not like the idea. He knew that his mother would not rest until she had found out where he was. Worse still, she might even go ask the police to help her find him. "Naw, Macacix, I'm going home. I don't like cops catching me when my ma is not there. I'm going home."

As he walked away, the whole little gang suddenly broke up and walked home their different ways. As they scattered, Macala went frantic with panic. With consternation twisted in his face and his arms floating like a blind man's in front of him, he looked half-comic as he stood on that mount of ash.

"Hey, hey, you guys won't leave me alone. We're de boys . . ."

He heard a sound of impatience behind him: "Aargh! Let them go, Macala." He turned round and reeled unsteadily a little as he saw Jungle standing there, not looking frightened at all.

"Wh-what you going to do, Jungle?"

Jungle took out his "gurkha" and scraped it across his palm from left to right, right to left. Then he said: "I'm going home, Macala," and that mournful expression crept across his countenance. "And when de cops come to get me tonight . . ." He made an ugly motion with his knife under his chin. He walked away with the slow, lanky movement of that gawky body of his.

By the time Macala decided to leave Maccauvlei, it was getting dark. But he knew where he was going. Rather unnecessarily, he skulked along the fences of the street, looking this way and that. Now and then, he would petrify at the zoom of a passing car or duck into an alley when headlights bore goldenly through the dark of the street. But ultimately he reached the open space where Gerty, Bertha, and Toby Streets used to be. He saw the dark building for which he was headed. He ran forward and stopped in front of it, but this side of the street. Slowly now. Somewhere here there is a night-watchman, a Zulu with a thick black beard and barbel moustache, black uniform and black face that rubbed him out of sight in the dark, and a gnarled knobkerrie known to have split skulls.

But Macala knew where the corrugated-iron fence had snarled out a lip of entrance for him. He went on his hands and knees, and crawled away from the immense double gate towards this entrance. He found it and coiled himself inside. He knew there were stacks of corrugated iron in this timber yard, and if he touched them, the racket would alert the night-watchman. So he did not go far, just nestled himself near his exit.

A little breeze was playing outside, hasting a piece of paper down the street, and now and then a bus or lorry would thunder by. But Macala slept, occasionally twitching in the hidden mechanics of sleep. Far from where he could hear, a woman's voice was calling stridently: "Mac-a-a-ala! Mac-a-a-a-la! Hai, that child will one day bring me trouble."

Rain

■ Richard Rive (South Africa)

Rain poured down, blotting out all sound with its sharp and vibrant tattoo. Dripping neon signs reflecting lurid reds and yellows in mirror-wet streets. Swollen gutters. Water overflowing and squelching on to pavements. Gurgling and sucking at storm-water drains. Table Mountain cut off by a grey film of mist and rain. A lost City Hall clock trying manfully to chime nine over an indifferent Cape Town. Baleful reverberations through a spluttering all-consuming drizzle.

Yellow light filters through from Solly's Grand Fish and Chips Palace. Door tight-shut against the weather. Inside stuffy with heat, hot bodies, steaming clothes and the nauseating smell of stale fish-oil. Misty patterns on the plate-glass windows and a messy pool where rain has filtered beneath the door and mixed with the sawdust.

Solly himself in shirt-sleeves, sweating, vulgar and moody. Bellowing at a dripping woman who has just come in.

"Shut 'e damn door. Think you live in a tent?"

"Ag, Solly."

"Don't ag me. You Coloured people can never shut blarry doors."

"Don' bloomingwell swear at me."

"I bloomingwell swear at you, yes."

"Come. Gimme two pieces 'e fish. Tail cut."

"Two pieces 'e fish."

"Raining like hell outside," the woman said to no one.

"Mmmmmm. Raining like hell," a thin befezzed Malay cut in.

"One an' six. Thank you. An' close 'e door behin' you."

"Thanks. Think you got 'e on'y door in Hanover Street?"

"Go to hell!" Solly cut the conversation short and turned to another customer.

The north-wester sobbed heavy rain squalls against the windowpanes. The Hanover Street bus screeched to a slithery stop and passengers darted for shelter in a cinema entrance. The street lamps shone blurredly.

Solly sweated as he wrapped parcels of fish and chips in a newspaper. Fish and chips. Vinegar? Wrap? One an' six, please. Thank you. Next. Fish and chips. No? Two fish. No chips? Salt? Vinegar? One an' six, please. Thank you! Next. Fish an' chips.

"Close 'e blarry door!" Solly glared daggers at a woman who had just come in. She half-smiled apologetically at him.

"You Coloured people are worse than Kaffirs."

She struggled with the door and then stood dripping in a pool of wet sawdust. Solly left the counter to add two presto-logs to the furnace. She moved out of the way. Another customer showed indignation at Solly's remark.

"You blooming Jews are always making Coloured people out."

"Go to hell!" Solly dismissed the attack on his race. Fish an' chips. Vinegar? Salt? One an' six. Thank you.

"Yes, madam?"

"Could you tell me when the bioscope comes out?"

"Am I the blooming manager?"

"Please."

"Half pas' ten," the Malay offered helpfully.

"Thank you. Can I stay here till then? It's raining outside."

"I know it's blarrywell raining, but this is not a Salvation Army."

"Please, Baas!"

This caught Solly unawares. He had had his shop in that corner of District Six since most could remember and had been called a great many unsavoury things down the years. Solly didn't mind. But this caught him unawares.

Please, Baas.

This felt good. His imagination adjusted a black bow-tie to an evening suit. Please, Baas.

"Okay, stay fer a short while. But when 'e rain stops you go!"

She nodded dumbly and tried to make out the blurred name of the cinema opposite, through the misted windows.

"Waitin' fer somebody?" Solly asked.

No response.

"I ask if yer waitin' fer somebody!"

The figure continued to stare.

"Oh, go to hell," said Solly, turning to another customer.

Through the rain blur Siena stared at nothing in particular. Dim visions of slippery wet cars. Honking and wheezing in the rain. Spluttering buses. Heavy, drowsy voices in the Grand Fish and Chips Palace. Her eyes travelled beyond the street and the water cascades of Table Mountain, beyond the winter of Cape Town to the summer of the Boland. Past the green grapelands of Stellenbosch and Paarl, and the stuffy wheat district of Malmesbury to the lazy sun and laughter of Teslarrsdal. A tired sun here. An uninterested sun. Now it seemed that the sun was weary of the physical effort of having to rise, to shine, to comfort and to set.

Inside the nineteenth-century gabled mission church she had first met Joseph. The church is still there, and beautiful, and the ivy climbs over it and makes it more beautiful. Huge silver oil-lamps suspended from the roof, polished and shining. It was in the flicker of the lamps that she had first become aware of him. He was visiting from Cape Town. She sang that night like she had never sung before. Her favourite psalm.

"Al ging ik ook in een dal der schaduw des doods. . . . Though I walk through the valley of the shadow of death. . . . *Der schaduw des doods."*

And then he had looked at her. Everyone had looked at her for she was good in solos.

"Ik zoude geen kwaad vreezen. . . . I will fear no evil."

And she had not feared but loved. Had loved him. Had sung for him. For the wide eyes, the yellow skin, the high cheek-bones. She had sung for a creator who could create a man like Joseph.

"Want gij zijt met mij; Uw stok en Uw staf, die vertroosten mij."

Those were black and white polka-dot nights when the moon did a gollywog cake-walk across a banjo-strung sky. Nights of sweet remembrances when he had whispered love to her and told her of Cape Town. She had giggled coyly at his obscenities. It was fashionable, she hoped, to giggle coyly at obscenities. He lived in one of those streets off District Six and was, he boasted, quite a one amongst the girls. She heard of Molly and Miena and Sophia and a sophisticated Charmaine who was almost a school-teacher and always spoke English. But he told her that he had only found love in Teslaarsdal. She wasn't sure whether to believe him. And then he had felt her richness and the moon darted behind a cloud.

The loud screeching of the train to Cape Town. Screeching loud enough to drown the protest of her family. The wrath of her father. The icy stares of Teslaarsdal matrons. Loud and confused screechings to drown her hysteria, her ecstasy. Drowned and confused in the roar of a thousand cars and a hundred thousand lights and a summer of carnival evenings which is Cape Town. Passion in a tiny room off District Six. Desire surrounded by four bare walls, and a rickety chair and a mounted cardboard tract that murmured, "Bless this House".

And the agony of the nights when he came home later and later and sometimes not at all. The waning of his passion and whispered names of others. Molly and Miena and Sophia. Charmaine. The helpless knowledge that he was slipping from her. Faster and faster. Gathering momentum.

"Not that I'm saying so but I only heard . . ."

"Why don't you go to bioscope one night and see for yourself. . . ."

"Marian's man is searching for Joseph. . . ."

Searching for Joseph. Looking for Joseph; knifing for Joseph. Joseph! Joseph!! JOSEPH!! Molly! Miena! Sophia! Names! Names! Names! Gossip. One-sided desire. Go to bioscope and see. See what? See why? When! Where!

And after he had been away a week she decided to see. Decided to go through the rain and stand in a sweating fish and chips shop owned by a blaspheming Jew. And wait for the cinema to come out.

The rain had stopped against the plate-glass window. A skin-soaking drizzle now set in. Continuous. Unending. Filming everything with dark depression. A shivering, weeping neon sign flickered convulsively on and off. A tired Solly shooting a quick glance at a cheap alarm clock.

"Half pas' ten, bioscope out soon."

Siena looked more intently through the misty screen. No movement whatsoever in the deserted cinema foyer.

"Time it was bloomingwell out." Solly braced himself for the wave of after-show customers who would invade his Palace.

"Comin' out late tonight, Missus."

"Thank you, Baas."

Solly rubbed sweat out of his eyes and took in her neat and plain figure. Tired face but good legs. A few late stragglers catching colds in the streets. Wet and squally outside.

"Your man in bioscope?"

She was intent on a khaki-uniformed usher struggling to open the door.

"Man in bioscope, Missus?"

The cinema had to come out some time or other. An usher opening the door, adjusting the outside gate. Preparing for the crowds to pour out. Vomited and spilt out.

"Man in bioscope?"

No response.

"Oh, go to hell!"

They would be out now. Joseph would be out. She rushed for the door, throwing words of thanks to Solly.

"Close the blarry door!"

She never heard him. The drizzle had stopped. An unnatural calm hung over the empty foyer, over the deserted street. Over her empty heart. She took up her stand on the bottom step. Expectantly. Her heart pounding.

Then they came. Pouring, laughing, pushing, jostling. She stared with fierce intensity but faces passed too fact. Laughing, roaring, gay. Wide-eyed, yellow-skinned, high cheek-boned. Black, brown, ivory, yellow. Black-eyed, laughing-eyed, gay, bouncing. No Joseph. Palpitating heart that felt like bursting into a thousand pieces. If she should miss him. She found herself searching for the wrong face. Solly's face. Ridiculously searching for hard blue eyes and a sharp white chin in a sea of ebony and brown. Solly's face. Missing half a hundred faces and then again searching for the familiar high cheek-bones. Solly. Joseph. Molly. Miena. Charmaine.

The drizzle restarted. Studying the overcoats instead of faces. Longing for the pale blue shirt she had seen in the shop at Solitaire. A bargain at £1.50. She had scraped and scrounged to buy it for him. A week's wages. Collecting her thoughts and continuing the search for Joseph. And then the thinning out of the crowd and the last few stragglers. The ushers shutting the iron gates. They might be shutting Joseph in. Herself out. Only the ushers left. And the uncompromising iron gates.

"Please is Joseph inside?"

"Who's Joseph?"

"Is Joseph still inside?"

"Joseph who?"

They were teasing her. Laughing behind her back. Preventing her from finding him.

"Joseph is inside!" she shouted frenziedly.

"Look, merrim, it's raining cats an' dogs. Go home."

Go home. To whom? To what? An empty room? An empty bed? A tract that shrieked its lie, "Bless this House"?

And then she was aware of the crowd on the corner. Maybe he was there. Running and peering into every face. Joseph. The crowd in the drizzle. Two battling figures. Joseph. Figures locked in struggle slithering in the wet gutter. Muck streaking down clothes through which wet bodies were silhouetted. Joseph. A blue shirt. And then she wiped the rain out of her eyes and saw him. Fighting for his life. Desperately kicking in the gutter. Joseph. The blast of a police-whistle. A pick-up van screeching to a stop.

"Please, sir, it wasn't him. They all ran away. Please, sir, he's Joseph. He done nothing. He done nothing, my Baas. Please, sir, he's my Joseph. Please, Baas!"

"*Maak dat jy weg kom.* Get away. *Voetsak!*"

"Please, sir, it wasn't him. They ran away! *Asseblief*, Baas."

Alone. An empty bed. An empty room.

Solly's Grand Fish and Chips Palace crowded out. People milling inside. Rain once more squalling and sobbing against the door and windows. Swollen gutters unable to cope with the giddy rush of water. Solly sweating to deal with the after-cinema rush.

Fish an' chips. Vinegar? Salt? One an' six. Thank you. Sorry, no fish. Wait five minutes. Chips on'y. Vinegar? Ninepence. Tickey change. Thank you. Sorry, no fish. Five minutes' time. Chips? Ninepence. Thank you. Solly paused for breath and stirred the fish.

"What's 'e trouble outside?"

"Bioscope, Solly."

"No, man, outside!"

"I say, bioscope."

"What were 'e police doin'? Sorry, no fish yet, sir. Five minutes' time. What were 'e police doin'?"

"A fight in 'e bloomin' rain."

"Jeesus, in 'e rain?"

"*Ja.*"

"Who was fightin'?"

"Joseph an' somebody."

"Joseph?"

"*Ja*, fellow in Arundel Street."

"Yes, I know Joseph. Always in trouble. Chucked him outta here a'reddy."

"Well, that chap."

"An' who?"

"Dinno."

"Police get them?"

"Got Joseph."

"Why were 'ey fightin'? Fish in a minute, sir."

"Over a dame."

"Who?"

"You know Miena who work by Patel? Now she. Her boy-friend caught 'em."

"In bioscope?"

"*Ja.*"

Solly chuckled deeply, suggestively.

"See that woman an' 'e police?"

"What woman?"

"Dame cryin' to 'e police."

"They say it's Joseph's dame."

"Joseph always got plenty 'e dames. F-I-S-H—R-E-A-D-Y!!! Two pieces for you, sir? One an' six. Shilling change. Fish an' chips? One an' six? Thank you. Fish on'y? Vinegar? Salt? Ninepence. Tickey change. Thank you!

"What you say about 'e woman?"

"They say Joseph's girl was crying to 'e police."

"Oh, he got plenty 'e girls."

"This one was living with him."

"Oh, what she look like? Fish, sir?"

"Okay. Nice legs."

Hmmmmm," said Solly. "Hey, close 'e damn door. Oh, you again."

Siena came in. A momentary silence. Then a buzzing and whispering.

"Oh," said Solly, nodding as someone whispered over the counter to him, "I see. She was waiting here. Mussta been waitin' for him."

A young girl in jeans giggled.

"Fish an' chips costs one an' six, madam."

"Wasn't it one an' three before?"

"Before the Boer War, madam. Price of fish go up. Potatoes go up an' you expect me to charge one an' three?"

"Why not?"

"Oh, go to hell! Next, please!"

"Yes, that's 'e one, Solly."

"Mmmm. Excuse me, madam." Turning to Siena, "Like some fish an' chips? Free of charge, never min' 'e money."

"Thank you, my Baas."

The rain now sobbed wildly as the shop emptied and Solly counted the cash in his till. Thousands of watery horses charging down the street. Rain drilling into cobbles and pavings. Miniature waterfalls down the sides of buildings. Blurred lights through unending streams. Siena listlessly holding the newspaper parcel of fish and chips.

"You can stay here till it clears up," said Solly.

She looked up tearfully. Solly grinned showing his yellow teeth.

"It's quite okay."

A smile flickered across her face for a second.

"It's quite okay by me."

She looked down and hesitated for a moment. Then she struggled against the door. It yielded with a crash and the north-wester howled into Solly's Palace.

"Close 'e blarry door!" he said, grinning.

"Thank you, my Baas," she said, as she shivered out into the rain.

NOVEL EXCERPTS

from The Flagellants

■ Carlene H. Polite

The bar was empty when Jimson and Ideal arrived. They had begun coming earlier in the day, now that they did not need the affirmation of the crowd, or seek an audience that would appreciate their being lovers. They had enjoyed being unveiled, shining with adoration and affinity. Now they understood each other's needs, quiet. They did not speak to communicate, touch to feel, or dance across the sawdust . . . any more.

"We are not made for this world, Ideal. This is not our time. You belong to the world of wafting incense and smoky tea, the world of white and ivory. You are my lover from the pages of books. You are too fragile to love me right now."

The bartender wiped the ring the glass had stamped upon the bar. The ring gave her mouth the impetus to form from its wet impression—a sigh.

"It's over, Jimson, I know it. Over as contained in the glass's wet ring. That's silly and a coward's foolish way to say it to you, isn't it? But you know how cowardly I am. Only you have made me stand up in the world and tell them all that I am—I beg your pardon—was in love. I still cannot believe it. We may as well stop our performance. Let's play to an empty house. Remember the times when we were gleaming with our light and love? We sought crowds that would readily see that we were in love. We listened for their applauding comments. Remember the cleaved warmth we left on the subway seats, park benches, bar stools? We played our roles beyond the cinematic dimension. The public properties of lovers achieved full utility when we bowed to the call. Now, we have unmasked each other and pointed up our undoing souls."

"Yes, we were love, Ideal. We still are. We are separate now, that's all. One would think that you have absorbed nothing of our time together, girl. Don't you ever take time to read my books; do you merely dust them? Impermanence is the law of the universe. We have saturated, mastered each other through understanding. We have talked too much. I have been trying to get this through your head. Nothing in life stays the same. Our first breath is our last. We are born and daily become dead, unborn."

"Please don't talk now. I want to hurry and cry before the crowd gets here. You know that I don't want them to see the affirmation of nothingness in our faces. Remember how we met, Jimson? We were something grand, something too, too beautiful. Remember the times when we could dance all night long? Those were the days when the Village was an institution, a city unto itself, the unofficial borough. Then came the invasion of the poetry-and-jazz boys who masturbated onstage, choking to death on toilet paper scrolls of pronouncements unfit for bordellos. Waiting their turns to appear, they scribbled spontaneous poems to the tones of their newly found idols. And please don't forget the part-time beats arriving from Canarsie, getting their acts together down in the subway station. A sign painter could have become rich painting signs for them that broadcasted how hip they were—because they smoked pot . . .

"What is this green-backed monstrosity, this stainless-steel erection, this glorified commune? The buildings are cleaned with Brillo. Probably, the people must agree to sign over their names and call themselves by numbers when they lease those characterless idiot boxes. Aw hell, yes, I love a Mies van der Rohe, a Le Courbusier, a Saarinen, a Frank Lloyd Wright; but, these boys designing the buildings that are cropping up down here now are contractors not architects. So many square rooms for so many square feet. The Green Flower was the place to go, the hangout. Remember it was so crowded, we had to dance back to back, belly to belly, side to side, inside your coat, under your hat; just so long as we could keep on dancing, do it up brown. Two or three people might have been wedged in between us; but who cared as long as we all kept the place swinging. Ray Charles was just beginning to be the man in New York. How many times was there a scene started by some weird drunk's mumbling that he had had too much of *Having a Woman Away 'Cross Town?* I never will forget the night the leather-jacket boys decided to look me over, daring you to object, silently threatening you with their mock force. They had me scared, though, with their brink-of-war strategy; but you won, you outstared them. They did nothing but sneaked away into the thick funk. When we got outside, remember, they were having a snowball fight? Wasn't it that winter's first snow? And Jimson, no one in New York knows Central Park any better than we do. I never knew it was so enormous, or had so many green grass laps and fade-aways that you cannot reach from here . . . You lose New York completely—the noise, grime, people, anything you want to lose.

"The morning we could hear the shade of Miles was too lovely. And who should be standing in the middle of nowhere, and charming trees, wiggling worms, blowing his horn to his heart's content, but Al. Remember? What ever happened to him? You can ask that about almost everyone you know in New York. You can strike up a crazy, wonderful friendship, cry the common blues, have a ball, then bam!—never see the soul again in life. And at the time you were being friends, you truly were . . . I guess this is all we can have of friendship. That everlasting, over the 'Hi! neighbor' back-fence bit is just about so much schmaltz. New York can make you break out of your cocoon and make you want life for whatever it damned well is; and, at the same time, send you retreating into your hatched cocoon. Who in New York knows their next-door, across-the-hall neighbor? You can share the toilet and the bath with a ghost—as far as that goes. You would never know the difference. I had forgotten the Peeping Tom until I got started on Central Park. He, I am sure, will not forget us. We toyed with his standard thrill of looking from a removed spot at hot-time lovers. We were not too cruel to him, though. He got his cookie; but we made him get it by transmitting anticipation, suggestion. He made Peeping Toms out of us—too much. He looked pathetic playing with himself to the beat of nothing but laughter. Did we egg his rhythm on, or did he egg on the rhythm of our laughter? It was not so funny when he made it. He looked so hurt, surprised; as if he did not know whether to run down his little hill to thank us or slap us for giving him the new experience of doing it with his mind only. We should have charged him entertainment tax, or he us—one of the two.

"You and I have always gotten into trouble for laughing. Funny . . . We were absolutely wild, Jimson. We tried it anywhere. The portable lovers on the waterfront, propped against interstate trucks, on the roof, down the hall, up the steps, up high, down low, sand, grass, water, on chairs, floors, the bookcase. We typed out a natural hymn on your typewriter, remember? Too bad we did not have paper in the machine. Wonder what we were saying. The upside-down, nailed-to-the-heights fools. I was never afraid, Jimson, truly afraid, in those days. The time I could have been frightened to death was the night we were roaming up Eighth Avenue and happened on the Puerto Rican confirmation party. Little girls dressed in head-to-toe white give me the creeps. I am able to see generations from now, maybe the year two thousand and fifty-six. I see them hermetically sealed within ornate picture frames, sepia-toned, indistinct. I see a member of the family bending over a mantel, holding them up to the light, peering, trying his best to see, and asking 'Who was this? How do we relate?' When the fellow asked me to dance and you said 'Hell no,' I almost died. The look on his face. Then his buddies gathered around lending him a terrorizing proportion. Then when he fired off in fast, clipped Puerto Rican, and I didn't answer—damn . . . I am forever running into someone in New York who thinks that I am passing for Negro. Now, that is a joke. It is true that being anything in New York, even Negro, is a whole lot better than being a Puerto Rican in New York. We have never had it so good . . . Remember when they were being sprayed when they got off the planes? Spray all the planes or hang it up.

"With some of these phony-time white people, though, I assume the identity. They are so amusing when they approach you with nasal twangs of Spanish, broken English, and sign language. You can't help but freedom-fight, defend everybody's lot. I can understand their willingness to make me feel at ease, comfortable, and cozy by speaking in a familiar way; but what they fail to realize is that the air of condescension stinks. Falsetto. How do they know? What makes them assume that you cannot understand basic English? Color? Well, now really . . . And then to be insulted for passing, for denying my assumed birthplace; he had had too much party, I guess. On him, too, you put your old, one-pointed stare. It works. I am here talking to you now; and this certainly does not look like heaven. I was loving you so much in those days, Jimson. I could have split my soul wide open to show off love. Anything you wanted to do with me, for me, to me, would have been all right . . . made me holler YES. Yes, it was love. It had to be; otherwise, how can I reconcile all the mess of pain I have caused, the chaos? If I do not think it was love, I am finished. Lock me up as a mad, demon bitch. I don't know what it is or was not, but I never will go through that again—not to the degree that we played. Some like it hard, close to the core, snipping at the cord. Jimson, maybe I am merely saving myself by calling it by the name of love; defiling the most common want, that most God-realizing transformed state where each is both . . . Perhaps we never know until we have been in it, until there is a distance between us negating self, subjectivity. The sad commentary is that then we are out of it. In order that I am able to refute the warnings of my blasé company, and believe that I have not wasted time, energy, violated my flesh, not appeared the utter ass, I must make this love. Anyway, I know what it is not. I can sit here all night talking heaps of garbage and wasting breath. It is an action beyond words. Flagellum. Lovers intuit, laugh and cry, grunt and groan. Pulp magazines and S-rate movies give them heavy dialogue up until the last moment; then, in slow motion, a door closes, a leaf falls, rain drops, snow flakes, music plays. Stop me, please; I have become a syrupy fool talking like a wet-eyed lush; but I will say again that if ever I loved anybody, Jimson, you are it. That's a mighty anemic-sounding 'if'—hummmm?"

"You still cannot see me as anything other than a blundering idiot, can you? Why is it you think me incapable of remembering how we came together? I came and got you, remember? You see, Ideal, that is one major fault of yours. You think no one capable of nostalgia and retrospection but yourself."

"Jimson, you know that is not true, now . . ."

"It is definitely true, woman. You have come to believe that you are some sort of fairy of good wish and true love. That is just about so much nonsense. It makes me sick at the stomach. And it is my fault. I have convinced you that you are the angel of mercy, the abdication of all my pain, my inspiration and virgin soul. Well, I am sorry. You are a woman, a weak woman, a girl whose very physicality bespeaks child. I see no soft, warm lap of the world in you. I see no responsible person, no listening voice, no affirmation of myself, no gropings toward myself in you . . . You are a witch and a yoke. I will die from you. Drink up your drink and let's get the hell out of this damned place. Come on, now."

The tone had been set . . . The liquor and drinking too fast falsely intoxicated them. They would use this intoxication as a final cue.

"You are the cryingest woman I have ever seen. Must you always start those damned tears welling up in your eyes? Believe me, I am no longer impressed by the sight of them. You had me fooled. You could stand here and cry forever, but I am going back home—so are you. Come now, little girl."

"I hate you. I hate you, you black dog. You simpering, trifling phony of a man. You are nothing. You are the shame and mistake of all my life. To think that I walked out on a tender, loving, giving man for some sick beast such as you."

"Ha! you should talk. What happened to the burning confession of your heart? Excuse me, I forgot that a woman's heart lies between her thighs. The tale of woe you told . . . He was too weak for you, too dead, too lacking. He didn't question you, or fight you, weight you with the heaviness of his manhood. You wanted him simply because he was older and you were the simple schoolgirl trying to impress friends and a college boy who had taken your virginity. And don't you ever forget it; you wanted him, he did not want you. You are a fool, I tell you. You are a fool. You sit here and, just like a fool, understand and forgive a man who responded with the openness of a mollusk. Again, I say he never loved you; but you refuse to hear what I say, Ideal. Never forgive an insult. You should hate him, get up each morning, go to bed each night, preparing his downfall, your revenge. He does not deserve your sympathy, your concession. Why? For what? You allow a few faint whispers to change your mind, a few I-love-you's, a few forgive-me's to make everything all right. What did he promise or offer you—nothing! He practically had to be put in jail, threatened with torture, before he consented to marry you. Public opinion . . . And, even now, he thinks he is the bargain, the prize package, the innocent one. He asked, begged, that you piss in his face. What does that mean? Ablution? Guilt? Adoration for you? Hell no! It means perversion, his inability to give, his inability to feel and realize you as a woman through his natural manhood. It takes some sick suppression to fascinate him. He made you not his wife, equal, or subject. He turned the emotion inward, upside down with an unwholesome idolatry. You became his master, his man. By begging you to enslave him, he became free to hate you, to renounce his virility. Mr. Ideal . . . You and your maudlin sentiment. I wish he would ask me to piss in his face; he would not have to beg. You will continue to be exploited by those less than you are so long as you allow your guilt-infested identification to beat you to death. In looking at him one time, you—no, not you—but someone with one degree of consciousness, an analytical adeptness, can readily perceive his masochism, his inadequacy for sensuousness, his lack of engendering a thrilling courtship and erotica with submission. He sees nothing as divine. In his self-indulgent indoctrination, he associates you with filth, uncleanliness. He really wishes a man to pour guts, essence, and masculinity upon that spot from which his own has escaped. He is only able to perceive the point-blank, the reality of a penny arcade, the neon-lit signposts. The damned eunuch, the passive whip. A good homosexual, and that is whom he truly desires, would laugh in his undynamic butt. They, too, seek a communicative exchange that negates difference, or, in their case, sameness, and creates the One. Even a money-hungry prostitute hates to see this kind of trick come calling. He means hard work, repulsion. His sort takes the last degree of quivering out of the flesh and leaves the love object cold, denuded, holding nothing but the thought—'What happened in his life? . . .' Don't give me that stuff about the love and comfort you had. You had a mirror, a rag on which to wipe your common, accumulated pain and lack. I should slap you down right here where you stand, you simple-minded whore."

The reeling couple stumbled and started, struggled and danced, across the street. New Yorkers hardly cared if they tore their respective brains out. Was love winning out? Absolutely no one was tearing through the streets proclaiming the virtues and divinity of love; or grabbing passers-by by the coat sleeve, fighting to explain the love in their hearts.

"Well, Mr. Jimson, I am not taking another step. I am going to stand right here, exactly where I am, and shout to the world the hell and much of love, yours and mine."

"Do it then! I could not care less. But you won't have me standing here to provide you with one forgotten line, one improvised gesture. Go to it, fool."

Jimson focused upon the gathering crowd, searching for that one look which would sanction his plight. Ideal overturned a wastebasket, mounted it, and looked every bit the girl who had played and climbed yellow hard-mud make-believe mountains. The old smells, the crawling creatures, the whirling colors, the shouts of rock bottom—exhuming themselves—flitted across her face supplying her with a multitude of excuses to really act a fool. The hysterical shrew was determined to play her part to the hilt.

"Yes, I am going to tell you, warn you. This is Ideal. Look, take a good look. I am love gone wrong. I am that thing, whatever it is, which masquerades in the name of love. I am the mouth that seeks kisses for its own enjoyment—because it likes the liquid chasm. I am the woman who gives up nothing in the name of love, the woman who gives up what she lacks in order to gain what she does not know. I am all feeling, incapable of reason, mistaking kindness and sensuality for passion. With a warped vista and undisciplined flounderings, I relish the idea of marriage as living with God."

Ideal was past the point of embarassment, of caring what people or "they" would say. Some figures in the crowd shook their heads and walked away. Some guessed that she was drunk, stoned, or carried away with histrionics.

"Yes . . . walk away if you like. I don't think you can hear what I am saying, anyhow. Ladies and gentlemen, I am most appreciative of those among you who choose to hear me out. I am not drunk. Of course, in the morning I will swear that my whisky instigated this little show."

She was reeking. Her hair was entangled in tears. Snot oozed from her nose and mouth. Her hand wiped and smeared the mess across her face. She glistened. Ranting was becoming her.

"Hey, Jimson, come back here and help me tell the story, the whole crying shame. Feed me fire while I tell them that I have discovered that you are not living the life that you so jealously constructed for yourself out of your solitary, confined imagination. You are not living the life that you fancy and dream about, that existence which you desire. You have cheapened the wish and image of whom you could become, how you could respond. You have made me understand your right and quest for liberty. Your complaints are valid. Vicariously, I can understand your plight. You say that you are a poet, that you must take the time and distance to write. I can understand your lack of interest for time-payment plans and twenty-year mortgages. There is no waft of an aromatic elixir in the smells of household detergents and cooking grease. There is no conscious, aesthetic design in wet diapers draped across a radiator. The Master Mathematician eludes us upon a daily grocery list and a basic budget of our bare necessity. I can understand a Jimson hating his necessary tasks, pouting at the time clock, and wishing that he would quickly or magically become his style of man. I can see a Jimson glad to get out of a green-metal filing room—away from the simultaneous smack of typewriter keys and chewing gum. I can see you making a complete revolution through a revolving door, walking out and not knowing just where to go—and not wanting to be home. I have been imagining you in such a shining manner, walking with the rhythm and ferocity of the free wind. Get 'em, Jim . . . I have been seeing you living your poems, constructing yourself exactly as if you, alone, were willing it. I can see you talking love and soft words into some woman's eyes. I can hear your misgivings about me—your justifications. I can see her giving the cool detachment that fires your blood. I saw you living your life for the sake of your soul's expressions. I was scared to death that you did not love, but I could see why . . . You broke my heart, Jimson, because you were not doing those things at all. You counterfeited the man. You did not become the thought of which you are capable. You sold out. You sold out in the name of common gossip. The story took on the traits of the housewife's soap opera, the forsaken artist's true confession."

Some minor scuffle flared up along the periphery of the crowd. Jimson, tussling with one of the onlookers, swung and chopped down the space. "Let him pass," someone said, "that's his woman up there." Jimson had changed his ultimatum. He had come back to get Ideal before she killed herself acting the complete fool.

"Ideal, please get down off that thing and come home. I know you are leaving me. How many times have you threatened me with that dried-up statement? You have made me understand that I am not your man, that I stink, that I am black and ugly, that I do not satisfy you in any way. I agree with you. I am crap and we both know it. Come on now, Ideal, get down. Come on, so that I can be left alone. I admit that I am weak, seduced by the moon. You could have helped me, though. You could have waited for me. I am out and I know it. I would have come back . . . You say that I have robbed you of your identity, that I stole your fire. Could it not be that we exchanged these things between us? If I do not accept the gift that you bring, the gift remains with you. Right now, I am unable to say what it is that I have taken from you. I have not opened the gift of you. The whole experience is intact."

"Good God, Jimson, you make me sound like a souvenir. Perhaps we have unwrapped too much of ourselves. We let go the tinsel, the element of surprise. We courted the spirit of love. We wind up, publicly, the same old story. Shame on us, Jimson. Shame on you for not tracking down your beautiful, poetic dream. You have cheated your talent. You have deceived your concept of man and artist. You are seeking escape and sensuality, romance and sympathy. Are you serious? You seek someone who is frightened to death of you, someone who answers yes to everything. You seek someone who affirms your destruction, who assists you in affirming your negation and denial. You are a fool, Jimson, in the white man's world. No, no, no, you are not. You are a coward and a provincial who sees everything desired as against the law. You use your color as a crutch. You use sex as an excuse. You know nothing of what you so arrogantly preach. You preach a selfishly adopted but finely Buddhistic view of the universe. Your philosophy is impenetrable by such a fool as I. You are the fabulous man, the artist, the lover. You preach a convincing sermon of man's stalking the earth in search of his way. I believe in you, but you have convinced me to a degree that you have not convinced yourself . . ."

"It is your vanity, Ideal, that is torn asunder. It is the concept of your becoming that is changed. It is your dream of originality that is polluted. Only your vanity is violated. You wanted a man, a genius with a predetermined giant's will to be the one who hurt you. You have constructed the only man in life whom you would allow to deceive you and stop loving you. It is you who have set up the man and the conditions by which you could be slain and wronged. It is your vanity that is pricked, since it is by the traditional and prosaic theme that your history will be made. What makes you think that the man whom you are able to imagine would, naturally, respond to you? Could he lose himself in you? Can you answer to his call and need, Ideal?"

Jimson's questions droned on and on. Not one word received more emphasis than the other. The tone of his voice remained, always, the same. One had to prepare to hear each word and intonation. His voice was whispered, conscious of breath. Only when one had flattered him would his voice assume another aspect. It became fragile and gleeful, giggling and lisping with all the commotion of childhood.

Ideal looked down at Jimson from atop her trash-basket throne. She wanted to believe the man's words. She wanted to fall down upon the ground before him, hug him around his knees, bury her head in his thighs, beg him to forgive her; instead, she balanced her drunken form and posed, as if she were awaiting the descension of a miracle that would restore them unto grace. The exhausted crowd shuffled in the waiting, and moved in upon Jimson and Ideal, flinging the torn-to-pieces lovers together.

"Kiss and make up," someone in the crowd advised. Ideal pushed away from Jimson.

"No, no, people . . . this is not it, this is not the miracle I am waiting for. You have pushed us together. I am waiting for the spirit to do it for us, not you."

She grabbed one of the onlookers as if to make an example of him. On second thought, she swept the onlooker, who did not resemble spirituality, aside like a swatted fly. Jimson struggled with the crazy woman to take her home. She fought him with the backbone of a mad dog.

"I give up, Ideal. It is your show. Please have it."

"Take your hands off me, you contrived fake and risk. You bizarre, haunting, beautiful man . . . don't put your hands on me. Yes, I hate you. I learned to relish hatred in being with you. You are too clever for me, my love. You do not think for one moment that I believe that saccharine, compassionate look in your eyes, do you? It is a filthy lie. You pretend because you cannot accept the boy you really are. You are saddened only because your public sees you standing out here with your guard dropped.

You are capable of great hatred. You hate with a power which demands that we give you our flesh, so that you may see our souls. You demand that the world empty its hard-earned purse, so that you may afford your aesthetic. You demand that the white man give you his identity, so that you may assume his color. What is your role, Jimson? Where is your place? What is your definite scheme for the universe? Whom will you blame, make wallow in the dust, kowtow to now?"

Tongue and mind were clapping, cutting through the night air with an eloquent clarity Ideal would be incapable of forming into language were it any other time, any other man . . . in life.

from Pimp: Story of My Life

■ "Iceberg Slim" (Robert Beck)

Chapter IV.: A Degree in Pimping

When I got back to Milwaukee, Mama and the street, my mind was straitjacketed into the pimp game. Back in the joint I had dreamed almost nightly. They were cruel playets.

They were fantastic. I would see myself gigantic and powerful like God Almighty. My clothes would glow. My underwear would be rainbow-hued silk petting my skin.

My suits were spun-gold shot through with precious stones. My shoes would be dazzling silver. The toes were as sharp as daggers. Beautiful whores with piteous eyes groveled at my feet.

Through the dream mist I would see shaped huge stakes. The whores' painted faces would be wild in fear. They would wail and beg me not to murder them on those sharp steel stakes.

I would laugh madly. Springs of scarlet would spurt from their behinds as I joyfully booted them crotch first onto the sharp pikes. They would flop around like dying chickens. They would finally fall away in a welter of blood into two red halves.

When I awoke my ticker would be earthquaking inside me. The hot volley of the savage thrill lay sticky wet between my trembling thighs.

I had other terrible dreams. I would be very tiny. A gargantuan Christ, in a sea of light, would be towering above me. In his anger his eyes would be blazing blue suns. His silky platinum hair would stand on end in his rage.

A shaft of purest white light would shoot from the tip of his index finger. He would point toward a woman. Her back would be turned to me. He would hand me a barbed leather whip.

Like a crash of summer thunder he would command, "Punish this evil woman. Destroy the devil inside her. The Lord so directs thee."

Eagerly I would grab the heavy whip in both hands. I would bring it down with all my force on the woman's back. She would just stand there. The scarlet would drain down from her slashed back. She would be standing to her knees in a river of blood.

She would turn her brown agonized face toward me. It would be Mama. I would be shaking and screaming in my sweat. It was horrible. I could never cut the dream off until its end. It had to run its fearful course. The dreams about Mama came until her death.

For a day or two following them, these dreams would recreate in daydreams. Sudden dark arrows of depression and regret would stab into that open sore in my mind. I would get high. The narcotics seemed to ward off like armor the stealthy arrows.

After a week of rest and Mama's soulfood, my color and strength came back. On a Saturday night I decked myself out in one of the vines and topcoat I had bought the day before Dalanski busted me.

I remembered the pimp rundowns at the joint. I had learned my first step had to be a fast cop. I needed a whore to hit the city scene. I had to get on that fast track to pimping.

I was only several months away from age twenty. My baby face was gone. I was six feet two. I was as thin as a greyhound on a crash diet. I went into an underworld bar, The 711 Club, crowded with pimps, whores, and thieves.

I stood at the far end of the bar stalling with a coke. I faced the front door. I turned and asked the slightly familiar elephant beside me about "Weeping" and "Party."

He turned his head. His dime-sized eyes got stuck in my fly's zipper as he looked me over head to toe. He remembered me.

He said, "About a month ago your 'boon coon' 'Party' caught sixty in the county. One of them tight pussys opened his nose wide enough to drive a freight train through. He caught a stud whamming it into her. The stud quit the scene. The broad had to go to a croaker to get 'Party's' shoe outta her ass."

Then after pausing to thumbnail a ball of snot from his trunk, he said, "Old 'Weeping' fell dead outside a shooting gallery in Saint Paul. Musta' shot some 'pure,' cause a lookout on the sidewalk heard him mumble before he croaked. "Well kiss my dead mammy's ass if this ain't the best 'smack' I ever shot."

The elephant again raised his hoof toward his filthy trunk. The sissy barkeep sat a fresh bottle of coke on the log before me. I yanked my eyebrows into a question mark.

He lisped, "The runty black bitch in the middle of the bar sent you a taste."

Without taking my eyes off his thin yellow face, I said, "Sugar, run her down to me. Is the bitch qualified? Is she a whore? Does she have a man?"

The corners of his mouth see-sawed. He slugged his soggy, dirty bar rag against my reflection on the bar top.

He almost whispered, "The bitch ain't nothing but a young skunk from Saint Louis. She ain't nothing but a jazzy 'jive whore.' I'm more whore than she is. She ain't got no man. She's a 'come' freak. She's 'Georgied' three bullshit pimps since she got here a month ago. If your game is strong you could play a 'hog' outta her ass. She ain't but eighteen."

I eased a bone from my pocket, put it on the bar for the fresh coke. I frantically remembered those pimp rundowns in the joint.

I said, "Tell the bitch no dice. I'll take care of the little things, and if she is qualified maybe I'll let her take care of the big things. Give the bitch a drink on me."

On the juke box Ella Fitzgerald was crying about her "little yellow basket."

The barkeep twinkle-toed toward her with the wire and drink. Through the blue mirror I zeroed my eyes in on the target. My ass bone starched on stiff point. Her big peepers were two sexy dancers in the velvet midnight of her cute Pekingese face.

Hot "scratch fever" streaked through me. I thought, if I could cop her and get a pimp's terms she would be out of pocket poison to all white tricks that "pinned" her.

Those pimps back in the joint sure knew basic whorology. I was glad my ears had flapped to all those rundowns.

They had said, "Chase a whore you get a chump's weak cop. Stalk a whore you get a pimp's strong cop."

My turn down of her measly first offer had her jumpy. It was a slick sharp hook twisting in the bitch's mind. Her juicy tongue darted out like a red lizard past her ivory teeth. It slithered over the full lips. She wiggled toward me in an uneven race with the bar keep. He was sliding her green drink between me and the elephant.

I heard a low excited trumpeting in the trunk of the elephant. He had dug her flawless "props" and "gourmet" rear end. It was rolling inside her glove-tight white dress.

I painted a lukewarm indifferent grin on my face as she perched on the stool. I noticed a roll of scratch wedged deep between the black peaks.

She said, "Who the hell are you, and what is that 'off the wall' shit you cracked on the bartender?"

My eyes were sub-zero spotlights on her face.

I said, "Bitch, my name is 'Blood,' and my wire wasn't 'off the wall.' It was real, like me. Bitch, you sure got a filthy, sassy 'job.' It could get your ass ruptured."

The big vein at the temple in the tiny dog face quivered. Her "rapper" was shrill.

She bleated, "I ain't no bitch. I'm a mother-fucking lady. The stud ain't been pulled outta his mammy's womb that kicks my ass. Goddamnit, call me Phyllis. Be a gentleman and respect me. I'm a lady."

The icy blasts busted the thermostat in my spotlights.

I could feel my cool spit on my lips as I roared, "You stinking black Bitch, you're a fake. There's no such thing as a lady in our world. You either got to be a bitch or a faggot in drag. Now Bitch, which is it? Bitch, I'm not a gentleman, I'm a pimp! I'll kick your funky ass. You gave me first 'lick.' Bitch, you're creaming to eat me up. I'm not a 'come' freak, you are. I'm a freak to scratch."

My blast had moved her. Those joint rundowns sure worked. I could see those sexy dancers were hot as hell there in the midnight. She was trying to conceal from me the freakish pain-loving bitch inside her.

She was comical like that fire-and-brimstone preacher. He was trying to hide his "hard on" from the cute sister in the front pew flashing her cat for him.

The broad was speechless. I had called all the shots. I turned toward the crapper.

As I walked away I bombed her. I said, "Bitch, I'm splitting when I come out of that crapper. I know your pussy is jumping for me. I know you want me for your man. Some lucky bitch is going to steal me from you. You better toss that bullshit out of your mind. Get straight Bitch, and tell me like it is on my way out. You had your chance. After tonight you don't have any."

Inside the crapper, I ripped a wad of paper from it's holder. I wrapped the saw buck and the four singles around it. What ever happened out there, I had to show a bankroll.

I stood there in the crapper. I was letting the heat seep deep into that bitch out there. Was I going to cop my first whore? My crotch was fluttery at the thought of it.

I walked out of the crapper. She was outside the door. I almost trampled her. I ignored her. I walked to the bar to pay my light tab. She was peering over my shoulder. I peeled the saw buck off.

I told the barkeep, "Steal the change and cop a 'hog.' "

His bedroom gray eyes sparkled. His delicate pinkie scooted the saw buck back to me across the log.

He said, "Sweetie, it's on me. Come back at two and cop a 'real girl.' "

She tugged at my sleeve as I turned from the bar. She looked up at me. Those dancers had stripped.

I looked down at the hot runt and said, "Well Bitch, it's your move. Do I cut you loose?"

She grabbed my shoulder. She pulled me down toward her. I could feel her hot breath on the side of my head. She popped that lizard tongue into my ear almost to my eardrum. It sent hot shivers through me. I stayed cool. I turned my head and knifed my teeth into the side of her neck. I don't know why she didn't bleed. She just moaned.

Then she whispered, "You cold-blooded sweet mother-fucker, I go for you. Let's go to my pad and 'rap.' "

We walked to the "slammer." I glanced back. The elephant was staring at us. His tongue was "frenching" his "chops." His trunk was twitching for a party.

On the sidewalk she handed me the key to her yellow thirty-six Ford. I was lucky. I had been taught to drive the laundry truck back in the joint. The Ford's motor sang a fine tune. It wasn't a pimp's "wheels," but it sure would make the trip to the city track.

I drove to her pad. On the way she played on me. She was setting me up for the "Georgia." That lizard thought my ear was a speedway. It did a hundred laps inside it. I was still green. I shouldn't have let her touch me.

Her pad was a trap for suckers all right. She had pasted luminous white stars on the hotel room's blue ceiling. There was one blue light. It glowed sexily from behind a three foot plaster copy of Rodin's "The Kiss."

There was a mirror over the bed. There were mirrors on the walls flanking the bed. There was a polar-bear rug gleaming whitely in front of a blue chaise lounge.

I sat on the lounge. She flipped on the portable record player. Ellington rippled out "Mood Indigo."

She slipped into a cell-sized bathroom. Its door was half shut. The "peke" was digging a washcloth into her armpits and "cat." She was nude. She sure was panting to swindle me out of my youth. I wondered if and where she had stashed that roll of scratch.

She came out belly dancing to the "Indigo" sex booster. She was a runt Watusi princess. Her curvy black body had the sheen of seal skin. I had one bitch of a time remembering the dialogue that covered this kind of a situation.

What had the pimps in the joint said: "You gotta' back up from them fabulous pussys. You gotta' make like you don't have a "swipe." You gotta' keep your mind on the scratch."

"Stay cold and brutal. Cop your scratch first. Don't let 'em 'Georgia' you. They'll laugh at you. They'll cut you loose like a trick after they've flim-flammed you. Your scratch cop is the only way to put a hook in their stinking asses."

She danced toward the head of the bed. She stooped over and raised the edge of the red carpet. Her rear end swayed to the "Indigo." It was grinning at me. It was theatre in the round for sure.

She danced toward me. She had two thin reefers in her hand. That box at the side of the bed had rejected and "Indigo" was encoring.

She stood between my legs. Even through the trouser cloth I could feel the hot dampness of her outer thighs. The inner surface of my knee caps tingled under the heat.

She quivered and rolled her jet satin belly under my nose. Her humming of the "Indigo" was low and throaty. She sure qualified as the package the pimps had warned about. My twenty-one month "cherry" was aching to chunk out.

She took a lighter off the cocktail table. She ran the sticks in and out of her mouth to get an even burn. She lit them and handed me one.

She said, "Daddy, this is light green 'pot' from 'chili gut' country. It will make us mellow. Why don't you take your clothes off?"

I took a deep pull on the stick of reefer. I looked up into the sultry dreamy eyes.

I parroted, "Bitch, don't put shit in the game. Business always comes before pleasure in my book. I'll take my clothes off when I know I'm taking them off with my whore. I don't sucker for the 'Georgia.' Jar loose from respectable scratch, Bitch."

I had heard it verbatim in the joint. It worked like a lie detector. The motor in her belly threw a rod. Her eyes had a far away look.

She was busy tailoring the con for me. She collapsed to a yogi squat on the polar bear rug. Her "moon" was winking at me. Her voice was bullshit sweet.

She warbled, "Sweetheart Daddy, you already shot me down. I'm your sweet bitch. I got a 'C' note coming from a trick with his nose open for me. He'll 'spring' for it tomorrow night. It's yours, but you got to wait. Now come on and put your freak baby to bed."

My system had been clean. The reefer was powerful. She didn't know how desperately I needed to pimp. She couldn't know she was the first. I couldn't let her escape.

I had to have a whore. That reefer was sending currents of anger and hatred through me in time with "Indigo." My mortal enemy squatted on that white rug.

I thought, "I'm going to murder this runt black bitch if she don't give me that scratch she had in her bosom."

Like a brute cop giving a heist man a last chance to confess, I said, "Bitch, give me that scratch you had between your tiddies."

Her peepers ballooned in surprise and anger.

She gritted, "You're pimping too hard, skinny ass nigger. I have changed my mind. Get your 'lid' and 'benny' and split."

The "Indigo" was on a torrid upbeat. Like brown-skin lightning I leaped erect from the chaise. I flung my right leg back.

I could feel the tendons at my hip socket straining. My eyes sighted for a heart shot. My needle-toed eleven triple-A shoe rocketed toward her.

The lucky runt turned a fraction of a second in time. The leather bomb exploded into her left shoulder blade. It knocked her flat on her belly. She lay there groaning.

Then like in the dreams in the joint, I kicked her rear end until my leg cramped. Through it all she just moaned and sobbed. I was soaked in sweat. Panting, I lay on the bear-skin beside her. I thrust my mouth against her ear.

In an icy whisper I said, "Bitch, do I have to kill you to make you my whore? Get up and give me that scratch."

She turned her head and looked into my eyes. There was no anger in them now, only fear and strange passion. Her tremulous mouth opened to speak. For a long moment nothing came out.

Then she whispered, "You got a whore, 'Blood.' Please don't kick me any more. I'm your little dog. I'll do anything you say. I love you, Pretty Daddy."

Her talons stabbed into the back of my neck as she tried to suck my tongue from its roots. I could taste her salty tears.

She wobbled to the record player. She lifted a corner of it. She slid that wad of scratch from beneath it. She rejected "Indigo." She put another platter on the turntable.

"Lady Day" was singing a sad lament. "My man don't love me, treats me awful mean. He's the meanest man that I ever seen."

I was standing on the bear skin. She came toward me with the scratch in her hand. She laid it in my palm. I riffled it in a fast count. It was respectable. It had to be over two bills. I was ready to let that "cherry" pop.

I scooped the ninety-pound runt up into my arms. I hit her hard on the tip of her chin. I carried her to the side of the bed. I hurled her onto it

She bounced and lay there on her back. She was breathing hard. Her legs were a wide pyramid.

I got out of my clothes fast. I snatched the top sheet off. I ripped it into four narrow strips. I tied her hands to the bed posts. I spread eagled her legs. With the longer strips, I tied her legs to the top of the springs at the sides of the bed.

She lay there a prisoner. I put her through the nerve shredding routines Pepper had taught me. She blacked out four times. She couldn't pull back from the thrilling, awful torture.

Finally, I took a straight ride "home." On the way I tried to smash the track. I reached my destination. The blast of hate was big enough to spawn a million embryo black pimps.

I untied her. We lay there in the dim blueness. The fake white stars glowed down on us. "Lady Day" still moaned her troubles.

I said, "Bitch, I want you to hump like Hell in these streets for a week. We're going to the big track in the city. Oh yes, this week we got to get that title to the Ford changed. I don't drive no bitch's wheels. It's got to be in my name, understand?"

She said, "Yes, Daddy, anything you say. Daddy, don't get angry, but I was bullshitting about that 'C' note trick."

I said, "Bitch, I knew that. Don't ever try to con me again."

I got up and put my clothes on. I peeled a fin off the scratch and put it on the dresser.

I said, "I want you in the street at six tonight. Stay out of the bars. Work the area around Seventh and Apple."

"I'll come through some time tonight. You be there when I show. If you get busted your name is Mary Jones. If you forget it I can't raise you fast. Have some scratch whenever I show."

I went down to the street. I got into my Ford. It roared to life. I drove toward Mama's. I felt good. I wasn't doing bad for a black boy just out of the joint.

I shuddered when I thought, what if I hadn't kept my ears flapping back there in the joint? I would be a boot black or porter for the rest of my life in the high walled white world. My black whore was a cinch to get piles of white scratch from that forbidden white world.

Mama was pressing a young customer's hair. She saw me get out of the Ford in front of the shop. She called me inside with a waggle of the pressing comb.

She said, "I have been worried. Where have you been all night? Where did you get the pretty little car? Did you find a job?"

I said, "A friend of mine let me borrow it. Maybe he'll sell it to me. I stayed with him all night. He's got a hundred-and-three fever. I'll try to find a job tomorrow."

She said, "There's a roast in the oven. Shut the gas off and eat. I hope, Son, you haven't been with Pepper."

I looked down at the nut brown, shapely girl getting her hair pressed.

I said, "Pepper? She's too old for me. I like young pretty brown-skin girls. Pepper's too yellow for me."

The young broad flashed her eyes up at me. She smiled. I winked and ran my tongue over my lips. She "dug" it. She blushed. I put her on file.

I turned and walked to the sidewalk. I went upstairs and attacked the roast.

I took a long nap. At five-thirty P.M. I went down and got into the Ford. I drove to Seventh and Apple. I parked.

At five minutes to six I saw Phyllis coming toward me. She was a block away. I fired the engine and pulled away.

It sure looked like I had copped a whore. I went back at midnight. She looked mussed up and tired. She got into the car.

I said, "Well, how goes it, Baby?"

She dug in her bosom and handed me a damp wad of bills. I counted it. It was a fin over half a 'C.'

She said, "I'm tired and nasty, and my shoulder and ass ache. Can I stop now, Daddy? I would like a pastrami and coffee and a bath. You know how you kicked me last night."

I said, "Bitch, the track closes at two. I'll take you to the sandwich and coffee. The bath will have to wait until the two o'clock breakdown. You needed your ass kicked."

She sighed and said, "All right, Daddy, anything you say."

I drove her to an open-air kosher joint. She kept squirming on the hard wooden bench. Her butt must have been giving her fits. She was silent until she finished the sandwich and coffee.

Then she said, "Daddy, please don't misunderstand me. I like a little slapping around before my man does it to me. Please don't be as cruel as you were last night. You might kill me."

I said, "Baby, never horse around with my scratch or try to play con on me. You blew my stack last night. You don't have to worry so long as you never violate my rules. I will never hurt you more than to turn you on."

I drove her back to the track. She got out of the car. As soon as she hit the sidewalk, two white tricks almost had a wreck pulling to the curb for her. She was a black money-tree all right.

The next day I took her to a notary. In ten minutes we walked out. She gave me the three bills back that I had paid her for the Ford.

It was legal now. She wasn't beefing. Her bruises were healing and she was ripe for another "prisoner of love" scene. She finished the week in great humping style. I had a seven-bill bankroll.

Sunday evening I packed the runt's bearskin and other things into the trunk of the Ford.

I parked around the corner from Mama's. I went up to get my things together. Mama caught me packing. Tears flooded her eyes. She grabbed me and held me tightly against her. Her sobbing was strangling her.

She sobbed, "Son, don't you love your Mama any more? Where are you going? Why do you want to leave the nice home I fixed for you? I just know if you leave I'll never see you again. We don't have anybody but each other. Please don't leave me. Don't break my heart, Son."

I heard her words. I was too far gone for her grief to register. I kept thinking about that freak, black money-tree in the Ford. I was eager to get to that fast pimp track in the city.

I said, "Mama, you know I love you. I got a fine clerk's job in a men's store in the city. Everybody in this town knows I'm an ex-con. I have to leave. I love you for making a home for me. You have been an angel to stick by me through those prison bits. You'll see me again. I'll be back to visit you. Honest, Mama, I will."

I had to wrestle out of her arms. I picked up my bags and hit the stairs. When I reached the sidewalk, I looked up at the front window. Mama was gnawing her knuckles and crying her heart out. My shirt front was wet with her tears.

from Howard Street

▇ Nathan C. Heard

Try as she would, Rosemary couldn't go back to sleep. The living room light was still on, which indicated that Hip hadn't gone to bed, so she got up, put on Franchot's robe, and went to sit with him.

He was still in the armchair with his head thrown back against the rest. He was blowing a thick stream of smoke up toward the pearl-white ceiling as he continued to think about Franchot and Gypsy Pearl. He'd already decided that Franchot could have her body all he wanted, but she wasn't going to be anybody's woman but his until he was ready to let her go. He reasoned that, after all, she was his bread and butter—he didn't try to take Franchot's job, did he?

"Gimme a smoke, Hip," Rosemary said, standing over him. He shook one out of the pack and indicated the matches which were lying on the coffee table. He had nothing to gain by being polite to Rosemary right now; she was just another broad who could light her own cigarettes.

She took a seat on the sofa and curled her legs up under her; she watched him as he continued to scan the ceiling. She wanted to talk about the threat to her love life, and he wanted to talk about the threat to his financial one, but both were afraid to admit that they had a situation they couldn't handle alone. An uncool dilemma was something that only squares fretted about. A down person didn't hang out problematic laundry like Blue Monday wash for everyone to dig: people peeped your hole card then, knew where you were at and saw that you weren't such-a-much after all.

Bothered by what she couldn't say, and in danger of saying it, Rosemary, in desperation, asked, "Why do you use that dope, Hip? That stuff gon' kill you one day." She was immediately sorry for intruding. She almost cringed as his gaze fell from the ceiling onto her with scathing

anger. "I didn't mean no harm," she said apologetically. "I just thought it'd
be interestin' to know, that's all. You don't have to answer if you don't
wanna. . . ."

"I don't?" he replied caustically. "Thanks for givin' me a choice." His
emaciated, tired face held a hypnotic spell over her; she could think of
nothing except how hollow his cheeks were and the sunken darkness that
surrounded his eyes. When she offered no further comment, he said, "I
use smack in order to live, Rosemary." There was no hostility in his voice
now.

She was relieved by his tone: "Aaah, I don't believe that. You could do
without that stuff if you really wanted to. Y'know, last week at our church,
a detective from the Narcotics Squad at headquarters gave a lecture—I
don't remember his name, Nastyrella or somethin' like that—anyway,
he—"

"I know the chump you talkin' about," Hip cut in: "Nazifella." He
lighted another cigarette without offering her one. "What'd he have to
say?"

"Well, he made it plain that people don't have to use dope, but they do
it to escape responsibility and to escape from life, not to live, like you
said. He said drug addicts were people who'd do anything—"

"Did he also tell you that they rob, rape, and kill when they got dope
in 'em? Did he say they were maniacs?" His voice had a vicious grating
in it. He looked as if he was about to jump up and attack her.

"He didn't say that, exactly—no," she replied timidly.

"But ain't that the impression the people got listenin' to 'im?"

"I guess some did. But he said the most dangerous kind was them that
needed a fix. He said they'd steal from their own family; take food right
outta their kids' mouths. Name it, he said, and a dope fiend would do it."

Hip said nothing for a long while. Then, with resignation, as if he'd
been through this many times, he said, "Y'know, I git so sick and tired of
hearin' and readin' about what squares, mothafuckin' fools, say about
junk. They so ignorant till it's a damn shame. Any tale that comes to their
minds they connect with junkies. What the hell do they know? Do they
use stuff? Do they know what a junkie goes through?—hell no! They read
in the papers about some punk who got stoned on goofballs and did somethin', and right away they go screamin' for junkies' heads because of this
lame, who wouldn't know dope from salt. Then some woman says a wild-
eyed man raped her, and right away everybody assumes a junkie did it. A
junkie with stuff in him don't bother nobody. You even got some dumb-
assed doctors out there who tell the public that a guy can git a habit from
smokin' pot—which is a fuckin' lie. But people believe that bull. I smoked
reefer for five straight years before I even knew what heroin was. How
come I didn't git no habit from it? I know a hundred people who smoke
pot—how come they ain't got no habits?" He stopped talking long enough
to snub out his cigarette and light another.

"You see this?" He held up the cigarette. "Well, you'll git a habit quicker
from smokin' this than you will from pot. The only reason pot ain't legal
is because the big-money whiskey makers got the government to outlaw it
because it was too much competition for them. A stud didn't have to buy

whiskey when he could git high from stuff that grew, unattended, in his own backyard. The whole thing is a drag. They hyped the public against smokin' pot so they could kill 'em—at a profit—with cancerous cigarettes and liver-destroyin' liquor. But when they can make sellin' death legal, it's awright, dig? That means they's honorable, yeah. So fuckin' moral till they ain't shit! I know where they at."

"But, Hip, they ain't got nothin' to do with you puttin' that stuff in you . . ."

"Oh, it ain't, huh?—that's what you think, woman. The outlook of the people in this country got everything to do with what they call 'the drug problem.' "

"Yeah, but why you have to use it, and why you seem to be blamin' people because you use it?"

"I ain't blamin' nobody. All I'm sayin' is that people oughta find out about somethin' before they go condemnin' it, that's all. It's just another case of ignorance bein' afraid of investigation. You wanna know why people use dope . . . I don't know. There's a lotta reasons, but unless a cat goes to a bug doctor and gits his head examined, they can only be guessed at. The one thing that'll make a junkie stop usin' is himself. Like they say: you can take the dope from the junkie, but you can't take the junkie from the dope."

"Well, why *you* use it?" Rosemary persisted. "Ain't you got no reason?"

"Sure, I got a million reasons. Take a look at the things that go on, like the way people act to each other, and you'll see plenty reasons. Every time I shoot up I'm sayin' to them: 'Fuck you *and* your system, lames!' "

Rosemary asked for another cigarette. After taking a long drag, she said, "I think your attitude is wrong, Hip. I mean, I can understand how somethin' that stands in the way of your goals can beat you down and all. But I think you gotta be strong; you gotta build up a physical and mental resistance, and a spiritual determination to go on as best you can, accepting things as they come."

"Shit, *your* attitude's wrong, not mine. You talk that passive junk and you don't git nowhere, not against aggressive and exploitin' people. You gotta rebel and fight! That's what junkies is doin': fightin' against hypocrisy like yours. They see how y'all 'good' citizens say one thing and do the exact opposite. Every time a junkie takes off he's rubbin' your face right in your own hypocritical shit. That's what y'all don't like about dope fiends—they take the freedom that y'all is scared to take. You keep on bein' passive and your behind'll be more familiar with shoe leather than your feet."

"I ain't passive, but I do believe in Christian ethics and law and order. That's more than you can say. I think you use dope just to be down. You think it's hip, and that makes you one of the elite in a sea of squares. You oughta be tryin' to make this a better country to live in insteada tryin' to tear it up by the roots!"

Both their voices were tinged with bitterness and spite now, though neither was outright angry. Hip smiled maliciously at her and said, "Sometimes I wish I could tear it up by the roots and start all over again. I betcha I could make it a hell of a better and more human than what it is."

"What would you do?—destroy everybody that don't use dope?" she asked derisively.

He ignored her remark. "I ain't botherin' nobody. I ain't ṇo cop and I ain't no soldier. I don't build no bombs and I don't fly no planes nowhere to drop none. I ain't no red-blooded American tryin' my damnedest to spill the red blood of other countries, and I ain't responsible for none of the mess in the world. I'm just a dope fiend. Why they persecute me? I ain't looking for nothin' but peace. Why they pick on me and call me one of the worse things in the world when they killin' people by the thousands— and gittin' ready to kill 'em by the millions? I ain't done nothin' to nobody. All I do is shoot good dope in my arm. Sure, I make an illegal dollar here and there and I don't follow no Christian ethic—but then, I don't claim none, neither. Y'all hypocrites can't say as much, can you?"

She thought for a moment before asking, in a softer tone now, "Do all that really justify you, Hip? Is you s'pozed to just lay down because you can't change the world? That's a sorry excuse to be a nothin' dope fiend, if you ask me."

"I ain't askin' you," he snapped. "I'm a dope fiend and love it. It kills me—lays me right out fine, baby."

"It's gon' kill you for real in the long run. Look at what happened to that man yesterday: dead on somebody's roof. That stuff not only ain't good for you, it's dangerous!"

He laughed at her. "Girl, it might not be good for me, but it's so damn good *to* me! When they found Tricky Dick on that roof it only proved that he was greedy and the dope was good. He blew his cool, that's all."

His manner abruptly changed; he seemed to be talking to himself as he murmured, "They sure is takin' a long time."

She was confused. "What you talkin' about, Hip?"

"Franchot and that whore," he said. Then, staring at her fixedly, he added, "Y'know, I think he tryin' to pull her. You dig what that means, don't you? If I blow her, you gon' blow him. You won't have no more man."

"What about you?" she replied tartly. "You won't have no woman, neither."

"Don't need none as long as the dope don't stop. A woman can't do nothin' for me but show me where some dope is and gimme the bread to buy it with."

"What you do for lovin'? Need a woman for that—unless you dig fags," she mocked.

"Only woman I need is the White Lady that rides through my veins. That's the only bitch that can git under my skin; and can't no woman do it as good as she can, baby, I'm tellin' you. When that White Lady's ready, a flesh-and-blood chick can stick a pepperoni up her slit for all I care—I don't need her, and that's the truth."

"Aw, Hip, you jivin'. You know ain't no dope can take the place of sex."

"Hah! That's what you think, woman, but let me tell you one thing. When a cat mixes some heroin and cocaine together and shoots it, he gits a nut—a real nut, right in his pants if he ain't careful. That's what's called speedballin', and, believe me, baby, you ball with a lotta speed!" He closed his eyes as if he were remembering his last speedball.

"Well," Rosemary said, slightly miffed at the insult to womanhood, "if it do all that, why you got Gypsy Pearl?"

"I done already told you—for dope money. If she didn't make no money I wouldn't be messin' with her. A bitch ain't no good to me if she ain't got nothin'. I can do bad by myself."

"You think that's right? You think prostitution is good, somethin' to be proud of?"

"Right? Good? Where you at, woman?—in the first century somewhere? If a woman wanna sell some and a man wanna buy it, what the hell is your phony morals gotta do with it? Yes, I not only think it's good and right, I know it is. A man is a natural pimp and a woman is a natural whore, anyway, regardless to what the law say. I dig natural law. Dig this. . . . Why you think a man shows off his wife to his boss? Why you think them politicians play up the fact that they married? And why you think the dumb bastards in this country won't vote for a bachelor for president? Lemme hip you, girl—it's because he ain't got no whore to show. That's pimpin' Christian style, this showin' of wives! So if you git right down to the nitty gritty, the man *is* livin' off the woman. Just think: all this shit we go through for a crack hung up between some legs! That's where it's at, baby."

"It still ain't like makin' a woman sell her body for money, though."

"Shit, it's worse!—because it's hypocritical. The only reason the squares make laws against prositution is because they full of secret envy for the pimps. Look at all the publicity and romantic worship that international playboys and broke royalty gits. The squares is jealous of them guys, but they can't do nothin' about it because the people love 'em. But me, they'll insult and even kill me, because I ain't a big enough pimp to tell 'em to kiss my behind. But I tell it to 'em anyway. As long as there's a woman out there willin' to give me the money she makes sellin' cunt, I'm gon' be smart enough to take it—and ain't gon' be no hypocrite about it, neither."

"Hip, if we had leaders like you, this would be one of the most corrupt countries in the world." Her hands were shaking as she lighted the cigarette he gave her.

"You think it ain't already? Is you stupid enough to think this morality stuff they preach is for real? Wow! Ain't nobody in this country got no business being dumb enough to believe that the leaders can rule without doin' all kinds of dirt—nobody can. This government ain't run morally and anybody who thinks so is a fool—anybody who says so is a damn liar."

Rosemary had had enough. She got up and went into the kitchen. The clock registered four forty-five. She reheated the coffe while Hip sat in silence in the living room. When it was steaming she brought it in and poured for both of them. Hip accepted the fact that their former conversation was closed when she asked, "Do you really think somethin's goin' on between them? You think he'll put me down for her if he can git her away from you?"

He knew she was really worried about the possibility of losing Franchot, but he couldn't resist getting in one last dig at her. "Didn't I just run it down to you?" he said coolly. "You's a whore, woman. You just ain't gittin' no money for doin' it. You ain't no more important to him than she is to me—can't you dig that? Damn right he gon' throw you over if he can git her, just like I'd git rid of her if I saw somethin' I dug better."

They fell silent, sipping their coffees. She wasn't a bad-looking woman, he thought; and in thinking, the inevitable idea spread its possibilities through his mind. His next statement was automatic: "Dig, Rosemary . . . I don't see no sense in us gittin' upset about them. Why don't we just switch? Like, I wouldn't mind diggin' things with you. You a pretty swingin' chick and you know where things at. If you put your mind to it, I bet you could make more money than she could anyway, y'know?"

She put her cup down so hard on the coffee table that it sloshed over and burned her hand, turning her anger into rage. "Is you askin' me to be a whore, Hip Ritchwood? You dirty, rotten dog. And after all that junk you was just tellin' me—You wait till Franchot come back, he'll strighten —"

"Aw, lay down, bitch. What you gittin' all shook up about? Puttin' on like you so insulted or somethin'. You oughta be flattered. Who the hell is you, anyway? I don't see much difference in whorin' and free-fuckin' like you doin'. At least a whore is a businesswoman—bitches like you ain't nothin' but free samples of the product. Little Miss Tight-pussy is insulted —ain't that a bitch? I'm the one oughta be insulted!"

Rosemary jumped up, glaring. Her throat was too full of fury to speak; when she tried she only stammered. She wouldn't give him the privilege of seeing her cry. She stormed out of the room and slammed the bedroom door behind her. Hip was caught up in a breathtaking fit of laughter.

A few minutes later he got up, went past the so definitely closed door of Franchot's bedroom, got his works out, and let the White Lady have her way with him. She subdued his body's tremble and gave his weary soul rest. She sent him soaring like a celestial body. He was God, making the world in his own image, peopled by nothing but down souls bursting with all the happiness he could dispense to them. Not a worry anywhere in his world; not a wrinkle on one soul's brow. This was where it was at. This was where it had to be.

He was sorry that he could never bring this heaven back to the sorry world of so-called reality. If only he could have—everything would be groovy . . . people would dig . . .

He went into a tight nod, slumped bonelessly down into the chair on which he sat; and again, as God of the world, he slew the squares like Franchot; vilified the women like Rosemary, who didn't know where it was at. Who thought that whores were made by men when, in truth, they were made by nature—born—just like pimps: as natural as a moist pussy.

from Houseboy

■ Ferdinand Oyono (Cameroon)

Madame asked the cook to find her a chambermaid and this morning he brought the girl he has found. He says she is the cousin of the niece of his sister's brother-in-law.

Very well developed at the back and her breasts still firm. She came barefoot, wearing a tailored jacket over her cloth and a single golden earring to set off her poverty. A real girl of the soil. Thick lips, black eyes and a sleepy expression on her face. She was waiting for Madame, sitting on the top step with a twig in her mouth.

The cook told us that he had only found out last night that they were related. Yes, she really was the cousin of the niece of his sister's brother-in-law.

"She's a town-girl," he told us, "she's never been back to the village. The whites are all crazy about her behind, well you've seen it, those lovely elephant's livers bulging beneath her cloth . . . but she'll never make her fortune. Her parents must have eaten a travelling salesman. She can't stop still in one place. She lived on the coast with a white man. He was talking about marrying her and taking her home with him. And you know, when a white man marries a daughter of our people, she's usually something very special. The white man had no heart left, the cousin of the niece of my sister's brother-in-law swallowed it up in one night. They say you could see him sitting all day long with Kalisia—that's her name—on his bony knees. Then, one morning, Kalisia went off, just like that, when the birds were off at the end of the dry season. The white man cried and moved heaven and earth to find her again. They were frightened he would go out of his mind and the Commandant in charge there had him sent home. Kalisia had had enough of whites and she lived for a long time with one of the coast negroes—you know, the ones with salty skins. Then she left him. She lived with other white men, other blacks, and other men who were not quite black and not quite white. Then she came back to Dangan like a bird comes to earth when it is tired of flying in the air . . ."

"And this is the one you have picked to be Madame's chambermaid?" asked Baklu, somewhat overwhelmed by this history. "There are plenty of women down in the township . . ."

"Madame said I must find a clean girl who understood French and was not a thief. I couldn't have found anyone better. And what is more, she knows whites better than any of us," he added, looking at each of us in turn.

"I'm afraid this girl will start trouble that will land us all in jail," said Baklu. "Any man with eyes can hardly see her without . . ."

The cook laughed.

"Are you talking about the Commandant or about one of us?" he asked. "I know the Commandant. He's the kind of white man who will always suppress his feelings however strong they are . . . Besides, his wife is here;

there is no danger. The Residence is not very big and I don't somehow see the Commandant climbing into a ditch . . ."

"You can't always rely on a sense of dignity in these matters," said Baklu, "especially with whites. Look at Madame . . ."

"We shall see," said the cook. "Women can sense these things. I can tell you that if Madame takes Kalisia on, it means that she doesn't think she's a danger . . ."

Nine o'clock came and Madame was still asleep. By now the heat of the sun had become overpowering. The skin began to toast pleasantly. Kalisia had stripped her shoulders. She drew her knees up under her chin and began to doze like the little grey lizard that was squatting in a scrap of newspaper just beside her. Baklu was stretched out on his stomach behind the washhouse and I was sitting at the top of the flight of steps waiting for Madame to wake up and letting a sense of warm well-being soak into my body.

Suddenly Madame's bedroom window opened. I woke up with a start. She rubbed her eyes and buttoned up the top of her pyjamas. She stretched herself, stifled a yawn and called me. She did not open the door but spoke to me through the partition. She sent me to change the water in her shower. She wanted to wash herself in cold water. At eleven o'clock, fresh as a day-old chick, she went on a tour of inspection of the rooms I had cleaned. She looked at the day's menu, went to see how much wine was left, drank the glass of lemon juice which I make for her every morning and began to go through the pile of letters waiting for her on the couch.

The cook came in. Madame asked him irritably what he wanted.

"Girl for chambermaid outside . . ." he said with a broad smile, bowing deeply.

The cook had a natural flair for showing respect. You have only to watch him making a bow before Madame or the Commandant. It begins with an imperceptible quivering of the shoulders. This gradually spreads through his whole body. Then his body as if it were under the sway of some mysterious force begins to bend slowly forward. He lets it go, his arms tight against his sides, his stomach pulled in until his head lolls on his breast. At the same time little dimples of laughter appear in his cheeks. When he has reached the position of a tree about to topple from the axe, he gives a broad grin.

Ever since Madame told him he was quite a gentleman the cook has felt his importance swelling daily after every bow.

He did not notice the icy look that Madame gave him over the top of the letter she was hurriedly reading.

"Where is she?" asked Madame.

The cook ran out and called Kalisia. She replied by a little humming sound and buttoned up her jacket. She pulled the twig she had been sucking out of her mouth and began to climb the steps nonchalantly. Everything about her seemed weary. She made no attempt to lift her feet which caught against every step as she climbed. She leaned in the doorway and gazed at us. Madame had gone back to reading her letter. She held it in one hand while with the other from time to time she tapped her cigarette-holder. The cook stood to attention by her side staring up at the ceiling.

At last Madame came to the end of her letter. She sighed and looked up at us each in turn.

"Bring the woman in," she said to the cook.

He signalled to Kalisia. She coughed, passed her hand over her lips and stepped into the room.

Madame put her mail to one side and crossed her legs. Kalisia stared at Madame with that look of insolent indifference that always infuriates her when it comes from an African. The contrast between the two women was striking. The African was completely calm with a calmness that seemed nothing could ever trouble. She looked at Madame without concern, with the vacant look of a ruminant sheep . . . Madame changed colour twice. Suddenly her dress became damp at the armpits. This wave of perspiration always heralded one of her rages. She looked Kalisia up and down. The corners of her mouth were turned down. She stood up. Kalisia was slightly taller. Madame began to walk round her. Kalisia although she pretended to be staring intently at her hands was now completely absent. Madame came back and sat down in front of her. She stamped her foot. The cook clicked his heels. Kalisia looked across to her kinsman, giving a tiny glance at Madame on the way. Madame went red. I turned my head away so as not to smile.

"Monsieur Toundi!" she thundered.

She lit a cigarette and inhaled. As she blew out the smoke her whole body seemed to go slack. Her forehead was beaded with drops of sweat.

"Have you been a chambermaid before?" she asked Kalisia.

"Yeeeeeesss," said Kalisia with a smile.

"Where was that?"

"Over there—by the sea," said Kalisia pointing with her arm westward towards the sea.

I could hardly hold myself. I bit my lips. Kalisia had a rather special idea of what her job was. I broke in and explained to Madame that she would have to put the question in a different way—something like, "Have you ever been a lady's houseboy?" Kalisia gave an "Ah" and told me in the vernacular that they would have had an interesting conversation at complete cross purposes.

Kalisia then admitted that she had never been a chambermaid in her life but that she would do her best to give satisfaction because from now on she did not want to earn her living in any other way. Madame seemed touched by this half-confession. At once, now that Kalisia had offered a kind of self-excuse, Madame regained her air of superiority.

"I will see what I can do for you," she said. "Toundi will show you round."

She dismissed us with the back of her hand.

"You can begin right away," she called after us.

Kalisia followed me into Madame's bedroom.

"These whites are rich," she said, looking round the room. "I like working for whites like these. You know, when they are poor they are as mean as a catechist . . . I once lived with a white man who used to count the lumps of sugar and measure the loaf after every meal. What are they like here?"

"All right when they are not angry," I said. "You'll see."

"The mistress is beautiful," said Kalisia. "A white woman with eyes like hers can't do without a man. Let me see" (she went to peep at Madame through a crack in the door), "I'd say she couldn't do without a man even for a fortnight . . . I bet she has a lover. Who is he?"

"You'll see for yourself?" I said.

"You rascal, you rogue, you sly devil," she shouted. "Slender hips like you've got are often the nest for a great big snake." She pinched my buttocks. "Don't think Madame doesn't know that as well!"

She made a grab at my sexual parts and gave a little hoarse cry.

"See, I was right," she said. "That's already had a taste of white flesh, I know. It's you. It's you that's Madame's man. I knew right away. You only have to look at her eyes when she talks to you."

This was really too much. Her familarity and abandon made me furious. I turned on her, my eyes blazing. She was dashed at once.

"I didn't mean to make you angry, my brother," she said, so repentant that my anger quickly drained away.

"It doesn't matter," I said. "Only you went a little too far . . ." We both smiled. She winked at me and we turned Madame's mattress.

"What is she like?" she asked me after a pause.

"Who?" I asked.

"Madame," she said.

I made a vague gesture.

"How many times do you do it a week?" she went on questioning.

I lifted up my arms in astonishment.

"Listen," I said. "Either you must keep your mouth shut or you must go back home. You may be crazy but I am not . . ."

"Oh, dear," she said. "So there really is nothing between you? Still, you're a man. Down on the coast, the houseboys sleep with their Madames, it's quite normal. Up here you're all too scared of the whites . . . It's silly to be so scared, I can tell you . . ."

"All right," I cut her off.

We spread the coverlet over the bed. Madame came into the room and made no comment on our work.

"She really is a woman," said the terrible Kalisia when Madame had gone.

Kalisia is going to work for two hours every day at the Residence. Still, she really is rather splendid.

from No Bride Price

■ David Rubadiri (Malawi)

The jukebox blazed away sixpences. In a corner of the room were "girls." Heavy make-up gave them a neutral expression. A mask that made them symbols of new womanhood. The Astronaut made every woman significant. It gave every girl a sex symbol. Behind their masks they looked interesting, exciting, but, at the same time, disgusting.

They wriggled in high-heeled shoes, their bottoms bursting through their tight dresses. "Bottoms" they called them. The music gained momentum. The tight dresses danced to the music. They bobbed up and down exposing dirty underclothes and highly greased brown thighs. A strong smell of sex engulfed the bar. The stench of overnight urine drifted through the windows. Empty bottles of beer lay about on ringed tables and on the floor. Flies perched around unwashed glasses and old beer bottles.

The music stopped. As the dancing girls flung themselves in exhaustion on the old couches they let off a strong smell of sweat and stale scent. Lombe felt the weight of the bodies as they thumped down. He was trying to make his beer last. These girls reminded him of Miria.

"Put on 'Julieta,'" demanded the fat one in a loud, crude voice.

"Oh! I am sick and tired of 'Julieta'," shouted back the other.

"Put on anything then—the place is so dull."

The slim girl fumbled in her bag for a sixpence. Abandoning the attempt, she cast a provocative masked look at Lombe. Lombe tried to look impassive—but when she crossed her legs and made a half serious attempt to pull her dress down, he became uncomfortable. He reached for his half-filled bottle and poured out a jet of beer to fill the glass with froth, to give him time to let the froth settle down so that the beer could last.

"You are early today, Mr. Lombe," the fat girl said.

Lombe gave a grunt.

"Shall we put some music on for you?"

The two girls giggled. The fat one was drunk. She reached forward to remove his now almost finished bottle of beer, parting her legs in an obscene and seductive manner. Lombe could see the dark, torn knickers. He remembered the evening he had taken this particular girl out. She had been young like Miria—straight from the village. Her first dress had looked gauchy on her. Her body was used to loose cloth. Her skin was tight. She had a mysterious shyness about her. When he had taken her out again she had given him gonorrhoea.

"Shall I get you another beer, Mr. Lombe?" she asked provocatively.

"Not just now—I am waiting for a friend."

The two girls held hands and giggled. The fat one lunged forward and wriggled to the jukebox. She gave it a hard kick on its side and it started to blare again. The girls now danced separately—each looking far into the distance and slowly gyrating her waist and bottom, reminiscent of the village female dancer who dances to the compulsive appeal of the drummer.

Chaudry walked in suspiciously as the music came to an end. The two girls stopped dancing and looked at him with surprise and amusement. Indians never came to these places. He reached in his pocket for a cigarette. Lombe gave a loud cough. Chaudry saw Lombe and with relief walked to where he sat.

"What a swinging place, Lombe," he said rather nervously.

"Have you never been here before?"

"No—not really. I have only peeped in from my car on several evenings."

"What will you have?"

"A beer, please. Watching that dancing made me thirsty."

They laughed. Lombe gave the order for two beers with more confidence.

"You are a lucky man—to be able to come to night-clubs like this. My people would not be amused if they heard that I came to the Astronaut."

"What do you do in the evenings then?"

"Oh, mainly the cinema, or simply driving around and watching you chaps enjoy yourselves from the window of my car. There is, of course, the T.V.," he added.

The fat girl brought the beer. She stared deliberately at Chaudry as she opened it—then poured it out for him. The slim girl came over and stretched out her hand in shy greeting. Chaudry shuffled around in embarrassment as the girl put on the jukebox again and started dancing, as it looked, specially for him.

"I like the slim one, Lombe—she really is pretty."

"I never knew you were interested in girls, Chaudry—especially African girls."

"Don't be daft. What do you think I am—a saint or something, man!"

More people came into the room. Some waved to Lombe and nodded to Chaudry. The place began to get noisy as beer was downed to the hearty slapping of the girls' bottoms. Sammy, an acquaintance of Lombe, came over to join them.

"How's life, boy—you look rather serious today?"

"Not really, Sammy. How are you? Meet my friend Chaudry."

"How are you, sir?"

"How do you do, Mr. Sammy. Nice place, isn't it?"

"Yah! Thank the Almighty for it. Some of us would be carcasses without it."

"I dare say."

"Hey, Lombe—congratulations on your promotion and all that. Going up the ladder, eh! When do we celebrate?"

"Sammy boy—it looks like the break I've been waiting for. But what a hell of a time to wait for it—Independence so far away behind."

"What about us, old boy—still cringing to that white boss, not even a wink from the Perm. Sec."

"Come off it, Sammy! You have a decent chap as Perm. Sec. When is the sandwich filling going to get thinner?"

"Not a hope. Two more whites arrived today. Contracts for four years."

"Well, efficiency and integrity, old boy."

"Efficiency and integrity, my foot! One of these days I am going to find the chief a good little bottom so that he can at least give me a nod. Have a beer on me, big civil servant."

"Thanks, Sammy, we are about to leave."

"Mr. Chaudry?"

"No, thanks very much—we are going to a reception very soon."

"Reception!" Sammy repeated the words with rehearsed wonder. "Lombe, since when have you started to attend receptions? Must be the new privileges of office, eh?"

"Get off, man. Chaudry's father is the Indian High Commissioner and they are having a reception this evening—National Day of India."

"Good to meet you, Mr. Chaudry," Sammy snapped back. "I hope we shall see more of you. Lombe is a great friend of mine—are you sure you will not have just one on me?"

"No, old man—not today. Will see you later."

Chaudry and Lombe stood up to go. Sammy watched them leave— then turned to the fat girl who had been patiently waiting for him to finish.

"What is the matter with him?" she asked provocatively.

Sammy looked at her, gave her a large wink, squeezed her hard and ordered her to go and fetch another beer. The jukebox played louder as the Astronaut filled with more people and noise.

4

Lombe felt the glow of the whisky begin to spread in his belly. He had been uncomfortable at Chaudry's house. The presence of the Ministers and all the big people from the Embassies had made him feel uncomfortable. Secretly, however, he felt that it was a great thing that a simple person like himself should be invited to such a party. To actually go to a party with one's Minister and Perm. Sec. and then to be sent home in a chauffeur-driven car was a new and exciting experience.

He settled down in the cushy leather seats of the Benz and felt good. The driver slowly moved the car out of the Embassy gates.

"Which way, sir?" he asked politely.

Suddenly Lombe saw the absurdity of the situation. He did not want to tell this man that a big shot like him lived in the African sector of the town. He felt big and wanted to impress him.

"Which way, sir?" the driver asked again.

Lombe had to think of an answer quickly.

"Oh! I have a lot of work to do before I go to my residence. Drive me to my office near Barclays Bank."

The driver was suitably impressed and drove on fast to the centre of the city where all the big and impressive offices were situated.

"You drive the Ambassador, driver?" Lombe asked.

"No, sir, me just be assistant driver. I drive much the madam in town."

"I see," said Lombe in an important manner.

They left the dimly lit, fashionable suburbs of the town and drove into the main street of the city. Lombe wondered what he would do when they reached the Bank. It was a cool night and there were a few people walking on the pavement. There was very little traffic on the road. The big car ran quietly and smoothly. Lombe suddenly wished he was a Minister. No wonder these people did everything they could to get votes from the people. Then his mind switched over to his little house in the African sector of the town. He saw a heavy-eyed Miria waiting for him. The thought made him feel angry. Why had this primitive girl played tricks with him? He would show her. He would go back and tell her to return to the Astronaut. If she worked there for a week no one would believe the story that he had made her pregnant. If she tried to do so, no one would believe her. They knew the tricks that these girls played on young men who were getting on in government and in business.

The solution was so simple. Why had he worried so much about it? He planned every move carefully. He would go to the house and not speak to Miria. In the morning, he would tell her to go back to the Astronaut. If she refused to get out of the house he would call in the police and tell them that she had stolen his money and was now refusing to leave the house. The threat should work.

The driver pulled in opposite the Bank. The street was deserted. To impress the driver Lombe jingled the keys in his pocket abstractedly. The driver left his seat in front and came to open the door for Lombe. He came out slowly, looking preoccupied. He turned sharply to the driver and said, "You can go now, driver."

"Thank you, sir." The driver saluted and drove off.

Lombe waited for the car to disappear into the night. The red lights at the back winked their way into the cool ambers of the street lights. Lombe was now alone. He felt cold and lonely. He had no money to take a taxi. The walk to his house would be about three miles. There was no alternative but to walk it.

The walk made him hot. He felt sober. He wondered why he had not asked the driver to drive him straight to his house. He found it painful to accept the truth. He only consoled himself with the thought that next time he went back to Chaudry's home the driver would spread the word amongst his friends that he was the big man at the Bank.

"You see that man there, Dickson?"

"No, man—who he be?"

"You not know him?"

"That one. Let me see. No, me not know him—who he be?"

"That be the big man at the Bank. He go there anytime to get money."

The driver would embellish the story to his friends.

He took off his jacket. He had now turned away from the main road on to a footpath that led to the African sector of the city. The grass was wet with dew. He stopped to roll his trousers up to his knees so that they would not get wet. The grass scratched his legs and made them itch. Frightened animals darted away from him into the bush as he walked along. Tomorrow he would put in his application for an advance to buy a car. The thought cheered him up.

There was a light in the house. That meant that Miria was there waiting for him. She had done this every day. He reached the corner of the house and paused for a moment to piss. At this time of the night the location was quiet. The good families slept early. The more active tenants were either at the beer houses, the Astronaut or visiting friends in other parts of the location. Next door someone was strumming a guitar and drunkenly singing about "My baby doll." He enjoyed pissing against the wall of his house. It gave him confidence and made him feel good. As he buttoned the fly of his trousers, a sharp, drunken voice of a woman pierced the night sharply. In the location one was used to women screaming. Voices of women being beaten by drunk husbands. Sometimes a man pleading with his wife to let him in and the wife declaiming loudly that she would not and that he had better go to his other woman. This voice tonight was claiming for money.

"You said you would give me five shillings."

"Shut up, woman," said the strong voice of a man.

"What do you think I am—a harlot?"

"Shut up you, woman, or I'll beat you up—beat you up so thoroughly that your mother will never recognize you again."

"You dare do that," she said at the top of her voice. "You dare do that if you are a man. Give me my money," she demanded.

"Shut up, woman," he kept on saying.

"No. I will not take your one shilling—what do you think I am, a harlot?" She repeated the word "harlot" with indignant loudness.

"Shut up, woman, before I smash you."

"Truth God, I am not going out until you give me my money."

"Then come back to bed if you are not going away," he said with bilious pleasure.

There was a noisy scuffle as the two naked bodies came to grips—rudely pushing furniture and beds in the dark. The heavy breathing could be heard even where Lombe stood. There was a loud thud as they fell down on the bed. Then silence.

Lombe finished buttoning his fly and prepared to enter the house. The door was open. He had expected to find the mess that he had left in the evening after the quarrel with Miria. The sitting room looked tidy. Miria had replaced the books on the shelves. As usual, some titles were upside down. She had even smoothed Lombe's ruffled suit. The great moment had come. He prepared to enter the bedroom and face Miria. With an air of self-confidence he pushed the door leading to the bedroom and stood square in it looking for Miria sitting on the bed waiting for him.

Miria had gone

DRAMA

The Electronic Nigger

■ Ed Bullins

The Electronic Nigger was first produced at the American Place Theatre on March 26, 1968. The production was directed by Robert MacBeth. Sets were designed by John Jay Moore, lighting by Roger Morgan. The cast was as follows:

MR. JONES	Wayne Grice
LENARD	Warren Pincus
MISS MOSKOWITZ	Jeanne Kaplan
MR. CARPENTIER	J. Errol Jaye
BILL	Roscoe Orman
SUE	Hedy Sontag
MARTHA	Helen Ellis
STUDENTS	Ronald A. Hirsch
	Maie Mottus

MR. JONES: *A light-brown-skinned man. Thirty years old. Hornrimmed glasses. Crewcut and small, smart mustache. He speaks in a clipped manner when in control of himself but is more than self-conscious, even from the beginning. Whatever, MR. JONES speaks as unlike the popular conception of how a negro speaks as is possible. Not even the fallacious accent acquired by many "cultured" or highly educated negroes should be sought, but that general cross-fertilized dialect found on various Ivy League and the campuses of the University of California. He sports an ascot.*

MR. CARPENTIER: *A large, dark man in his late thirties. He speaks in blustering orations, many times mispronouncing words. His tone is stentorian, and his voice has an absurdly ridiculous affected accent.*

BILL: *Twenty-two years old. Negro.*

SUE: *Twenty years old. White.*

LENARD: *Twenty-one. A fat white boy.*

MISS MOSKOWITZ: *Mid-thirties. An aging professional student.*

MARTHA: *An attractive negro woman.*

Any number of interracial students to supply background, short of the point of discouraging a producer.

Scene: *A classroom of a Southern California junior college.*
Modern decor. New facilities:
Light green blackboards, bright fluorescent lighting, elongated rectangular
tables, seating four to eight students, facing each other, instead of the
traditional rows of seats facing toward the instructor. The tables are stag-
gered throughout the room and canted at angles impossible for the instruc-
tor to engage the eye of the student, unless the student turns toward him
or the instructor leaves his small table and walks among the students.
It is seven o'clock by the wall-clock; twilight outside the windows indicates
a fall evening. A NO SMOKING sign is beneath the clock, directly above
the green blackboards, behind the instructor's table and rostrum.
The bell rings.
Half the STUDENTS *are already present.* MISS MOSKOWITZ *drinks coffee*
from a paper cup; LENARD *munches an apple, noisily. More* STUDENTS
enter from the rear and front doors to the room and take seats. There is
the general low buzz of activity and first night anticipation of a new eve-
ning class.
BILL *comes in the back door to the room;* SUE *enters the other.* THEY
casually look about them for seats and indifferently sit next to each other.
JONES *enters puffing on his pipe and smoothing down his ascot.*
The bell rings.

MR. JONES (*Exhaling smoke*): Well . . . good evening . . . My name is
Jones . . . ha ha . . . that won't be hard to remember, will it? I'll be
your instructor this semester . . . ha ha . . . Now this is English 22E . . .
Creative Writing.
LENARD: Did you say 22E?
MR. JONES: Yes, I did . . . Do all of you have that number on your cards?
. . . Now look at your little I.B.M. cards and see if there is a little 22E
in the upper left hand corner. Do you see it?

(CARPENTIER *enters and looks over the class*)

MISS MOSKOWITZ (*Confused*): Why . . . I don't see any numbers on my
card.
MR. JONES (*Extinguishing pipe*): Good . . . now that everyone seems to
belong here who is here, we can get started with our creativity . . . ha
ha . . . If I sort of . . .
MISS MOSKOWITZ (*Protesting*): But I don't have a number!
LENARD (*Ridicule*): Yes, you do!
MISS MOSKOWITZ: Give that back to me . . . give that card back to me
right now!
LENARD (*Pointing to card*): It's right here like he said . . . in the upper
left-hand corner.
MISS MOSKOWITZ (*Snatching card*): I know where it is!
MR. JONES: Now that we all know our . . .
MR. CARPENTIER: Sir . . . I just arrived in these surroundings and I have
not yet been oriented as to the primary sequence of events which have
preceded my entrance.

MR. JONES: Well, nothing has . . .

MR. CARPENTIER (*Cutting*): If you will enlighten me I'll be eternally grateful for any communicative aid that you may render in your capacity as professor *de la classe.*

MR. JONES: Well . . . well . . . I'm not a professor, I'm an instructor.

BILL: Just take a look at your card and see if . . .

MR. CARPENTIER: Didn't your mother teach you any manners, young man?

BILL: What did you say, fellah?

MR. CARPENTIER: Don't speak until you're asked to . . .

MR. JONES: Now you people back there . . . pay attention.

MISS MOSKOWITZ: Why, I never in all my life . . .

MR. JONES: Now to begin with . . .

SUE: You've got some nerve speaking to him like that. Where did you come from, mister?

MR. JONES: Class!

MR. CARPENTIER: Where I came from . . . *mon bonne femme* . . . has no bearing on this situational conundrum . . . splendid word, conundrum, heh, what? Jimmie Baldwin uses it brilliantly on occasion . . .

MR. JONES: I'm not going to repeat . . .

MR. CARPENTIER: But getting back to the matter at hand . . . I am here to become acquainted with the formal aspects of authorcraft . . . Of course I've been a successful writer for many years even though I haven't taken the time for the past ten years to practice the art-forms of fiction, drama or that very breath of the muse . . . poesy . . .

MR. JONES: Sir . . . please!

BILL: How do you turn it off?

LENARD: For christ sake!

MR. CARPENTIER: But you can find my name footnoted in numerous professional sociological-psychological-psychiatric and psychedelic journals . . .

MR. JONES: If you'll please . . .

MR. CARPENTIER: A. T. Carpentier is the name . . . notice the silent T . . . My profession gets in the way of art, in the strict aesthetic sense, you know . . . I'm a Sociological Data Research Analysis Technician Expert. Yes, penalology is my field, naturally, and I have been in over thirty-three institutions across the country . . . in a professional capacity, obviously . . . ha ho ho.

MR. JONES: Sir!

LENARD: Geez!

MR. CARPENTIER: Here are some of my random findings, conclusions, etc. which I am re-creating into a new art-form . . .

SUE: A new art-form we have here already.

BILL: This is going to be one of those classes.

MR. CARPENTIER: Yes, young lady . . . Socio Drama . . .

MR. JONES: All right, Mr. Carpenter.

MR. CARPENTIER (*Corrects*): Carpentier! The T is silent

MR. JONES: Okay. Complete what you were saying. . . .

MR. CARPENTIER: Thank you, sir.

MR. JONES: . . . and then . . .

MR. CARPENTIER: By the way, my good friend J. J. Witherthorn is already dickering with my agent for options on my finished draft for a pilot he is planning to shoot of *Only Corpses Beat the Big House* which, by the way, is the title of the first script, taken from an abortive *novella narratio* I had begun in my youth after a particularly torrid affair with one Eulah Mae Jackson . . .

MR. JONES: Good . . . now let's . . .

MR. CARPENTIER: Of course, after I read it some of you will say it resembles in some ways *The Quare Fellow,* but I have documented evidence that I've had this plot outlined since . . .

BILL: Question!

SUE: Won't somebody do something?

BILL: *Question!*

MR. JONES (*To* BILL): Yes, what is it?

MR. CARPENTIER (*Over*): . . . Of course I'll finish it on time . . . the final draft, I mean . . . and have it to J. J. far ahead of the deadline but I thought that the rough edges could be chopped off here . . . and there . . .

MR. JONES (*Approaching anger*): Mr. Carpentier . . . if you'll please?

MR. CARPENTIER (*Belligerent and glaring*): I beg your pardon, sir?

(MARTHA *enters*)

MR. JONES: This class must get under way . . . immediately!

MARTHA (*To* MR. JONES): Is this English 22E?

MR. CARPENTIER: Why, yes, you are in the correct locale, *mon jeune fil.*

MR. JONES: May I see your card, Miss?

MR. CARPENTIER (*Mutters*): Intrusion . . . non-equanimity . . .

MISS MOSKOWITZ: Are you speaking to me?

MR. JONES (*To* MARTHA): I believe you're in the right class, miss.

MARTHA: Thank you.

MR. JONES (*Clears throat*): Hummp . . . huump . . . well, we can get started now.

MR. CARPENTIER: I emphatically agree with you, sir. In fact . . .

MR. JONES (*Cutting*): Like some of you, I imagine, this too is my first evening class . . . And I'd . . .

MISS MOSKOWITZ (*Beaming*): How nice!

LENARD: Oh . . . oh . . . we've got a green one.

MR. JONES: Well . . . I guess the first thing is to take the roll. I haven't the official roll sheet yet, so . . .
. . . please print your names clearly on this sheet of paper and pass it around so you'll get credit for being here tonight.

BILL: Question!

MR. JONES: Yes . . . you did have a question, didn't you?

BILL: Yeah . . . How will we be graded?

SUE: Oh . . . how square!

MR. JONES (*Smiling*): I'm glad you asked that.

MISS MOSKOWITZ: So am I.

LENARD: You are?

MR. JONES: Well . . . as of now everybody is worth an A. I see all students as A students until they prove otherwise . . .

MISS MOSKOWITZ: Oh, how nice.

MR. JONES: But tonight I'd like us to talk about story ideas. Since this is a writing class we don't wish to waste too much of our time on matters other than writing. And it is my conclusion that a story isn't a story without a major inherent idea which gives it substance . . .

MISS MOSKOWITZ: How true.

MR. JONES: And, by the way, that is how you are to retain your A's. By handing in all written assignments on time and doing the necessary outside work . . .

LENARD: Typewritten or in longhand, Mr. Jones?

MR. JONES: I am not a critic, so you will not be graded on how well you write but merely if you attempt to grow from the experience you have in this class . . . this class is not only to show you the fundamentals of fiction, drama and poetry but aid your productivity, or should I say creativity . . . ha ha . . .

MR. CARPENTIER (*Admonishing*): You might say from the standpoint of grammar that fundamentals are essential but . . .

MR. JONES (*Piqued*): Mr. Carpentier . . . I don't understand what point you are making!

MR. CARPENTIER (*Belligerent*): Why . . . why . . . you can say that without the basics of grammar, punctuation, spelling, etc. . . . that these neophytes will be up the notorious creek without even the accommodation of a sieve.

SUE: *Jesus!*

LENARD (*Scowling*): Up the where, buddy?

MISS MOSKOWITZ: I don't think we should . . .

BILL: It's fantastic what you . . .

MARTHA: Is this really English 22E?

MR. JONES: Now wait a minute, class. Since this is the first night, I want everyone to identify themselves before they speak. All of you know my name . . .

MARTHA: I don't, sir.

MR. CARPENTIER: You might say they will come to grief . . . artistic calamity.

MR. JONES: Ohhh . . . It's Jones . . . Ray Jones.

LENARD: Didn't you just publish a novel, Mr. Jones?

MARTHA: Mine's Martha . . . Martha Butler.

MR. JONES: Oh, yes . . . yes, a first novel.

MR. CARPENTIER (*Mutters*): Cultural lag's the real culprit!

BILL (*To* SUE): I'm Bill . . . Bill Cooper.

SUE: Pleased . . . just call me Sue. Susan Gold.

MR. JONES: Now . . . where were we? . . .

MR. CARPENTIER: In the time of classicism there wasn't this rampant commerce among Philistines . . .

MR. JONES: Does someone . .

MISS MOSKOWITZ: Story ideas, Mr. Jones.
MR. JONES: Oh, yes.

(*Hands are raised.* LENARD *is pointed out*)

LENARD: I have an idea for a play.
MR. JONES: Your name, please.
LENARD: Lenard . . . Lenard Getz. I have an idea for a lavish stage spectacle using just one character.
MR. CARPENTIER: It won't work . . . it won't work!
SUE: How do you know?
MISS MOSKOWITZ: Let Lenard tell us, will ya?
MR. CARPENTIER (*Indignant*): Let him! Let him, you say!
MR. JONES (*Annoyed*): Please, Mr. Carpentier . . . please be . . .
MR. CARPENTIER (*Glaring about the room*): But I didn't say it had to be done as parsimoniously as a Russian play. I mean only as beginners you people should delve into the simplicity of the varied techniques of the visual communicative media and processes.
MR. JONES: For the last time . . .
MR. CARPENTIER: Now take for instance cinema . . . or a tele-drama . . . some of the integrative shots set the mood and that takes technique as well as craft.
MR. JONES: I have my doubts about all that . . . but it doesn't have anything to do with Lenard's idea, as I see it.
MR. CARPENTIER: I don't agree with you, sir.
MR. JONES: It's just as well that you don't. Lenard, will you go on, please?
LENARD: Ahhh . . . forget it.
MR. JONES: But, Lenard, won't you tell us your idea?
LENARD: No!
MISS MOSKOWITZ: Oh . . . Lenard.
MR. CARPENTIER: There is a current theory about protein variation . . .
MR. JONES: Not again!
SUE (*Cutting*): I have a story idea!
MISS MOSKOWITZ: Good!
MR. JONES: Can we hear it . . . Miss . . . Miss . . . ?
SUE: Miss Gold. Susan Gold.
MR. JONES: Thank you.
SUE: Well, it's about a story that I have in my head. It ends with a girl or woman, standing or sitting alone and frightened. It's weird. I don't know where I got *that* theme from! . . . There is just something about one person, alone, that is moving to me. It's the same thing in movies or in photography. Don't you think if it's two or more persons, it loses a dramatic impact?
MR. JONES: Why, yes, I do.
MISS MOSKOWITZ: It sounds so psychologically pregnant!
LENARD: It's my story of the stupendous one-character extravaganza!

(*A few in the class hesitantly clap*)

MR. CARPENTIER (*In a deep, pontifical voice*): Loneliness! Estrangement! Alienation! The young lady's story should prove an interesting phenomena—it is a phenomena that we observe daily.

MISS MOSKOWITZ: Yes, it is one of the most wonderful things I've ever heard.

MR. JONES (*Irritated*): Well, now let's . . .

MR. CARPENTIER: The gist of that matter . . .

MR. JONES: I will not have any more interruptions, man. Are you all there!

MR. CARPENTIER: I mean only to say that it is strictly in a class of phenomenology in the classic ontonological sense.

MR. JONES: There are rules you must observe, Mr. Carpentier. Like our society, this school too has rules.

MR. CARPENTIER: Recidivism! Recidivism!

MARTHA: Re-sida-what?

MR. CARPENTIER (*Explaining*): Recidivism. A noted example of alienation in our society. We have tape-recorded AA meetings without the patients knowing that they were being recorded. In prison we pick up everything . . . from a con pacing his cell . . . down to the fights in the yard . . . and I can say that the milieu which creates loneliness is germane to the topic of recidivism.

MR. JONES: What? . . . You're a wire-tapper, Mr. Carpentier?

MR. CARPENTIER: Any method that deters crime in our society is most inadequate, old boy.

BILL: A goddamned fink!

LENARD: I thought I smelled somethin'.

MR. CARPENTIER: Crime is a most repetitive theme these days. . . . The primary purpose of we law enforcement agents is to help stamp it out whatever the method.

MR. JONES: Carpentier!

MR. CARPENTIER: Let the courts worry about . . .

MR. JONES: But, sir, speaking man to man, how do you feel about your job? Doesn't it make you uneasy knowing that your race, I mean, our people, the Negro, is the most victimized by the police in this country? And you are using illegal and immoral methods to . . .

MR. CARPENTIER: Well, if you must personalize that's all right with me . . . but, really, I thought this was a class in creative writing, not criminology. I hesitate to say, Mr. Jones, that you are indeed out of your depth when you engage me on my own grounds . . . ha ha . . .

(MR. JONES *has taken off his glasses and is looking at* MR. CARPENTIER *strangely.*)

MARTHA (*Raising voice*): I have a story idea . . . it's about this great dark mass of dough . . .

BILL: Yeah . . like a great rotten ham that strange rumbling and bubbling noises come out of . . .

SUE: And it stinks something awful!

LENARD: Like horseshit!

MISS MOSKOWITZ: Oh, my.

MR. JONES: Class! Class!

MR. CARPENTIER (*Oblivious*): The new technology doesn't allow for the weak tyranny of human attitudes.

MR. JONES: You are wrong, terribly wrong.

MR. CARPENTIER: This is the age of the new intellectual assisted by his tool, the machine, I'll have you know!

MR. JONES (*Furious*): Carpentier! . . . That is what we are here in this classroom to fight against . . . we are here to discover, to awaken, to search out human values through art!

MR. CARPENTIER: Nonsense! Nonsense! Pure nonsense! All you pseudo-artistic types and humanists say the same things when confronted by truth.

(*Prophetically*)

This is an age of tele-symbology . . . phallic in nature, oral in appearance.

MR. JONES: Wha' . . . I don't believe I follow you. Are you serious, man?

MR. CARPENTIER: I have had more experience with these things so I can say that the only function of cigarettes is to show the cigarette as a symbol of gratification for oral types . . . Tobacco, matches, Zig Zag papers, etc. are all barter items in prison. There you will encounter a higher incident of oral and anal specimens. I admit it is a liberal interpretation, true, but I don't see how any other conclusion can be drawn!

MR. JONES: You are utterly ineducable. I suggest you withdraw from this class, Mr. Carpentier.

MISS MOSKOWITZ: Oh, how terrible.

BILL: Hit the road, Jack.

MR. CARPENTIER: If I must call it to your attention . . . in a tax-supported institution . . . to whom does that institution belong?

LENARD: That won't save you, buddy.

MR. JONES: Enough of this! Are there any more story ideas, class?

MR. CARPENTIER (*Mumbling*): It's councilmatic . . . yes, councilmatic . . .

MISS MOSKOWITZ: My name is Moskowitz and I'd like to try a children's story.

MR. CARPENTIER: Yes, yes, F. G. Peters once sold a story to the Howdie Dowdie people on an adaptation of the *Cherry Orchard* theme . . . and Jamie Judson, a good friend of mine . . .

MR. JONES: Mr. Carpentier . . . please. Allow someone else a chance.

MR. CARPENTIER: Why, all they have to do is speak up, Mr. Jones.

MR. JONES: Maybe so . . . but please let Mrs. Moskowitz . . .

MISS MOSKOWITZ (*Coyly*): That's Miss Moskowitz, Mr. Jones.

MR. JONES: Oh, I'm sorry, Miss Moskowitz.

MISS MOSKOWITZ: That's okay, Mr. Jones . . . Now my story has an historical background.

MR. CARPENTIER: Which reminds me of a story I wrote which had a setting in colonial Boston . . .

LENARD: Not again. Not again, for chrissakes!

MR. CARPENTIER: Christopher Attucks was the major character . . .

SUE: Shhhhhh . . .

BILL: Shut up, fellow!

MR. CARPENTIER (*Ignoring them*): The whole thing was done in jest . . . the historical inaccuracies were most hilarious . . . ha ho ho . . .

MR. JONES: *Mr. Carpentier ! ! !*

(MR. CARPENTIER *grumbles and glowers*)

MISS MOSKOWITZ: Thank you, Mr. Jones.

MR. JONES: That's all right . . . go on, please.

MISS MOSKOWITZ: Yes, now this brother and sister are out in a park and they get separated from their mother and meet a lion escaped from the zoo and make friends with him.

LENARD: And they live happily ever afterwards.

MISS MOSKOWITZ: Why, no, not at all, Lenard. The national guard comes to shoot the lion but the children hide him up a tree.

BILL (*To* SUE): I got the impression that it was a tall tale.

SUE: Not you too?

LENARD: I thought it had a historical background.

MARTHA: Can you convince children that they can easily make friends out of lions and then hide them up trees?

LENARD: I got that it's pretty clear what motivated the lion to climb the tree. If you had a hunting party after you wouldn't . . .

MR. CARPENTIER (*Cutting*): Unless you give the dear lady that liberty . . . you'll end up with merely thous and thees!

MR. JONES: What?

MISS MOSKOWITZ (*Simpering*): Oh, thank you, Mr. Carpentier.

MR. CARPENTIER (*Beau Brummel*): Why, the pleasure is all mine, dear lady.

MR. JONES: Enough of this! Enough of this!

MISS MOSKOWITZ (*Blushing*): Why, Mr. Carpentier . . . how you go on.

MR. CARPENTIER: Not at all, my dear Miss Moskowitz . . .

MISS MOSKOWITZ: Call me Madge.

MR. JONES (*Sarcastic*): I'm sorry to interrupt this . . .

MR. CARPENTIER: A.T. to you . . . A.T. Booker Carpentier at your service.

MR. JONES: . . . This is a college classroom . . . not a French boudoir.

MISS MOSKOWITZ (*To* JONES): Watch your mouth, young man! There's ladies present.

MARTHA (*To* MOSKOWITZ): Don't let that bother you, dearie.

LENARD: What kind of attitude must you establish with this type of story and do you create initial attitudes through mood?

MR. JONES (*Confused*): I beg your pardon?

MR. CARPENTIER (*Answering*): Why, young man, almost from the beginning the central motif should plant the atmosphere of . . .

MR. JONES: Thank you, Mr. Carpentier!

MR. CARPENTIER: But I wasn't . . .

BILL (*Cutting*): To what audience is it addressed?

SUE: Good for you!

MISS MOSKOWITZ: Why, young people, of course. In fact, for children.

MR. CARPENTIER: I hardly would think so!

MARTHA: Oh, what kinda stuff is this?

MISS MOSKOWITZ: Mr. Carpentier . . . I . . .

MR. JONES: Well, at least you're talking about something vaguely dealing with writing. Go on, Mr. Carpentier, try and develop your . . .

MR. CARPENTIER: A question of intellectual levels is being probed here . . . The question is the adult or the child . . . hmm . . . *Robinson Crusoe, Gulliver's Travels, Alice in Wonderland, Animal Farm* can all be read by children, dear lady, but the works have added implication for the adult . . . in a word, they are potent!

MARTHA: You're talking about universality, man, not audience!

MR. CARPENTIER: Do you know the difference?

LENARD (*Challenges* CARPENTIER): What's the definition of audience?

MR. CARPENTIER: Of course, I don't use myself as any type of criteria, but I don't see where that story would appeal to my sophisticated literary tastes, whereas . . .

MR. JONES: Now you are quite off the point, Mr. Carpentier.

BILL: He thinks we should all write like the Marquis de Sade.

SUE: Yeah, bedtime tales for tykes by Sade.

MISS MOSKOWITZ: I think you're trying to place an imposition of the adult world on the child's.

MR. JONES: The important thing is to write the story, class. To write the story!

MR. CARPENTIER: Well, I think that the story was not at all that emphatic . . . it didn't emote . . . it didn't elicit my . . .

MISS MOSKOWITZ (*Confused*): Why didn't it?

MR. CARPENTIER: I don't think the child would have the range of actual patterns for his peer group in this circumstantial instance.

MARTHA: What, man?

LENARD: I got the impression that the protagonists are exemplary.

MR. JONES: Class, do you think this story line aids the writer in performing his functions? . . . The culture has values and the writer's duties are to . . .

MR. CARPENTIER: No, I don't think this story does it!

SUE: Why not?

MR. CARPENTIER: It is fallacious!

MISS MOSKOWITZ: But it's only a child's story, a fantasy, Mr. Carpentier!

MR. JONES: Yes, a child's story . . . for children, man!

MR. CARPENTIER: But it doesn't ring true, dear lady. The only way one can get the naturalistic speech and peer group patterns and mores of children recorded accurately . . .

MR. JONES (*begins a string of "Oh God's" rising in volume until* MR. CARPENTIER *finishes his speech*): Oh God, Oh, God, *Oh, God, Oh, God*, OH, GOD!

MR. CARPENTIER: . . . is to scientifically eavesdrop on their peer group with electronic listening devices and get the actual evidence for any realistic fictionalizing one wishes to achieve.

MR. JONES (*Scream*): NO! ! !

MR. CARPENTIER (*Query*): No?

MR. JONES (*In a tired voice*): Thomas Wolfe once said .

MR. CARPENTIER (*Ridicule*): Thomas Wolfe!

MR. JONES: "I believe that we are lost here in America, but I believe we shall be found." . . . Mr. Carpentier . . . let's hope that we Black Americans can first find ourselves and perhaps be equal to the task . . . the burdensome and sometimes evil task, by the way . . . that being an American calls for in these days.

MR. CARPENTIER: Sir, I object!

MR. JONES: Does not the writer have some type of obligation to remove some of the intellectual as well as political, moral and social tyranny that infects this culture? What does all the large words in creation serve you, my Black brother, if you are a complete whitewashed man?

MR. CARPENTIER: Sir, I am not black nor your brother . . . There is a school of thought that is diametrically opposed to you and your black chauvinism . . . You preach bigotry, black nationalism, and fascism! . . . The idea . . . black brother . . . intellectual barbarism! . . . Your statements should be reported to the school board—as well as your permitting smoking in your classroom.

SUE: Shut up, you Uncle Tom bastard!

BILL (*Pulls her back*): That's for me to do, not you, lady!

MR. JONES: Four hundred years. . . . Four hundred . . .

LENARD: We'll picket any attempt to have Mr. Jones removed!

MARTHA (*Disgust*): This is adult education?

MISS MOSKOWITZ (*To* MR. CARPENTIER): I bet George Bernard Shaw would have some answers for you!

MR. CARPENTIER: Of course when examining G. B. Shaw you will discover he is advancing Fabian Socialism.

BILL: Who would picket a vacuum?

LENARD: Your levity escapes me.

SUE: Your what, junior?

MR. JONES: Let's try and go on, class. If you'll . . .

MR. CARPENTIER (*To* MISS MOSKOWITZ): Your story just isn't professional, miss. It doesn't follow the Hitchcock formula . . it just doesn't follow . . .

MISS MOSKOWITZ: Do you really think so?

MR. JONES: Somehow, I do not believe that you are quite real, Mr. Carpentier.

LENARD (*To* MR. CARPENTIER): Have you read *The Invisible Man*?

BILL: Are you kidding?

MR. CARPENTIER: Socio Drama will be the new breakthrough in the theatrical-literary community.

MR. JONES: Oh, Lord . . . not again. This is madness.

MR. CARPENTIER: Combined with the social psychologist's case study, and the daily experiences of some habitant of a socio-economically depressed area, is the genius of the intellectual and artistic craftsman.

MR. JONES: Madness!

MISS MOSKOWITZ: Socio Drama . . . how thrilling.

MR. JONES: Don't listen to him, class . . . I'm the teacher, understand?

MR. CARPENTIER: Yes, yes . . . let me tell you a not quite unique but nevertheless interesting phenomenon . .

MR. JONES: Now we know that there is realism, and naturalism and surrealism . . .

MR. CARPENTIER: . . . an extremely interesting phenomenon . . . adolescent necrophilia!

MARTHA: Oh, shit!

MR. JONES: I have a degree. . . . I've written a book. . . . Please don't listen . . .

MISS MOSKOWITZ: It sounds fascinating, Mr. Carpentier.

MR. CARPENTIER: Yes, tramps will freeze to death and kids, children, will punch holes in the corpses . . .

LENARD: Isn't that reaching rather far just to prove that truth is stranger than fiction?

SUE: I have a story about crud and filth and disease . . .

MR. JONES: And stupidity and ignorance and vulgarity and despair . . .

MR. CARPENTIER: I go back to my original point . . . I go back to necrophilia!

BILL: And loneliness . . . and emptiness . . . and death.

MR. CARPENTIER: Cadavers! Cadavers! Yes, I come back to that! . . . Those findings could almost be case studies of true cases, they are so true in themselves, and that's where the real truth lies . . . Verily, social case histories of social psychologists . . .

MISS MOSKOWITZ (*Enraptured*): Never . . . never in all my experience has a class aroused such passionate response in my life!

LENARD: I don't believe it!

MR. JONES: But I have read Faulkner in his entirety . . .

MR. CARPENTIER: These people in New York, Philadelphia, Boston, Chicago, San Francisco . . . and places like that . . .

MR. JONES: I cut my teeth on Hemingway . . .

MR. CARPENTIER: . . . they just get drunk and die in the streets . . .

MR. JONES: *Leaves of Grass* is my Bible . . . and Emily Dickinson . . .

MR. CARPENTIER: . . . and then they are prone to suffer adolescent and urchin necrophilia!

MR. JONES (*Frustrated*): . . . Emily Dickinson has always been on my shelf beside *Mother Goose*.

MR. CARPENTIER: It's curiosity . . . not a sickness . . . curiosity!

MR. JONES: I don't want much . . . just to learn the meaning of life.

MARTHA: Will you discover it here, Ray?

LENARD: But how can anybody be so sure?

MR. CARPENTIER (*Offhand*): We happen to own some mortuaries . . . my family, that is . . . and it is our experience that children will disarrange a corpse . . . and if we don't watch them closely . . .

MR. JONES: Booker T. Washington walked barefooted to school! Think of that! Barefooted!

MR. CARPENTIER: Once as a case study in experimental methods I placed a microphone in a cadaver and gave some juvenile necrophilics unwitting access to my tramp.

(JONES *almost doubles over and clutches his stomach; his hands and feet twitch*)

MR. JONES: I'd like to adjourn class early tonight . . . will everyone please go home?

MR. CARPENTIER: What I'm saying is this . . . with our present cybernetic generation it is psycho-politically relevant to engage our socio-philosophical existence on a quanitatum scale which is, of course, pertinent to the outer-motivated migration of our inner-oriented social compact. Yes! Yes, indeed, I might add. A most visionary prognosis, as it were, but . . . ha ho ho . . . but we pioneers must look over our bifocals, I always say . . . ha ha ha . . . giving me added insight to perceive the political exiguousness of our true concomitant predicament. True, preclinical preconsciousness gives indication that our trivialization is vulva, but, owing to the press of the press our avowed aims are maleficent! True! Yes, true! And we are becoming more so. In areas of negative seeming communications probing our error factors are quite negligible. . . . For instance . . . Senator Dodd getting a pension for someone who has gotten abducted and initiated at a Ku Klux meeting . . . well . . . It's poesy! . . . Monochromatic!

LENARD: What's our assignment for next week, Mr. Jones?

MISS MOSKOWITZ: I have something to show you, Mr. Jones.

MARTHA: Are you okay, Mr. Jones?

MR. JONES: Ray . . . just Ray . . . okay?

SUE: Do you have office hours, Mr. Ray?

MR. JONES: I just want everybody to go home now and think about what has happened tonight . . . and if you want to be writers after this then please don't come back to this class.

I've just published an unsuccessful novel, as you know, and I thought I'd teach a while and finish my second one and eat a bit . . . But I think I'd rather not, eat well, that is, so you won't see me next week but if any of you'd like a good steady job I could recommend you . . .

MR. JONES: Reading is the answer. It must be . . . cultivating the sensibilities . . . Plato. . . . Aristotle. . . . Homer. . . . Descartes. . . . and Jones . . . I've always wanted to carry the Jones banner high.

BILL (*To Sue*): Hey, I've got some pretty good grass that just came in from Mexico.

SUE: Yeah? You have, huh?

BILL: It's at my pad . . . would you like to stop by?

SUE: How far?

BILL: A couple of blocks.

SUE: Okay. It might be interesting.

MR. CARPENTIER (*To a student*): Ubiquitous! A form of reference which exposes . . .

(BILL *and* SUE *exit. Students begin filing out.* MARTHA *walks over to* MR. JONES, *though the other students are gathered about* MR. CARPENTIER)

MARTHA: You look tired, Ray.

MR. JONES: Yeah . . . yeah . . . I've been reading a lot. The classics are consuming.

MARTHA: Yes, I've heard. Why don't we stop by my place and I'll fix drinks and you can relax . . .

MR. JONES: Okay . . . okay . . . but my ulcer's bothering me . . . Mind if I drink milk?

MARTHA: It's not my stomach.

(*She helps him off*)

MR. CARPENTIER: Who's that French poet . . . Balu . . .

LENARD: Bouvier?

MR. CARPENTIER: . . . Bali . . . Blau? . . .

(MISS MOSKOWITZ *shows* MR. CARPENTIER *a bound manuscript as he deposits his own in his briefcase*)

MISS MOSKOWITZ: Will you please look at my few labors of love when you find time, Mr. Carpentier?

(*He shoves it in the case beside his own*)

LENARD (*Gathering his books*): Mr. Carpentier?

MR. CARPENTIER (*Snapping clasps on his briefcase*): Yes, Lenard.

LENARD (*Pushing himself between* CARPENTIER *and other students*): What weight does language have on the contemporary prevalence to act in existential terms?

MR. CARPENTIER (*Leads them off*): When the writer named the crow "Caw Caw" it was onomatopoeia in practice, of course . . . but too it became the Egyptian symbol of death.

LENARD: The crow.

(MISS MOSKOWITZ *giggles.*
They all exit crowing: "Caw caw caw caw caw . . .")

BLACKNESS

Madheart

■ LeRoi Jones

A MORALITY PLAY

Characters

BLACK MAN (*late twenties, early thirties*)
BLACK WOMAN (*twenties, with soft natural hair, caught up in gaylay*)
MOTHER (*Black woman in fifties, business suit, red wig, tipsy*)
SISTER (*Black woman in twenties, mod style clothes, blonde wig*)
DEVIL LADY (*Female with elaborately carved white devil mask*)

DEVIL LADY: You need pain. (*coming out of shadows with neon torch, honky-tonk calliope music*) You need pain, ol nigger devil, pure pain, to clarify your desire.

BLACK MAN (*turns slowly to look at her, raises his arms, straight out, parallel to the floor, then swiftly above his head, then wide open in the traditional gesture of peace*): God is not the devil. Rain is not fire nor snow, or old women dying in hallways.

DEVIL LADY: There is peace.

BLACK MAN: There is no peace.

DEVIL LADY: There is beauty.

BLACK MAN: None that you would know about.

DEVIL LADY: There is horror.

BLACK MAN: There is horror. There is . . . (*pause, as if to cry or precipitate a rush of words which does not come*) only horror. Only stupidity. (*rising to point at her*) Your stale pussy weeps paper roses.

DEVIL LADY: And horror.

BLACK MAN: Why aren't you dead? Why aren't you a deader thing than nothing is?

DEVIL LADY: I am dead and can never die.

BLACK MAN: You will die only when I kill you. I raise my hand to strike. (*pulling out sword*) I raise my hand to strike. Strike. Strike. (*waving the sword, and leaping great leap*) Bitch devil in the whistling bowels of the wind. Blind snow creature.

A fanfare of drums. Loud, dissonant horns. The action freezes. The lights dim slowly, on the frozen scene. The ACTORS *fixed. The music rises. Lights are completely off. Then a flash. On. On. Off. Off. As if it was an SOS signal. Then the music changes, to a slow insinuating, nasty blues. Rock. Rock. Voices offstage begin to pick up the beat, and raise it to falsetto howl. Scream in the sensual moan.*

VOICES: Rock. Rock. Love. Me. Love. Me. Rock. Heaven. Heaven. Ecstasy. Ecstasy. Ooooahhhhummmmah-ah-ahoooooh. Let Love. Let Rock. Let Heaven. All love. All love, like rock . . .

Lights go up full. Silence. The action continues. The actors, from the freeze, come to life, but never repeat this initial action; as if in slow motion

BLACK MAN: Hear that?? Hear those wild cries. Souls on fire. Fire. Floods of flame. Hear that. Ol humanless bitch. Dead judge.
DEVIL LADY: I am the judge. I am the judge. (*She squats like old Chinese*) The judge. (*rolls on her back, with skirt raised, to show a cardboard image of Christ pasted over her pussy space. A cross in the background.*) My pussy rules the world thru newspapers. My pussy radiates the great heat. (*She rolls back and forth on the floor panting.*)
BLACK MAN: The great silence. Serenades of brutal snow. You got a cave, lady?
VOICES: Blood. Snow. Dark cold cave. Illusion. Promises. Hatred and Death. Snow. Death. Cold. Waves. Night. Dead white. Sunless. Moonless. Forever. Always. Iceberg Christians, pee in the ocean. Help us. We move. (*music again, over all, the high beautiful falsetto of a fag. The traditional love song completely taking over*)

BLACK
(*Lights up, the* WHITE WOMAN *lies in the middle of the stage with a spear, or many arrows stuck in her stomach and hole. As the lights come up, the singing subsides to a low hum.* THREE BLACK WOMEN *enter slowly* (MOTHER, SISTER, WOMAN), *humming now softly.*
The BLACK MAN *is standing just a few feet away from the skewered* WHITE WOMAN. HE *is gesturing with his hands, at the prone figure, like* HE *is conjuring or hypnotizing.*)

BLACK MAN: You will always and forever, be dead, and be dead, and always you will be the spirit of deadness, or the cold stones of its promise. (*He takes up a huge wooden stake and drives it suddenly into her heart, with a loud thud as it penetrates the body, and crashes deep in the floor.*) Beautiful. (*preoccupied and still unaware of the* BLACK WOMEN) Beautiful. (*He makes to repeat his act, and one of the women speaks*)
MOTHER: No. Mad man. Stop!
SISTER: She is old and knows. Her wisdom inherits the earth. (*stepping forward suddenly at* DEVIL LADY) I love you. I love the woman in my sleep. I cannot love death.
WOMAN: Perhaps we are intruding. (*The two women turn and stare at her, and form a quick back-off circle to point at her casually and turn their heads. The* WOMAN's *head is wrapped in a modest headrag, and her natural hair cushions her face in a soft remark. Pointing*) You want the whole thing.
BLACK MOTHER: You want the whole thing, baby. (*advancing*) The earth, the sky.
BLACK SISTER: You must leave what the womb leaves. The possibility of all creation.
BLACK MAN: The dead do not sing. Except through the sawdust lips of

science fiction jigaboos, who were born, and disappeared, in a puff
of silence at the foot of the Woolworth heir's cement condom.

DEVIL LADY (*from the floor, moaning through her teeth, from beyond
the grave. Let there be music, and setting, to indicate that these words
come from behind the veil.*): OOOOOOOOAHHHHHHHH . . . My
pussy throbs above the oceans, forcing weather into the world.

BLACK MAN: The cold.

BLACK MOTHER: The light and promise. (*from an ecstatic pose, suddenly
turns into a barker, selling young black ass*) Uhyehhh. Eh? Step right
up. Get your free ass. (*starts moving wiggle—suggestively*) Come on,
fellahs—

BLACK SISTER: And free enterprise.

DEVIL LADY: Enter the prize. And I am the prize. And I am dead. And
all my life is me. Flowing from my vast whole, entire civilizations.

BLACK WOMAN (*almost inadvertently*): That smell. I knew I'd caught
it before.

BLACK MAN: Broom sticks thrust up there return embossed with zombie
gold.

BLACK MOTHER: Out of the bowels of the sun. I slap around drunk up
Lenox. Stumble down 125th into the poet who frowns at me, lost in
my ways. You'd think that ol nigger was worth something.

BLACK SISTER (*dazed*): It's just . . . just . . . (*staggers toward the dead
WOMAN*) . . . that I wanted to be something like her, that's all.
(*weeps but tries to hold it*)

WOMAN: Yet she be a stone beast, ladies! A stone ugly pagan. Israelites
measure your beauty by what the filthy bitch looks like, lying around
an old sore.

BLACK MAN: An old punctured sore with the pus rolled out.

SISTER (*falling to her knees. Screams.*): Aiiiieeeee . . . it could be me,
that figure on the floor. It could be me, and backward out of the newspaper dreams of my American life. Out of the television enemas
poured through my eyes out of my mouth onto the floor of everybody's
life. I hate so. I am in love with my hatred. Yet I worship this beast
on the floor, because—

BLACK WOMAN: Because you have been taught to love her by background
music of sentimental movies. A woman's mind must be stronger than
that.

BLACK MAN: A black woman. (*throws his hands above his head*) A black
woman! Wouldn't that be something?

(*The dead* WHITE WOMAN's *body wiggles in a shudder and releases,
dead.*)

WOMAN (*Her voice goes up to high long sustained note.*): I am black
and am the most beautiful thing on the planet. Touch me if you
dare. I am your soul.

MOTHER: What is wrong with the niggers, this time? I'm old and I hump
along under my wig. I'm dying of oldness. I'm dying of the weight.
The air is so heavy. (*taken by more somber mood*) And dying all the

time. Diseased. Broken. Sucking air from dirty places. Your mother. Shit filthiness. In a cheap mink. In a frozen roach funeral.

SISTER: Brazen bitch. You trying to steal my shit?

MOTHER: Make for the exit, child, before you bleed on somebody. (*They begin to have at each other. Breathing hard and cursing. The* BLACK WOMAN *backs away, hands at her mouth, terrified.*)

WOMAN (*Coming close to the* MAN, *as the* WOMEN *begin to fight in aggravated pantomimed silence. Clock gongs away, maybe fifty times. Slow sudden insinuating drums, and brushes. The* TWO WOMEN *fighting clutch each other and fight more stiffly, finally subsiding into a frozen posture.*): What do you want, black man? What can I give you? (*in a calm loving voice*) Is there a heart bigger than mine? Is there any flesh sweeter, any lips fatter and redder, any thighs more full of orgasms?

BLACK MAN (*leaning toward her*): Sweet pleasure. (*he touches her arm.*)

DEVIL LADY (*beginning to moan on the floor*): Oooooooooooooooaaaaaa-aaaa. My white pussy is beating the air. My navel is raw and ready to be attached. I come back from the dead 'cause I wanna.

BLACK MAN: Oh, bullshit. Go back, for christsakes.

WOMAN: Christ was a pagan. A stumble bum in the Swedish baths of philosophy. (*The* TWO WOMEN *struggle suddenly on the floor. With violence and slobbering*)

TWO WOMEN: Fuckingbitch Fuckingbitch Fuckingbitch Fuckingbitch Fuckingbitch Fuckingbitch Fuckingbitch Fuckingbitch Fuckingbitch Fuckingbitch Fuckingbitch—

WOMAN: Thing on the floor, be still. I'm tired of your ignorant shamble. Let me be alone in the world with women and men, and your kind be still in the grave where you have fun. (DEVIL LADY *screams with throbbing thighs.* MOTHER *and* SISTER *begin crawling across the floor to the* DEVIL LADY. *She writhes and stiffens in death. The* MOTHER *whimpers, the* SISTER *gags, and weeps and whines.*)

SISTER: My dead sister reflection. Television music. Soft lights and soft living among the buildings.

WOMAN: She went for luxury.

BLACK MAN: I used to see her in white discotheque boots and sailor pants. (*pointing to the crawling women*) This is the nightmare in all of our hearts. Our mothers and sisters groveling to white women, wanting to be white women, dead and hardly breathing on the floor. Look at our women dirtying themselves. (*runs and grabs wig off of* SISTER's *head*) Take off filth. (*He throws it onto the dead* WOMAN's *body.*) Take your animal fur, heathen. (*laughs*) Heathen. Heathen. I've made a new meaning. Let the audience think about themselves, and about their lives when they leave this happening. This black world of purest possibility. (*laughs*) All our lives we want to be alive. We scream for life.

WOMAN: Be alive, black man. Be alive, for me. For me, black man. (*kisses him*) And love me. Love, Me.

BLACK MAN: Women assemble around me. I'm gonna sing for you now, in my cool inimitable style. About my life. About my road, and where it's taking me now. Assemble, sweet black ladies, ignorant or true, and let me run down the game of life.

WOMAN: Get up, you other women, and listen to your man. This is no fattening insurance nigger graying around the temples. This is the soulforce of our day to day happening universe. A man.

SISTER: A man. Dammit. Dance. (*change*) Men. What do they do? Hang out. Niggermen. If I have to have a niggerman, give me a faggot, anyday.

MOTHER (*laughing high voice and sweeping her hand*): Oh, chil', I know the kind you mean. Uhh, so sweet. I tell you. But . . . a white boy's better, daughter. Don't you forget it. Just as sof' and sweet as a pimple. (*spies* BLACK WOMAN *still standing separate and looking confused, hands covering her ears*) Haha . . . (*hunching or trying to hunch* SISTER) Haaha, will you look at that simple bitch. My lan', chil', why don't you straighten up and get in the world?

SISTER: Yeh, Desideria, why don't you make up your mind?

BLACK MAN: What is this? (*To* BLACK WOMAN) What's all this mouth mouth action? Why don't these women act like women should? Why don't they act like Black Women? All this silly rapping and screaming on the floor. I should turn them over to the Black Arts and get their heads relined.

WOMAN: They've been tricked and gestured over. They hypnotized, that's all. White magic.

BLACK MAN: White Magic. Yes. (*raising his stake, suddenly*) Maybe this dead thing's fumes are sickening the air. I'll make sure it's dead. (*he strikes*)

SISTER (*screams as* BLACK MAN *stabs the* DEVIL LADY. *Grabs her heart as if the* MAN *had struck her.*): Oh, God, you've killed me, Nigger.

BLACK MAN: What? (*wheels to look at her*)

WOMAN: You're killed if you are made in the dead thing's image, if the dead thing on the floor has your flesh, and your soul. If you are a cancerous growth. Sad thing.

SISTER: I'm killed and in horrible agony, and my own brother did it. (*staggering around stage. Finally falls in great overdramatic climax*) My own bro . . . ther. (*falls*)

BLACK MAN: Oh, God! (*rushes over to her*) Is this child my sister?

WOMAN: No, get away from her. She is befouled.

BLACK MAN: But my own sister . . . I've killed her.

WOMAN: She's not even dead. She just thinks she has to die because that white woman died. She's sick.

BLACK MAN (*stands over* SISTER, *pondering what the* WOMAN *has said*): Hmmmmmm.

MOTHER: You've killed her. You've killed my baby. (*rushes over to* MAN *and starts beating him on the chest. She's weeping, loud and disconsolately.*) You've killed my own sweet innocent girl. My own sweet innocent girl . . . she never had a chance. She could'a been somebody.

WOMAN: Woman, you're crazy.

BLACK MAN: I killed my sister. (*mumbling*)

MOTHER: No, I'm not the crazy one. You are all crazy. Stuntin' like this. All that make believe. And you ki—led your own flesh. And this ol nappy head bitch agitated the whole shit. (*weeps*) My baby, she never had a chance. She never even got a chance to be nobody. Oh, God, why's my life so fucked up? And you, man, you killed your own sister. I hope that shit you talk's enough to satisfy you. Or that nappy head bitch.

WOMAN: Why don't you find out something before you show how long ignorance can claim a body? An old woman like you should be wise . . . but you not wise worth a mustard seed.

MOTHER: You talk to me with respect, whore . . . or I'll—(*threatening gesture*)

WOMAN: What? Or you'll beat me with your wig? You're streaked like the devil. And that pitiful daughter of yours is not even dead. But she'll act dead as long as she licks on that Devil Woman.

BLACK MAN: My mother, my sister, both . . . like television dollbabies, doing they ugly thing. To mean then, me, and what they have for me, what I be then, in spite my singing, and song, to stand there, or lay there, like they be, with the horizon blowing both ways, to change, God damn . . . and be a weight around my neck . . . a weight . . .

MOTHER: Well, leave us alone, murderer . . . punk ass murderer. Gimme a drink an' shut up. And drag that whore's mouth shut, too.

WOMAN: You shut up. And get back in your dead corner with the other rotting meat.

BLACK MAN: I've killed my sister. And now watch my mother defiled, thrown in a corner.

WOMAN: If she was your mother, she'd be black like you. She'd come at you to talk to you, about old south, and ladies under trees, and the soft wet kiss of her own love, how it made you fight through sperm to arrive on this planet whole . . . (*soft laugh*) . . . and beautiful.

BLACK MAN: Who're you . . . to talk so much . . . and to stand apart from this other jive? The lousy score's two to one, diddybops! (MOTHER *starts singing a sad dirge for the daughter, trailing around the body, throwing kisses at the still figures . . .*)

MOTHER: Yohoooooo, Yohoooooo, daw daw daw daw daw daw daw yodaw hoooodaw deee. All the beauty we missed. All the cool shit. All the sad drinking in crummy bars we missed. All the crissmating and crossbreeding and holy jive in the cellars and closets. The cool flirts in the ladies' meeting. The meeting of the ex-wives. All the Belafontes and Poitiers and hid unfamous nigger formers, hip still on their lawns, and corn and wine, and tippy drinks with green stuff with cherries and white cats and titles, all the television stuff, and tapdances, and the soft music, and stuff. All of it gone. Dead child, save me, or take me . . . (*She bows, kisses the two bodies.*) . . . or save me, take me with you . . . Daw daw doooodaw daw ding ding daw do do dooon . . . (*She trails sadly around the bodies.*)

BLACK MAN: This is horrible. Look at this.

WOMAN: It's what the devil's made. You know that. Why don't you stop

pretending the world's a dream or puzzle. I'm real and whole . . .
(*holds out her arms*) And yours, only, yours, but only as a man will
you know that.

BLACK MAN: You are . . .

WOMAN: I'm the black woman. The one who disappeared. The sleep-
walker. The one who runs through your dreams with your life and
your seed. I am the black woman. The one you need. You know this.
Now you must discover a way to get me back, Black Man. You and
you alone, must get me. Or you'll never . . . Lord . . . be a man. My
man. Never know your own life needs. You'll walk around white ladies
breathing their stink, and lose your seed, your future to them.

BLACK MAN: I'll get you back. If I need to.

WOMAN (*laughs*): You need to, baby . . . just look around you. You better
get me back, if you know what's good for you . . . you better.

BLACK MAN (*Looking around at her squarely, he advances*): I better?
. . . (*a soft laugh*) Yes. Now is where we always are . . . that now
. . . (*he wheels and suddenly slaps her crosswise, back and forth across
the face.*)

WOMAN: Wha??? What . . . oh love . . . please . . . don't hit me. (*He
hits her, slaps her again.*)

BLACK MAN: I want you woman, as a woman. Go down. (*He slaps again*)
Go down, submit, submit . . . to love . . . and to man, now, forever.

WOMAN (*weeping, turning her head from side to side*): Please don't hit
me . . . please . . . (*She bends.*) The years are so long, without you,
man, I've waited . . . waited for you . . .

BLACK MAN: And I've waited.

WOMAN: I've seen you humbled, black man, seen you crawl for dogs
and devils.

BLACK MAN: And I've seen you raped by savages and beasts, and bear
bleach-shit children of apes.

WOMAN: You permitted it . . . you could . . . do nothing.

BLACK MAN: But now I can (*He slaps her . . . drags her to him, kissing
her deeply on the lips.*) That shit is ended, woman, you with me, and
the world is mine.

WOMAN: I . . . oh love, please stay with me . . .

BLACK MAN: Submit, for love.

WOMAN: I . . . submit. (*she goes down, weeping*) I submit . . . for
love . . . please love. (*The MAN sinks to his knees and embraces her,
draws her with him up again. They both begin to cry and then laugh,
laugh, wildly at everything and themselves.*)

BLACK MAN: You are my woman, now, forever. Black woman.

WOMAN: I am your woman, and you are the strongest of God. Fill me
with your seed. (*They embrace. MOTHER is now crawling around on
her knees*)

MOTHER: Tony Bennett, help us please. Beethoven, Peter Gunn . . . deliver us in our sterling silver headdress . . . oh please deliver us.

BLACK MAN: This is enough of this stuff. Get up, supposed-to-be-mother,
and drag that supposed-to-be-sister up, too. This stuff is over and
done. Get up or so help me, you die with the dead bitch you worship.

MOTHER: What I care? Batman won't love me without my yellowhead daughter. I'm too old for him or Robin. I can't paint soupcans, the junk I find is just junk, my babies stick in they eyes, I'm sick in the big world, and white shit zooms without me. I'm a good fuck and an intelligent woman . . . frankly . . . frankly . . . (*laughs. Turns to look at the* MAN) Fuck both of you stupid ass niggers . . . you'll never get no light . . . Daughter . . . Daughter . . . put on your wig and wake up dancing. The old Italian wants you to marry him.

BLACK MAN: Why won't these women listen? Why do they want to die?

WOMAN: The white one's fumes strangle their senses. The thing's not dead.

BLACK MAN: I've killed it. And death must come to the thing. I'll do it again. (*shouts*) Die, you bitch, and drag your mozarts into your nasty hole. Your mozarts stravinskys stupid white sculpture corny paintings deathfiddles, all your crawling jive, drag it in and down with you, your officebuildings blowup in your pussy, newspapers poison gasses congolene brain stragglers devising ways to deal death to their people, your smiles, your logic, your brain, your intellectual death, go to a dead planet in some metal bullshit, dissolve, disappear, leave your address in the volcano, and turn into the horrible insects of a new planet . . . but leave. I am the new man of the earth, I command you . . . Command bullshit. (*He runs over and stomps the dead* WHITE WOMAN *in her face.*) This kinda command. (*He drags her over to the edge of the stage, and drops her off.*) Into the pit of deadchange, slide bitch slide. (*Smoke and light shoot up where she lands.*)

WOMAN: Yes. Yes . . .

MOTHER: You fool. You crazy thing . . . get out of here.

WOMAN: Why don't you listen . . . or die, old hag!

BLACK MAN (*grabs* MOTHER *by the arm, drags her over to the edge*): Look down in there, smell those fumes. That's ashy death, bitchmother, stinking filthy death. That's what you'll be. Smell it. Look at it!

MOTHER: You fool, you mess with the gods, and shit will belt you.

WOMAN: Listen, old woman, this is a man speaking, a black man. (MAN *shakes the* MOTHER *violently*).

BLACK MAN: Yes, you listen.

MOTHER: No, no . . . (*She pulls away . . . goes to* SISTER *who's now starting to turn over, fan and shake herself*) Get away . . . you've killed my daughter . . . you . . . what, she's still breathing??

WOMAN: I told you she was . . . "sick actress from Broome Street."

MOTHER: Oh, daughter . . . the Italian called you jest a while ago. Get up, pussycat, mama's worried so about you. You hungry? (*She pulls out a box lunch from her brassiere.*) You must be starved.

SISTER (*wakes up, looks around, senses the* DEVIL WOMAN *is missing, dead*): Where . . . where's she . . . ooh . . . Where's my body . . . my beautiful self? Where? What'd you do, you black niggers? What'd you do to me? Where'd you hide me? Where's my body? My beautiful perfumed hole?

MOTHER: The hairy nigger killed you, daughter, dropped you in a . . . pit.

SISTER: What! OOOOOOOOOO . . . (*horrible shriek*) OOOOOOOOOO . . .

here . . . OOOOO . . . (*runs toward* BLACK MAN) You beast bastard . . . OOOOOOOO . . . Where'd you stick my body . . .

(MAN *grabs her and tosses her to the floor,* MOTHER *goes over to comfort her*)

MOTHER: Oh, please, pussycat . . . ain't you hungry a little bit? I saved some dinner for you. Eat something, pussycat, baby, don't aggravate yourself. You'll ruin your complexion. Don't let these niggers upset you.

SISTER: Oh, God, I know . . . he's killed me. He's dropped me in that pit. (*weeps unconsolably*)

WOMAN: Bitchfool.

SISTER: You jealous 'cause you ain't blonde like me, nigger. You shut up and get outta here with that nigger . . . You get outta here . . . get outta here. So help me I'll kill you . . . get outta here, get outta here, get outta here . . . (*screams, turns into mad raving creature, runs, puts wig back on head, pulls it down over her eyes, runs around stage screaming,* MOTHER *chasing her, trying to feed her from the box*)

MOTHER: Please . . . oh, please, baby . . . jest a little bit a greens, they's flavored with knuckles . . . oh, pussycat, please, you'll be alive agin . . . that nigger can't stop you . . . pussycat . . .

BLACK MAN (*Stunned, staring, tears coming to his eyes, the* WOMAN *comes to comfort him.*): What can I do . . .

WOMAN: Baby, baby . . .

BLACK MAN: My mother . . . and sister . . . crazy white things slobbering . . . God help me.

WOMAN: Oh, baby, you can't help it . . . you just can't help it.

(*The two women finally fall in the middle of the stage, holding each other, the older* WOMAN *feeding the* SISTER, *with a spoon, out of a small pot, some collard greens. The* SISTER *still sobs.*)

SISTER: OOOOOHhhhhhh God, God help me . . .

BLACK MAN: But this can't go, this stuff can't go. They'll die or help us, be black or white and dead. I'll save them or kill them. That's all. But not this shit . . . not this . . . horrible shit. (MAN *runs over and gets firehose, brings it back and turns it on the two women*) Now, let's start again, women. Let's start again. We'll see what you get . . . life . . . or death . . . we'll see . . . (*He sprays them and they struggle until they fall out. Then the* MAN *and* WOMAN *stand over the two on the floor.*)

WOMAN: You think there's any chance for them?? You really think so??

BLACK MAN: They're my flesh. I'll do what I can. (*looks at her*) We'll both try. All of us, black people.

                                                                    Curtain

from The Rhythm of Violence

■ Lewis Nkosi (South Africa)

An interracial group of left-wing students in Johannesburg carouse nervously at a party in the basement apartment building belonging to Mary, an English student, awaiting the midnight detonation of a bomb that they have planted in the City Hall, filled with Afrikaaners, one of whom is the father of Sarie who knows nothing of the plot. The following is from Act 1.

Scene IV

Same as before. This time the young people can be seen milling around in the back room, drinking coffee. The party is nearing an end. Before the action begins, there is a harsh throb of jazz, much more insistent than previously, with jarring rude phrases constantly being interpolated in the continuous rhythm. When the music subsides, TULA and SARIE emerge through the panel door from the back room, carrying their mugs of coffee. They sit gingerly in the foreground of the stage. There is noticeably more warmth, a greater ease, between the two. When the light picks out their faces, they seem to be glowing with an innocent, youthful gravity and concern for each other.

SARIE: Now it seems that coming here was the most important thing I have done in a long, long while.

TULA: You can't imagine how glad I am you came.

SARIE: All night we seem to have done nothing but talk and talk, and yet, somehow, I seem to have discovered something important and vital. I can't explain it to you.

TULA: I know how you feel because this is exactly how I feel. It's like stumbling upon something precious, something you want to keep. I suppose the pain of discovery is the fear of losing.

SARIE: We can't be losers, because we care, and caring breeds regard; and now that I know something of your affection, even the political problem seems less heavy, less frightful.

TULA: I'm frightened, though. Precisely because I care. There seems to be no way of preserving the important things when history grinds on its course, and yet one wants to preserve the things that one has affection for.

SARIE: There must be a way of redirecting history to avoid tragedy, provided there is enough love. I am a woman, so my optimism is boundless. I don't feel despondent. I used to, but now that I know there must be many people who feel like you on your side, I think I feel more strengthened.

TULA: You know it's very important that I see you again soon; I'm even ashamed to admit it.

SARIE: Oh, please don't . . . because you make me feel important. I just wish that it were not so difficult with all the laws controlling our lives.

TULA: Maybe we can meet for lunch at the university canteen from time to time and talk.

SARIE: Maybe we can too!

TULA: You don't mind if we do have lunch together sometimes?

SARIE: Why I would love to. I don't care what they think.

TULA: It doesn't have to be often.

SARIE: We can meet as often as it is reasonable. Anyway, I always have lunch mostly with people who don't interest me in the least. I'd love to have lunch with you. There's so much to talk about! May I take your cup?

TULA: No, no. I'll take them in for you. (*They both get up.*)

SARIE: That's all right! I'll take them in. (*She goes away with the cups.*) I'll be right back.

TULA *paces the floor. Although his face still retains something of its usual gravity, it is now touched by a dreamy quality. We hear a few bars of soft, fragile melody. The music is interrupted by* JULIE's *voice from the back room.*

JULIE: So I say to him, Carmine, if there's one thing I can't stand, it's a boy who remains uncommitted in this country, in spite of the grave problems. There's absolutely no excuse for cowardice or indifference!

SARIE *makes her appearance again immediately after this short speech. She and* TULA *move quickly toward each other, and spontaneously* TULA *takes* SARIE's *hand.*

TULA: Won't your father be wondering where you are tonight?

SARIE: He won't be back until very late. He's gone to the Party rally.

TULA: Oh, I see . . . (*Too abruptly.*) Where did you say?

SARIE: At the National Party rally.

TULA (*manifestly agitated*): You mean at the City Hall?

SARIE: Yes . . . (*Looking at his face, which he is trying to keep averted.*) What's the matter, Tula? I hope you don't hold that against me. Do you?

TULA: Oh, no. No! You can't understand! You can't know what it means!

SARIE (*alarmed*). What do you mean? It can't be that important to us, what my father does!

TULA: No. I don't mean that at all. (*He makes to move away.*)

SARIE: Wait! And you know what, Tula? He's gone to tender his resignation to the Party. It's a great night for him! That is something, Tula. He may be no Liberal, but at least he is making a break with the Government régime. You can't imagine what a great step it is for him. He's been nervous all day long. I could see it the way he walked about the house! I could see it the way he stared absent-mindedly at things! Twice I asked him something, and he kept saying, yes, yes, although he wasn't listening to anything I was saying. (TULA *is more agitated and wants to break away from her.*) Tula, the way your face has changed suddenly frightens me. Something must be wrong. It's not my father? (TULA *shakes his head vigorously.*) No, then what is it? You must tell me! It's very important to me!

Rapidly he walks away into the back room, followed closely behind by SARIE. *Immediately, he comes out from the back room followed by* GAMA, JIMMY, *and* CHRIS.

GAMA: What's the matter with you? (*He looks at the clock and back to* TULA.) What is it?

JIMMY: What is it, Tula?

GAMA (*shakes him roughly by the shoulders*): What is it? Can't you talk.

TULA (*wiping his face with the back of his hand*): Her father! Her father! The only parent she's got too!

CHRIS: What do you mean, Tula?

JIMMY: Whose father?

GAMA: What are you talking about?

TULA: The Afrikaner girl who's here tonight! Sarie Marais!

JIMMY: What happened to her father? Just tell us slowly what the matter is.

TULA: Her father is at the City Hall right now! At the National Party rally! If anything happens tonight, he will be there too! He'll get hurt with the lot!

The group is stunned. They all turn to the clock; it is eleven forty-five.

GAMA (*in distress*): How stupid! How damn stupid! What a damn stupid thing!

TULA: We've got to put the bomb off! We can't go on with it! There's still time to run down to the City Hall and put the whole thing off!

GAMA (*recovering from shock*): No! Nothing's to be put off!

TULA (*close to hysteria*): Are you crazy? He's the only parent she's got! That girl has nobody but her father! We can't let him get hurt.

JIMMY: Damn it! Why did we have to get mixed up with her? Why did she have to come sniffing here?

TULA: We can't let the bomb go off!

GAMA: Shut up, will you! You're not giving orders to anybody here! The bomb shall go off as planned! We can't help it if her father is a National Party supporter! He's just as guilty as any other white supremacist! He must perish with the rest!

TULA: He is not a National Party supporter!

CHRIS: What's he doing at the City Hall tonight? Why didn't she tell me about this earlier?

TULA: He's gone there to tender his resignation! He's making a break with the Party! She told me so herself!

The whole group begins pacing up and down like caged lions without any means of escape from the dilemma. Only TULA *has made his decision and stands accusingly before them.*

GAMA: Don't just stand there accusingly! It's not our fault her father is at the City Hall tonight!

TULA: We can still do something! Disconnect the whole thing!

GAMA: No, we can't! It's too late!

TULA: It's not too late! If we didn't argue about this, somebody would be running down already!

GAMA (*furiously shaking him and pushing him off*): Listen, stupid! We've worked hard preparing for this! We've run grave risks! We can't just put it off for one white supremacist who's suddenly suffered a "crisis of conscience." What's the matter with you anyway! Are you in love with her? That's right! You want us to risk our necks rushing down to the City Hall because of your sentimental reasons!

TULA: Don't people mean anything to you? She's alone! She has no relatives! Her father is the only one she's got in the world!

GAMA: People mean something to me. That's why I am involved in this. Because I care about people! Hundreds of black people have been shot down mercilessly by these brutes! You don't remember that. No! And you talk about caring for people! For one white man you want to put off something that's important! Something that might mean the beginning of a change in this country! You call that caring about people?

JIMMY (*trying to be reasonable about it*): Have you told her about the plans to blow up the City Hall?

TULA: No. She doesn't know it! She thinks me a friend and here am I, murdering her father in cold blood!

JIMMY: Calm down, Tula! We are all in this! We both feel sympathy for her! But we must keep our heads!

TULA: Keep our heads and her father is just about losing his!

CHRIS: Isn't there a way of removing the father from the City Hall without telling him the reason?

GAMA: When the news breaks, her father will suspect something and she will suspect us! We can't even explain this to her! We don't know her well enough to tell her we are behind the blowing up of the City Hall!

TULA (*desperately*): You can go on arguing about it! I'm going down to cut the wire off!

He rushes toward the door. GAMA *runs after him and grabs him by the shoulders. There is a struggle and* GAMA *hits his younger brother with a fist repeatedly in the stomach until he sags down.*

GAMA: You're not running to any City Hall! Damn fool! You asked for this!

The girls and the boys pile out of the back room during the struggle. They are still all asking what's happened. CHRIS, JIMMY, *and* GAMA *are mute. Neither does* TULA *explain what it is all about.* SARIE *rushes to* TULA, *who is still on the floor and is groaning. She lifts his face between her hands and tries to find out what the matter is, but* TULA *keeps shaking his head*

MARY: Gama, did you hit him?

GAMA: Yes, I hit him!

MARY: You really hit him? Your own brother? And for what?

GAMA: He was going to do something stupid! And don't ask me what!

MARY (*furiously*): Gama, I don't want to see you again! And don't ever touch me again! You're a cruel, heartless bully, and I can't stand bullies!

GAMA: Wait a minute! You don't even know what he was going to do! You don't know a thing! Why do you always have to rush to conclusions?

MARY: What conclusions are you talking about? You hit him, didn't you? Jimmy, what was the quarrel about this time?

KITTY: Jimmy, what happened?

JIMMY (*evading the questions*): Look, this is not the time to talk about it.

The girls help SARIE *move* TULA *to the back room to look after his condition.*

CHRIS: What are we going to do about it?

JIMMY: There's nothing we can do about it.

GAMA: It's none of our fault!

CHRIS: Maybe we can telephone anonymously and give him the message that his daughter has been seriously hurt! Anything to get him out of there.

JIMMY: That's a good idea, Chris! That's a splendid idea! Gama, what do you think?

GAMA (*agitated*): Ya, maybe it will work! What's the City Hall phone number?

JIMMY: We can telephone the lobby, and somebody will send the message into the conference hall.

GAMA: Okay, Jimmy, you call!

GAMA, CHRIS, *and* JIMMY *move toward the telephone, where* JIMMY *dials the number of the City Hall. There is a long quiet, with only the purring of the telephone and the vague voices from the back room. The three young people stand tensely around the telephone. There is no answer.*

JIMMY (*slamming the telephone back to the cradle*): Not a damn answer! Too busy dreaming up crazy apartheid schemes to even answer the telephone! (*He paces up and down.*)

GAMA: Why do we have to bother? We can't help it if he is there! (*The others nod half-heartedly.*) I mean, I care and all that, but what can we do about it?

CHRIS: There's danger that anybody who goes down to the City Hall might be intercepted by the police. The whole City Hall is ringed by the police.

JIMMY: You're absolutely right, Chris! We might be caught in the act of cutting off wires! There's nothing more distressing than being punished for an aborted plan.

Every pause now is marked by increased tension.

GAMA: Goddammit! It's not as if we asked him to be there!

Pause.

CHRIS: Thank heavens she doesn't know yet!

JIMMY: She'll soon know! Chris, how the hell did you get mixed up with her?

CHRIS: Wait a minute, Jimmy! Don't try and start pushing the blame onto me now! This group is non-racial! So, we meet a Boer girl at the university who's interested in joining, and we ask her to come along! How could I have known her father was to be at the City Hall tonight?

GAMA: Okay! Okay! Nobody's blaming you! This is nobody's fault! Besides, it's almost time for the bomb to go off! (*With a deliberate attempt at levity.*) Ah, who cares? One Boer gets blown up because he happens to be in the wrong place at the wrong time! It's not the first time it's happened. Hundreds of black people have been killed by Boers! It's a pity if one good Boer gets on the rails of history and gets ground up with the rest. (*Pause. Suddenly.*) Jimmy, what do you think? You think I am right or wrong? Tell me.

JIMMY (*uncertainly*): Right. Maybe . .

GAMA: Maybe what? Jimmy, do you think I'm right or wrong? Why do you say maybe?

JIMMY: I mean, maybe we should try that number again.

GAMA: Okay, maybe we will get an answer this time.

They move off toward the telephone, where JIMMY *tries again. There is complete stillness, during which we can almost hear the breathing of the three young men. After a while* JIMMY *replaces the receiver with an irritated bang.*

JIMMY: They're about to be blown off the face of the earth, and they can't even answer a telephone! Too busy with the damned apartheid policies to bother!

CHRIS (*slowly, dejectedly*): I suppose that's it! There's nothing more to be done!

GAMA (*agitated*): Suppose that's it? What else is there to do? We can't destroy everything we've planned for months because of one crazy Boer bastard! Why did he have to be there! Why did she have to come here!

CHRIS: Stop putting the blame on her! That girl was invited to join this group! When all of you started a non-racial organization, nobody bothered to think about Boers joining!

JIMMY: Nobody's saying Boers shouldn't join this organization! We are not racialists!

CHRIS: Well, both of you talk as if you're blaming me for having brought this girl to the party.

GAMA: No, no! We're not blaming you! It's just that she's made everything that was right seem wrong suddenly. (*The other young people who have been in the back room come out. Everybody is remarkably tense. Occasionally their eyes are riveted to the clock.*) Is there anything left to drink? Mary, is there anything left to drink?

She doesn't answer him.

JULIE: Everybody's been guzzling drinks all night! Now you want a drink!

GAMA: Jimmy, give me a cigarette, will you?

JIMMY (*to* KITTY, *after searching his pockets unsuccessfully*): Blackie, what did I do with my cigarettes?

KITTY: How should I know? Did you give them to me?

GAMA: What's the matter with everybody suddenly?

MARY (*exploding*): What's the matter with you? You're stalking the room like a lion. Look at you!

GAMA: Well, what of it! Maybe I am a lion!

MARY: Stop shouting! You're going to bring all the neighbours running here! Are you all shot up or something?

GAMA: Who's shot up? I don't get shot up that easily! I'll see this through!

SARIE *and* TULA *come in from the back room. There is suddenly a dead quiet again. They stand separately. Tension mounts and is only broken by the drunken entrance of* SLOWFOOT, *who stumbles and falls but manages to save the bottle of brandy he has been hiding from everybody. He looks around searchingly at the group, then takes a sip from the bottle.* TULA *slips out unnoticed.*

SLOWFOOT (*grinning sardonically*): Ah, I can see a sombre quiet rests heavily upon this illogical conglomeration of the flotsam and jetsam of society! (*Nobody responds to him. He sizes up the group and tries again.*) A dead stillness! I see. Only drunks are not impressed by the sober solemnity of history!

JIMMY: And history is not impressed by the solemn sogginess of a drunkard's mind!

SLOWFOOT: Ah, Jimmy, my boy! I knew you would rise up to the occasion!

GAMA: Will that clot shut up! He's getting on my nerves!

SLOWFOOT (*whistles drunkenly and stumbles forward*): Hey, waita minute! Listen who's talking now! The tough cool boy! The wonderboy who's in truck with history! And for the first time he's unsure like the rest of us mortals! Gama, rise and shine; immortality is passing you by!

GAMA: If somebody doesn't stop that drunk, I swear I'm going to punch him on his blabbering mouth!

SLOWFOOT: Ah, it "was the best of times, it was the worst of times . . . it was the time of wisdom, it was the time of foolishness!" (*He stumbles forward.*) A time of extreme stupidity! You see, Gama, my boy, you're not the original thing! There've been revolutions before!

GAMA *rushes to punch him one, but he is intercepted by* JIMMY's *swift action.*

GAMA: Damn him! Somebody get this drunk out of here before he gets hurt!

JIMMY: Gama, calm down, for God's sake! Everybody's flying off the handle. What's the matter with everybody?

SLOWFOOT: Nothing's the matter with me. (*Pause.*) Okay, what did I say wrong? Did I say anything wrong? If I did, I heartily apologize—like a gentleman. (GAMA *snatches the bottle from him.*) Now, waita minute,

Gama! That's a very arbitrary measure! Even a drunk has a democratic right to retain his bottle—I mean—for all practical purposes. I deman' an explanation why my bottle is being impounded. (GAMA *takes a swig from the bottle. He raises it against the light and discovers there is pretty little left in it. He empties down his throat the rest of the contents and throws the bottle away.*) Ah, the maestro needed a shot in the arm too!

GAMA: And you need a shot in the head!

JIMMY (*suddenly*): Where's Tula? What's happened to Tula?

SARIE: He said he was going to get some fresh air.

JIMMY: What? Oh, my God!

GAMA: What? When did he leave? What happened? Where did he say he was going? Talk, can't you? Goddammit! (*He shakes the bewildered girl.*)

SARIE: Don't! You're hurting me! (MARY *pulls* GAMA *away.*) What's the matter with all of you What's the matter with everybody here? What are you planning? What's going on? (JIMMY *and* GAMA *have rushed outside to search for* TULA.) Something is going on here that I don't know about!

LILI: Mary, what's the matter? Do you know what the excitement's all about?

MARY: How should I know? Why ask me? I was in there drinking coffee, and I come out here and there's a general commotion. I don't know what it's all about! (GAMA *and* JIMMY *come in again.*) Gama, is there something wrong?

GAMA (*moving toward the centre of the stage. A note of hysteria*): You bet something is wrong! Sweet brother of mine has run down there to watch the whole thing happen! He's goin' to be the major witness! Who knows, maybe he's even goin' to sing to the police! Warn them! I bet he's goin' to do that! He's goin' to rush into the hall and tell all those people to get out before it happens! (GAMA *begins to shout in a deranged fashion.*) Get out all you good people! Get out before we blow you up! Can you hear me? Get out of the damned City Hall! You only have five minutes to do it! Get out now or be blown off, goddammit! Can anybody hear me? No, nobody can hear me! Not a damn single person can hear me! You're all too damn busy cooking up your crazy apartheid policies to listen, to care! Well you can damn well perish! All of you perish, and see if I care! I tell you it's your damn fault if you———

We begin to hear the clock strike the hour of midnight. Suddenly there are rumblings at a distance. Loud explosions, detonations, can be heard within two miles. Then sirens begin to scream, ambulance and police cars. The lights on stage are shaken as though by an explosion; they falter as though a power plant has been affected. A wild jazz rhythm can be heard blending with the rhythmic detonations offstage. The explosions stop suddenly. The whole group rushes for the door. The lights falter and die out suddenly.

Curtain.

POETRY

from Libretto for the Republic of Liberia

■ Melvin B. Tolson

Do

      Liberia?
No micro-footnote in a bunioned book
     Homed by a pedant
     With a gelded look:
      You are
The ladder of survival dawn men saw
In the quicksilver sparrow that slips
     The eagle's claw!

      Liberia?
No side-show barker's bio-accident,   10
     No corpse of a soul's errand
     To the Dark Continent:
      You are
The lightning rod of Europe, Canaan's key,
     The rope across the abyss,
Mehr licht for the Africa-To-Be!

      Liberia?
   No haply black man's X
Fixed to a Magna Charta without a magic-square
By Helon's leprous hand, to haunt and vex: 20
      You are
The Orient of Colors everywhere,
The oasis of Tahoua, the salt bar of Harrar,
To trekkers in saharas, in sierras, with Despair!

      Liberia?
   No oil-boiled Barabas,
No Darwin's bulldog for ermined flesh,
No braggart Lamech, no bema's Ananias:

You are
Libertas flayed and naked by the road   30
To Jericho, for a people's five score years
Of bones for manna, for balm an alien goad!

Liberia?
No pimple on the chin of Africa,
No brass-lipped cicerone of Big Top democracy,
No lamb to tame a lion with a baa:
You are
Black Lazarus risen from the White Man's grave,
Without a road to Downing Street,
Without a hemidemisemiquaver in an Oxford stave!   40

Liberia?
No Cobra Pirate of the Question Mark,
No caricature with a mimic flag
And golden joys to fat the shark:
You are
American genius uncrowned in Europe's charnel-house.
Leave fleshpots for the dogs and apes; for Man
The books whose head is golden espouse!

Liberia?
No waste land yet, nor yet a destooled elite,   50
No merry-andrew, an Ed-dehebi at heart,
With St. Paul's root and Breughel's cheat:
You are
The iron nerve of lame and halt and blind,
Liberia and not Liberia,
A moment of the conscience of mankind!

Re

The Good Gray Bard in Timbuktu chanted:
"Brow tron lo—eta ne a ne won oh gike!"

Before Liberia was, Songhai was: before
America set the raw foundling on Africa's   60
Doorstep, before the Genoese diced west,
Burnt warriors and watermen of Songhai
Tore into *bizarreries* the uniforms of Portugal
And sewed an imperial quilt of tribes.

In Milan and Mecca, in Balkh and Bombay,
Sea lawyers in the eyeservice of sea kings
Mixed liquors with hyperboles to cure deafness.

Europe bartered Africa crucifixes for red ivory,
Gewgaws for black pearls, *pierres d'aigris* for green gold:
Soon the rivers and roads became clog almanacs!   70

The Good Gray Bard in Timbuktu chanted:
"Wanawake wanazaa ovyo! Kazi yenu wazungu!"

Black Askia's fetish was his people's health:
The world his world, he gave the Bengal light
Of Books the Inn of Court in Songhai. *Beba mzigo!*
The law of empathy set the market price,
Scaled the word and deed: the gravel-blind saw
Deserts give up the ghost to green pastures!

Solomon in all his glory had no Oxford,
Alfred the Great no University of Sankoré: 80
Footloose professors, chimney sweeps of the skull,
From Europe and Asia; youths, souls in one skin,
Under white scholars like El-Akit, under
Black humanists like Bagayogo. *Karibu wee!*

The Good Gary Bard in Timbuktu chanted:
"Europe is an empty python in hiding grass!"

Lia! Lia! The river Wagadu, the river Bagana,
Became dusty metaphors where white ants ate canoes,
And the locust Portuguese raped the maiden crops,
And the sirocco Spaniard razed the city-states,   90
And the leopard Saracen bolted his scimitar into
The jugular vein of Timbuktu. *Dieu seul est grand!*

And now the hyenas whine among the barren bones
Of the seventeen sun sultans of Songhai,
And hooded cobras, hoodless mambas, hiss
In the gold caverns of Falémé and Bambuk,
And puff adders, hook scorpions, whisper
In the weedy corridors of Sankoré. *Lia! Lia!*

The Good Gray Bard chants no longer in Timbuktu:
"The maggots fat on yeas and nays of nut empires!"   100

Ti

O Calendar of the Century,
red-letter the Republic's birth!
O Hallelujah,
oh, let no *Miserere*

venom the spinal cord of Afric earth!
Selah!   260

"*Ecco homo!*"
the blind men cowled in azure rant
before the Capitol,
between the Whale and Elephant,
where no longer stands Diogenes' hearse
readied for the ebony mendicant,
nor weeping widow Europe with her hands
making the multitudinous seas incarnadine
or earth's *massebôth* worse:
O Great White World, thou boy of tears, omega hounds   270
lap up the alpha laugh and *du-haut-en-bas* curse.
Selah!

O Africa, Mother of Science
. . . *lachen mit yastchekes* . . .
What dread hand,
to make tripartite one august event,
sundered Gondwanaland?
What dread grasp crushed your biceps and
back upon the rack
chaos of chance and change   280
fouled in Malebolgean isolation?
What dread *elboga* shoved your soul
into the *tribulum* of retardation?
melamin or melanin dies to the world and dies:
Rome casketed herself in Homeric hymns.
Man's culture in barb and Arab lies:
The Jordan flows into the Tiber,
the Yangtze into the Thames,
the Ganges into the Mississippi, the Niger
into the Seine.
                                                                        290

Judge of the Nations, spare us: yet,
fool latins, alumni of one school,
on Clochan-na-n'all, say *Phew*
. . . *Lest we forget! Lest we forget!* . . .
to dusky peers of Roman, Greek, and Jew.
Selah!
Between Yesterday's wars
now hot now cold
the grief-in-grain of Man
dripping dripping dripping
from the Cross of Iron
dripping
drew jet vampires
of the Skull;

Between Yesterday's wills of Tanaka, between 470
golden goblet and truckling trull
and the ires
of rivers red with the reflexes of fires,
the ferris wheel
of race, of caste, of class
dumped and alped cadavers till the ground
fogged the Pleiades with Gila rot: Today the mass,
the Beast with a Maginot Line in its Brain,
the staircase Avengers of base alloy,
the *vile canaille—Gorii!*—the *Bastard-rasse,* 480
the *uomo qualyque,* the *hoi barbaroi,*
the *raya* in the *Oeil de Boeuf,*
the *vsechelovek,* the *descamisados,* the *hoi polloi,*
the Raw from the Coliseum of the Cooked,
Il Duce's Whore, Vardaman's Hound—
unparadised nobodies with maps of Nowhere
ride the merry-go-round!
Selah!

NOTES

LINE
7. Cf. Dryden, *All for Love,* II, i:
"... upon my eagle's wings
I bore this wren, till I was tired of soaring,
and now he mounts above me."
11. Cf. Raleigh, *The Soul's Errand.*
15. V. Nietzsche, *Thus Spake Zarathustra.*
18. Cf. Shakespeare, *Othello,* III, iii:
"Haply, for I am black ..."
19. *Magic-square:* a symbol of equality. The diagram consists of a number of small squares each containing a number. The numbers are so arranged that the sum of those in each of the various rows is the same. Cf. Thomson, *The City of Dreadful Night,* XXI, 1061.
20. Cf. Willis, *The Leper.*
30. The motto of Liberia: "The love of liberty brought us here."
32. Cf. Carlyle: "God has put into every white man's hand a whip to flog a black man."
38. Cf. the tavern scenes in Boulton's comic opera, *The Sailor's Farewell.*
42. *Cobra Pirate.* V. Hardy, *Les Grands Etapes de l'Histoire du Maroc,* 50–54. *The Question Mark.* The shape of the map of Africa dramatizes two schools of thought among native African scholars. To the Christian educator, Dr. James E. Kwegyir Aggrey, it is a moral interrogation point that challenges the white world. According to Dr. Nnamdi Azikiwe, the leader of the nationalistic movement on the West Coast, foreigners consider it "a ham-bone designed by destiny for the carving-knife of European imperialism." I have found very fruitful the suggestions and criticisms of Professor Diana Pierson, the Liberian, and Dr. Akiki Nyabongo, the Ugandian. I now know that the Question Mark is rough water between Scylla and Charybdis.
43. Cf. Bismarck: "They [Negroes] appear to me to be a caricature of the white man."

44. Cf. Shakespeare, *Henry IV*, III, i:
    "A foutra for the world and worldlings base!
    I speak of Africa and golden joys."
46. Cf. Emerson: "While European genius is symbolized by some majestic Corinne crowned in the capitol at Rome, American genius finds its true type in the poor negro soldier lying in the trenches by the Potomac with his spelling book in one hand and his musket in the other." V. Maran, *Batouala*, 9: "Civilization, civilization, pride of the Europeans and charnel-house of innocents, Rabindranath Tagore, the Hindu poet, once, at Tokio told what you are! You have built your kingdom on corpses."
48. *The books whose head is golden.* Cf. Rossetti, *Mary's Girlhood.*
50. *Destooled.* On the Gold Coast the "Stool" is the symbol of the soul of the nation, its Magna Charta. In 1900, Sir Frederick Hodgson, Governor of the Gold Coast, demanded that the Ashantis surrender their "Stool." They immediately declared war. "Destooling" is a veto exercised by the sovereign people over unpopular rulers.
51. *Ed-dehebi:* "The Master of Gold." He was the conqueror of Songhai, with its fabulous gold mines.
54. *The iron nerve.* Cf. Tennyson, *Ode on the Death of the Duke of Wellington.*
56. V. the address of Anatole France at the bier of Emile Zola.
57. Cf. *A Memoir of Tennyson*, Vol. I, 46, the letter of Arthur Hallam to William Gladstone on the Timbuktu prize poem: "I consider Tennyson as promising fair to be the greatest poet of our generation, perhaps of our century." V. Delafosse, *Les Noirs de L'Afrique.* The Schomburg Collection, in Harlem, contains many rare items on the civilization at Timbuktu. Dr. Lorenzo Turner's *Africanism in the Gullah Dialects*, by tracing West Coast derivatives to their Arabic and Moslem and Portuguese cultural roots, has revealed the catholicity and sophistication of African antiquity and exploded the theory of the Old English origin of the Gullah dialects.
58. I am informed that variations of this *eironeia* or mockery may be found in scores of African languages. It means here: "The world is too large—that's why we do not hear everything." Cf. Pliny, *Historia Naturalis*, II: "There is always something new from Africa." Also Swift:
    "So geographers, in Afric maps,
    With savage pictures fill their gaps . ."
69. *Black pearls.* V. Shakespeare, *Two Gentlemen of Verona*, V, i. Also *Othello*, II, i:
    "Well prais'd! How if she be black and witty?"
    Mr. J. A. Rogers treats the subject and time and place adequately in *Sex and Race.*
72. *Wanawake wanazaa ovyo:* "The women keep having children right and left." *Kazi yenu wazungu:* "It's the work of you white men."
75. *Beba mzigo:* "Lift the loads." This repetend is tacked on *ex tempore* to ballads growing out of a diversity of physical and spiritual experiences.
80. V. Du Bois, *The World and Africa*, a book to which I am deeply indebted for facts.
81. The nomadic pedagogues gathered at Timbuktu are not to be confused with the *vagantes* of the *Carmina Burana.*
82. *Souls in one skin.* V. Firdousi, *The Dream of Dakiki*, I, A.
84. *Karibu wee.* Among primitives hospitality is a thing poetic—and apostolic. *Jogoo linawika: Karibu wee.* "The rooster crows: Welcome!" *Mbuzi wanalia: Karibu wee.* "The goats bleat: Welcome."
87. *Lia.* The word means "weep" and seems to follow the patterns of "*otototoi*" in the Aeschylean chorus.

92. *Dieu seul est grand.* These first words of Massillon's exordium, delivered at the magnificent funeral of Louis XIV, brought the congregation to its feet in the cathedral. For an account of the destruction of Timbuktu, see the *Tarikh el-Fettach.* The *askia* Issahak, in a vain attempt to stop the Spanish renegades at Tondibi, used cows as Darius had used elephants against the Macedonian phalanx.

100. *Nut empires.* Cf. Sagittarius, *New Statesman and Nation,* May 1, 1948, the poem entitled "Pea-Nuts":
> "The sun of Empire will not set
> While Empire nuts abound."

258. *Miserere.* Cf. Newman, *The Definition of a Gentleman:* ". . . we attended the Tenebrae, at the Sestine, for the sake of the Miserere . . ."

262. *Cowled in azure:* the cloak of deceit and false humility. Cf. Hafiz, *The Divan (Odes),* V, translated by Bicknell.

264. *Whale and Elephant:* the symbols Jefferson used to designate Great Britain with her navy under Nelson and France with her army under Napoleon. V. Anderson, *Liberia,* X.

269. *Massebôth:* "sacred pillars." Cf. Genesis, XXVIII, xviii. Also the J author.

270. *Thou boy of tears.* Cf. Shakespeare, *Coriolanus,* V, v.

274. *Lachen mit vastchekes:* "laughing with needles being stuck in you"; ghetto laughter.

275. Cf. Blake, *The Tiger.*

276. Cf. Hardy, *The Convergence of the Twain.*

286. V. Pycraft, *Animals of the World,* 1941–1942. *A fortiori,* the American trotter is "a combination of barb and Arab on English stock."

287. V. Christy, *The Asian Legacy and American Life.* This book contains vital facts on Oriental influences in the New Poetry. What I owe the late Professor Arthur E. Christy, a favorite teacher, is not limited to the concept of "the shuttle ceaselessly weaving the warp and weft of the world's cultural fabric."

293. *Clochan-na-n'all:* "the blind men's stepping-stones." Cf. Ferguson, *The Welshmen of Tirawley.*

297. V. Aeschylus, *Agamemnon.*

464. *Grief-in-grain.* The "grain" I have in mind in this figure consists of the dried female bodies of a scale insect found on cacti in Mexico and Central America. The dye is red and unfading. Cf. Henley, *To James McNeill Whistler, in toto.*

479. Cf. Cavafy, *The Footsteps.*

480. *Gorii.* The voyage of the Carthaginian general Hanno carried him as far as what is now Liberia. The aborigines he saw were called *Gorii,* which later Greek and Latin scholars turned into "gorilla." However, to Hanno's interpreter and in the Wolof language today, the expression means "These too are men."

482. *Raya.* In the Turkish conquest of the Southern Slavs, the maltreated people became *raya* or cattle. Conquest salves its conscience with contempt. Among the *raya* for five hundred years, the ballads of the wandering *guslars* kept freedom alive. *Oeil de Boeuf:* a waiting room at Versailles. Cf. Dobson, *On a Fan That Belonged to the Marquise de Pompadour.*

483. *Vsechelovek:* "universal man." In spite of its global image, this concept has a taint of *blut und boden.* Ever since Dostoevski, in a eulogy on Pushkin, identified the latter's genius with *vsechelovek,* the term has created pros and cons. Cf. the Latin: "Paul is a Roman and not a Roman." *Descamisados:* "the shirtless ones."

484. The line was suggested by the history of the *Crudes* and *Asados* of Uruguay

485. *Il Duce's Whore.* V. *Ciano Diaries 1939–43*, edited by Gibson. This is one of the "many instances of the vast contempt in which Il Duce held his people."
486. Cf. Milton, the outline of *Adam Unparadised.*

from The Panther and the Lash

■ Langston Hughes

Harlem

> Here on the edge of hell
> Stands Harlem—
> Remembering the old lies,
> The old kicks in the back,
> The old "Be patient"
> They told us before.
> Sure, we remember.
> Now when the man at the corner store
> Says sugar's gone up another two cents,
> And bread one,
> And there's a new tax on cigarettes—
> We remember the job we never had,
> Never could get,
> And can't have now
> Because we're colored.
> So we stand here
> On the edge of hell
> In Harlem
> And look out on the world
> And wonder
> What we're gonna do
> In the face of what
> We remember.

Prime

> Uptown on Lenox Avenue
> Where a nickel costs a dime,
> In these lush and thieving days
> When million-dollar thieves
> Glorify their million-dollar ways

In the press and on the radio and TV—
　　But won't let me
　　Skim even a dime—
I, black, come to my prime
In the section of the niggers
Where a nickel costs a dime.

The Backlash Blues

Mister Backlash, Mister Backlash,
Just who do you think I am?
Tell me, Mister Backlash,
Who do you think I am?
You raise my taxes, freeze my wages,
Send my son to Vietnam.

You give me second-class houses,
Give me second-class schools,
Second-class houses
And second-class schools.
You must think us colored folks
Are second-class fools.

When I try to find a job
To earn a little cash,
Try to find myself a job
To earn a little cash,
All you got to offer
Is a white backlash.

But the world is big,
The world is big and round,
Great big world, Mister Backlash,
Big and bright and round—
And it's full of folks like me who are
Black, Yellow, Beige, and Brown.

Mister Backlash, Mister Backlash,
What do you think I got to lose?
Tell me, Mister Backlash,
What you think I got to lose?
I'm gonna leave you, Mister Backlash,
Singing your mean old backlash blues

　　　You're the one,
　　　Yes, you're the one
　　　Will have the blues.

Who but the Lord

I looked and I saw
That man they call the Law.
He was coming
Down the street at me!
I had visions in my head
Of being laid out cold and dead,
Or else murdered
By the third degree.

I said, O, Lord, if you can,
Save me from that man!
Don't let him make a pulp out of me!
But the Lord he was not quick.
The Law raised up his stick
And beat the living hell
Out of me!

Now I do not understand
Why God don't protect a man
From police brutality.
Being poor and black,
I've no weapon to strike back
So who but the Lord
Can protect me?

We'll see.

Still Here

I been scared and battered.
My hopes the wind done scattered.
        Snow has friz me,
        Sun has baked me,
Looks like between 'em they done
        Tried to make me
Stop laughin', stop lovin', stop livin'—
        But I don't care!
        I'm still here!

Words Like Freedom

There are words like *Freedom*
Sweet and wonderful to say.
On my heartstrings freedom sings
All day everyday.

There are words like *Liberty*
That almost make me cry.
If you had known what I know
You would know why.

Little Song on Housing

Here I come!
Been saving all my life
To get a nice home
For me and my wife.

> *White folks flee—*
> *As soon as you see*
> *My problems*
> *And me!*

Neighborhood's clean,
But the house is old,
Prices are doubled
When I get sold:
Still I buy.

> *White folks fly—*
> *Soon as you spy*
> *My wife*
> *And I!*

Next thing you know,
Our neighbors all colored are.
The candy store's
Turned into a bar:
White folks have left
The whole neighborhood
To my black self.

> *White folks, flee!*
> *Still—there is me!*
> *White folks, fly!*
> *Here am I!*

Final Call

SEND FOR THE PIED PIPER AND LET HIM PIPE THE RATS
     AWAY.
SEND FOR ROBIN HOOD TO CLINCH THE ANTI-POVERTY
     CAMPAIGN.

SEND FOR THE FAIRY QUEEN WITH A WAVE OF THE
  WAND
TO MAKE US ALL INTO PRINCES AND PRINCESSES.
SEND FOR KING ARTHUR TO BRING THE HOLY GRAIL.
SEND FOR OLD MAN MOSES TO LAY DOWN THE LAW.
SEND FOR JESUS TO PREACH THE SERMON ON THE
  MOUNT.
SEND FOR DREYFUS TO CRY, *"J'ACCUSE!"*
SEND FOR DEAD BLIND LEMON TO SING THE *B FLAT
  BLUES.*
SEND FOR ROBESPIERRE TO SCREAM, *"ÇA IRA! ÇA IRA!
  ÇA IRA!"*
SEND (GOD FORBID—HE'S NOT DEAD LONG ENOUGH!)
FOR LUMUMBA TO CRY "FREEDOM NOW!"
SEND FOR LAFAYETTE AND TELL HIM, "HELP! HELP ME!"
SEND FOR DENMARK VESEY CRYING, "FREE!"
FOR CINQUE SAYING, "RUN A NEW FLAG UP THE MAST."
FOR OLD JOHN BROWN WHO KNEW SLAVERY COULDN'T
  LAST.
SEND FOR LENIN! (DON'T YOU DARE!—HE CAN'T COME
  HERE!)
SEND FOR TROTSKY! (WHAT? DON'T CONFUSE THE ISSUE,
  PLEASE!)
SEND FOR UNCLE TOM ON HIS MIGHTY KNEES.
SEND FOR LINCOLN, SEND FOR GRANT.
SEND FOR FREDERICK DOUGLASS, GARRISON, BEECHER,
  LOWELL.
SEND FOR HARRIET TUBMAN, OLD SOJOURNER TRUTH.
SEND FOR MARCUS GARVEY (WHAT?) SUFI (WHO?)
  FATHER DIVINE (WHERE?)
DuBOIS (WHEN?) MALCOLM (OH!) SEND FOR STOKELY.
  (NO?) THEN
SEND FOR ADAM POWELL ON A NON-SUBPOENA DAY.
SEND FOR THE PIED PIPER TO PIPE OUR RATS AWAY.

(And if nobody comes, send for me.)

from Selected Poems

■ Robert Hayden

A Ballad of Remembrance

Quadroon mermaids, Afro angels, black saints
balanced upon the switchblades of that air
and sang. Tight streets unfolding to the eye
like fans of corrosion and elegiac lace
crackled with their singing: Shadow of time. Shadow of blood.

Shadow, echoed the Zulu king, dangling
from a cluster of balloons. Blood,
whined the gun-metal priestess, floating
over the courtyard where dead men diced.

What will you have? she inquired, the sallow vendeuse
of prepared tarnishes and jokes of nacre and ormolu,
what but those gleamings, oldrose graces,
manners like scented gloves? Contrived ghosts
rapped to metronome clack of lavalieres.

Contrived illuminations riding a threat
of river, masked Negroes wearing chameleon
satins gaudy now as a fortuneteller's
dream of disaster, lighted the crazy flopping
dance of love and hate among joys, rejections.

Accommodate, muttered the Zulu king,
toad on a throne of glaucous poison jewels.
Love, chimed the saints and the angels and the mermaids.
Hate, shrieked the gun-metal priestess
from her spiked bellcollar curved like a fleur-de-lis:

As well have a talon as a finger, a muzzle as a mouth,
as well have a hollow as a heart. And she pinwheeled
away in coruscations of laughter, scattering
those others before her like foil stars.

But the dance continued—now among metaphorical
doors, coffee cups floating poised
hysterias, decors of illusion; now among
mazurka dolls offering death's-heads
of cocaine roses and real violets.

Then you arrived, meditative, ironic,
richly human; and your presence was shore where I rested

released from the hoodoo of that dance, where I spoke
with my true voice again.

And therefore this is not only a ballad of remembrance
for the down-South arcane city with death
in its jaws like gold teeth and archaic cusswords;
not only a token for the troubled generous friends
held in the fists of that schizoid city like flowers,
but also, Mark Van Doren,
a poem of remembrance, a gift, a souvenir for you.

Incense of the Lucky Virgin

Incense of the Lucky Virgin,
High John the Conqueror
didn't bring him home again,
didn't get his children fed,
      get his children fed.

I prayed and what did prayer avail?
My candles held no power.
An evening came I prayed no more
and blew my candles out,
      oh blew my candles out.

Put on your Sunday ribbon-bows,
Cleola, Willie Mae;
you, Garland, go
and shine your Sunday shoes,
      make haste and shine your shoes.

They were so happy they forgot
they were hungry, daddyless.
Except Cleola maybe—she
wasn't asking, Where we going,
      Mommy, where we going?

Garland was too quick for me
(he didn't yell once as he ran);
Cleola, Willie Mae
won't be hungry any more,
      oh they'll never cry and hunger any more.

Summertime and the Living . . .

Nobody planted roses, he recalls,
but sunflowers gangled there sometimes,
tough-stalked and bold

and like the vivid children there unplanned.
There circus-poster horses curveted
in trees of heaven
above the quarrels and shattered glass,
and he was bareback rider of them all.

No roses there in summer—
oh, never roses except when people died—
and no vacations for his elders,
so harshened after each unrelenting day
that they were shouting-angry.
But summer was, they said, the poor folks' time
of year. And he remembers
how they would sit on broken steps amid

The fevered tossings of the dusk, the dark,
wafting hearsay with funeral-parlor fans
or making evening solemn by
their quietness. Feels their Mosaic eyes
upon him, though the florist roses
that only sorrow could afford
long since have bidden them Godspeed.

Oh, summer summer summertime—

Then grim street preachers shook
their tambourines and Bibles in the face
of tolerant wickedness;
then Elks parades and big splendiferous
Jack Johnson in his diamond limousine
set the ghetto burgeoning
with fantasies
of Ethiopia spreading her gorgeous wings.

Runagate, Runagate

I

Runs falls rises stumbles on from darkness into darkness
and the darkness thicketed with shapes of terror
and the hunters pursuing and the hounds pursuing
and the night cold and the night long and the river
to cross and the jack-muh-lanterns beckoning beckoning
and blackness ahead and when shall I reach that somewhere
morning and keep on going and never turn back and keep on going

      Runagate
          Runagate
              Runagate

Many thousands rise and go
many thousands crossing over

> O mythic North
> O star-shaped yonder Bible city

Some go weeping and some rejoicing
some in coffins and some in carriages
some in silks and some in shackles

> Rise and go or fare you well

No more auction block for me
no more driver's lash for me

> If you see my Pompey, 30 yrs of age,
> new breeches, plain stockings, negro shoes;
> if you see my Anna, likely young mulatto
> branded E on the right cheek, R on the left,
> catch them if you can and notify subscriber.
> Catch them if you can, but it won't be easy.
> They'll dart underground when you try to catch them,
> plunge into quicksand, whirlpools, mazes,
> turn into scorpions when you try to catch them.

And before I'll be a slave
I'll be buried in my grave

> North star and bonanza gold
> I'm bound for the freedom, freedom-bound
> and oh Susyanna don't you cry for me

> Runagate

> Runagate

II

Rises from their anguish and their power,

> Harriet Tubman,

> woman of earth, whipscarred,
> a summoning, a shining

> Mean to be free

And this was the way of it, brethren brethren,
way we journeyed from Can't to Can.

Moon so bright and no place to hide,
the cry up and· the patterollers riding,
hound dogs belling in bladed air.
And fear starts a-murbling, Never make it,
we'll never make it. *Hush that now,*
and she's turned upon us, levelled pistol
glinting in the moonlight:
Dead folks can't jaybird-talk, she says;
you keep on going now or die, she says.

Wanted   Harriet Tubman   alias The General
alias Moses   Stealer of Slaves

In league with Garrison   Alcott   Emerson
Garrett   Douglass   Thoreau   John Brown

Armed and known to be Dangerous

Wanted   Reward   Dead or Alive

Tell me, Ezekiel, oh tell me do you see
mailed Jehovah coming to deliver me?

Hoot-owl calling in the ghosted air,
five times calling to the hants in the air.
Shadow of a face in the scary leaves,
shadow of a voice in the talking leaves:

Come ride-a my train

Oh that train, ghost-story train
through swamp and savanna movering movering,
over trestles of dew, through caves of the wish,
Midnight Special on a sabre track movering movering,
first stop Mercy and the last Hallelujah.

Come ride-a my train

Mean mean mean to be free.

from Selected Poems

■ Gwendolyn Brooks

Negro Hero

to suggest Dorie Miller

I had to kick their law into their teeth in order to save them.
However I have heard that sometimes you have to deal
Devilishly with drowning men in order to swim them to shore.
Or they will haul themselves and you to the trash and the fish beneath.
(When I think of this, I do not worry about a few
Chipped teeth.)

It is good I gave glory, it is good I put gold on their name.
Or there would have been spikes in the afterward hands.
But let us speak only of my success and the pictures in the Caucasian
  dailies
As well as the Negro weeklies. For I am a gem.
(They are not concerned that it was hardly The Enemy my fight was
  against
But them.)

It was a tall time. And of course my blood was
Boiling about in my head and straining and howling and singing me
  on.
Of course I was rolled on wheels of my boy itch to get at the gun.
Of course all the delicate rehearsal shots of my childhood massed in
  mirage before me.
Of course I was child
And my first swallow of the liquor of battle bleeding black air dying
  and demon noise
Made me wild.

It was kinder than that, though, and I showed like a banner my
  kindness.
I loved. And a man will guard when he loves.
Their white-gowned democracy was my fair lady.
With her knife lying cold, straight, in the softness of her sweet-
  flowing sleeve.
But for the sake of the dear smiling mouth and the stuttered promise
  I toyed with my life.
I threw back!—I would not remember
Entirely the knife.

Still—am I good enough to die for them, is my blood bright enough
  to be spilled,

Was my constant back-question—are they clear
On this? Or do I intrude even now?
Am I clean enough to kill for them, do they wish me to kill
For them or is my place while death licks his lips and strides to them
In the galley still?

(In a southern city a white man said
Indeed, I'd rather be dead;
Indeed, I'd rather be shot in the head
Or ridden to waste on the back of a flood
Than saved by the drop of a black man's blood.)

Naturally, the important thing is, I helped to save them, them and a
    part of their democracy.
Even if I had to kick their law into their teeth in order to do that for
    them.
And I am feeling well and settled in myself because I believe it was
    a good job,
Despite this possible horror: that they might prefer the
Preservation of their law in all its sick dignity and their knives
To the continuation of their creed
And their lives.

Beverly Hills, Chicago

> *"and the people live till they have white hair"*—E. M. PRICE

The dry brown coughing beneath their feet,
(Only a while, for the handyman is on his way)
These people walk their golden gardens.
We say ourselves fortunate to be driving by today.

That we may look at them, in their gardens where
The summer ripeness rots. But not raggedly.
Even the leaves fall down in lovelier patterns here.
And the refuse, the refuse is a neat brilliancy.

When they flow sweetly into their houses
With softness and slowness touched by that everlasting gold,
We know what they go to. To tea. But that does not mean
They will throw some little black dots into some water and add sugar
    and the juice of the cheapest lemons that are sold,

While downstairs that woman's vague phonograph bleats, "Knock me
    a kiss."
And the living all to be made again in the sweatingest physical
    manner
Tomorrow. . . . Not that anybody is saying that these people have no
    trouble.

Merely that it is trouble with a gold-flecked beautiful banner.
Nobody is saying that these people do not ultimately cease to be. And
Sometimes their passings are even more painful than ours.
It is just that so often they live till their hair is white.
They make excellent corpses, among the expensive flowers. . . .

Nobody is furious. Nobody hates these people.
At least, nobody driving by in this car.
It is only natural, however, that it should occur to us
How much more fortunate they are than we are.

It is only natural that we should look and look
At their wood and brick and stone
And think, while a breath of pine blows,
How different these are from our own.

We do not want them to have less.
But it is only natural that we should think we have not enough.
We drive on, we drive on.
When we speak to each other our voices are a little gruff.

Truth

And if sun comes
How shall we greet him?
Shall we not dread him,
Shall we not fear him
After so lengthy a
Session with shade?

Though we have wept for him,
Though we have prayed
All through the night-years—
What if we wake one shimmering morning to
Hear the fierce hammering
Of his firm knuckles
Hard on the door?

Shall we not shudder?—
Shall we not flee
Into the shelter, the dear thick shelter
Of the familiar
Propitious haze?

Sweet is it, sweet is it
To sleep in the coolness
Of snug unawareness.

The dark hangs heavily
Over the eyes.

The Bean Eaters

They eat beans mostly, this old yellow pair.
Dinner is a casual affair.
Plain chipware on a plain and creaking wood,
Tin flatware.

Two who are Mostly Good.
Two who have lived their day,
But keep on putting on their clothes
And putting things away.

And remembering . . .
Remembering, with twinklings and twinges,
As they lean over the beans in their rented back room that is full of
    beads and receipts and dolls and cloths, tobacco crumbs, vases and
    fringes.

We Real Cool

The Pool Players.
Seven at the Golden Shovel.

We real cool. We
Left school. We

Lurk late. We
Strike straight. We

Sing sin. We
Thin gin. We

Jazz June. We
Die soon.

The Ballad of Rudolph Reed

Rudolph Reed was oaken.
His wife was oaken too.
And his two good girls and his good little man
Oakened as they grew.

"I am not hungry for berries.
I am not hungry for bread.

But hungry hungry for a house
Where at night a man in bed

"May never hear the plaster
Stir as if in pain.
May never hear the roaches
Falling like fat rain.

"Where never wife and children need
Go blinking through the gloom.
Where every room of many rooms
Will be full of room.

"Oh my home may have its east or west
Or north or south behind it.
All I know is I shall know it,
And fight for it when I find it."

It was in a street of bitter white
That he made his application.
For Ruloph Reed was oakener
Than others in the nation.

The agent's steep and steady stare
Corroded to a grin.
*Why, you black old, tough old hell of a man,
Move your family in!*

Nary a grin grinned Rudolph Reed,
Nary a curse cursed he,
But moved in his House. With his dark little wife,
And his dark little children three.

A neighbor would *look*, with a yawning eye
That squeezed into a slit.
But the Rudolph Reeds and the children three
Were too joyous to notice it.

For were they not firm in a home of their own
With windows everywhere
And a beautiful banistered stair
And a front yard for flowers and a back yard for grass?

The first night, a rock, big as two fists.
The second, a rock big as three.
But nary a curse cursed Rudolph Reed.
(Though oaken as man could be.)

The third night, a silvery ring of glass.
Patience ached to endure.

But he looked, and lo! small Mabel's blood
Was staining her gaze so pure.

Then up did rise our Rudolph Reed
And pressed the hand of his wife,
And went to the door with a thirty-four
And a beastly butcher knife.

He ran like a mad thing into the night.
And the words in his mouth were stinking.
By the time he had hurt his first white man
He was no longer thinking.

By the time he had hurt his fourth white man
Rudolph Reed was dead.
His neighbors gathered and kicked his corpse.
"Nigger—" his neighbors said.

Small Mabel whimpered all night long,
For calling herself the cause.
Her oak-eyed mother did no thing
But change the bloody gauze.

from In the Mecca

Boy Breaking Glass

> *To Marc Crawford*
> *from whom the commission*

Whose broken window is a cry of art
(success, that winks aware
as elegance, as a treasonable faith)
is raw: is sonic: is old-eyed première.
Our beautiful flaw and terrible ornament.
Our barbarous and metal little man.

"I shall create! If not a note, a hole.
If not an overture, a desecration."

Full of pepper and light
and Salt and night and cargoes.

"Don't go down the plank
if you see there's no extension.

Each to his grief, each to
his loneliness and fidgety revenge.

Nobody knew where I was and now I am no longer there."

The only sanity is a cup of tea.
The music is in minors.

Each one other
is having different weather.

"It was you, it was you who threw away my name!
And this is everything I have for me."

Who has not Congress, lobster, love, luau,
the Regency Room, the Statue of Liberty,
runs. A sloppy amalgamation.
A mistake.
A cliff.
A hymn, a snare, and an exceeding sun.

■   Paul Vesey (Samuel W. Allen)

View from the Corner

Now the thing the Negro has *got* to do—
   I looked from my uncle to my dad
Yes, but the trouble with the *Negro* is—
   I looked from my dad to my uncle
I know, but the *first* thing the Negro has got to do—
   It was confusing.

This fellow, the Negro, I thought excitedly,
   must be in a very bad fix—
We'd all have to jump in and help—
   —such trouble—
   —all these things to do—
I'd never heard of anybody with so many things to do—
   Got to do!

I intensely disliked such things
   —go to school, wash your ears, wipe the dishes—
And what the *Negro* had to do sounded worse than that!
He was certainly in a fix, this Negro, whoever he was.

I was much concerned as I looked quietly at my uncle—
Now the thing the Negro has *got* to do—!

In My Father's House

A reverie

In my father's house, when dusk had fallen
I was alone on the dim first floor
I sensed someone, a power, desirous
Of forcing the outer door.
              How shall I explain—

I bolted it securely
And was locking the inner when
Somehow I was constrained to turn
To see it quietly open again.

Transfixed before the panther night
My heart gave one tremendous bound
Paralyzed, my feet refused
The intervening ground.
              How shall I say—

I was in the house and dusk had fallen
I was alone on the earthen floor
I knew there was a power
Lurking beyond the door.

I bolted the outside door
And was closing the inner when
I noticed the first had swung open again
My heart bound and I knew it would be upon me I rushed to the door
It came upon me out of the night and I rushed to the yard
If I could throw the ball the stone the spear in my hand
Against the wall my father would be warned but now
Their hands had fallen on me and they had taken me and I tried
To cry out but O I could not cry out and the cold grey waves
Came over me O stifling me and drowning me.

A Moment Please

When I gaze at the sun
   I walked to the subway booth
   for change for a dime
And know that this great earth

Two adolescent girls stood there
     alive with eagerness to know
is but a fragment from it thrown
     all in their new found world
     there was for them to know
in heat and flames a billion years ago,
     they looked at me and brightly asked
     "Are you Arabian?"
that then this world was lifeless
     I smiled and cautiously
     —for one grows cautious—
     shook my head.
as, a billion hence
     "Egyptian?"
it shall again be,
     Again I smiled and shook my head
     and walked away.
what moment is it that I am betrayed,
     I've gone but seven places now
Oppressed, cast down,
     and from behind comes swift the sneer
or warm with love or triumph?
     "Or nigger?"
     A moment, please
What is it that to fury I am roused?
     for still it takes a moment
What meaning for me
     now
in this homeless clan
     I'll turn
the dupe of space
     and smile
the toy of time?
     and nod my head.

That's Mighty Fine

> *In the mid Fifties, Willie McGee was executed in Missis-*
> *sippi for an alleged rape. Outside the prison, at the signal*
> *of his death, a waiting crowd sent up a rebel cheer.*

I was, I say, delighted with the splendid death row
Straight, boy, gleaming, pretty in the sun.

Because I mocked ole Willie down the last mile
Howled down his wretched hymn
Jabbered at his prayer
Almighty God, I say, the Almighty God, son conferred on me

the combination to the kingdom
A worthy God
who scorns the knives of niggers pleading.

Come along, now, Willie
You can make it
Only try.
You musn't, I say, son
    you musn't keep God waiting
    (with a twinkle in my eye)
Come right in
  take off your li'l ole robe
  no, please
  you sit down.
He screamed
  frothing at the mouth
  in a spastic frenzy
  til it got downright disagreeable—
So I pushed him.

When, at last
  we got the nigger dead
God Almighty said,
  Ah say, son
  that wuz mighty fine.

My Friend

To Jim

I have a friend
who reads higher mathematics and postquantum physics in his
    leisure.
He is, and has been for some time, a so-called Negro.
When he was a boy
He won a contest for the nation's high school students.
The prize was a four-year scholarship to college.
They found out he was colored
And they gave him a pin.

Even some of the Committee didn't like it
But the Daughters of the American Revolution were giving
                    part of the money
And the Daughters said, unfortunately,
                    it would offend our way of life.

Now my friend is not happy with his country.
He went to a so so school
and has a so so job

But not a so so feeling toward his so-called country.
He laughs a wild and high pitched laugh
> at the famed loyalty of the so-called Negro.
He is quickly and violently roused on the subject.
I'd publish every state secret I got my hands on,
> he almost shouts.
I, of course, tell him I don't believe this
And I point out it bees unpatriotic
> > undemocratic
> > and unamerican
And what is more,
the C.I.A. will get you, if you don't . . . watch . . . out!
He seems to think I'm joking, laughs evil
and carries on.

His friends used to say
If Stalin were to rise from his coffin
Day or lovely night
And call for a volunteer
> to lead a tank battalion through Mississippi—
There would be no problem.
Sometimes when I see his face
> at some innocent remark about the land of the free
I recall the war photos of the grim red tank commanders moving
> on Berlin
I think how lucky Mississippi would be to have them
> > moving in
> > > instead of him
My friend.

from Spirits Unchained

■ Keorapetse W. Kgositsile
(South African exile in America since 1960)

To Fanon*

Tears,
hiding behind a doomed god
no longer define
the soul
because of your shock therapy

---

* Frantz Fanon (1924–1961), Martinique-born, Paris-trained Negro psychiatrist, whose books delineate world black revolution.

history's psychosis will be cured
once soft shack-born melodies explode
in love-loving hollers
in the womb of the future
exposing the shallow trenches
of make-belief history to the fury
of the midday sun
and now lovers weaving
their dreams into infinite
realities with ghetto charms will
with the light of the poet
show Jesus miracles

Lumumba Section*

Searching past what we see and hear
Seering past the pretensions of knowledge
We move to the meeting place,
The pulse of the beginning the end and the beginning
In the stillnesses of the night
We see the gaping wounds where
Those murderers butchered your flesh
As they butchered the flesh of our land
Spirit to spirit we hear you
Then blood on blood comes the pledge
Swift as image, in spirit and blood
The sons and daughters of our beginnings
Boldly move to post-white fearlessness
Their sharpnesses at the murderer's throat
Carving your song on the face of the earth
In the stillnesses of the night
Informed by the rhythm of your spirit
We hear the song of warriors
And rejoice to find fire in our hands
"Ain't no mountain high enough . . ." Dig it,
The silences of the wind know it too
"Ain't no valley low enough . . ."
Freedom, how do you do!

Spirits Unchained

(For Brother Max Stanford)

Rhythm it is we
walk to against the evil

* Patrice Emery Lumumba, Congolese Prime Minister, assassinated in Katanga, 1961

of monsters that try to kill the Spirit
It is the power of this song
that colors our every act
as we move from the oppressor-made gutter
Gut it is will move us from the gutter
It is the rhythm of guts
blood black, granite hard
and flowing like the river or the mountains
It is the rhythm of unchained Spirit
will put fire in our hands
to blaze our way
to clarity to power
to the rebirth of real men

Brother Malcolm's Echo

Translated furies ring
on the page not thoughts
about life
but what should be
real people and things
loving love
this is real
the human Spirit moves
what should be
grinning molotov cocktails
replenishing the fire
WATTS happening
SHARPEVILLE burning
much too damn talking
is not
what's happening

Mandela's Sermon*

Blessed are the dehumanized
For they have nothing to lose
But their patience.

False gods killed the poet in me. Now
I dig graves
With artistic precision.

* Nelson Mandela, South African lawyer and leader of African National Congress until 1961, when he and other black leaders were imprisoned after a trial lasting four years.

from Song Of Lawino

■ Okot p'Bitek (Uganda)

I

Husband, now you despise me
Now you treat me with spite
And say I have inherited the stupidity of my aunt;
Son of the Chief,
Now you compare me
With the rubbish in the rubbish pit,
You say you no longer want me
Because I am like the things left behind
In the deserted homestead.
You insult me.

Stop despising people
As if you were a little foolish man,
Stop treating me like saltless ash.*
Become barren of insults and stupidity;
Who has ever uprooted the Pumpkin?

II

My husband treats me roughly.
The insults:
Words cut more painfully than sticks!
He says my mother is a witch,
That my clansmen are fools
Because they eat rats,
He says we are all Kaffirs.
We do not know the ways of God,
We sit in deep darkness
And do not know the Gospel,
He says my mother hides her charms
In her necklace
And that we are all sorcerers.

He says Black people are primitive
And their ways are utterly harmful,
Their dances are mortal sins
They are ignorant, poor and diseased!

* Salt is extracted from the ash of certain plants and also from the ash of the dung of domestic animals. The ash is put in a container with small holes in its bottom, water is then poured on the ash, and the salty water is collected in another container placed below. The useless saltless ash is then thrown on the pathway and people tread on it. (p'Bitek)

219

Ocol says he is a modern man,
A progressive and civilized man,
He says he has read extensively and widely
And he can no longer live with a thing like me
Who cannot distinguish between good and bad.

He says I am just a village woman,
I am of the old type,
And no longer attractive.

Ocol is no longer in love with the old type.
He is in love with a modern girl;
The name of the beautiful one
Is Clementine.

Brother, when you see Clementine!
The beautiful one aspires
To look like a white woman;
Her lips are red-hot
Like glowing charcoal,
She resembles the wild cat
That has dipped its mouth in blood,
Her mouth is like raw yaws
It looks like an open ulcer,
Like the mouth of a fiend!
Tina dusts powder on her face
And it looks so pale;
She resembles the wizard
Getting ready for the midnight dance;

I am not angry
With the woman with whom
I share my husband
I do not fear to compete with her.

All I ask
Is that my husband should stop the insults,
My husband should refrain
From heaping abuses on my head.
He should stop being half-crazy,
And saying terrible things about my mother.
Listen, Ocol, my old friend,
The ways of your ancestors
Are good,
Their customs are solid
And not hollow
They are not thin, not easily breakable
They cannot be blown away

By the winds
Because their roots reach deep into the soil.

Listen, my husband,
You are the son of a Chief.
The pumpkin in the old homestead
Must not be uprooted!

III

I was made chief of girls
Because I was lively,
I was bright,
I was not clumsy or untidy
I was not dull,
I was not heavy and slow.

I did not grow up a fool
I am not cold
I am not shy
My skin is smooth
It still shines smoothly in the moonlight

When Ocol was wooing me
My breasts were erect
And they shook
As I walked briskly,
And as I walked
I threw my long neck
This way and that way
Like the flower of *lyonno* lily
Waving in a gentle breeze.

I was the Leader of the girls
And my name blew
Like a horn
Among the Payira.
And I played on my bow harp
And praised my love.

You trembled
When you saw the tattoos
On my breasts
And the tattoos below my belly button;
And you were very fond
Of the gap in my teeth!

My husband says
He no longer wants a woman

With a gap in her teeth,
He is in love
With a woman
Whose teeth fill her mouth completely
Like the teeth of war-captives and slaves.

My husband is angry
Because, he says,
I cannot keep time
And I do not know
How to count the years.

Ocol has brought home
A large clock
It goes tock-tock-tock-tock
And it rings a bell.

He winds it first
And then it goes!
But I have never touched it.
I am afraid of winding it.

I wonder what causes
The noise inside it!
And what makes it go!

On the face of the clock
There are writings
And its large single testicle
Dangles below.
It goes this way and that way
Like a sausage-fruit
In a windy storm.

I do not know
How to tell the time
Because I cannot read
The figures.

I do not know
How to keep the white man's time.
My mother taught me
The way of the Acoli*
And nobody should

---

* The Acoli tribe, numbering about 250,000 members, flourishes in Northern Uganda. Their customs have been described by Anna Apoko, an Acoli, in "Growing Up in Acoli," *East African Childhood*, edited by Lorene Fox (1967). Mr. p'Bitek, the author, is also a member of the Acoli (or Acholi) tribe.

Shout at me
Because I know
The customs of our people!
When the baby cries
Let him suck milk
From the breast.
There is no fixed time
For breast feeding.

It is true
White man's medicines are strong,
But Acoli's medicines
Are also strong.
The sick gets cured
Because his time has not yet come.

But when the day has dawned
For the journey to Pagak
No one can stop you,
White man's medicines,
Acoli medicines,
Crucifixes, rosaries,
Toes of edible rats,
The horn of the rhinoceros
None of them can block the path
That goes to Pagak!

When Mother Death comes
She whispers
Come,
And you stand up
And follow
You get up immediately,
And you start walking
Without brushing the dust
On your buttocks.

You do not resist,
You must not resist.
You cannot resist!

But Ocol, my husband,
If you are not yet utterly dead
And fit only for the stomach of the earth,
If your heart-string
Is not yet completely cut,
Take courage,
Take a small amount of millet porridge,
Let them prop you up,

Drink some fish soup
Slowly, slowly
You will recover.

Let them drop simsim oil
Into the holes of your ear,
Let them scoop out the gum
That has filled your ears for so long,
The thick dust you collected
From the altar
And the chaff
From the books
And the useless things,
From the magazines and newspapers,
And the radio and television!

Brush your tongue
So thickly coated with bitter insults;
Here is warm water
There is some salt in it,
Gargle it,
Clean your mouth

Spit out the insults with the water!
The abuses you learnt
From your white masters
And the stupid stubbornness,
Spit them down with water.

And, son of the Bull,
When you are completely cured
When you have gained your full strength
Go to the shrine of your fathers,
Prepare a feast,
Give blood to your ancestors
Beg forgiveness from them
And ask them to give you
A new spear
A new spear with a sharp and hard point.
A spear that will crack the rock.

Ask for a spear that you will trust,
One that does not bend easily
Like the earth-worm.
Ask them to restore your manhood!
For I am sick
Of sharing a bed with a woman!

And I as your first wife,
Mother of your first-born,

Mother of your son and daughter,
I have only one request.

All I ask
Is that you give me one chance,
Let me praise you,
Son of the chief!
Let me dance before you,
My love,
Let me show you
The wealth in your house,
Ocol, my husband,
Son of the Bull,
Let no one uproot the Pumpkin.

from Coups de Pilon

■　David Diop (Dakar, Senegal)

Listen Comrades

Listen comrades of the struggling centuries
To the keen clamour of the Negro from Africa to the
 Americas
They have killed Mamba
As they killed the seven of Martinsville
Or the Madagascan down there in the pale light on the
 prisons
He held in his look comrades
The warm faith of a heart without anguish
And his smile despite agony
Despite the wounds of his broken body
Kept the bright colours of a bouquet of hope
It is true that they have killed Mamba with his white hairs
Who ten times poured forth for us milk and light
I feel his mouth on my dreams
And the peaceful tremor of his breast
And I am lost again
Like a plant torn from the maternal bosom
But no
For there rings out higher than my sorrows
Purer than the morning where the wild beast wakes
The cry of a hundred people smashing their cells
And my blood long held in exile

The blood they hoped to snare in a circle of words
Rediscovers the fervour that scatters the mists
Listen comrades of the struggling centuries
To the keen clamour of the Negro from Africa to the
    Americas
It is the sign of the dawn
The sign of brotherhood which comes to nourish the
    dreams of men.

The Renegade

My brother you flash your teeth in response to every
    hypocrisy
My brother with gold-rimmed glasses
You give your master a blue-eyed faithful look
My poor brother in immaculate evening dress
Screaming and whispering and pleading in the parlours of
    condescension
We pity you
Your country's burning sun is nothing but a shadow
On your serene 'civilized' brow
And the thought of your grandmother's hut
Brings blushes to your face that is bleached
By years of humiliation and bad conscience
And while you trample on the bitter red soil of Africa
Let these words of anguish keep time with your
    restless step—
Oh I am lonely so lonely here.

Africa

Africa my Africa
Africa of proud warriors in ancestral savannahs
Africa of whom my grandmother sings
On the banks of the distant river
I have never known you
But your blood flows in my veins
Your beautiful black blood that irrigates the fields
The blood of your sweat
The sweat of your work
The work of your slavery
The slavery of your children
Africa tell me Africa
Is this you this back that is bent
This back that breaks under the weight of humiliation
This back trembling with red scars

And saying yes to the whip under the midday sun
But a grave voice answers me
Impetuous son that tree young and strong
That tree there
In splendid loneliness amidst white and faded flowers
That is Africa your Africa
That grows again patiently obstinately
And its fruit gradually acquire
The bitter taste of liberty.
And the myths burn around me
Around me the wigs of learning
In great fires of joy in the heaven of your steps
You are the dance
And burn false gods in your vertical flame
You are the face of the initiate
Sacrificing his childhood before the tree-god
You are the idea of All and the voice of the Ancient
Gravely rocketed against our fears
You are the Word which explodes
In showers of light upon the shores of oblivion.

Nigger Tramp

You who move like a battered old dream
A dream transpierced by the blades of the mistral
By what bitter ways
By what muddy wanderings of accepted suffering
By what caravels drawing from isle to isle
The curtains of Negro blood torn from Guinea
Have you carried your old coat of thorns
To the foreign cemetery where you read the sky
I see in your eyes the drooping halts of despair
And dawn restarting the cottonfields and mines
I see Soundiata the forgotten
And Chaka the invincible
Fled to the seabed with the tales of silk and fire
I see all that
Martial music sounding the call to murder
And bellies that burst open amid snowy landscapes
To comfort the fear crouched in the entrails of cities
O my old Negro harvester of unknown lands
Lands of spice where everyone could live
What have they done with the dawn that lifted on your
    brow
With your bright stones and sabres of gold
Now you stand naked in your filthy prison
A quenched volcano exposed to other's laughter

To others' riches
To others' hideous greed
They called you Half-White it was so picturesque
And they shook their great jaws to the roots
Delighted at a joke not malicious in the least
But I what was I doing on your morning of wind and tears
On that morning drowned in spray
Where the ancient crowns perished
What did I do but endure seated upon my clouds
The nightly agonies
The unhealing wounds
The petrified bundles of rags in the camps of disaster
The sand was all blood
And I saw the day like any other day
And I sang Yéba
Yéba like a delirious beast
O buried promise
O forsaken seed
Forgive me Negro guide
Forgive my narrow heart
The belated victories the abandoned armour
Have patience the Carnival is over
I sharpen the hurricane for the furrows of the future
For you we will remake Ghana and Timbuktu
And the guitars shuddering with a thousand strokes
Great mortars booming under the blows
Pestles
Pounding
From house to house
In the coming day.

The Black Revolts

ASSERTIONS AND ARGUMENTS

An Interview with an Architect of Négritude: Césaire

■ Ellen Conroy Kennedy

We had arrived in the middle of the First World Festival of Negro Arts, a three week international spectacle held in the Senegalese capital in April 1966 bringing together from Africa, Europe, the Caribbean, North and South America black artists, writers, performers, scholars, in expositions of every art form from ancient to contemporary in handicraft, sculpture, painting, dance, theater, music, films, literature—the whole prefaced by a week-long Colloquium on "The Function and Meaning of Negro Art in the Life of the People." (See NEGRO DIGEST—June, July, August, September 1966)

The exhilaration was contagious. My own was dampened only by the fatigue of a transatlantic flight and the knowledge we had missed by just a few hours the "Nuit de la Poésie," a gala evening of dramatic readings by the Senegalese actor Bachir Touré, followed by the solemn awarding of Festival prizes in the numerous categories of competition.

A poetry reading the key event of a Festival of Negro Arts? Yes. But for the self-affirmative poetry through which 30 years earlier a small group of African and West Indian students in Paris found their authentic voice, re-discovered what they called their "négritude" the 1966 Festival would never have taken place. It was through this extraordinary body of writings—the poems of Aimé Césaire, Léopold Senghor, Birago and David Diop, Bernard Dadié, Jacques Rabemananjara and others—that "négritude" first found expression. It has matured since then from a simple protest against cultural assimilation into a cultural philosophy now articulated by Léopold Senghor, president of Senegal, as a new humanism in which the Negro's special contribution to world culture will at last have a fully recognized share. So the marriage of a gala poetry reading and the awarding of Festival prizes was particularly fitting.

I scanned the pages of Dakar Matin for a report of the evening and the literary prizes. The elder poets, Aimé Césaire and Léopold Senghor, for example, were not in the running, of course. From their group had come the juries to single out for honors writers of a younger generation. Césaire, who invented "négritude," philosophical premise of the Festival, and leader of the literary school grown up around it, had headed the

French language literary jury, I read, while the American poet Langston Hughes was chairman of the English language section. It was these elders, whose work is still so little translated and so little known in the United States, who drew my interest most. Theirs were the works I knew and would teach. I would have a chance to meet many of them, I was soon told, at a special post-Colloquium session where the Madagascan poet-statesman Jacques Rabemananjara would speak, two evenings later.

That evening, Aimé Césaire, Léon Damas, Alioune Diop, Bernard Dadié, Birago Diop, most of the Festival's French language literary notables (though not that visitor-from-another-planet, Evgeny Yevtuschenko) were circulating among the crowd gathered in the lobby of the Assemblée Nationale. The effect was rather like seeing Mallarmé, Rimbaud, Verlaine, Corbière, and Laforgue all in one room. Only Négritude's Baudelaire, President Senghor, seemed to be missing. Yet his presence was felt in every way but the physical, since the Festival was surely his creation more than any other single person's.

Langston Hughes was on hand, too, autographing books in green ink with wide round Palmer method letters. For Mr. Hughes was one of the surviving grand old men of the 1920's Harlem Renaissance. His poems and stories, together with those of Claude MacKay, Countee Cullen and Jean Toomer, had had a profound impact on the originators of Négritude, Negro students from French colonies in Africa and the Caribbean who read them in Paris a decade later.

Like Hughes, Césaire was seated at a card table, chatting with clusters of admirers, writing gracious dedications in copies of the various works they presented him: his poetry, *Les armes miraculeuses, Ferrements, Cadastre;* his plays, one of which, *La tragédie du roi Christophe,* later marked a high point of the Festival, with Senghor and Haile Selassie in gala attendance; his essays, the *Discours sur le colonialisme,* the *Lettre à Maurice Thorez* (his 1957 resignation from the French Communist Party), and his study of the Haitian revolutionary, *Toussaint l'Ouverture.*

I recognized him instantly, with something of a start. Yet how could one have expected to find the same young militant whose dark face, incendiary eyes and radiant white smile glow forth from a 1945 photograph?[1] Today, in his fifties, the poet's eyes are softened with spectacles, his face a trifle lined and heavier, his fervor perhaps not dampened, but seasoned by more than 20 years as poet parliamentarian. For the former lycée professor is also the longtime mayor of his home town Fort-au-France and Deputy from his island Martinique to the Chambre des Députés in Paris.

Turning his attention toward us, Césaire flashed his invincible, magnetic smile. Edouard Maunick, the young Mauritian poet we had met the day before, murmured an introduction. I passed Monsieur Césaire several volumes to autograph, mentioning my regret at not having found a copy of his first, and still best-known work, *Cahier d'un retour au pays natal.* This is the poem the late André Breton, dean of French surrealists, called

---

[1] In Lilyan Kesteloot's book, *Aimé Césaire, Poètes d'aujourdhui* 85, Seghers, Paris, 1962.

"nothing less than the greatest lyric monument of our time," in which he discovered "that major tone which distinguishes great from lesser poets." Publication of *Les armes miraculeuses* just after World War II, and of the first complete edition of the *Cahier* soon afterwards, established Césaire in the front rank of French poets. He was hailed as the great renewer of Surrealism, though his originality was far more than simply stylistic. The ethnic element, his magnificent messianic identification with all peoples of African heritage, these thematic qualities were still more distinctive. The poet's close friend, Senghor, has spoken of the *Cahier's* "parturition in pain," the pain of its genesis in the 25 year old poet's anguished confrontation with the misery of his island, his people, his race. A dramatic monologue of some 60 pages, his "notes on a return to the native land" begins as a bitterly ironic inventory of rage, despair, and frustration, to become an exorcism and then an acceptance, an immense surging affirmation of the poet's "Negroness, of *all* Negroness, and a personal dedication to its cause.

> . . . you know it is not from hate for
> other races that I seek to be the plowman of
> This single race

> . . . what I wish
> for the universal hunger
> for the universal thirst

> is to shake it free at last
> to summon from its inner depths
> the succulence of fruit.

If Léon Damas' startling poems, *Pigments* (1937), were the first rejection of cultural assimilation, Césaire's *Cahier* (written in 1938) was the first direct lyric proclamation of Négritude. His words, as Jean-Paul Sartre has put it, "do not describe Négritude, they do not designate it, they do not copy it from outside as a painter does a model; they *make* it; they compose it under our eyes." One of the great poems of our century, the *Cahier d'un retour au pays natal* is the literary movement's inspirational "emblem," the one incomparable work to which all African and West Indian poets in French refer, in whose stature they are measured.

Alas, the *Cahier* was temporarily out of print, Césaire said. And when would there be a new American edition? I knew there had been a bilingual version of only 1,000 copies with translations by Ivan Goll and Lionel Abel, published in 1947 by Brentano's in New York. Surely it was time it were available again! A Cuban refugee we knew owned Wilfredo Lam's original drawings for another edition, the French-Spanish one, published in Havana in 1944. Couldn't an American publisher put them together for a new French-English edition? "Why not?" smiled Césaire. And as for the drawings, if the old ones were not enough, perhaps Wilfredo would make new ones! Had he Lam's address? Yes, in a notebook at his brother's villa, where he was staying during the Festival. The poet jotted down a phone number on a tiny leaf of graphed notepaper, asking us to call a few days later, since he was leaving the city that evening. Césaire, and one or two other close friends, Maunick later told us, would be spending those few days in Casamance, the lush Southern part of Senegal, as guests of President Senghor. But now others were waiting to speak to the poet. We said goodbye and moved on.

The interview itself came about unexpectedly. I phoned on the appointed afternoon. Césaire had just lunched. He would be tied up the following day, our last in Dakar; but now he had an hour to spare before the dress rehearsal of *La tragédie du roi Christophe*. (Césaire's play about the rise and fall of Henri-Christophe, despot ruler of independent 18th-century Haiti, was a highpoint of the Festival. Its pertinence to the careers of certain contemporary African statesmen was not lost on the Dakar audience.) Would my husband and I care to come over right away? We were delighted, and asked if we could bring along a journalist friend who was also anxious to meet him.

The taxi left us in front of a large townhouse, just visible through the iron gate in a six-foot high wall. We rang, and Césaire himself came down to meet us, ushering us through a small garden, up a flight of stairs to the parlor floor. We stepped through a corridor into a spacious high-ceilinged room, its coolness refreshing after the almost blinding sunshine outside. A tall, shuttered window on the far side was open, letting in the sea breeze that brings relief in Dakar even from the intense midday heat. Leaning out, one caught a green glimpse, framed in the deep blue of sky and water, of the ancient fortress island, Gorée. Here for more than 200 years, captives from the African interior were held prisoner in slave-depots before their deportation West to the Americas. A museum now, the prison can be reached by motor launch from the harbor of Dakar in 15 minutes. During the Festival it was the scene of a nightly sound-and-light spectacular.

We shook hands, and I introduced the journalist friend who had accompanied us. Did Monsieur Césaire understand English? More or less, he indicated, though he preferred not to try to speak it. We decided to put our questions in French, and I would interpret if needed. Occasionally, as we talked, he would repeat a question in French, to check that he had understood it properly. As he spoke, I noticed he had the trace of a lisp. It interfered not at all with the warmth, the thoughtfulness and precision with which he talked, sometimes moving forward in his chair, occasionally breaking into smiles, pausing or altering his inflection to emphasize a point.

Interviewers: What are your impressions of the Festival, generally?
Césaire: Ah! The Festival is a real event, an historical achievement. For President Senghor, it is the realization of a 30-year wish. He has dreamed of organizing a festival of Negro arts since his student days in Paris. And here at last in Dakar are writers, artisans, artists, and performers from 34 countries of Africa, the U.S.A., the Antilles, Brazil

—all together—along with Africanists, and experts of all kinds. It is a meeting and a confrontation—the very first—of the performing and visual arts of the entire Negro world.

Interviewers: What is the Festival's particular meaning for you?

Césaire: It demonstrates, I think, that despite the differences that exist, there is a remarkable unity in the Negro world. To go further, I think it heralds the advent of African unity.

Interviewers: Unity, in the face of such vast political, economic, geographical and cultural diversity?

Césaire: Yes! I remember discussing this on various occasions with your Melville Herskovits [the late, distinguished anthropologist]. He always insisted that for him Africa was a vast number of different and unconnected cultures, while I held and continue to hold that despite this undeniable fact, there is something that transcends those differences, an underlying cultural unity.

Interviewers: If the Festival is the realization of a long-held dream, how is it related to the Negro Writers and Artists conferences [organized by the cultural review, *Présence Africaine*] of 1956 in Paris, and 1959 in Rome?

Césaire: The Festival is simply a more complete artistic manifestation. The earlier meetings were merely of intellectuals, a forum for the exchange of ideas. This has been the role of the Colloquium at the present Festival.

Interviewers: Has the concept of Négritude changed since you and Senghor originated it back in the 1930's?

Césaire: Not at all. The question now is to remain faithful to it, to develop it. It is not Négritude which has changed, but the historical situations. For a long time Négritude served as an *arme de guerre* in the political struggle against colonialism. Since independence, it has been able to take on a more constructive emphasis. *If anything, Négritude is more necessary today, than ever!* It has moral and ethical implications that should concern everyone. It must be valid for the whole Negro world. It is a philosophy which is emerging, bringing unity, making a synthesis of the traditional and the modern. It can have a vital role in directing the evolution of Africa. For we do not want the future of Africa left to chance.

You see, now that Négritude has been restored to its true dimensions, we can ask ourselves why Africa needs art, its own art. Quite simply because Africa has entered definitively into the *mouvance* of Western civilization. There is an obvious withering, a drying up in Western civilization, whose impact on the world is enormous. Africa must have its own art as a protection against acculturation, in order to retain its own personality.

Interviewers: What do you mean when you say Western civilization is drying up?

Césaire: That the European-American technical civilization which has overrun the world has come to an impasse. Modern man, master of the technical, has become the prisoner of objects, of categories, of the concepts he has created. He is the victim of "thingification," a process which tends to replace the real world with convenient summaries, with substitutes for nature that deprive it of its aura of the marvelous.

Interviewers: We understand you had a rather strong reaction to the address last week by Monsieur André Malraux. [Césaire had made a stinging rebuttal to remarks by André Malraux, Minister of Culture in the DeGaulle government, in the latter's speech to the Colloquium, later adapted as "Behind the Mask of Africa," in the *New York Times* Magazine, May 15, 1966. Though Césaire's remarks had reportedly left the spectators cheering, we were not sure his disagreement was well-founded.]

Césaire: Yes. It seemed to me that Malraux put the question badly [the question of the future of African art]. He said the modern African will never revive the emotion from which his ancestors sculpted the masks, that this inspiration "no less than what once inspired the cathedrals, is forever lost."

The problem is not to remake the masks, any more than it was for Europeans to remake the cathedrals. France did not end with the cathedrals, nor Italy with the Renaissance, nor Germany with Hegel! Every epoch illustrates the permanent genius of a race, people, a nation. The power of renewal is the very sign of the strength of a people, a culture. The problem of African art can only be posed in human terms. The black African artist recreates the world, animates the object. It is from his heart, his guts, his pulse that he brings forth his creation. If the African artist were merely to copy his past, failure would be the inevitable result. We want an African art which springs from the African's contemporary emotional response. This will be the measure of tomorrow's African and of tomorrow's Africa.

Interviewers: Is this then the function and meaning of Negro art in the life of the people—the theme of the Colloquium?

Césaire: Yes, and this is Senghor's hope for this First World Festival of Negro Arts, to stimulate such a renaissance, to mark Africa's coming of age as a producer and not just a consumer of culture. For to Senghor, you know, culture is an affair of state.

Interviewers: M. Césaire, as the inventor of the term, which you first used in the *Cahier* nearly 30 years ago, may we ask for your definition of a word we have been using throughout this interview?

Césaire: La Négritude? Yes. It has been so often abused, misrepresented, that it must be defended, and defined. Négritude is the simple realization of the fact of being black, the acceptance of this fact, of its cultural and historical consequences. In the time of abomination, in the years 1930 to 1940, Négritude was a moment of human consciousness. We [French-speaking] Negroes, caught by the white man in a deformative prism of stereotypes, reminded him, rather vehemently, I admit, that true humanism is one and indivisible, that it is only born of the dialogue between men of good will, who have rid themselves of mutual distrust and hatred. Négritude has never been anything else but an irritated and impatient postulation of fraternity. Impatient because we were being humiliated and we were being mutilated.

Interviewers: You speak first of Africa, but also of the rest of the Negro world. What role does Négritude have, or could it have, for example, in the United States? We find it a concept not generally understood in our country.

Césaire: Superficially, the tradition of Négritude is lost in the U.S.A., the French Antilles, Brazil. I mean among the Negro *bourgeoisie.* These people are terribly correct, terribly formal with each other, less instinctive, less spontaneous. This is the price they have paid in assimilating an alien culture. But Négritude is always there among the ordinary people.

Interviewers: Here you seem to describe Négritude as a particularly "Negro" way of being-in-the-world, rather than as you described it before, in terms of a philosophy which can give the Negro's group life, or Africa's cultural life, direction and meaning. Can you give us other examples of what you mean by Négritude as an underlying cultural unity?

Césaire: One finds it in dress, dance, songs, movement, in physical types. Just a day or two ago, as I was travelling in Casamance, I saw an old woman whose every motion, whose very face and expressions, reminded me of my own grandmother in Martinique.

Interviewers: You feel there is this underlying unity despite the obvious variations in physical types and in culture, not only among continental Africans today, but among their descendants in the Americas?

Césaire: Certainly there is variation. And no one would deny it. This diversity among Negroes must not be sacrificed. It enriches us. Just as we know Negro culture enriches Western civilization.

Interviewers: The other day we heard Ousmane Soce Diop (Senegalese Ambassador to the U.S. and U.N.) enlarge on this point at a P.E.N. club reception. He said that Négritude's insistence on the black man's unique contributions to world culture stands against the trend toward what he called "the universal standardization of man"—an idea you also express.

Césaire: Yes, he's quite right. You know, by the way, Ousmane Soce was the first African I met in Paris, in 1932. It was he who introduced me to Senghor.

Interviewers: M. Césaire, what are the prospects for other Festivals after this one?

Césaire: We hope that a second Festival can be organized within three to five years, perhaps the next time by an English-speaking country—for example, Nigeria. Nigeria has the largest Negro population in the world.

Interviewers: But we understand from Dr. Dike [Kenneth Dike, Chancellor of the University of Ibadan, and, like Césaire, a Vice-President of the Festival's International Committee] that such a Festival might well prove too costly an undertaking for his government during the next few years.*

Césaire: Yes, perhaps. But then there is Brazil—perhaps there may be a Festival in Rio de Janeiro. . . .

---

* The date of this interview is April 1966, some months prior to the opening of regional hostilities in Nigeria.

Interviewers: Why not the United States? Doesn't our country have the second largest Negro population in the world? How about a Festival in Washington? Think of it. A Festival of Negro arts where once there was a March-on-Washington. Imagine for a setting the combined resources of the Mall, Howard University, the National Gallery, the JFK Cultural Center . . .

Césaire: [Smiling, perhaps at our naiveté]: But that's up to you Americans, isn't it?

from Cahier d'un retour au pays natal

■ Aimé Césaire (Translated by Emile Snyder)

ô lumière amicale
ô fraîche source de la lumière
ceux qui n'ont inventé ni la poudre ni la boussole
ceux qui n'ont jamais su dompter la vapeur ni
l'électricité
ceux qui n'ont exploré ni les mers ni le ciel
mais ceux sans qui la terre ne serait pas la terre
gibbosité d'autant plus bienfaisante que la terre
déserte
davantage la terre
silo où se préserve et mûrit ce que la terre a de
plus terre
ma négritude n'est pas une pierre, sa surdité ruée
contre la clameur du jour
ma négritude n'est pas une taie d'eau morte sur
l'oeil mort de la terre
ma négritude n'est ni une tour ni une cathédrale

elle plonge dans la chair rouge du sol
elle plonge dans la chair ardente du ciel
elle troue l'accablement opaque de sa droite patience.

Eia pour le Kaïlcédrat royal!
Eia pour ceux qui n'ont jamais rien inventé
pour ceux qui n'ont jamais rien exploré
pour ceux qui n'ont jamais rien dompté

mais ils s'abandonnent, saisis, à l'essence de toute
chose
ignorants des surfaces mais saisis par le mouvement de toute chose
insoucieux de dompter, mais jouant le jeu du monde

véritablement les fils aînés du monde
poreux à tous les souffles du monde
aire fraternelle de tous les souffles du monde
lit sans drain de toutes les eaux du monde
étincelle du feu sacré monde
chair de la chair du monde palpitant du mouvement même du monde!
    Tiède petit matin de vertus ancestrales

Sang! Sang! tout notre sang ému par le coeur
mâle du soleil
ceux qui savent la féminité de la lune au corps
d'huile
l'exaltation réconciliée de l'antilope et de l'étoile

ceux dont la survie chemine en la germination de
l'herbe!
Eia parfait cercle du monde et close concordance!

Ecoutez le monde blanc
horriblement las de son effort immense
ses articulations rebelles craquer sous les étoiles
dures
ses raideurs d'acier bleu transperçant la chair
mystique
écoute ses victoires proditoires trompeter ses défaites
écoute aux alibis grandioses son piètre trébuchement

Pitié pour nos vainqueurs omniscients et naïfs!

Eia pour la douleur aux pis de larmes réincarnées
pour ceux qui n'ont jamais rien exploré
pour ceux qui n'ont jamais rien dompté

Eia pour la joie
Eia pour l'amour
Eia pour la douleur aux pis de larmes réincarnées.

et voici au bout de ce petit matin ma prière virile
que je n'entende ni les rires ni les cris, les yeux
fixés sur cette ville que je prophétise, belle,

donnez-moi la foi sauvage du sorcier
donnez à mes mains puissance de modeler
donnez à mon âme le trempe de l'épée

je ne me dérobe point. Faites de ma tête une tête
de proue
et de moi-même, mon coeur, ne faites ni un père,

ni un frère,
ni un fils, mais le père, mais le frère, mais le fils,
ni un mari, mais l'amant de cet unique peuple.

Faites-moi rebelle à toute vanité, mais docile à
son génie
comme le poing à l'allongée du bras!

Faites-moi commissaire de son sang
faites-moi dépositaire de son ressentiment
faites de moi un homme de terminaison
faites de moi un homme d'initiation
faite de moi un homme de recueillement
mais faites aussi de moi un homme d'ensemencement

faites de moi l'exécuteur de ces oeuvres hautes
voici le temps de se ceindre les reins comme un
vaillant homme—

Mais les faisant, mon coeur, préservez-moi de toute
haine

O friendly light
O fresh source of light
those who have invented neither gunpowder nor compass
those who tamed neither steam nor electricity
those who explored neither the sea nor the sky
but those without whom the earth would not be the earth
    gibbosity all the more beneficient, as the deserted earth is all the
more earth
    silo where is ripened and preserved what is earthiest in earth
    my Negritude is not a stone, its deafness thrown against the
clamour of the day
    my Negritude is not a speck of dead water on the dead eye of earth
    my Negritude is neither a tower nor a cathedral

    it thrusts into the red flesh of the soil
    it thrusts into the warm flesh of the sky
    it digs under the opaque dejection of its rightful patience

Eia for the royal *Kailcedrat!*
Eia for those who invented nothing
for those who have never discovered
for those who have never conquered

    but, struck, deliver themselves to the essence of all things,
    ignorant of surfaces, but taken by the very movement of things
    not caring to conquer, but playing the game of the world

truly the elder sons of the world
porous to all the breath of the world
fraternal space of all the breath of the world
bed without drain of all the waters in the world
spark of the sacred fire of the world
flesh of the flesh of the world
panting with the very movement of the world
Tepid dawn of ancestral virtues

Blood! Blood! All our blood stirred by the male heart of the sun
Those who know the feminine nature of the moon's oily flesh
the reconciled exultation of the antelope and the star
those whose survival moves in the germination of grass
Eia! perfect circle of the world and close concordance!

Hear the white world
horribly fatigued by its immense effort
its rebellious articulations crack under the hard stars
its inflexibilities of blue steel pierce the mystic flesh
hear its treacherous victories trumpeting its defeats
hear with grandiose alibis the pitiful stumbling

Mercy for our omniscient and naive conquerors!

Eia for grief at the udders of reincarnated tears
For those who explored nothing
For those who never mastered

Eia for joy
Eia for love
Eia for grief at the udders of reincarnated tears

Here at the end of the dawn is my virile prayer
that I may not hear the laughter or the cries, my eyes fixed on this
city which I prophesy shall be beautiful
give me the savage faith of the sorcerer
give my hands the power to mould
give my soul the sword's temper
I won't evade. Make my head a prow

and of myself, my heart, make neither a father nor a brother
nor a son, but the father, the brother, the son,
not the husband, but the lover of this unique people.

Make me refractory to vanity, but docile to their genius
as the fist to the extended arm!

make me commissar of their blood
make me trustee of their resentments

make me a man of termination
make me a man of initiation
make me a man of meditation
but also make me a man of germination

make me the executioner of these mighty deeds
this is the time to gird one's loins like a valiant man

but so doing, my heart, preserve me from all hatred

A Conversation with Léopold Senghor

■ Translated from French to English by
Rosey E. Pool

*During his state visit to the United States in the fall of 1966, President
Léopold Senghor of Senegal, the poet and philosopher of Negritude,
paused in Washington, D.C., for a relaxed conversation with some of his
friends.*

*The talk which ensued was taped, and a portion of it is published here.
The emphasis, of course, is on the statements made by President Senghor
in response to questions and comments made by the three people with
whom he talked. Although the President speaks English, he is more at
home in his native French, and it is in that language that he conversed.
The French was translated into English by Dr. Rosey E. Pool, who took
part in the conversation. Following is an identification of the conversa-
tionalists who, in the transcription, are not always identified:*

Dr. Rosey E. Pool, anthropologist (*Beyond the Blues*) and teacher, who
recently ended her second stint as Visiting Professor of English at Alabama A & M College at Huntsville.

Samuel Allen, who writes poetry under the name *Paul Vesey* and who
is Chief Legal Advisor to the Ministry of Justice, Department of Community Relations.

Wilfred Cartey, professor of Literature at Columbia University and
Chairman of the Literature Section of the United States Association of
African Studies.

Cartey: Poet, philosopher, statesman, "I salute you in the silence" and
I and my colleagues here would like to honor you. This afternoon we also
want to look for "the humming of fragrances," we want to plunge into
the libations of Negritude and, also, Mr. President, we want to touch the
silence which flashes in the night of your poetry. So, for us here this leaves
a question which tantalizes. I mean about a kind of unity between the

poet and the politician, the great writer and the head of state. Is there a discord or is there harmony between the two?

Senghor: No, I don't think there is a discord. In a way, the upheaval was the beginning of it all. In the beginning of their lives, I think all poets are like that, but I, myself, was somewhat swerving between my family and the missionaries who instructed me in the Catholic religion. I swerved somewhat between the African Negro tradition and the French culture I was being taught. I swerved between the Black African animist tradition and the Christian tradition, which I was being taught. That, I think, was my first upheaval. When I was studying at Liberman I had many occasions to explain this. I had a professor who told me that we were savages, that we had no traditions, that we had no civilization, that we were merely responsive to the hollow sound of the word and that we didn't put ideas behind the words. That Father, Father LeLouze, was really my teacher because, on the one hand, I reacted against the things he told me; I was a child, I had no reasoning, but I had intuition about a Black African civilization. I had the intuition that we had roots in a profound spiritual tradition, but, at the same time, I took in the Father's teaching and I believe that is the reason why I have always taken care to put an idea or an emotion behind the words, and that I have made it a habit to be suspicious of the mere music of words, because I was indeed extremely sensitive to this music of words. And so, I was led to an ideal, the ideal to defend this civilization which one denied us, the ideal of making this civilization manifest, of illustrating it. I was then 15 years old, and my ideas were rather confused. I think that all my research got its orientation at that point. Look, at that time I had a twofold ideal; in the first place, I wanted to be a priest in order to save my people, so to speak; and I wanted to be a professor and teach. Therefore, I do not think there is an antithesis between, on the one hand, religion, and political activities on the other. Neither do I have the impression that there is an antithesis between literary activities at universities and political activities. That is the reason why I think that all these different activities are just different complemental means to the same end. At the start I was split, but now no more.

Question: That means, I suppose, that now word and action are one?

Senghor: I believe that the word helps the deed and the deed helps the word. I think that is still very African. For instance, take the sculptor who carves a mask; he has learned a skill, hasn't he: the skill of carving. And he has also learned to carve under the observation of certain laws, certain rules. Right? But at the same time he executes a religious action when he carves the sculpture. Like this: this mask becomes the personification of what I call the idea—emotion. Or, if you like, the mask will be the materialization of a myth, an image symbol. And there is not just the material, the technical side, there is also the spiritual. And while this sculptor carves, he sings a song, he sings a poem and he weaves a poem. And there you see the significant and the significance. The image and the idea living in symbiosis.

Question: Excuse me for interrupting you, Mr. President. Do I understand you correctly that there would be a fusion between African animism and the Christian faith? Does that enter into Negritude?

Senghor: No. I mean, in the beginning, I was torn between Black African animism and Christianity. If I had been a Muhammedan I might have said I was torn between Black African animism and Islam. But, there again, I have arrived at a kind of synthesis. When you read the Bible or when you read the Koran, or nowadays, when you read a book of "Yesterday's Arabs," and today I got the confirmation of all this, look at the Semites: at their root there is first a kind of crossbreed between the Negroids who lived all over North Africa and the Middle East and the Semites who came afterwards. And I have a friend, a Jew, Albert Memi, who is writing a study which will have the title: "Judaism and Negritude." And I have often said it, in an article for instance about the Concilium and about the black priests, I have said that it was their task to bring Christianity back to its tradition, to the tradition of the word-word.

Question: You mean . . . ?

Senghor: . . . the word—symbol. You see, in this way Black African animism, Christianity and Islam are not opposites . . . animism and Christianity and Islam are on the same level, the level of the word-symbol.

Question: Does this mean that the word-symbol of Negritude is a kind of religion?

Senghor: It is a kind of religion. You know very well that in Black Africa there is no contrast between religion, art, and skill. The arts—poetry, the mask—it is all part of *the* religion. The arts are merely a way to express religion to the people. During the Christian middle ages this was the same; all the arts lived in the cathedrals, in the religious services. One could say that division and dychotomy began in the Renaissance when the contrast between the sacred and the civilian- or lay-world came into being.

Question: Seen like this, Negritude would be linked with the navel of Europe.

Senghor: But . . . but. . . .

Question: That's what you said, didn't you?

Senghor: But . . . but I think, on a very ancient level, Negritude rejoins the total of civilization and the symbol civilizations. There is something which I've said somewhere, something that has touched me . . . Some years ago I visited in Paris an exposition of Gallic art. It makes me smile because in the beginning we were taught that 2,000 years ago our country was called France and our ancestors the Gallic. But when I went to see that exposition I was stunned. That Gallic art resembled Negro art, and I began to ask myself why Gallic art looked like Negro art and, finally, I think those Gauls. . . . Now look at the Scots, the Welsh, the British, the people of the Auvergne, they are passionate people; you could say . . . there are those Celts and those Negroes, they are mystic people; they are people of mysticism who express themselves in images and rhythm. I recommend the book of ancient Gaelic poetry to you; you will see how it absolutely resembles . . . ?

Question: The same thing . . .

Senghor: Read the old Hebrew poems, the ancient Egyptian; read the old Arabic poetry before the Islamic period.

Question: I think Dr. Pool wants to ask you something with regard to this subject.

Miss Pool: Mr. President, there is a question that rose in me; please allow me to ask you this out of my 'Blanchitude.' Is it possible . . . do you think it is possible for a white man or a white woman to identify absolutely with Negritude, to, put it like this, not to appreciate or to look at Negritude sympathetically but to really live Negritude?

Senghor: Certainly I think this is possible because, in essence, the qualities which I have discovered in Negritude—imagery, symbolism, rhythm —are equally found in other races. For instance, priests, and artists, must have the gift of imagery, of symbolism, of rhythm. In principle they must, I mean . . .

Question: Excuse me.

Senghor: Yes?

Question: Is there such a thing as . . . how do I say this . . . as identification with tropical man?

Senghor: I'll get to that. I think that all the qualities are apparent in all races, on all continents. But look, a certain race or a certain continent will lean on one quality, the other on a different one. Since the Renaissance, the Europeans have leaned heavily on discursive reasoning, on analysis, etc., while Black Africa, and even the Arabs, have been leaning on intuitive reasoning, on intuition, symbols. But still I think that a white individual can identify with Black people. Look, since the rise of jazz, since the American influence which has spread the jazz, the Negro dance, American dance, we find that American music, that Negro-American music, that American Negro dance has invaded the world. And nowadays we see the revolt of the youth of Europe against the older generation. In fact, this European youth, those who dance . . .

Question: Excuse me a moment, but there is a difficult question: If the Negritude of inspiration is of an intuitive spirit, how then can a Black man enter industrial society? There is your famous "New York" poem; is that sufficient in the 20th century, this spirit, this infusion of warmth?

Senghor: Yes . . .

Question: Human nature?

Senghor: . . . Yes; I think that is possible. In Montreal I lectured on the subject of "Francophonie," and I showed how Descartes was uniquely cartesian, analytical and how, by contrast, Pascal adds to the cartesian idea, the spirit of the faith, and how in the 20th century a man like Pierre Telhard de Chardin associates himself with him, one could say reason, analytical reason, cartesian reason and intuitive reason. And again, in our days, knowledge is no longer the same as in the days of Descartes—I mean, a string of abstract evidences. In modern knowledge enters the element of experience, the fact, an element of intuition. And it is Einstein who said that, in our days, the intuition of a mystic is needed for contemporary science.

Question: I believe, excuse me, Sir, that this is the question: that nowadays, e.g. in this country . . . is it possible to enter into the 20th century with intuition, with faith and all that . . . in a machine country?

Senghor: Yes, but . . .

Question: . . . and with power.

Senghor: But one can enter into the 20th century; that is what we are trying to do. In our schools we put high value on two things: the study of the French language, that is of an analytical language, a discursive language, and the study of mathematics, because we must become rationalist persons. But, at the same time, we encourage the arts, because man consists of two elements. This matches in the first place the Black African tradition. For the African Negro there is a male and a female element in every individual; an element of discursive reason and an element of intuitive reason. And, in our days, epistemology, that is the science of knowledge, has changed. It is no longer sufficient to re-think, to analyze an object in order to know it, but we must also *live* this object . . . And there is a sociologist who studies the American Negro. He says that in order to know the American Negro it is not enough to do, like, e.g. Melvin Herskovits, and set up ethnological analyses with statistics, etc. One must live like the Negro. And this man took something to transform himself and he lived as a Negro. He had the intuition inside the Negro. In this way is in our time complete knowledge a symbiosis of discursive reason and intuitive reason . . .

Question: Excuse me . . .

Senghor: In my opinion . . .

Question: All right, but is this also true with regard to mastering the exterior world? All modern science?

Senghor: Exactly. In our days, in order to master the exterior world, we must overtake cartesian rationalism, we must overtake positivism, and intellectualism. We need enthusiasm, intuition, don't we? And it has been observed that the young scholars of our time, the young scholars of today, are more and more intuitive, and that discovery is a kind of enthusiasm.

Question: In that way, can we say that now the world is approaching a kind of intuitive philosophy which will guide and direct the other philosophies of the world?

Senghor: No, I don't say that, I believe . . .

Question: In a mixture?

Senghor: No. I believe that the world . . . really that we are arriving at a universal civilization in which man, if you like to put it that way, will produce in himself the symbiosis of the qualities of all races, and particularly the symbiosis of the white European and the Black African. You see, more and more . . .

Question: Like, perhaps, you, Mr. President, said it yourself in 1959 at the occasion of the Second Conference (of Negro Writers and Artists) when you said that the world must be animated, the entire world; that is what you said, didn't you, and is that what you want to convey now?

Senghor: Yes, yes. Look, for instance what produces the power of the United States? Every day, in the United States 150 most important books or scientific articles are published. One could say that America is now the prototype of technological civilization, the prototype of industrial civilization. And, at the same time, thanks to the Black people, one meets among the American nation a spontaneous kind of people, really a people of spontaneity and today's America rejoins . . . today's America lives in symbiosis within herself, a symbiosis of the most rational, the utmost technological and at the same time the enthusiasm of the Negro. Look . . .

Question: In its very essence?
Senghor: In its very essence. Look, at the World Festival of Negro Arts many people said that the performances of the American Negroes were the best. Why? Because there we have . . . the American Negro has retained his Negro enthusiasm, the Negro intuition. And, isn't it, at the same time, he expresses this with the technological perfection which is American. Whether this concerns Duke Ellington or the Du Paur choir, whether it is in the ballet, the Harlem ballet . . .
Question: Does this mean that the gift of African man is spontaneity and then intuition?
Senghor: In my opinion . . .
Question: And then what, sir?
Senghor: You know that is very difficult to say.
Question: So I believe . . .
Senghor: Briefly: I believe that the Black Africans have indeed brought in intuition and artistic expression. I mean philosophical intuition, ontological intuition, in the deepest sense of the word, that which the Germans call "Weltanschauung," and on the other hand they brought artistic expression. I believe that the Black man has contributed this. And what did the white man bring? He brought the idea of method and technology.
Question: But with regard to the Festival, Mr. President, I think I could see at the Festival in the African dance and music manifestations, something which was a combination of intuition and a very high level of professionalism. It was not only the Americans, but indeed it was the Mali companies, for instance, who were really very great professionals and also with all the intuition and the fervor of Africa. And, in your opinion, what is the significance of such a Festival? Not just for those who took part in it, but also for the world at large?
Senghor: But it is evident that the Negro of our days has undergone the technological influence of Europe, whether he knows it or not. The Mali show was very good because there was a certain technique, and that was inspired by Europe, wasn't it? But there is also an African technique, that must be said . . .
Question: Indeed.
Senghor: But the African technique is the result of experience, comes from experience rather than from discursive analysis. In the same way the chief diseases were cured by Africans before the arrival of the white man. I remember that, in the early days, when yellow fever occurred, the European physicians could not cure the yellow fever, but the African doctors did cure the fever. Today we have, for instance, anti-biotics. We have found them through groping our way about, through experiences, through intuition, whereas the white man has arrived at the same result via analysis, not through experience but through experiment.
Question: I have a question, Mr. President. It is always dangerous to ask a poet to explain his poetry, but I think you have said in respect of

the man of politics and the statesman, something which contradicts somewhat your poem "Chacka." There the great warrior kills "Holivé" because he can not be both, that is to say he cannot be statesman, warrior, head of his people and, at the same time, a poet, a sensitive man. Is there a contradiction . . . ?

Senghor: No, no.

Question: Am I mistaken?

Senghor: No. You see, "Chacka" is a legend. Now what is a legend? It is an idea, an idea expressed in a concrete form. First, we have the historical fact. "Chacka" killed his bride, he killed his mother too. That is not my invention. Right? And he did it in order to realize a political dream. All right, we could say I wanted to express myself this way: the contradiction which exists relates to the extreme demands of politics and private life, but, quite obviously, I did not myself act like Chacka . . . Or in this way: remember the seventeenth century, there was in the theatre, in the French threatre, a similar legend or a similar myth treated by different poets. We have the same legends, the same historical facts, treated in different ways by Corneille or Racine. Each of them takes a myth and expresses himself across it. Take Césaire, he has just written *Une saison en Enfer* (*Some Time in Hell*), and in *Saison en Enfer,* he makes (Patrice) Lumumba, doesn't he, a great political figure, a prophet. I said to him: "But Lumumba, I have little admiration for Lumumba. In his life he was, let's face it, a rather mediocre man who could not control his passions." And he said to me: "That does not matter! All I wanted to express was an idea." And he was right.

Question: I agree with you, I agree.

Question: Tell me something, Mr. President.

Senghor: Yes. If you see an apparent contradiction, there is an apparent contradiction, but I myself changed the facts in order to express myself.

Question: So, in the ideal sense, there is no contradiction.

Senghor: No, that's right. In life the contradiction does exist, but a poem is life re-arranged; one modifies the balance of the relations as they are found in life.

Question: Now, Mr. President, if you had to select one of your poems for recitation, which one would you choose?

Senghor: Ah . . . when I was younger I knew all my poems by heart, but now, unfortunately, I do not know them by heart. And the ones I prefer, I can't tell you that, because usually I am all wrapped up in my latest one, in my most recent poem, and that is why I have no preference. I could say the poem which is the best expression of myself is always the one I wrote last.

Question: So right.

Question: May I ask you in which poem of our, American, literature you find evidence of Negritude?

Senghor: Ah, in Langston Hughes; Langston Hughes is the most spontaneous as a poet and the blackest in his expression. For me, it is Langston Hughes and also the popular poems of Sterling Brown. You see? It appears to me that Langston Hughes and Sterling Brown are the most Negro. I do not say that theirs are the best poems on an artistic level. Take, for instance, Countee Cullen. It has often been said that Countee Cullen was so sophisticated, that he was a *bourgeois*. He is beautiful, because there is drama in Cullen's work, there is pain, there is drama. He has beauty, but the songs of Langston Hughes are pure, spontaneous and simple.

Question: So, in consequence, spontaneity, purity, simplicity, etc. . . . is that the element of the poetry of Damas, to mention one? If we change the subject a little.

Senghor: Exactly.

Question: Has he got all these things?

Senghor: I'd like to say, yes, because among all of us Damas is one of the most spontaneous, one who is most Negro. I must say that, in order to judge the human quality of a poem—I do not say its philosophical quality—the best one can do is ask the women. You will find that women are very spontaneous, and I know many women who love Damas, who prefer Damas and understand him. In a certain sense, Damas is the blackest among us. I am working on a study about the rhythm in the poetry of Damas; it is absolutely Negro rhythm and in that way resembles Langston Hughes very much.

Question: I know you also know the young American poets. Among them there are some who are indeed Negro poets, I think . . .

Senghor: Right. I do not know them well enough; I'd like to know them. I got as far as Bruce Wright, and O'Higgins . . . But I know that since there are young poets, and Langston Hughes and I have agreed, that when I have time I shall meet some on the evening of the sixth, if I do not have a dinner to attend I could meet Negro-American writers. I told him I especially wanted to meet the young ones because I know the older writers and that I wanted to have a bath of youth and wanted to see the new trends.

Question: There are some who are indeed Black, Mr. President.

Question: Mr. President, Mme. Pool, Mr. Allen, and myself can indeed thank you most warmly for having been here with us, and in the name of the U.S.I.A. we wish you God-speed! Thank you, Sir.

Senghor: I too thank you. Before we end I want to say that we owe a great deal to the United States. Indeed, with regard to our Negritude, we have depended largely on the teachings of our professors of ethnology, anthropology on the subject of Black African civilizations. But, was it not the "New Negro" movement, the movement of the "Negro Renaissance," with Alain Locke and the others, was it not they who stimulated us to do as they did, to write poetry! In this way, and at this moment, I want to give to America that which is due to her, that is to say to have been, in a way, the initiator of Negritude.

The Defense and Illustration of Négritude*

■ Léopold Sédar Senghor
President, Republic of Senegal

We deeply appreciate the honor that devolves upon us at the First World Festival of Negro Arts to welcome so many talents from the four continents, from the four horizons of the spirit. But what honors us most of all and what constitutes your greatest merit is the fact that you will have participated in an undertaking much more revolutionary than the exploration of the cosmos: the elaboration of a new humanism which this time will include the totality of humanity on the planet Earth.

Senegal welcomes you, therefore, as distinguished guests and first of all, Dakar greets you, thus fulfilling its mission. For Dakar, a black plowshare cast in the fertile ocean, has always answered the call of the trade-winds and welcomed visitors arriving by sea or by air. Thus we can enter into a dialogue, the mainspring of civilizations, or at any rate, of culture.

Here we are, here you are assembled. Ethnologists and sociologists, historians and linguists, writers and artists. Your task will be to seek out, to spell out the *function of Negro art* in the life of the black man. The function, or rather the signs. But, basically, you will probe beyond those signs to discover their meaning. Today, more modestly, as an old *militant of Négritude,* I should like to say less about the function and meaning of Negro art—which I have tried to treat elsewhere—than about the function and significance that we Senegalese attribute to this First World Festival of Negro Arts. In a word, if we have assumed the terrible responsibility of organizing this Festival, it is for the *Defense and Illustration of Négritude.*[1]

For people are continuing here and there throughout the world to deny African art as well as Négritude, by which I mean the Negro values of civilization. And when they can no longer deny Negro art because it is so evident they try to contest its originality: its human truth.

African art has been denied on the pretext that it presents different forms. And in fact, if it is indeed an entity, it is in the diversity of its fields, its types, even its styles. Like European art which under its Italian, French, German, Russian, or Swedish appearance derives from Greco-Latin civilization: from discursive reason animated by Christianity. Like European art which, subjected to frequent revolutions, nevertheless remains European in its fundamental characteristics. To return to African art, it is all the more a unit because, if its function is always to actualize its object, I mean its matter, its nature on the contrary is always to express

---

* The address delivered at the opening of the Colloquium on Negro Art and Culture, which launched the First World Festival of Negro Arts at Dakar in April, 1966.

[1] This is a paraphrase of a famous sixteenth century French title: *La Défense et Illustration de la langue française.* The word "illustration" here has the special meaning: making illustrious.

it's object by means of the same signs: in the same profound style which is precisely to *stylize* it.

As a result one can not long deny Negro art because the Europeans themselves were the first to discover and to define it—the Negro Africans preferred to live it. The most eminent European artists and writers defended it, from Pablo Picasso to André Malraux whose presence here I salute as conclusive evidence. And I need not speak about the African and American Negro writers and artists who, between the two World Wars and since 1945 have won the attention of a world torn apart and which, because it was torn asunder, was seeking its unity, its authenticity.

Unable then to deny Negro art they have tried to minimize its originality, claiming that it had no monopoly either over emotion or over the analogical image, not even over the rhythm. And it is true that every genuine artist has these gifts whatever his continent, his race, his nation may be. Nevertheless Rimbaud had to claim kinship with Négritude, Picasso had to be overwhelmed by a Baoulé mask, Apollinaire had to sing of wooden fetishes before Western European art would consent, after two thousand years to abandon *physéôs mimésis* (the imitation of nature). It is in large measure the fault of Negro art—a very fortunate fruitful fault —that the artists of that same Western World are inspired today like Bazaine by the "most obscure effort of instinct and sensitivity," and that, like Masson, they define the work of art as "a simple play of forms and values that are legibly organized." In brief, a simple rhythm: "a play of forces" my friend Soulages would have said, because rhythm is harmonious movement in that it signifies forms.

But it is not only a question of defending the Negro art of the past as it is exhibited today in the Musée Dynamique; it is even more a matter of making it illustrious by showing what it is in the middle of the twentieth century: a gusher that does not run dry, a basic, significant element of the civilization of the universal which is being constructed before our eyes by us and for us, by all and for all.

And first of all for the Negro writers and artists as is evidenced by the exposition of contemporary art which bears the meaningful title "Tendencies and Confrontation." And so, after the first and then the second World War, from everywhere—Africa, America and the very heart of Europe— young black men and girls have risen, like young trees pruned by those two wars. From the depth of their ancestral experiences, from the depth of their more recent experiences as slaves and as colonized people or simply as men of this century, wide open to all contributions, they have discovered, along with a new vision of the world, the new words of the new Negro, words that they provided. Their works did not need to be placed in anthologies or in museums to fulfill that function which is to express life, to represent it, so as to help men, all men, to live better.

To help their black brothers, before all others. Think of the former black slaves of America deported from mother Africa. If they did not surrender to the *taedium vitae* (tedium of life); if they did not give up, like other races destined to die in weak, sorrowful languor, it was because they had carried within them from the motherland, along with the "lust for life," that creative power which is the original trademark of art. For art is nothing other than this primal gesture of *Homo sapiens* (thinking man) who, representing life by the symbolic image, intensifies it by rhythm, thus magnifying it to give it the value of eternity. Such at least is Negro art and to refer again to the Negro Americans, the art of Negro spirituals and the blues. The most ordinary labor of the peasant, the most painful labor of the slave, vivified because it is magnified by the word, by the song, by the dance: by the rhythmic energy which is the very stuff of life.

But slavery belongs to the past. Today in Senegal, to take a current example, the new national art, rooted in the black basalt of Cap Vert, is being built up once again in Dakar, a crossroads swept by all the pollens in the world as well as by images and ideas. Saving us from despair this Negro art sustains us in our effort toward economic and social development, in our *determination to live.* So too do our poets, short story writers and novelists, our singers and dancers, our painters and sculptors, our musicians. Whether they paint violent mystical abstractions or the noble elegance of royal African courtships; whether they sculpt the national lion or fantastic monsters; whether they dance the Development Plan or sing the diversification of crops, the Negro African artists, the Senegalese artists of today help us to live today, to live a better, more abundant life. To live more, that is to say, more intensely, reinforcing the high tension that characterized the North Sudanese Negro African civilization, to live better in order to resolve the concrete problems that condition our future.

Listening to me, one might believe that Negro art is only a *technique:* an ensemble of means at the service of a civilization of the comfortable or, in any case, at the service of material production. Let me explain: I have spoken not merely of economic *growth,* but of *development,* that is to say the correlative and complementary totality of matter and spirit, of the economic and social, of the body and the soul. I have spoken at the same time of the production of material goods and spiritual goods. When I speak of *Négritude,* I am referring to a civilization where art is at once technique and vision, handicraft and prophecy; where art expresses, in the words of Ogotemmêli: "the identity of material gestures and spiritual forces." The same aged Negro said the other day: "The weaver sings as he pushes his shuttle and his voice continues the chain, aiding and leading the chant of the ancestors." This means simply that all art in Black Africa —weaving, sculpture, painting, music and dance—is speech, or better still the *Word,* I mean *Poetry.* In fact, form and colors, timbres and tones, movement, even the materials used by the artists have the effectiveness of the Word provided they are rhythmic. For speech, having become the Word, because it has the rhythm of the primeval movement, the form of things named, recreates them, makes them more present, *more true.* Thus it accomplishes the action of the Creator because, by renewing that action, it prolongs it by art which, once again, eternizes the life of things and beings by vivifying and magnifying that life. Beyond its vital function, this is *the significance of Negro art:* It makes us resemble God by having us participate in its creation.

I have almost finished. By helping the defense and illustration of Negro art, Senegal is conscious of helping to build the Civilization of the Universal.

In fact, even before our national independence, during the past twenty years or so, we have never stopped basing our policy on *Dialogue*. In all fields and essentially in the realm of culture. For culture is the first requisite and the final objective of all development. But, to dialogue with others, to take part in the common work of conscientious, determined men who springing up everywhere in the world, to bring new values to the symbiosis of complementary values by which the Civilization of the Universal is determined, we Negroes need to be ourselves at long last in our dignity, our regained identity.

To be ourselves by cultivating our own values as we have rediscovered them in the sources of Negro art. Because those values spring from biological, geographical and historical data, they are over and beyond the profound unity of humanity, the hallmark of our originality in thought, feeling and action. To be ourselves, not without borrowing, not by procuration, but rather by our own personal and collective effort and for ourselves. Otherwise, we should merely be poor copies of others in the *Musée vivant*, as the Negroes of America were in slavery days, until the end of the nineteenth century. Just as we African Negroes were in the days of colonization, until the eve of the Second World War.

Between the two World Wars, what the young black men and girls of my generation wanted was to abandon the imitative spirit of the old regime, to regain, along with the sentiment of our dignity, the creative spirit which had been for thousands of years the seal of Négritude, as revealed by the rupestrian art of the African continent. We meant to become once again *producers of civilization* like our ancestors. For we were conscious of the fact that the humanism of the twentieth century, which can only be the civilization of the universal, would be impoverished if it excluded a single continent. Once again, the problem is posed in terms of complementarity, of dialogue and interchange, not of opposition or racial hatred. Moreover, how could we Negroes reject the scientific and technical discoveries of the European and North American peoples? Thanks to those discoveries Man is seen transforming man himself as well as nature.

Ladies and Gentlemen:

You researchers and professors, artists and writers are the real humanists of the present day. Because Senegal has chosen to be the fatherland of dialogue and interchange, Senegal wishes to be your second country. In any event, it hopes that the great dialogue that begins here today will contribute to the construction of the Earth: to the fulfillment of Man.

from Selected Poems

■ Léopold Sédar Senghor

Black Woman

Naked woman, black woman
Clothed with your colour which is life, with your form which is beauty!
In your shadow I have grown up; the gentleness of your hands was
  laid over my eyes.
And now, high up on the sun-baked pass, at the heart of summer, at
  the heart of noon, I come upon you, my Promised Land,
And your beauty strikes me to the heart like the flash of an eagle.

Naked woman, dark woman
Firm-fleshed ripe fruit, sombre raptures of black wine, mouth making
  lyrical my mouth
Savannah stretching to clear horizons, savannah shuddering beneath
  the East Wind's eager caresses
Carved tom-tom, taut tom-tom, muttering under the Conqueror's fingers
Your solemn contralto voice is the spiritual song of the Beloved.

Naked woman, dark woman
Oil that no breath ruffles, calm oil on the athlete's flanks, on the
  flanks of the Princes of Mali
Gazelle limbed in Paradise, pearls are stars on the night of your skin
Delights of the mind, the glinting of red gold against your watered
  skin
Under the shadow of your hair, my care is lightened by the neigh-
  bouring suns of your eyes.

Naked woman, black woman,
I sing your beauty that passes, the form that I fix in the Eternal,
Before jealous Fate turn you to ashes to feed the roots of life.

Ndéssé or Blues

Once Spring brought down the ice-floes turning to torrents all my
  slack streams
And my young sap leapt at the first caress on the tender bark.
But now, at July's heart I am blinder than Winter at the pole.
My wings beat, are broken on the bars of the narrow sky
My weariness a soundproof vault where no ray breaks.
What is the sign, the secret knock that will open to me?
How can I reach the gods of the distant spears?

Royal summer of the distant South, you will come, yes, but too late, in a dying September!
In what book find the ardour of your reverberation?
On the pages of what book, of what inaccessible lips the frenzy of your love?
Worn out by the wound of my impatience. O the sound of the rain among the monotonous leaves.
Just play me your 'Solitude', Duke, and I will cry myself to sleep.

Spring Song

For a black girl with a pink heel

I

Bird songs rise up washed in the primitive sky
The green smell of grass rises, April.
I hear the breath of dawn stirring the white clouds of my curtains
I hear the sun's song on my melodious shutters
I feel a breathing and the memory of Naett on my bare neck that tingles
And my blood's complicity in spite of me whispers down my veins.
It is you my darling, O listen to the breeze already warm in the April of another continent
O listen when the wings of migrating swallows slip by, glazed with blue
Listen to the black and white rustle of the storks at the tips of their unfolded sails
Listen to the message of spring from another age, another continent
Listen to the message from distant Africa and the song of your blood!
I listen to the sap of April, singing in your veins.

II

You said to me:
Listen my friend to the far-off, muffled, precocious rumble of the storm like a fire rolling through the bush
My blood shouts with pain in the frenzy of my head, heavy, delivered over to electric currents.
Down there the sudden storm, the firing of the white coasts of the white peace of my Africa.
And in the night when there is thunder of rending metal
Hear, closer to us, for two hundred miles, all the howlings of moonless jackals and the catlike mewings of bullets
Hear the sharp roar of the guns and the trumpeting of hundred-ton monsters.
Is that still Africa, that shuffling coast, that order of battle, that long rectilinear line, that line of steel and fire?

But listen to the hurricane of the eagle strongholds, the aerial squadrons firing from every side
Blasting capital cities in a second of lightning.
And great trains leap over the cathedrals
And superb cities flame, yellower drier than grass in the dry season.
See high towers, men's pride, fall like forest giants with a noise of debris and rubbish
See the buildings of cement and steel melt like soft wax at the feet of God.
And the blood of my black brothers boils in the streets, redder than Nile—under what anger of God?
And the blood of my black brothers, the *tirailleurs* of Senegal, each drop shed is a point of fire in my side.
Tragic Spring. Spring of blood. Is that then your message, Africa?
O my friend—O how shall I hear your voice? See your black face soft to my brown cheek my brown joy
Since I must stop my eyes and ears?'

III

I said to you:
'Listen to the silence beneath the flamboyant tempers of the storm
The voice of Africa soaring above the anger of the long guns
The voice of your heart your blood, listen to it beneath the madness of your head your cries.
Is it her fault if God has asked the first-fruits of her harvests
The fairest ears, the fairest bodies chosen with patience from a thousand peoples?
Is it her fault if God makes of her sons rods to chastise the pride of the nations?
Listen to her blue voice in the air washed of hate, see the priest pour his libations at the foot of the funeral mound.
She proclaims the excitement that makes bodies tremble under the warm breath of April
She proclaims the longing wait for renewal in the fever of this spring
The life that makes two newborn babies cry at the edge of the hollow tomb.
She says your kiss is stronger than hate and death.
I see at the bottom of your troubled eyes, the calm light of Summer
I breathe between your hills the sweet headiness of harvests.
Ah! that dew of light on the trembling wings of your nostrils!
And your mouth is a bud swelling in the sun
And like a wine-coloured rose that will open at the song of your lips.
Listen to the message, dark friend with rosy heels.
I listen to your amber heart springing in silence and in Springtime.

New York

Jazz orchestra: solo trumpet

I

New York! At first your beauty confused me, and your great long-
legged golden girls.
I was so timid at first under your blue metallic eyes, your frosty smile
So timid. And the disquiet in the depth of your skyscraper streets
Lifting up owl eyes in the sun's eclipse.
Your sulphurous light and the livid shafts (their heads dumbfounding
the sky)
Skyscrapers defying cyclones on their muscles of steel and their
weathered stone skins.
But a fortnight on the bald sidewalks of Manhattan
—At the end of the third week the fever takes you with the pounce of
a jaguar
A fortnight with no well or pasture, all the birds of the air
Fall suddenly dead below the high ashes of the terraces.
No child's laughter blossoms, his hand in my fresh hand
No mother's breast. Legs in nylon. Legs and breasts with no sweat
and no smell.
No tender word for mouths are lipless. Hard cash buys artificial hearts.
No book where wisdom is read. The painter's palette flowers with
crystals of coral.
Insomniac nights O nights of Manhattan, tormented by fatuous fires,
while the klaxons cry through the empty hours
And dark waters bear away hygienic loves, like the bodies of children
on a river in flood.

II

It is the time of signs and reckonings
New York! It is the time of manna and hyssop.
Only listen to God's trombones, your heart beating to the rhythm of
blood your blood.
I have seen Harlem humming with sounds and solemn colour and
flamboyant smells
—(It is tea-time for the man who delivers pharmaceutical products)
I have seen them preparing at flight of day, the festival of the Night.
I proclaim there is more truth in the Night than in the day.
It is the pure hour when God sets the life before memory germinating
in the streets
All the amphibious elements shining like suns.
Harlem Harlem! I have seen Harlem Harlem! A breeze green with
corn springing from the pavements ploughed by the bare feet of
dancers In

Crests and waves of silk and breasts of spearheads, ballets of lilies and fabulous masks
The mangoes of love roll from the low houses under the police horses' hooves.
I have seen down the sidewalks streams of white rum and streams of black milk in the blue haze of cigars.
I have seen the sky at evening snowing cotton flowers and wings of seraphim and wizard's plumes.
Listen, New York, listen to your brazen male voice your vibrant oboe voice, the muted anguish of your tears falling in great clots of blood
Listen to the far beating of your nocturnal heart, rhythm and blood of the drum, drum and blood and drum.

III

New York! I say to New York, let the black blood flow into your blood
Cleaning the rust from your steel articulations, like an oil of life
Giving your bridges the curve of the hills, the liana's suppleness.
See, the ancient times come again, unity is rediscovered the reconciliation of the Lion the Bull and the Tree
The idea is linked to the act the ear to the heart the sign to the sense.
See your rivers murmuring with musky caymans, manatees with eyes of mirage. There is no need to invent the Mermaids.
It is enough to open your eyes to the April rainbow
And the ears, above all the ears to God who with a burst of saxophone laughter created the heavens and the earth in six days.
And on the seventh day, he slept his great negro sleep.

Statement

■   LeRoi Jones

I said before, "The Destruction Of America," was the Black Poet's role . . . to contribute as much as possible to that. But now, I realize that the Black Poet ought also try to provide a "post american form," even as simple vision, for his people.

We must study the present, and the past, and outline a maximum security and consciousness for our people's future. By past I mean, for instance "African and Arabic language, studies here would place our eyes on documents sacred to us. The study of hieroglyphs would open the mind of the Black man back into a time of his strength."* Perhaps by studying

* From "The Book Of Life," L. J. unpublished

and understanding Pre-american or Pre-white forms we will know how to strengthen any Black post-american form.

We must, in the present, be missionaries of Blackness, of consciousness, actually. In the coming chaos, any place of knowledge, any vessel, then, will want to know, "What To Do." Tell them now, as you would then. As they run through the streets looking for safety.

As a people we have no control of 20th-century communications media among ourselves, to, by, and for each other. (As separated from white communication.) We have only a few newspapers, most not really ours. But print is not the 20th century anyway . . . the 20th century is movies and television, but also the 45 rpm record.

But at the broadest, deepest, level of consciousness, aside from a few literary and poetry magazines, we have no communication at all. Except word of mouth, letters, &c.

And it strikes me that communication is one of our tragic problems. White people talk through our people's mouths. Black reality provides the lie to a great deal of television reality, but so much goes through and lodges inside Black people's heads. (Just its *sound*, whine of death, is deadly to us. The images worse. They make us kill ourselves, or long to die like white people.)

The poet is the precisest shaper of language, image, and communications' media. The Black poet must give his life to communicating to Black people, the precise circumstance of contemporary universal consciousness. (It might mean crossing the 7th century with the 21st, illuminating the 20th, &c . . .)

And this is the shaping of the future (BUILDINGS LIKE JOHN COLTRANE SOLOS), the task for which the study of past and present, the close analysis, is fitted.

A Black Criterion

■   Clarence Major

The black poet confronted with western culture and civilization must isolate and define himself in as bold a relief as he can. He must chop away at the white criterion and destroy its hold on his black mind because seeing the world through white eyes from a black soul causes death. The black poet must not attempt to create from a depth of black death. The true energy of black art must be brought fully into the possession of the black creator. The black poet must stretch his consciousness not only in the direction of other non-western people across the earth, but in terms of pure reason and expand the mind areas to the far reaches of creativity's endlessness to find new ways of seeing the world the black poet of the west is caught up in.

If we black poets see ourselves and our relationships with the deeper elements of life and with all mankind perhaps we can also break thru the tangled ugly white energy of western fear and crime.

We are in a position to know at first hand the social and political ma chinery that is threatening to destroy the earth and we can use a creative and intellectual black criteria on it.

I believe the artist does owe something to the society in which he is involved; he should be involved fully. This is the measure of the poet, and the black poet in his—from a white point of view—invisibility must hammer away at his own world of creative criticism of this society. A work of art, a poem, can be a complete "thing"; it can be alone, not preaching, not trying to change men, and though it might change them, if the men are ready for it, the poem is not reduced in its artistic status. I mean we black poets can write poems of pure creative black energy right here in the white West and make them works of art without falling into the cheap market place of bullshit and propaganda. But it is a thin line to stand on.

We are the "eye" of the West really.

We must shake up not only our own black brothers but the superficial and shoddy people stumbling in the brainlessness of the western decline. We must use our black poetic energy to overthrow the western ritual and passion, the curse, the dark ages of this death, the original sin's impact on a people and their unjust projection of it upon us black people; we must lead ourselves out of this madness and if our journey brings out others—perhaps even white people—then it will be good for us all. We must use our magic, as brother Leroi says.

The nightmare of this western sadism must be fought with a superior energy and black poetic spirit is a powerful weapon.

With the poem, we must erect a spiritual black nation we all can be proud of. And at the same time we must try to do the impossible—always the impossible—by bringing the poem back into the network of man's social and political life.

Total life is what we want.

from The African Image

■ Ezekiel Mphahlele (South Africa)

At the conference of the American Society of African Culture held at Philadelphia, I hit upon a vague desire among some Negroes, to dislodge themselves culturally and seek a reorientation in African values. Mr. Samuel Allen, the Negro poet who writes under the name of Paul Vesey, presented a paper analysing *négritude* as seen and felt by Aimé Césaire, Léopold Sédar Senghor, and interpreted by Sartre. Briefly, here are Mr. Allen's signposts: Mr. Alioune Diop, secretary of the Paris-born Society of

African Culture, gives as the *raison d'être of a négritude* the fact that the world has been taught there is no culture other than the West's, no universal values which are not hers. The effort to determine the common elements of Negro African culture is but one phase of an historic renaissance which has only begun to reshape the image of man upon the earth. *Négritude*, then, is the complete ensemble of values of African culture, and the vindication of the dignity of persons of African descent.

Jacques Rabemananjara, the Malagassy poet, says the unity of Negro culture is an act of faith. Aimé Césaire is said to be reflecting the essence of *négritude* when he says in a poem:

> Hail the royal Kailcedrat!
> Hail those who have invented nothing!
> Who have explored nothing!
> But they abandon themselves, possessed, to the essence of all things,
> Heedless of taming, but playing the game of the world. . . .

Sénghor finds the African's heightened sensibility and his strong emotional quality as his chief psychic traits. Two sources, he says, explain the origin of the psychic profile of the Negro African: the millenniums of his tropical experience and the agricultural nature of his existence; the heat and humidity of tropical regions and a pastoral closeness to the earth and the rhythms of its seasons. Emotion, he finds, is at the heart of *négritude*: 'emotion is Negro.'

Ranged against these opinions, Mr. Allen records, are those of the late Richard Wright (on American Negro poetry): its common characteristics, its rebelliousness, its intensity, its despair, can be attributed to the common social factor of oppression. Sénghor, on the other hand, finds in a poem by Wright an intensity which he considers as peculiarly African. George Lamming (Jamaican writer): politics is the only ground for a universal Negro sympathy. Peter Abrahams (South African born and now living in Jamaica): any singularities in the Negro's creative art can be attributed to the social fact of his rejection by the West.

Although Mr. Allen objectively reports these views, he himself asserts that Africa is looked to by many for a 'new humanism, for new psychic ways, for a vital force.' Earlier, in a paper included in a publication of AMSAC, *The American Negro Writer and his Roots*, Mr. Allen had said: 'Let us consider briefly the possible relevance of this concept (*négritude*) to the work of the American Negro writer or, to put it differently, its validity for a writer in our cultural situation. I think it has a role. This is not necessarily so for all of us, the writer not being a soldier marching to command. He writes, when he writes most creatively, pursuant to his own individual and most deeply felt need. The racial accident of his birth may have little influence or only indirect influence on the purpose of his writing. . . .

'It is probably true also that it was not by chance that this concept, negritude, originated among the poets rather than among those working in prose. Except for certain highly imaginative works, the novelist writes within a framework of what we term reality. He must in part concern himself with Plato's shadows—with plot and setting. His characters must grow up. He is constrained to a certain degree of reasonableness. The poet has probably a greater chance to penetrate, at once without apology and without a setting of the worldly stage, to the deepest levels of his creative concern. And so, perhaps what we are saying may have greater applicability to poetry than to prose.'

Mr. Allen had also observed that for Sénghor the *négritude* of a poem was *less the theme than the style* (my italics); 'its characteristic manner, the intensity of its passion, its rhythmic flow or the quality of its imagery, whether he writes of a ritual dance in Dahomey, of the Brittany sea coast, or of the nature of God and Man.'

Look at this poem by Aimé Césaire, of which Mr. Allen renders a translation in order to demonstrate how Césaire emphasizes the 'dynamic quality' of *négritude:*

> My negritude is not a rock, its deafness hurled against the clamour of the day
> My negritude is not a film of dead water on the dead eye of the earth
> My negritude is neither a tower nor a cathedral
> It plunges into the red flesh of the earth
> It plunges into the burning flesh of the sky
> It pierces the opaque prostration by its upright patience.

The theme is, of course, clearly *négritude*. Because the poem is a passionate outcry, a self-vindication, it has an intensity of style, of imagery: 'its deafness hurled against the clamour of the day'; 'the burning flesh of the sky'; 'upright patience.' Abstract ideas are given a concrete meaning. What have we proved? An intensely conceived subject begets—or calls for —intensity of style; so that it becomes irrelevant to talk about theme and style separately. What is so distinctively *négritude* about that? One could find in Baudelaire an intensity to match this. The difference would be that Baudelaire wouldn't talk *négritude,* but Césaire does, because he *is* Negro. So we go back to the theme, the subject of all this talk.

The main reason why *négritude* has enchanted a few American Negro writers consists in their resistance against the tendency on the part of the outside world and their fellow-Americans to regard their work as a tributary to some major American stream, or against the desire among other writers to join the mainstream of American culture, 'a desire for obliteration and passive absorption by the majority.'

The American Negro has the right to seek his roots in Africa if he wishes to, for all the good it might do his art. We must realize that he is living through a series of crises. Mr. Arthur Davis, another Negro writer, lays bare the predicament of his people most ably in his essay in the AMSAC publication referred to above. He says now that the lynching days are all but over, the enemy that gave Negro writers a common purpose is capitulating, and integration is taking place, the most fruitful literary tradition of Negro writing has been shattered: the protest element is being destroyed; the spiritual climate for integration exists, he says, and 'it becomes almost a tragic experience because it means (especially for the writer in his middle years) giving up a tradition in which he has done

his apprentice and journeyman work, giving it up when he is prepared to
make use of that tradition as a master craftsman.' Some writers have
tried to shift the emphasis from the protest aspect to the problems and
conflicts within their Negro group itself, while retaining the Negro character and background. Some even write about whites. Frank Yerby, for instance, with ten or more best-selling novels in succession, has never used
a Negro background or Negro principal characters. Mr. Davis says that he
hopes from the integration crisis his people 'will move permanently into
full participation in American life—social, economic, political, and literary. . . . He (the Negro artist) will discover what we all know in our
objective moments, that there are many facets of Negro living—humorous,
pathetic and tragic—which are not directly touched by the outside world.

It seems to me, an outsider, that the Negro's commitment is so huge
in his country that he will probably find it more profitable to concern himself with producing good art inside his social climate, as a 'native son.' If
he finds the American civilization frustrating, he should realize that it is
not a parochial malady. Everywhere, especially in Africa, we are up against
this invasion by the white world upon our sense of values. It was a healthy
thing to discover that the Negro's image of the African was changing to
the good. Until President Nkrumah, Dr. Nnamdi Azikiwe, Tom Mboya,
Julius Nyerere, Dr. Hastings Banda went to the United States, the Negro
thought of the African as a primitive man whose jungle existence had
largely outlived the processes of education. The Americans saw these men
on TV and heard especially Nyerere and Mboya brilliantly weather the
storm of pressmen's questions and often make them look silly. Both middle-class and working-class Negroes told us how revealing these pictures
were. I still cannot explain the ignorance of some of the literate Negroes,
when United States publishers tell us the book market is glutted with
books on Africa, many of them quite good. Negro porters, taxi-drivers,
spontaneously revealed their pride in Africa. One old man stopped three of
us visiting Africans in Harlem to ask who we were. Then he told us, quite
emotionally, how stunned he was by the articulateness of the African
leaders he saw on television. On the other hand, we were told, French-
speaking Africans who were coming to the United States on and off despised what they regarded as the Negro's lack of fight in response to so
much discrimination aimed at them. It reminded me that our French-
speaking brothers need a heavy course on African affairs. They just don't
seem to know the social forces at work in African countries south of the
Equator. They are too often apt to bring a philosophical mind to political
and cultural questions in a changing continent.

How similar the American Negro's cultural predicament is to ours in
South Africa and in other multi-racial communities. The needle that reg-
isters your response as a writer swings between protest and romantic
writing, and then, when you are spiritually emancipated, the needle quiv-
ers around the central point—the meeting point between rejection and
acceptance. Then you know both how excruciating and exciting it is to be
the meeting point of two streams of consciousness and the paradoxes they
pose. That is what makes our art. If there is any *négritude* in the black

man's art in South Africa, it is because we *are* African. If a writer's tone is healthy, he is bound to express the African in him. Stripped of Sénghor's philosophic musings, the African traits he speaks of can be taken for granted: they are social anthropology. We who grew up and were educated in Africa do not find anything new in them. Simply because we respond intensely to situations is no reason why we should think non-Africans are incapable of doing so, or that we are the only section of the human race who are full of passionate intensity. These traits are not anything we need make slogans about, in terms of art. Or are we supposed to dig up the bones of Victorian aesthetes and start beating our drums with them? In my struggle to overcome the artistic difficulty that arises when one is angry most of the time and when one's sense of values is continually being challenged by the ruling class, I have never thought of calling my *négritude* to my aid, except when writing protest material. But is not this elementary—shall I call it 'underdoggery'?—that Sénghor is talking about? Even he must know, however, that his philosophy will contain his art only up to a point: it won't chain his art for long. He must know that his *négritude* can at best be an attitude, a pose, where his art is concerned, just as it was a pose in my protest writing. Excessive protest poisons one's system, and thank goodness I'm emancipated from that. The anger is there, but I can harness it.

excerpt *from* The Wretched of the Earth

■ Frantz Fanon (Martinique)

When we consider the efforts made to carry out the cultural estrangement so characteristic of the colonial epoch, we realize that nothing has been left to chance and that the total result looked for by colonial domination was indeed to convince the natives that colonialism came to lighten their darkness. The effect consciously sought by colonialism was to drive into the natives' heads the idea that if the settlers were to leave, they would at once fall back into barbarism, degradation and bestiality.

On the unconscious plane, colonialism therefore did not seek to be considered by the native as a gentle, loving mother who protects her child from a hostile environment, but rather as a mother who unceasingly restrains her fundamentally perverse offspring from managing to commit suicide and from giving free rein to its evil instincts. The colonial mother protects her child from itself, from its ego, and from its physiology, its biology and its own unhappiness which is its very essence.

In such a situation the claims of the native intellectual are no luxury but a necessity in any coherent programme. The native intellectual who takes up arms to defend his nation's legitimacy and who wants to bring proofs to bear out that legitimacy, who is willing to strip himself naked to study the history of his body, is obliged to dissect the heart of his people.

Such an examination is not specifically national. The native intellectual who decides to give battle to colonial lies fights on the field of the whole continent. The past is given back its value. Culture, extracted from the past to be displayed in all its splendour, is not necessarily that of his own country. Colonialism, which has not bothered to put too fine a point on its efforts, has never ceased to maintain that the Negro is a savage; and for the colonist, the Negro was neither an Angolan nor a Nigerian, for he simply spoke of "the Negro." For colonialism, this vast continent was the haunt of savages, a country riddled with superstitions and fanaticism, destined for contempt, weighed down by the curse of God, a country of cannibals—in short, the Negro's country. Colonialism's condemnation is continental in its scope. The contention by colonialism that the darkest night of humanity lay over pre-colonial history concerns the whole of the African continent. The efforts of the native to rehabilitate himself and to escape from the claws of colonialism are logically inscribed from the same point of view as that of colonialism. The native intellectual who has gone far beyond the domains of Western culture and who has got it into his head to proclaim the existence of another culture never does so in the name of Angola or of Dahomey. The culture which is affirmed is African culture. The Negro, never so much a Negro as since he has been dominated by the whites, when he decides to prove that he has a culture and to behave like a cultured person, comes to realize that history points out a well-defined path to him: he must demonstrate that a Negro culture exists.

And it is only too true that those who are most responsible for this racialisation of thought, or at least for the first movement towards that thought, are and remain those Europeans who have never ceased to set up white culture to fill the gap left by the absence of other cultures. Colonialism did not dream of wasting its time in denying the existence of one national culture after another. Therefore the reply of the colonised peoples will be straight away continental in its breadth. In Africa, the native literature of the last twenty years is not a national literature but a Negro literature. The concept of Negro-ism, for example, was the emotional if not the logical antithesis of that insult which the white man flung at humanity. This rush of Negro-ism against the white man's contempt showed itself in certain spheres to be the one idea capable of lifting interdictions and anathemas. Because the New Guinean or Kenyan intellectuals found themselves above all up against a general ostracism and delivered to the combined contempt of their overlords, their reaction was to sing praises in admiration of each other. The unconditional affirmation of African culture has succeeded the unconditional affirmation of European culture. On the whole, the poets of Negro-ism oppose the idea of an old Europe to a young Africa, tiresome reasoning to lyricism, oppressive logic to high-stepping nature, and on one side stiffness, ceremony, etiquette and scepticism, while on the other frankness, liveliness, liberty and—why not?—luxuriance: but also irresponsibility.

The poets of Negro-ism will not stop at the limits of the continent. From America, black voices will take up the hymn with fuller unison. The «black world» will see the light and Busia from Ghana, Birago Diop from Senegal, Hampaté Ba from the Soudan and Saint-Clair Drake from Chicago will not hesitate to assert the existence of common ties and a motive power that is identical.

This historical necessity in which the men of African culture find themselves to racialise their claims and to speak more of African culture than of national culture will tend to lead them up a blind alley. Let us take for example the case of the African Cultural Society. This society had been created by African intellectuals who wished to get to know each other and to compare their experiences and the results of their respective research work. The aim of this society was therefore to affirm the existence of an African culture, to evaluate this culture on the plane of distinct nations and to reveal the internal motive forces of each of their national cultures. But at the same time this society fulfilled another need: the need to exist side by side with the European Cultural Society, which threatened to transform itself into a Universal Cultural Society. There was therefore at the bottom of this decision the anxiety to be present at the universal trysting place fully armed, with a culture springing from the very heart of the African continent. Now, this Society will very quickly show its inability to shoulder these different tasks, and will limit itself to exhibitionist demonstrations, while the habitual behaviour of the members of this Society will be confined to showing Europeans that such a thing as African culture exists, and opposing their ideas to those of ostentatious and narcissistic Europeans. We have shown that such an attitude is normal and draws its legitimacy from the lies propagated by men of Western culture. But the degradation of the aims of this Society will become more marked with the elaboration of the concept of Negro-ism. The African Society will become the cultural society of the black world and will come to include the Negro dispersion, that is to say the tens of thousands of black people spread over the American continents.

The Negroes who live in the United States and in Central or Latin America in fact experience the need to attach themselves to a cultural matrix. Their problem is not fundamentally different from that of the Africans. The whites of America did not mete out to them any different treatment from that of the whites that ruled over the Africans. We have seen that the whites were used to putting all Negroes in the same bag. During the first congress of the African Cultural Society which was held in Paris in 1956, the American Negroes of their own accord considered their problems from the same standpoint as those of their African brothers. Cultured Africans, speaking of African civilisations, decreed that there should be a reasonable status within the state for those who had formerly been slaves. But little by little the American Negroes realized that the essential problems confronting them were not the same as those that confronted the African Negroes. The Negroes of Chicago only resemble the Nigerians or the Tanganyikans in so far as they were all defined in relation to the whites. But once the first comparisons had been made and subjective feelings were assuaged, the American Negroes realized that the objective problems were fundamentally heterogeneous. The test cases of civil liberty whereby both whites and blacks in America try to drive back racial discrimination have very little in common in their principles and objectives with the heroic fight of the Angolan people against the detestable Portuguese colonialism. Thus, during the second congress of the African Cultural Society the American Negroes decided to create an American society for people of black cultures.

Negro-ism therefore finds its first limitation in the phenomena which take account of the formation of the historical character of men. Negro and African-Negro culture broke up into different entities because the men who wished to incarnate these cultures realized that every culture is first and foremost national, and that the problems which kept Richard Wright or Langston Hughes on the alert were fundamentally different from those which might confront Léopold Senghor or Jomo.

If the action of the native intellectual is limited historically, there remains nevertheless the fact that it contributes greatly to upholding and justifying the action of politicians. It is true that the attitude of the native intellectual sometimes takes on the aspect of a cult or of a religion. But if we really wish to analyse this attitude correctly we will come to see that it is symptomatic of the intellectual's realization of the danger that he is running in cutting his last moorings and of breaking adrift from his people. This stated belief in a national culture is in fact an ardent, despairing turning towards anything that will afford him secure anchorage. In order to ensure his salvation and to escape from the supremacy of the white man's culture the native feels the need to turn backwards towards his unknown roots and to lose himself at whatever cost in his own barbarous people. Because he feels he is becoming estranged, that is to say because he feels that he is the living haunt of contradictions which run the risk of becoming insurmountable, the native tears himself away from the swamp that may suck him down and accepts everything, decides to take all for granted and confirms everything even though he may lose body and soul. The native finds that he is expected to answer for everything, and to all comers. He not only turns himself into the defender of his people's past; he is willing to be counted as one of them, and henceforward he is even capable of laughing at his past cowardice.

This tearing away, painful and difficult though it may be, is however necessary. If it is not accomplished there will be serious psycho-affective injuries and the result will be individuals without an anchor, without a horizon, colourless, stateless, rootless—a race of angels. It will be also quite normal to hear certain natives declare "I speak as a Senegalese and as a Frenchman . . ." "I speak as an Algerian and as a Frenchman . . ." The intellectual who is Arab and French, or Nigerian and English, when he comes up against the need to take on two nationalities, chooses, if he wants to remain true to himself, the negation of one of these determinations. But most often, since they cannot or will not make a choice, such intellectuals gather together all the historical determining factors which have conditioned them and take up a fundamentally "universal standpoint."

This is because the native intellectual has thrown himself greedily upon Western culture. Like adopted children who only stop investigating the new family framework at the moment when a minimum nucleus of security crystallises in their psyche, the native intellectual will try to make European culture his own. He will not be content to get to know Rabelais and Diderot, Shakespeare and Edgar Allen Poe; he will bind them to his intelligence as closely as possible:

La dame n'était pas seule
Elle avait un mari
Un mari très comme il faut
Qui citait Racine et Corneille
Et Voltaire et Rousseau
Et le Père Hugo et le jeune Musset
Et Gide et Valéry
Et tant d'autres encore[1]

But at the moment when the nationalist parties are mobilising the people in the name of national independence, the native intellectual sometimes spurns these acquisitions which he suddenly feels make him a stranger in his own land. It is always easier to proclaim rejection than actually to reject. The intellectual who through the medium of culture has filtered into Western civilisation, who has managed to become part of the body of European culture—in other words who has exchanged his own culture for another—will come to realise that the cultural matrix, which now he wishes to assume since he is anxious to appear original, can hardly supply any figureheads which will bear comparison with those, so many in number and so great in prestige, of the occupying power's civilisation. History, of course, though nevertheless written by the Westerners and to serve their purposes, will be able to evaluate from time to time certain periods of the African past. But, standing face to face with his country at the present time, and observing clearly and objectively the events of today throughout the continent which he wants to make his own, the intellectual is terrified by the void, the degradation and the savagery he sees there. Now he feels that he must get away from white culture. He must seek his culture elsewhere, anywhere at all; and if he fails to find the substance of culture of the same grandeur and scope as displayed by the ruling power, the native intellectual will very often fall back upon emotional attitudes and will develop a psychology which is dominated by exceptional sensitivity and susceptibility. This withdrawal which is due in the first instance to a begging of the question in his internal behaviour mechanism and his own character brings out, above all, a reflex and contradiction which is muscular.

This is sufficient explanation of the style of those native intellectuals who decide to give expression to this phase of consciousness which is in process of being liberated. It is a harsh style, full of images, for the

---

[1] The lady was not alone; she had a most respectable husband, who knew how to quote Racine and Corneille, Voltaire and Rousseau, Victor Hugo and Musset, Gide, Valéry and as many more again. (René Depestre: Face à la nuit.)

image is the draw-bridge which allows unconscious energies to be scattered on the surrounding meadows. It is a vigorous style, alive with rhythms, struck through and through with bursting life; it is full of colour, too, bronzed, sun-baked and violent. This style, which in its time astonished the peoples of the West, has nothing racial about it, in spite of frequent statements to the contrary; it expresses above all a hand-to-hand struggle and it reveals the need that man has to liberate himself from a part of his being which already contained the seeds of decay. Whether the fight is painful, quick or inevitable, muscular action must substitute itself for concepts.

If in the world of poetry this movement reaches unaccustomed heights, the fact remains that in the real world the intellectual often follows up a blind alley. When at the height of his intercourse with his people, whatever they were or whatever they are, the intellectual decides to come down into the common paths of real life, he only brings back from his adventuring formulas which are sterile in the extreme. He sets a high value on the customs, traditions and the appearances of his people; but his inevitable, painful experience only seems to be a banal search for exoticism. The sari becomes sacred, and shoes that come from Paris or Italy are left off in favour of pampooties, while suddenly the language of the ruling power is felt to burn your lips. Finding your fellow countrymen sometimes means in this phase to will to be a nigger, not a nigger like all other niggers but a real nigger, a Negro cur, just the sort of nigger that the white man wants you to be. Going back to your own people means to become a dirty wog, to go native as much as you can, to become unrecognizable, and to cut off those wings that before you had allowed to grow.

The native intellectual decides to make an inventory of the bad habits drawn from the colonial world, and hastens to remind everyone of the good old customs of the people, that people which he has decided contains all truth and goodness. The scandalised attitude with which the settlers who live in the colonial territory greet this new departure only serves to strengthen the native's decision. When the colonialists, who had tasted the sweets of their victory over these assimilated people, realise that these men whom they considered as saved souls are beginning to fall back into the ways of niggers, the whole system totters. Every native won over, every native who had taken the pledge not only marks a failure for the colonial structure when he decides to lose himself and to go back to his own side, but also stands as a symbol for the uselessness and the shallowness of all the work that has been accomplished. Each native who goes back over the line is a radical condemnation of the methods and of the regime; and the native intellectual finds in the scandal he gives rise to a justification and an encouragement to persevere in the path he has chosen.

If we wanted to trace in the works of native writers the different phases which characterise this evolution we would find spread out before us a panorama on three levels. In the first phase, the native intellectual gives proof that he has assimilated the culture of the occupying power. His writings correspond point by point with those of his opposite numbers in the mother country. His inspiration is European and we can easily link up these works with definite trends in the literature of the mother country. This is the period of unqualified assimilation. We find in this literature coming from the colonies the Parnassians, the Symbolists and the Surrealists.

In the second phase we find the native is disturbed; he decides to remember what he is. This period of creative work approximately corresponds to that immersion which we have just described. But since the native is not a part of his people, since he only has exterior relations with his people, he is content to recall their life only. Past happenings of the bye-gone days of his childhood will be brought up out of the depths of his memory; old legends will be reinterpreted in the light of a borrowed estheticism and of a conception of the world which was discovered under other skies.

Sometimes this literature of just-before-the-battle is dominated by humour and by allegory; but often too it is symptomatic of a period of distress and difficulty, where death is experienced, and disgust too. We spew ourselves up; but already underneath laughter can be heard.

Finally in the third phase, which is called the fighting phase, the native, after having tried to lose himself in the people and with the people, will on the contrary shake the people. Instead of according the people's lethargy an honoured place in his esteem, he turns himself into an awakener of the people; hence comes a fighting literature, a revolutionary literature, and a national literature. During this phase a great many men and women, who up till then would never have thought of producing a literary work, now that they find themselves in exceptional circumstances —in prison, with the Maquis or on the eve of their execution—feel the need to speak to their nation, to compose the sentence which expresses the heart of the people and to become the mouthpiece of a new reality in action.

The native intellectual nevertheless sooner or later will realize that you do not show proof of your nation from its culture but that you substantiate its existence in the fight which the people wage against the forces of occupation. No colonial system draws its justification from the fact that the territories it dominates are culturally non-existent. You will never make colonialism blush for shame by spreading out little-known cultural treasures under its eyes. At the very moment when the native intellectual is anxiously trying to create a cultural work he fails to realize that he is utilising techniques and language which are borrowed from the stranger in his country. He contents himself with stamping these instruments with a hall-mark which he wishes to be national, but which is strangely reminiscent of exoticism. The native intellectual who comes back to his people by way of cultural achievements behaves in fact like a foreigner. Sometimes he has no hesitation in using a dialect in order to show his will to be as near as possible to the people; but the ideas that he expresses and the preoccupations he is taken up with have no common yardstick to measure the real situation which the men and the women of his country know. The culture that the intellectual leans towards is often no more than a stock of particularisms. He wishes to attach himself to the people; but instead he only catches hold of their outer garments. And these outer garments are merely the reflection of a hidden life, teeming and perpetually in motion. That extremely obvious objectivity which seems to characterise a people is in fact only the inert, already forsaken result of frequent, and not always very coherent adaptations of a much more fundamental substance which itself is continually being renewed. The man of culture, instead of setting out to find this substance, will let himself be hypnotised by these mummified fragments which because they are static are in fact symbols of negation and outworn contrivances. Culture has never the translucidity of custom; it abhors all simplification. In its essence it is opposed to custom, for custom is always the deterioration of culture. The desire to attach oneself to tradition or bring abandoned traditions to life again does not only mean going against the current of history but also opposing one's own people. When a people undertakes an armed struggle or even a political struggle against a relentless colonialism, the significance of tradition changes. All that has made up the technique of passive resistance in the past may, during this phase, be radically condemned. In an under-developed country during the period of struggle, traditions are fundamentally unstable and are shot through by centrifugal tendencies. This is why the intellectual often runs the risk of being out of date. The peoples who have carried on the struggle are more and more impervious to demagogy; and those who wish to follow them reveal themselves as nothing more than common opportunists, in other words latecomers.

In the sphere of plastic arts, for example, the native artist who wishes at whatever cost to create a national work of art shuts himself up in a stereotyped reproduction of details. These artists, who have nevertheless thoroughly studied modern techniques and who have taken part in the main trends of contemporary painting and architecture, turn their back on foreign culture, deny it and set out to look for a true national culture, setting great store on what they consider to be the constant principles of national art. But these people forget that the forms of thought and what it feeds on, together with modern techniques of information, language and dress have dialectically reorganised the people's intelligences and that the constant principles which acted as safeguards during the colonial period are now undergoing extremely radical changes.

The artist who has decided to illustrate the truths of the nation turns paradoxically towards the past and away from actual events. What he ultimately intends to embrace are in fact the cast-offs of thought, its shells and corpses, a knowledge which has been stabilised once and for all. But the native intellectual who wishes to create an authentic work of art must realise that the truths of a nation are in the first place its realities. He must go on until he has found the seething pot out of which the learning of the future will emerge.

Before independence, the native painter was insensible to the national scene. He set a high value on non-figurative art, or more often was specialised in still-lifes. After independence his anxiety to rejoin his people will confine him to the most detailed representation of reality. This is representative art which has no internal rhythms, an art which is serene and immobile, evocative not of life but of death. Enlightened circles are in ecstasies when confronted with this «inner truth» which is so well expressed; but we have the right to ask if this truth is in fact a reality, and if it is not already outworn and denied, called in question by the epoch through which the people are treading out their path towards history.

In the realm of poetry we may establish the same facts. After the period of assimilation characterised by rhyming poetry, the poetic tom-tom's rhythms break through. This is a poetry of revolt; but it is also descriptive and analytical poetry. The poet ought however to understand that nothing can replace the reasoned, irrevocable taking up of arms on the people's side.

We must not therefore be content with delving into the past of a people in order to find coherent elements which will counteract colonialism's attempts to falsify and harm. We must work and fight with the same rhythm as the people to construct the future and to prepare the ground where vigorous shoots are already springing up. A national culture is not a folklore, nor an abstract populism that believes it can discover the people's true nature. It is not made up of the inert dregs of gratuitous actions, that is to say actions which are less and less attached to the ever-present reality of the people. A national culture is the whole body of efforts made by a people in the sphere of thought to describe, justify and praise the action through which that people has created itself and keeps itself in existence. A national culture in under-developed countries should therefore take its place at the very heart of the struggle for freedom which these countries are carrying on. Men of African cultures who are still fighting in the name of African-Negro culture and who have called many congresses in the name of the unity of that culture should to-day realize that all their efforts amount to is to make comparisons between coins and sarcophagi.

There is no common destiny to be shared between the national cultures of Senegal and Guinea; but there *is* a common destiny between the Senegalese and Guinean nations which are both dominated by the same French colonialism. If it is wished that the national culture of Senegal should come to resemble the national culture of Guinea, it is not enough for the rulers of the two peoples to decide to consider their problems—whether the problem of liberation is concerned, or the trade-union question, or economic difficulties—from similar view-points. And even here there does not seem to be complete identity, for the rhythm of the people and that of their rulers are not the same. There can be no two cultures which are completely identical. To believe that it is possible to create a black culture is to forget that niggers are disappearing, just as those people who brought them into being are seeing the break-up of their economic and cultural supremacy.[2] There will never be such a thing as

---

[2] At the last school prize-giving in Dakar, the president of the Senegalese Republic, Leopold Senghor, decided to include the study of the idea of Negro-ism in the curriculum. If this decision was due to an anxiety to study historical causes, no one can criticise it. But if on the other hand it was taken in order to create black self-consciousness, it is simply a turning of his back upon

black culture because there is not a single politician who feels he has a vocation to bring black republics into being. The problem is to get to know the place that these men mean to give their people, the kind of social relations that they decide to set up and the conception that they have of the future of humanity. It is this that counts; everything else is mystification, signifying nothing.

In 1959, the cultured Africans who met at Rome never stopped talking about unity. But one of the people who was loudest in the praise of this cultural unity, Jacques Rabemananjara, is today a minister in the Madagascan government, and as such has decided, with his government, to oppose the Algerian people in the General Assembly of the United Nations. Rabemananjara, if he had been true to himself, ought to have resigned from the government and denounced those men who claim to incarnate the will of the Madagascan people. The ninety thousand dead of Madagascar have not given Rabemananjara authority to oppose the aspirations of the Algerian people in the General Assembly of the United Nations.

It is around the peoples' struggles that African-Negro culture takes on substance, and not around songs, poems or folklore. Senghor, who is also a member of the Society of African Culture and who has worked with us on the question of African culture, is not afraid for his part either to give the order to his delegation to support French proposals on Algeria. Adherence to African-Negro culture and to the cultural unity of Africa is arrived at in the first place by upholding unconditionally the peoples' struggle for freedom. No one can truly wish for the spread of African culture if he does not give practical support to the creation of the conditions necessary to the existence of that culture; in other words, to the liberation of the whole continent.

I say again that no speech-making and no proclamation concerning culture will turn us from our fundamental tasks: the liberation of the national territory; a continual struggle against colonialism in its new forms; and an obstinate refusal to enter the charmed circle of mutual admiration at the summit.

from White Man, Listen!

■   Richard Wright

The Psychological Reactions of Oppressed People

Buttressed by their belief that their God had entrusted the earth into their keeping, drunk with power and possibility, waxing rich through

---

history which has already taken cognizance of the disappearance of the majority of Negroes.

trade in commodities, human and non-human, with awesome naval and merchant marines at their disposal, their countries filled with human debris anxious for any adventures, psychologically armed with new facts, white Western Christian civilization during the fourteenth, fifteenth, sixteenth, and seventeenth centuries, with a long, slow, and bloody explosion, hurled itself upon the sprawling masses of colored humanity in Asia and Africa.

I say to you white men of the West: Don't be too proud of how easily you conquered and plundered those Asians and Africans. You had unwitting allies in your campaigns; you had Fifth Columns in the form of indigenous cultures to facilitate your military, missionary, and mercenary efforts. Your collaborators in those regions consisted of the mental habits of the people, habits for which they were in no way responsible, no more than you were responsible for yours. Those habits constituted corps of saboteurs, of spies, if you will, that worked in the interests of European aggression. You must realize that it was not your courage or racial superiority that made you win, nor was it the racial inferiority or cowardice of the Asians and Africans that made them lose. This is an important point that you must grasp, or your concern with this problem will be forever wide of the facts. How, then, did the West, numerically the minority, achieve, during the last four centuries, so many dazzling victories over the body of colored mankind? Frankly, it took you centuries to do a job that could have been done in fifty years! You had the motive, the fire power, the will, the religious spur, the superior organization, but you dallied. Why? You were not aware exactly of what you were doing. You didn't suspect your impersonal strength, or the impersonal weakness on the other side. You were as unconscious, at bottom, as were your victims about what was really taking place.

Your world of culture clashed with the culture-worlds of colored mankind, and the ensuing destruction of traditional beliefs among a billion and a half of black, brown, and yellow men has set off a tide of social, cultural, political, and economic revolution that grips the world today. That revolution is assuming many forms, absolutistic, communistic, fascistic, theocratistic etc.—all marked by unrest, violence, and an astounding emotional thrashing about as men seek new objects about which they can center their loyalties.

It is of the reactions, tortured and turbulent, of those Asians and Africans, in the New and Old World, that I wish to speak to you. Naturally I cannot speak for those Asians and Africans who are still locked in their mystical or ancestor-worshiping traditions. They are the voiceless ones, the silent ones. Indeed, I think that they are the doomed ones, men in a tragic trap. Any attempt on their part to wage a battle to protect their outmoded traditions and religions is a battle that is lost before it starts. And I say frankly that I suspect any white man who loves to dote upon those "naked nobles," who wants to leave them as they are, who finds them "primitive and pure," for such mystical hankering is, in my opinion, the last refuge of reactionary racists and psychological cripples tired of their own civilization. My remarks will, of necessity, be confined to those Asians and Africans who, having been partly Westernized, have a quarrel with the West. They are the ones who feel that they are oppressed. In a sense, this is a fight of the West with *itself*, a fight that the West blunderingly began, and the West does not to this day realize that it is the sole responsible agent, the sole instigator. For the West to disclaim responsibility for what it so clearly did is to make every white man alive on earth today a criminal. In history as in law, men must be held strictly responsible for the consequences of their historic actions, whether they intended those consequences or not. For the West to accept its responsibility is to create the means by which white men can liberate themselves from their fears, panic, and terror while they confront the world's colored majority of men who are also striving for liberation from the irrational ties which the West prompted them to disown—ties of which the West has partially robbed them.

Let's imagine a mammoth flying saucer from Mars landing, say, in a peasant Swiss village and debouching swarms of fierce-looking men whose skins are blue and whose red eyes flash lightning bolts that deal instant death. The inhabitants are all the more terrified because the arrival of these men had been predicted. The religious myths of the Western world —the Second Coming of Christ, the Last Judgment, etc., have conditioned Europeans for just such an improbable event. Hence, those Swiss natives will feel that resistance is useless for a while. As long as the blue strangers are casually kind, they are obeyed and served. They become the Fathers of the people. Is this a fragment of paperback science fiction? No. It's more prosaic than that. The image I've sketched above is the manner, by and large, in which white Europe overran Asia and Africa. (Remember the Cortés-Montezuma drama!)

But why did Europe do this? Did it only want gold, power, women, raw materials? It was more complicated than that.

The fifteenth-, sixteenth-, and seventeenth-century neurotic European, sick of his thwarted instincts, restless, filled with self-disgust, was looking for not only spices and gold and slaves when he set out; he was looking for an Arcadia, a Land's End, a Shangri-la, a world peopled by shadow men, a world that would permit free play for his repressed instincts. Stripped of tradition, these misfits, adventurers, indentured servants, convicts and freebooters were the most advanced individualists of their time. Rendered socially superfluous by the stifling weight of the Church and nobility, buttressed by the influence of the ideas of Hume and Descartes, they had been brutally molded toward attitudes of emotional independence and could doff the cloying ties of custom, tradition, and family. The Asian-African native, anchored in family-independence systems of life, could not imagine why or how these men had left their homelands, could not conceive of the cold, arid emotions sustaining them. . . . Emotional independence was a state of mind not only utterly inconceivable, but an attitude toward life downright evil to the Asian-African native—something to be avoided at all costs. Bound by a charged array of humble objects that made up an emotionally satisfying and exciting world, they, trapped by their limited mental horizon, could not help thinking that the white men invading their lands had been driven forcibly from their homes!

Living in a waking dream, generations of emotionally impoverished colonial European whites wallowed in the quick gratification of greed, reveled in the cheap superiority of racial domination, slaked their sensual thirst in illicit sexuality, draining off the dammed-up libido that European morality had condemned, amassing through trade a vast reservoir of economic fat, thereby establishing vast accumulations of capital which spurred the industrialization of the West. Asia and Africa thus became a neurotic habit that Europeans could forgo only at the cost of a powerful psychic wound, for this emotionally crippled Europe had, through tne centuries, grown used to leaning upon this black crutch.

But what of the impact of those white faces upon the personalities of the native? Steeped in dependence systems of family life and anchored in ancestor-worshiping religions, the native was prone to identify those powerful white faces falling athwart his existence with the potency of his dead father who had sustained him in the past. Temporarily accepting the invasion, he transferred his loyalties to those white faces, but, because of the psychological, racial, and economic luxury which those faces derived from their domination, the native was kept at bay.

Today, as the tire of white domination of the land mass of Asia and Africa recedes, there lies exposed to view a procession of shattered cultures, disintegrated societies, and a writhing sweep of more aggressive, irrational religion than the world has known for centuries. And, as scientific research, partially freed from the blight of colonial control, advances, we are witnessing the rise of a new genre of academic literature dealing with colonial and post-colonial facts from a wider angle of vision than ever possible before. The personality distortions of hundreds of millions of black, brown, and yellow people that are being revealed by this literature are confounding and will necessitate drastic alteration of our past evaluations of colonial rule. In this new literature one enters a universe of menacing shadows where disparate images coalesce—white turning into black, the dead coming to life, the top becoming the bottom—until you think you are seeing Biblical beasts with seven heads and ten horns rising out of the sea. Imperialism turns out to have been much more morally foul a piece of business than even Marx and Lenin imagined!

An agony was induced into the native heart, rotting and pulverizing it as it tried to live under a white domination with which it could not identify in any real sense, a white domination that mocked it. The more Westernized that native heart became, the more anti-Western it had to be, for that heart was now weighing itself in terms of white Western values that made it feel degraded. Vainly attempting to embrace the world of white faces that rejected it, it recoiled and sought refuge in the ruins of moldering tradition. But it was too late; it was trapped; it found haven in neither, This is the psychological stance of the elite of the populations, free or still in a state of subjection, of present-day Asia and Africa; this is the profound revolution that the white man cast into the world; this is the revolution (a large part of which has been successfully captured by the Communists) that the white man confronts today with fear and paralysis.

"Frog Perspectives"

I've now reached that point where I can begin a direct descent into the psychological reactions of the people across whose lives the white shadow of the West has fallen. Let me commence by presenting to you concept number one: "Frog Perspectives."

This is a phrase I've borrowed from Nietzsche to describe someone looking from below upward, a sense of someone who feels himself lower than others. The concept of distance involved here is not physical; it is psychological. It involves a situation in which, for moral or social reasons, a person or a group feels that there is another person or group above it. Yet, physically, they all live on the same general material plane. A certain degree of hate combined with love (ambivalence) is always involved in this looking from below upward and the object against which the subject is measuring himself undergoes constant change. He loves the object because he would like to resemble it; he hates the object because his chances of resembling it are remote, slight.

Proof of this psychological reality can be readily found in the expressions of oppressed people. If you ask an American Negro to describe his situation, he will almost always tell you:

"We are rising."

Against what or whom is he measuring his "rising"? It is beyond doubt his hostile white neighbor.

At Bandung, Carlos Romulo of the Philippines said:

"I think that over the generations the deepest source of our own confidence in ourselves had to come from the deeply rooted knowledge that the white man was *wrong*, that in proclaiming the superiority of his race, *qua race,* he stamped himself with his own weakness and confirmed all the rest of us in our dogged conviction that we could and would reassert ourselves as men. . . ."

The "we" that Romulo speaks of here are the so-called "colored" peoples of the world. It is quite clear here that it is against the dominance of the white man that Romulo measures the concept of manhood. Implied in his statement is the feeling or belief that the white man has, by his presence or acts, robbed the colored peoples of a feeling of self-respect, of manhood. Once more we are confronted with the problem of distance, a psychological distance, a feeling that one must regain something lost.

At Bandung, in 1955, President Sukarno of Indonesia spoke as follows:

"The peoples of Asia and Africa wield little physical power. Even their economic strength is dispersed and slight. We cannot indulge in power politics. Diplomacy for us is not a matter of the big stick. Our statesmen, by and large, are not backed up with serried ranks of jet bombers."

Listen to the above words with a "third ear" and you will catch echoes of psychological distance; every sentence implies a measuring of well-being, of power, of manners, of attitudes, of differences between Asia and Africa and the white West. . . . The core of reality today for hundreds of millions resides in how unlike the West they are and how much and quickly they must resemble the West.

This "frog perspective" prevails not only among Asians and Africans who live under colonial conditions, but among American Negroes as well. Hence, the physical nearness or remoteness of the American or European white has little or nothing to do with the feeling of distance that is engendered. We are here dealing with values evoked by social systems or colonial regimes which make men feel that they are dominated by powers stronger than they are.

The "Whiteness" of the White World

This "frog perspective" which causes Asians, Africans, American or West Indian Negroes to feel their situation in terms of an "above" and a "below" reveals another facet of the white world, that is, its "whiteness" as seen and felt by those who are looking from below upwards.

It would take an effort of imagination on the part of whites to appreciate what I term "the reality of whiteness" as it is reflected in the colored mind. From the inside of an American Black Belt, from the perspective of an African colony where 90 per cent of the population is black, or from China, India, or Indonesia where the white man is a rare sight or a distinct minority, the Western white world shrinks in size. The many national states which make up that white world, when seen from the interior of colored life lying psychologically far below it, assumes a oneness of racial identity. This aspect of "whiteness" has been re-enforced by a "gentleman's agreement" (of centuries' standing) implemented by treaties and other forms of aid between the big colony-owning powers to support one another in their colonial difficulties. Of course, of late, there have been some exceptions to this rule. For example, today Germans are prone to boast that they and they alone among the European powers have no record of recent exploitation of Asians and Africans. The Americans can say that they were largely responsible for the liberation of Indonesia. And when the Germans and Americans say this they are expecting that Asians and Africans make a distinction between them and the other colony-owning European states. Yet this distinction is hardly ever made. Why? Because the "whiteness" of Europe is an old reality, stemming from some five hundred years of European history. It has become a tradition, a psychological reality in the minds of Asians and Africans.

I have on occasion heard an Englishman express horror at the French policy in North Africa; and I've heard Frenchmen condemn both the British and the American systems of racial practices. On the other hand, the Spanish claim that they and they alone treated the colored peoples fairly and justly: they married them, etc. In making these boastful claims of their virtues in dealing with their colored colonial subjects, all of these European nations forget that they are contending with a reality which they themselves created deep in the minds of their subject people.

Whose hands ran the business enterprises? White hands. Whose hands meted out the law? White hands. Whose hands regulated the money? White hands. Whose hands erected the churches? White hands. Thus, when the white world is viewed from inside the colored world, that world is a block-world with little or no divisions.

I've heard liberal-minded Frenchmen express genuine horror at the lynching of a Negro by Mississippi whites. But to an Asian or an African it was not a Mississippi white man who did the lynching; it was just a Western white man. It is difficult for white Western Europe to realize how tiny Europe is in the minds of most of the people of the earth. Europe is indeed one world, small, compact, white, apart. . . .

This "whiteness" of the white world, this "frog perspective," this pathos of distance that I've been describing—these are not static qualities; they have their dynamic aspects which I shall now proceed to present to you.

Negative Loyalty

The foremost quality of action which one finds among so many colonial peoples is a kind of negative loyalty to the West among the educated elite. This negative loyalty is a kind of yearning under almost impossible conditions to identify with the values of the white world, since their own traditions have been shattered by that world. Perhaps this yearning to identify with the values of the white world is stronger among American Negroes and West Indian Negroes than any other sections of the colored people in the world. The reason for this is simple: The Negroes in America and in the British West Indies live within the confines of the white cultures that dominate them—cultures that limit and condition their impulses and actions.

Let me illustrate this from the American Negro point of view. The Negro American is the only American in America who says: "I want to be an American." More or less all the other Americans are born Americans and take their Americanism for granted. Hence, the American Negro's effort to be an American is a self-conscious thing. America is something outside of him and he wishes to become part of that America. But, since color easily marks him off from being an ordinary American, and since he lives amidst social conditions pregnant with racism, he becomes an American who is not accepted as an American, hence a kind of negative American.

The psychological situation resulting from this stance is a peculiar one. The Negro in America is so constantly striving to become an American that he had no time to become or try to become anything else. When he becomes a publisher, he is a "Negro" publisher; when he becomes a physician, he is a "Negro" physician; when he becomes an athlete, he is a "Negro" athlete. This is the answer to the question that so many people have asked about American Negroes: Why do not American Negroes rebel? Aside from the fact that they are a minority and their rebellion would be futile, they haven't got time to rebel. Why are Negroes so loyal to America? They are passionately loyal because they are not psychologically free enough to be traitors. They are trapped in and by their loyalties. But that loyalty has kept them in a negative position.

This negative loyalty is widespread also in Asia and Africa. The elite that I've met in Asia and Africa were striving desperately to build societies most nearly like those of the Western states. Nkrumah, Nasser, Sukarno, Nehru, are all Western-educated men striving to make a Western dream come true in non-Western conditions of life. They too share with the American Negro certain negative aspects of loyalty. Each of the four men I've named has come under heavy criticism by white Westerners. (This tragic problem of the elite I shall deal with a little later.)

The psychological dynamics of the Westernized non-Westerner, that is Western-trained and educated Asians and Africans, assume truly strange and compounded psychological patterns. The stance of negative loyalty leads to a whole variety of ironic attitudes. I shall describe this reality briefly under the heading of *acting*.

Acting

What? Am I saying that Asians and Africans and colored people in general are good actors? No. I'm not speaking of the theater. I'm saying that the situation of their lives evokes in them an almost unconscious tendency to hide their deepest reactions from those who they fear would penalize them if they suspected what they really felt. Do I mean to imply that Asians and Africans and American Negroes are not honest people, that they are agents of duplicity? I do not. They are about as honest as anybody else, but they are cautious, wise, and do not wish to bring undue harm upon themselves. Hence, they act. Let me recite an experience of mine. I recently had lunch one day, in Paris, with an Englishman interested in Asia and Africa, and with a West Indian Negro social scientist. The Englishman kept asking me questions about Asians', Africans', and American Negroes' reactions to their plight, and I kept answering quite openly and frankly. I noticed, as I talked, that the West Indian Negro social scientist kept glowering at me, shaking his head, showing acute evidence of something akin to anger. Finally he could contain himself no longer and he blurted out:

"Wright, why are you revealing all of our secrets?"

Unwittingly, I had hurt that man. Desperately I sought to allay his feelings. I had thought that we were three free, modern men who could talk openly. But, no. The West Indian Negro social scientist felt that I was revealing racial secrets to the white race.

"Listen," I said, "the only secret in Asia and Africa and among oppressed people as a whole is that there is no secret."

That did it. He threw up his hands in disgust and exclaimed:

"You have now revealed the profoundest secret of all!"

The scope and intensity of this Asian-African and Negro acting depend on the degree of white hostility that they confront. In America, this acting is a perfected system; it is almost impossible for the white man to determine just what a Negro is really feeling, unless that white man, like a Gunnar Myrdal, is gifted with a superb imagination. In a recent interview William Faulkner, Nobel Prize winner, declared that he could not imagine himself a Negro for two minutes! A strange statement to come from a man with an undoubtedly rich imagination. The American Negro's adversary is next door to him, on the street, on the job, in the school; hence, acting has become almost a second nature with him. This acting regulates the manner, the tone of voice, even, in which most American Negroes speak to white men. The Negro's voice is almost always pitched high when addressed to a white man; all hint of aggressiveness is purged from it. In some instances an educated Negro will try to act as uneducated as possible in order not to merit rebuff from whites.

In Asia and Africa this acting exists, but in a looser form. Not being as intimately related to the Western white man in their daily lives as the American Negro, the Asian and African do not need to practice this dissimulation to the degree that the American Negro does. Yet it is there. There are Asians and Africans who, when confronting whites, will swear proudly that they have never felt any racial feelings at all, that such feelings are beneath them, and will proceed to act in a Western manner. Yet, when alone or among themselves, they will confess their feelings freely and bitterly. I believe that it was only at Bandung that the full content of Asian and African racial feelings were expressed publicly and for the first time in all their turgid passion. They were among themselves and could confess without shame.

This "acting" is one of the secrets that my West Indian social scientist did not want me to talk about. He felt that I was making the Negro, the Asian, and the African transparent, vulnerable to white attack. On the other hand, it is my conviction that the sooner all of these so-called secrets are out in the open, the sooner both sides, white and colored, realize the shadows that hem them in, the quicker sane and rational plans can be made. Let us go one step further into this business of secrets.

The educated Asian, African, or American Negro who longs to escape his debased position, who longs to have done with acting, who longs to convert his negative loyalty into something positive, will encounter ideology sponsored by labor leaders or revolutionaries, the most powerful and appealing of which is that of Marxism. In short, one minority section of the white society in or under which he lives will offer the educated elite of Asia and Africa or black America an interpretation of the world which impels to action, thereby assuaging his feelings of inferiority. Nine times out of ten it can be easily pointed out that the ideology offered has no relation to the plight of the educated black, brown or yellow elite. Yet, what other road is there out of his Black Belt? His captured homeland? His racial prison? But that ideology does solve something. It lowers the social and racial barriers and allows the trapped elite of Asia and Africa and black America the opportunity to climb out of its ghetto. In Asia almost all the national revolutionaries I met had received aid from the hands of Marxists in their youth. The same was true of the black politicians of the Gold Coast, even though Marxism did not even remotely pertain to their non-industrial society. The same is true of the Negro in the United States where there prevailed an absurd theory, Marxist in origin, that the Negro constituted a separate nation.

Ideology as Intimacy

The fear inspired by white domination breeds a tendency, as I have said, to make Asians and Africans act, pretend. And this same almost unconscious tendency to pretension will spur them to pretend to accept an ideology in which they do not believe. They accept it in order to climb out of their prisoners. Many a black boy in America has seized upon the rungs of the Red ladder to climb out of his Black Belt. And well he may, if there are no other ways out of it. Hence, ideology here becomes a means towards social intimacy.

Yes, I know that such a notion is somewhat shocking. But it is true. And in your heart, you know it's true. Many an African in Paris and London, and many a Negro in New York and Chicago, crossed the class and racial line for the first time by accepting the ideology of Marxism, whether he really believed it or not. The role of ideology here served as a function; it enabled the Negro or Asian or African to meet revolutionary fragments of the hostile race on a plane of equality. No doubt the oppressed, educated young man said to himself: "I don't believe in this stuff, but it works." In the Gold Coast young revolutionary Africans told me that, as soon as they had gained their freedom, they were going to erect a statue to the English white woman, thereby celebrating friendships that had redeemed days and weeks of loneliness. "If it had not been for them, we would have lost," they told me.

Resistance

Now, the most natural reaction, the most human response, to the revelation I've just made is to reject it and declare that no such psychological reaction exists. And the tendency to deny psychological traits of the sort I've just revealed leads me to my next concept: Resistance. There is a state of mind among the elite of Asia and Africa and the Negroes of America to reject that which they imagine hurts, degrades, or shames them. It is painful to realize that one is not free enough to make clean and honest decisions, that one has to "use" ideologies for one's own personal benefit. It is a state of mind that compels people to protect themselves against truths that wound; it is a deep, unconscious mechanism that prompts one to evade, deny, or seek explanations for problems other than those that prevail, for one does not wish to acknowledge a state of affairs that induces a loss of face.

I had the experience in both Asia and Africa of receiving intimate, unprompted confessions of how Indonesians felt about the Dutch, of how the Africans felt about the British, but as soon as those confessions appeared in print, there were hasty and passionate denials on the part of the very men who had given me their confessions.

Oppressed people have two sets of feelings: one for home consumption and one for export. I must say in all fairness that this duality of attitude has really aided the Asian and African in his dealing with white Westerners. In almost every instance of colonial revolt, the white Westerner has had absolutely no inkling of the revolt until it burst over his head, so carefully hidden had the rebels kept their feelings and attitudes. In short, oppression helps to forge in the oppressed the very qualities that eventually bring about the downfall of the oppressor.

STORIES

New Life at Kyerefaso

■ Efua Sutherland (Ghana)

Shall we say
Shall we put it this way

Shall we say that the maid of Kyerefaso, Foruwa, daughter of the Queen Mother, was as young as a deer, graceful in limb? Such was she, with head held high, eyes soft and wide with wonder. And she was light of foot, light in all her moving.

Stepping springily along the water path like a deer that had strayed from the thicket, springily stepping along the water path, she was a picture to give the eye a feast. And nobody passed her by but turned to look at her again.

Those of her village said that her voice in speech was like the murmur of a river quietly flowing beneath shadows of bamboo leaves. They said her smile would sometimes blossom like a lily on her lips and sometimes rise like sunrise.

The butterflies do not fly away from the flowers, they draw near. Foruwa was the flower of her village.

So shall we say

Shall we put it this way, that all the village butterflies, the men, tried to draw near her at every turn, crossed and crossed her path? Men said of her, "She shall be my wife, and mine, and mine, and mine."

But suns rose and set, moons silvered and died and as the days passed Foruwa grew more lovesome, yet she became no one's wife. She smiled at the butterflies and waved her hand lightly to greet them as she went swiftly about her daily work:

"Morning, Kweku,
Morning, Kwesi,
Morning, Kodwo,"
but that was all.

And so they said, even while their hearts thumped for her:
"Proud!
Foruwa is proud . . . and very strange."
And so the men when they gathered would say:

"There goes a strange girl. She is not just stiff-in-the-neck proud, not just breasts-stuck-out-I-am-the-only-girl-in-the-village proud. What kind of pride is hers?"

The end of the year came round again, bringing the season of festivals. For the gathering of corn, yams and cocoa there were harvest celebrations. There were bride-meetings too. And it came to the time when the Asafo companies should hold their festival. The village was full of manly sounds, loud musketry and swelling choruses.

The path-finding, path-clearing ceremony came to an end. The Asafo marched on towards the Queen Mother's house, the women fussing round them, prancing round them, spreading their cloths in the way.

"Osee!" rang the cry. "Osee!" to the manly men of old. They crouched like leopards upon the branches.

> Before the drums beat
> Before the danger drums beat, beware!
> Before the horns moaned
> Before the wailing horns moaned, beware!

They were upright, they sprang. They sprang. They sprang upon the enemy. But now, blood no more! No more thundershot on thundershot.

But still we are the leopards on the branches. We are those who roar and cannot be answered back. Beware, we are they who cannot be answered back.

There was excitement outside the Queen Mother's courtyard gate.

"Gently, gently," warned the Asafo leader. "Here comes the Queen Mother."

> Spread skins of the gentle sheep in her way.
> Lightly, lightly walks our Mother Queen.
> Shower her with silver,
> Shower her with silver for she is peace.

And the Queen Mother stood there, tall, beautiful, before the men and there was silence.

"What news, what news do you bring?" she quietly asked.

"We come with dusty brows from our path-finding, Mother. We come with tired thorn-pricked feet. We come to bathe in the coolness of your peaceful stream. We come to offer our manliness to new life."

The Queen Mother stood there, tall and beautiful and quiet. Her fan-bearers stood by her and all the women clustered near. One by one the men laid their guns at her feet and then she said:

"It is well. The gun is laid aside. The gun's rage is silenced in the stream. Let your weapons from now on be your minds and your hands' toil.

"Come, maidens, women all, join the men in dance for they offer themselves to new life."

There was one girl who did not dance.

"What, Foruwa!" urged the Queen Mother. "Will you not dance? The men are tired of parading in the ashes of their grandfathers' glorious deeds. That should make you smile. They are tired of the empty croak: 'We are men, we are men.'

"They are tired of sitting like vultures upon the rubbish-heaps they have piled upon the half-built walls of their grandfathers. Smile, then, Foruwa, smile.

"Their brows shall now indeed be dusty, their feet thorn-pricked, and 'I love my land' shall cease to be the empty croaking of a vulture upon the rubbish-heap. Dance, Foruwa, dance!"

Foruwa opened her lips and this was all she said: "Mother, I do not find him here."

"Who? Who do you not find here?"

"He with whom this new life shall be built. He is not here, Mother. These men's faces are empty; there is nothing in them, nothing at all."

"Alas, Foruwa, alas, alas! What will become of you, my daughter?"

"The day I find him, Mother, the day I find the man, I shall come running to you, and your worries will come to an end."

"But, Foruwa, Foruwa," argued the Queen Mother, although in her heart she understood her daughter, "five years ago your rites were fulfilled. Where is the child of your womb? Your friend Maanan married. Your friend Esi married. Both had their rites with you."

"Yes, Mother, they married and see how their steps once lively now drag in the dust. The sparkle has died out of their eyes. Their husbands drink palm wine the day long under the mango trees, drink palm wine and push counters across the draughtboards all the day, and are they not already looking for other wives? Mother, the man, I say, is not here."

This conversation had been overheard by one of the men and soon others heard what Foruwa had said. That evening there was heard a new song in the village.

> There was a woman long ago,
> Tell that maid, tell that maid,
> There was a woman long ago,
> She would not marry Kwesi,
> She would not marry Kwesi,
> She would not, would not, would not.
> One day she came home with hurrying feet,
> I've found the man, the man, the man,
> Tell that maid, tell that maid,
> Her man looked like a chief,
> Tell that maid, tell that maid,
> Her man looked like a chief,
> Most splendid to see,
> But he turned into a python,
> He turned into a python
> And swallowed her up.

From that time onward there were some in the village who turned their backs on Foruwa when she passed.

Shall we say
Shall we put it this way

Shall we say that a day came when Foruwa with hurrying feet came running to her mother? She burst through the courtyard gate; and there she stood in the courtyard, joy all over. And a stranger walked in after her and stood in the courtyard beside her, stood tall and strong as a pillar. Foruwa said to the astonished Queen Mother:

"Here he is, Mother, here is the man."

The Queen Mother took a slow look at the stranger standing there strong as a forest tree, and she said:

"You carry the light of wisdom on your face, my son. Greetings, you are welcome. But who are you, my son?"

"Greetings, Mother," replied the stranger quietly, "I am a worker. My hands are all I have to offer your daughter, for they are all my riches. I have travelled to see how men work in other lands. I have that knowledge and my strength. That is all my story."

Shall we say
Shall we put it this way,
strange as the story is, that Foruwa was given in marriage to the stranger.

There was a rage in the village and many openly mocked saying, "Now the proud ones eat the dust."

Yet shall we say
Shall we put it this way,
that soon, quite soon, the people of Kyerefaso began to take notice of the stranger in quite a different way.

"Who," some said, "is this who has come among us? He who mingles sweat and song, he for whom toil is joy and life is full and abundant?"

"See," said the others, "what a harvest the land yields under his ceaseless care."

"He has taken the earth and moulded it into bricks. See what a home he has built, how it graces the village where it stands."

"Look at the craft of his fingers, baskets or *kente*,[1] stool or mat, the man makes them all."

"And our children swarm about him, gazing at him with wonder and delight."

Then it did not satisfy them any more to sit all day at their draught-boards under the mango trees.

"See what Foruwa's husband has done," they declared; "shall the sons of the land not do the same?"

And soon they began to seek out the stranger to talk with him. Soon they too were toiling, their fields began to yield as never before, and the women laboured joyfully to bring in the harvest. A new spirit stirred the village. As the carelessly built houses disappeared one by one, and new

[1]kente: a kind of cloth.

homes built after the fashion of the stranger's grew up, it seemed as if the village of Kyerefaso had been born afresh.

The people themselves became more alive and a new pride possessed them. They were no longer just grabbing from the land what they desired for their stomach's present hunger and for their present comfort. They were looking at the land with new eyes, feeling it in their blood, and thoughtfully building a permanent and beautiful place for themselves and their children.

"Osee!" It was festival-time again. 'Osee! Blood no more. Our fathers found for us the paths. We are the roadmakers. They bought for us the land with their blood. We shall build it with our strength. We shall create it with our minds."

Following the men were the women and children. On their heads they carried every kind of produce that the land had yielded and crafts that their fingers had created. Green plantains and yellow bananas were carried by the bunch in large white wooden trays. Garden eggs, tomatoes, red oil-palm nuts warmed by the sun were piled high in black earthen vessels. Oranges, yams, maize filled shining brass trays and golden calabashes. Here and there were children proudly carrying colourful mats, baskets and toys which they themselves had made.

The Queen Mother watched the procession gathering on the new village playground now richly green from recent rains. She watched the people palpitating in a massive dance towards her where she stood with her fan-bearers outside the royal house. She caught sight of Foruwa. Her load of charcoal in a large brass tray which she had adorned with red hibiscus danced with her body. Happiness filled the Queen Mother when she saw her daughter thus.

Then she caught sight of Foruwa's husband. He was carrying a white lamb in his arms, and he was singing happily with the men. She looked on him with pride. The procession had approached the royal house.

"See!" rang the cry of the Asafo leader, "See how the best in all the land stands. See how she stands waiting, our Queen Mother. Waiting to wash the dust from our brows in the coolness of her peaceful stream. Spread skins of the gentle sheep in her way, gently, gently. Spread the yield of the land before her. Spread the craft of your hands before her, gently, gently.

"Lightly, lightly walks our Queen Mother, for she is peace."

NOVEL EXCERPTS

from A Man of the People

■ Chinua Achebe (Nigeria)

Chapter Seven

Chief Nanga was a born politician; he could get away with almost any-thing he said or did. And as long as men are swayed by their hearts and stomachs and not their heads the Chief Nangas of this world will continue to get away with anything. He had that rare gift of making people feel— even while he was saying harsh things to them—that there was not a drop of ill will in his entire frame. I remember the day he was telling his min-isterial colleague over the telephone in my presence that he distrusted our young university people and that he would rather work with a European. I knew I was hearing terrible things but somehow I couldn't bring myself to take the man seriously. He had been so open and kind to me and not in the least distrustful. The greatest criticism a man like him seemed cap-able of evoking in our country was an indulgent: "Make you no min' am."

This is of course a formidable weapon which is always guaranteed to save its wielder from the normal consequences of misconduct as well as from the humiliation and embarrassment of ignorance. For how else could you account for the fact that a Minister of Culture announced in public that he had never heard of his country's most famous novel and received applause—as indeed he received again later when he prophesied that be-fore long our great country would produce great writers like Shakespeare, Dickens, Jane Austen, Bernard Shaw and—raising his eyes off the script— Michael West and Dudley Stamp.

At the end of the function Mr. Jalio and the Editor of the *Daily Matchet* came forward to congratulate him and to ask for copies of the speech. Chief Nanga produced two clean copies from his file, bent down at the table and amended the relevant portions in his own fair hand by the addi-tion of those two names to the list of famous English writers.

I knew the Editor already from a visit he had paid the Minister a few days earlier. A greasy-looking man, he had at first seemed uneasy about my presence in the room and I had kept a sharp look out for the slightest hint from Chief Nanga to get up and leave them. But no hint was given. On the contrary I felt he positively wanted me to stay. So I stayed. Our visitor took a very long time to come to the point, whatever it was. All I could gather was that he had access to something which he was holding back in Chief Nanga's interest. But it was clear that the Minister did not attach very great importance to whatever it was; in fact he appeared to be sick and tired of the man but dared not say so. Meanwhile the journalist told us one story after another, a disgusting white foam appearing at the corners of his mouth. He drank two bottles of beer, smoked many cigarettes and then got a "dash" of five pounds from the Minister after an account of his trouble with his landlord over arrears of rent. Apparently it was not a straightforward case of debt but, since the landlord and the journalist came from different tribes, the element of tribalism could not be ruled out.

"You see what it means to be a minister," said Chief Nanga as soon as his visitor left. His voice sounded strangely tired and I felt suddenly sorry for him. This was the nearest I had seen him come to despondency. "If I don't give him something now, tomorrow he will go and write rubbish about me. They say it is the freedom of the Press. But to me it is nothing short of the freedom to crucify innocent men and assassinate their character. I don't know why our government is so afraid to deal with them. I don't say they should not criticize—after all no one is perfect except God —but they should criticize constructively. . . ." So that other afternoon when the journalist came forward to get a copy of the speech and shouted: "First rate, sir; I shall put it in the front page instead of a story I have promised the Minister of Construction," I just wondered if he ever suspected where he and his stories would be if Chief Nanga had his way.

It must have been about eight o'clock—it was certainly dark—when we left the exhibition to drive back home. As soon as the car moved I dovetailed my fingers into Elsie's on her lap and threw the other arm across her shoulders in a bold, proprietary gesture.

"That was a beautiful speech and you didn't have much time to go over it," I said, just to get some talk going while privately I throbbed with expectation. An image that had never until then entered my mind appeared to me now. I saw Elsie—or rather didn't see her—as she merged so completely with the darkness of my room, unlike Jean who had remained half undissolved like some apparition as she put her things on in the dark.

"When an old woman hears the dance she knows her old age deserts her," replied Chief Nanga in our language. I laughed more loudly than the proverb deserved and then translated it for Elsie who spoke a different language. We used the laughter to get a little closer so that the arm I had over her shoulder slipped under her arm to her breast, and I pressed her against my side.

When we got back, Chief Nanga and I had whisky while Elsie went upstairs to change.

Incidentally, when on our first return from the hospital Chief Nanga had told his steward to take Elsie's bags to his absent wife's room I had been greatly alarmed. But then I had quickly reassured myself that he was merely displaying great tact and delicacy, and I felt grateful just as I had done when he had told us of the all-night Cabinet meeting.

There was only a short flight of stairs between my room on the ground floor and where Elsie was being installed. When all was silent I would go up quietly, tap on her door, find her waiting and take her downstairs to my room, and we could pretend that our host was none the wiser.

We had an excellent dinner of rice, ripe plantains and fried fish. Elsie, looking ripe and ready in a shimmering yellow dress, took us back to the President of the Writers' Association and his funny garb. I found myself putting up a feeble kind of defence.

"Writers and artists sometimes behave that way," I said.

"I think he will heed my advice," said Chief Nanga. "He is a well-comported young man."

This surprised me a great deal. I suppose it was Jalio's flattering words in introducing the Minister that did it; or more likely Chief Nanga had not missed the almost deferential manner in which one of the ambassadors had approached Jalio with a copy of his book for an autograph. I remember looking at Chief Nanga then and seeing astonishment and unbelief on his face, but I did not think it was enough to persuade him to call Jalio "a well-comported young man" so soon after their clash.

The words "well-comported" struck me almost as forcibly as the sentiment they conveyed. I couldn't say whether it was right or wrong, and in any case you felt once again that such distinctions didn't apply here. Chief Nanga was one of those fortunate ones who had just enough English (and not one single word more) to have his say strongly, without inhibition, and colourfully. I remember his telling me of a "fatal accident" he once had driving from Anata to Bori. Since he was alive I had assumed that someone else had been killed. But as the story unfolded I realized that "fatal" meant no more than "very serious."

I retired soon after dinner so that the others might take the cue. And Elsie did. The second time I peeped out she was no longer there in the sitting-room. But Chief Nanga sat on stolidly looking at the file of the speech he had already given. Every two minutes or so I came to the door and peeped out and there he was. Could he be asleep? No, his eyes seemed to be moving across the page. I was getting quite angry. Why didn't he take the blessed file to his study? But perhaps what hurt me most was the fact that I could not muster up sufficient bravado to step into the sitting-room and up the stairs. Perhaps he even expected me to do so. Let me say that I do not normally lack resolution in this kind of situation; but Chief Nanga had, as it were, cramped my style from the very first by introducing an element of delicacy into the affair, thus making it not so much a question of my own resolution as of my willingness to parade Elsie before a third person as a common slut. So there was nothing for it but wait in anger. I sat on my bed, got up again and paced my room barefoot and in pajamas.

It seemed a full hour before Chief Nanga finally switched the lights off and turned in. I gave him about five to ten minutes to settle down in his bed while I had time to steady myself from the strain of the last hour and the unsettling effect which imminent fulfilment always has on me. Then I began to tiptoe upstairs running my palm up the wooden railing for guidance. By the time I got to the landing my eyes were fairly at home in the darkness and it was easy finding Elsie's door. My hand was already on the knob when I heard voices within. I was transfixed to the spot. Then I heard laughter and immediately turned round and went down the stairs again. I did not go into my room straight away but stood for long minutes in the sitting-room. What went on in my mind at that time lacked form and I cannot now set it down. But I remember finally deciding that I was jumping to conclusions, that Chief Nanga had in all probability simply opened the connecting door between the two rooms to say good-night and exchange a few pleasantries. I decided to give him a minute or two more, and then discarding this pussy-footed business go up boldly and knock on Elsie's door. I went back to my room to wait, switched on the bedside lamp which was worked by a short silvery rope instead of a normal switch, looked at my watch which I had taken off and put on a bedside stool. It was already past half-past ten. This stung me into activity again. I hadn't thought it was so late. I rushed into the sitting-room and made to bound up the stairs when I heard as from a great distance Elsie deliriously screaming my name.

I find it difficult in retrospect to understand my inaction at that moment. A sort of paralysis had spread over my limbs, while an intense pressure was building up inside my chest. But before it reached raging point I felt it siphoned off, leaving me empty inside and out. I trudged up the stairs in the incredible delusion that Elsie was calling on me to come and save her from her ravisher. But when I got to the door a strong revulsion and hatred swept over me and I turned sharply away and went down the stairs for the last time.

I sat on my bed and tried to think, with my head in my hands. But a huge sledgehammer was beating down on my brain as on an anvil and my thoughts were scattering sparks. I soon realized that what was needed was action; quick, sharp action. I rose to my feet and willed myself about gathering my things into the suitcase. I had no clear idea what I would do next, but for the moment that did not trouble me; the present loomed so large. I brought down my clothes one at a time from the wardrobe, folded them and packed them neatly; then I brought my things from the bathroom and put them away. These simple operations must have taken me a long time to complete. In all that time I did not think anything particularly. I just bit my lower lip until it was sore. Occasionally words like "Good Heavens" escaped me and came out aloud. When I had finished packing I slumped down in the chair and then got up again and went out into the sitting-room to see if the sounds were still coming. But all was now dark and quiet upstairs. "My word!" I remember saying; then I went to wait for Elsie. For I knew she would come down shedding tears of shame and I would kick her out and bang the door after her for ever. I waited and waited and then, strange as it may sound, dozed off. When I started awake I had that dull, heavy terror of knowing that something terrible had happened without immediately remembering what it was. Of course the uncertainty lasted only one second, or less. Recollection and panic followed soon enough and then the humiliating wound came alive again and began to burn more fresh than when first inflicted. My watch said a few minutes past four. And Elsie had not come. My eyes misted, a thing that had not happened to me in God knows how long. Anyway the tears hung back. I took off my pajamas, got into other clothes and left the room by the private door.

I walked for hours, keeping to the well-lit streets. The dew settled on my head and helped to numb my feeling. Soon my nose began to run and as I hadn't brought a handkerchief I blew it into the roadside drain by closing each nostril in turn with my first finger. As dawn came my head began to clear a little and I saw Bori stirring. I met a night-soil man carrying his bucket of ordure on top of a battered felt hat drawn down to hood his upper face while his nose and mouth were masked with a piece of black cloth like a gangster. I saw beggars sleeping under the eaves of luxurious department stores and a lunatic sitting wide awake by the basket of garbage he called his possession. The first red buses running empty passed me and I watched the street lights go off finally around six. I drank in all these details with the early morning air. It was strange perhaps that a man who had so much on his mind should find time to pay attention to these small, inconsequential things; it was like the man in the proverb who was carrying the carcass of an elephant on his head and searching with his toes for a grasshopper. But that was how it happened. It seems that no thought—no matter how great—had the power to exclude all others.

As I walked back to the house I tried in vain to find the kind of words I needed to speak to Chief Nanga. As for Elsie I should have known that she was a common harlot and the less said about her the better.

Chief Nanga was outside his gate apparently looking out for me when I came round the last bend. He happened just then to be looking in the opposite direction and did not see me at once. My first reaction on seeing him was to turn back. Fortunately I did not give in to that kind of panic; in any case he turned round just then, saw me and began to come towards me.

"Where have you been, Odili?" he asked. "We—I—have been looking for you; I nearly phoned nine-nine-nine."

"Please don't talk to me again," I said.

"What . . . ! Wonders will never end! What is wrong, Odili?"

"I said don't talk to me again," I replied as coolly as possible.

"Wonders will never end! Is it about the girl? But you told me you are not serious with her; I asked you because I don't like any misunderstanding. . . . And I thought you were tired and had gone to sleep . . ."

"Look here, Mr. Nanga, respect yourself. Don't provoke me any more unless you want our names to come out in the newspapers today." Even to myself I sounded strange. Chief Nanga was really taken aback, especially when I called him mister.

"You have won today," I continued, "but watch it, I will have the last laugh. I never forget."

Elsie was standing at the door with arms folded across her bust when I came in at the gate. She immediately rushed indoors and disappeared.

When I brought out my suitcase Chief Nanga, who had not said another word since I insulted him, came forward and tried to put a hand on my shoulder in one last effort at reconciliation.

"Don't touch me!" I eased my shoulders away like one avoiding a leper's touch. He immediately recoiled; his smile hardened on his face and I was happy.

"Don't be childish, Odili," he said paternally. "After all she is not your wife. What is all this nonsense? She told me there is nothing between you and she, and you told me the same thing . . . But anyway I am sorry if you are offended; the mistake is mine. I tender unreserved apology. If you like I can bring you six girls this evening. You go do the thing sotay you go beg say you no want again. Ha, ha, ha, ha!"

"What a country!" I said. "You call yourself Minister of Culture. God help us." And I spat; not a full spit but a token, albeit unmistakable, one.

"Look here, Odili," he turned on me then like an incensed leopard, "I will not stomach any nonsense from any small boy for the sake of a common woman, you hear? If you insult me again I will show you pepper. You young people of today are very ungrateful. Imagine! Anyway don't insult me again-o. . . ."

"You can't do a damn-all," I said. "You are just a bush . . ." I cut myself short and walked out, lumbering my suitcase past Dogo the one-eyed stalwart who had presumably heard our voices and come out from the Boys' Quarters in his sleeping loin-cloth to investigate.

"Na this boy de halla so for master im face?" I heard him ask.

"Don't mind the stupid idiot," said Chief Nanga.

"E no fit insult master like that her and comot free. Hey! My frien'!" he shouted, coming after me. "Are you there?" His voice was full of menace.

I was then half-way to the outside gate. I turned boldly round but on second thoughts said nothing, turned again and continued.

"Leave am, Dogo. Make e carry im bad luck de go. Na my own mistake for bring am here. Ungrateful ingrate!"

I was now at the gate but his voice was loud and I heard every word.

I took a taxi to my friend Maxwell's address. Maxwell Kulamo, a lawyer, had been my classmate at the Grammar School. We called him Kulmax or Cool Max in those days; and his best friends still did. He was the Poet Laureate of our school and I still remember the famous closing couplet of the poem he wrote when our school beat our rivals in the Inter-collegiate Soccer Competition:

Hurrah! to our unconquerable full backs.
(The writer of these lines is Cool Max.)

He was already fully dressed for Court (striped trousers and black coat) and was eating breakfast when I arrived. The few words I spoke to Nanga and the fairly long taxi ride had combined to make it possible for me to wear a passable face.

"Good gracious!" Max shouted, shaking my hand violently. "Diligent! Na your eye be this?" Diligent was a version of Odili I had borne at school.

"Cool Max!" I greeted him in return. "The writer of these lines!" We laughed and laughed and the tears I had not shed last night came to my eyes. Max suspected nothing and even thought I was just coming from home. I told him rather shamefacedly that I had been in town for the past few days but hadn't found it possible to contact him. He took this to be a reference to his having no telephone in the house, a fact which in turn could be a reflection on his practice.

"I have been on the waiting list for a telephone for two months," he said defensively. "You see, I have not given anyone a bribe, and I don't know any big gun . . . So you have been staying with that corrupt, empty-headed, illiterate capitalist. Sorry-o."

"Na matter of can't help," I said. "He na my old teacher, you know."

I was dipping my bread in the cup of hot cocoa drink Max's boy had made for me. Chief Nanga and Elsie already seemed so distant that I could have talked about them like casual acquaintances. But I was not going to delay Max by talking now. And in any case I had no wish to make him think that I only remembered him when I could no longer enjoy the flesh-pots of Chief Nanga's home.

Within minutes I was already feeling so relaxed and at ease here that I wondered what piece of ill-fate took me to Chief Nanga in the first place.

from The Second Round

■   Lenrie Peters (Gambia)

Chapter Two

The Kawas lived in a modest house on Charles Street opposite the Boys' High School. The walls were of timber painted a reddish brown colour, the roof was aluminium and there was a porch for taking the air on warm evenings.

Mrs Kawa had stayed awake through the previous night tossing in bed restlessly and accompanying the chimes of the clock with sobs. Even she had despaired of ever seeing her only son again. Long before the Rhode Island cock had decided to wake the neighbours Mrs Kawa was up, arranging and attending to a thousand necessities. Though nervous with expectation she went about it methodically and unhurriedly. The family photographs which were put away at her husband's death were again hung round the walls with their venerated collection of dust and cobwebs, just as they had been before her son left home.

Mrs Kawa had decided on a grand welcome for her son if it was the very last thing she did, and as he had specifically asked to be spared the traditional welcome on disembarkation she had planned his reception at home. It was what her husband would have wished. No one was going to point a finger at her for stinting. The house was accordingly amply filled with food and drink. The scent of flowers on the tables helped the flavour from the heavily spiced mounds of cooked mutton, poultry and rice to intoxicate the guests. The drummers and dancers had arrived early and, squatting on the sand in the yard, had been warming their throats and drums for hours. Only one slight hitch had occurred during the course of the morning when the Principal of the school had protested against the "rowdy palaver" of the celebrations. At this insult Mrs Kawa, who had never said an angry word in her life, thrust her head out of the window to hear the school singing *Rule Britannia!* and had told him to mind his own business.

She had moved her own things out of the only large bearoom kept cool by window shutters and made homely with the aroma of medicinal potions, ginger and liniment. She had set the pillow in the middle of the brass-limbed bed with the mosquito net neatly drawn back. "I shall sleep in the small bedroom," she had mused with tender satisfaction.

As the taxi rounded the corner of Charles Street the "look-outs" gave the signal and the drummers struck out, moving in rhythm towards the gate, each cadence from the drums punctuated by an ecstatic nasal shriek from the master drummer.

Mrs Kawa hurried to her favourite chair at the end of the corridor facing the door and wiped away a furtive tear. There Dr Kawa had often sat on her knee as a boy and heard the family history handed down—all except the unmentionable interlude of the Slave Trade. In her excitement she could not find either a comfortable or natural position. First she folded her arms across her chest and decided it looked too sombre. Then she rested them on the arms of her chair and thought this attitude lacked warmth. Her heart was beating so quickly that she felt she could not trust it not to leap clean out of her chest. Meanwhile she chewed a green pepper to calm her nerves and keep her blood pressure where it ought to be.

When Dr Kawa walked through the door she thought she would faint with joy, but she managed to get up from her chair, her arms spread out and her head tilted to one side. She observed him keenly and lovingly as he walked towards her, noting every mark of change in his eyes, his walk, even his thoughts. Murmuring a prayer with her eyes closed she flung herself at him and held his head to her breast for a consummate moment of happiness. Then with tears rolling freely down her face she released him to the crowd of well-wishers who had swarmed in like locusts ready and able to devour the new crop.

Dr Kawa was overwhelmed by the welcome and embarrassed by the open show of affection and subtle indictment in the way he was greeted.

"You have been away a long time," one said.

"Now I have seen you again I can die in peace," another.

In the midst of the rejoicing he felt slightly irritated because he could not measure up to the warm-heartedness around him nor find suitable words in reply. Mrs Kawa, recognizing his difficulty, proudly led the singing of a hymn in thanksgiving.

"Amen!" shouted an old man who had already armed himself with a bottle of lager and was searching for an opener.

"God has sent him back to oss, and we are grr-ateful," responded a wiry old woman, sensing the moment of ecstasy approaching.

"And God said, for he was lost and is found. Kill the fatted calf, bo!" recited a younger man as he made his way towards the bottles at the other end of the room. Each outburst drew a conducted sigh from the company while the school bell from across the street added its timorous assent. There was joy and friendship, music and laughter.

Mrs Kawa indeed killed the fatted calf. She kept open house for a week, feasting all who came. Habitual spongers practically took up residence at the little house, systematically mopping up the drink.. When finally the barrel ran dry, contented belches were to be heard all over Freetown. This was the signal for the old Mammies to invade the Kawa residence.

These dear rheumatoids arrived in twos and threes with the perspicacity of vultures descending on the ripped-open carcass of a deer; but though scavengers they looked, they were as clear-minded and extortionate as any Lebanese trader. Some knew the address, some had to be led to it, but all arrived.

They blessed Dr Kawa, admired his patriotism and he in return warmed their shaking hands with neatly-folded currency. They thanked him for the unexpected blessing from God, but as they could not break into his gift before they had prayed for him in the darkness of their own bed-rooms, could he find it in his heart to add their return bus fares to it? Which he did.

If it was an expensive welcome which he could only have avoided by remaining in England, nevertheless it served as a useful investment and an infallible advertising campaign. Even before he had begun to lay his professional hand on the community, the rumour had spread that he was the best doctor Freetown had seen for many years.

Unfortunately for him, the rush of welcomers had scarcely slackened when the traditional end-of-the-month calls fell due, and, while the former depended on his good-will and sentiment, the latter involved a strict call to duty.

The marauders told him that everything about him, his generosity, yes! especially his generosity, his affability and kind eyes had convinced them that all his years away from home in that hard and bitter country of Europe had not deprived him of his respect and understanding for their ancient customs. They were moved to tears because he had not forgotten any single one of them. They who had nursed him as a boy and watched him grow up until the day when, God willing, he had put on his first pair of full-length trousers. They who had prevented his exasperated father— of dear memory—from throwing his son through the windows on those nights when as a baby in arms, he would keep everybody awake with his crying. What heavenly memories returned to them as clearly as if they were incidents of yesterday. His kindness to them—slaves who had done no more than their duty and deserved only as much. All this they said, with eyes darting from the wonder of his face to that of the sky.

Only, they went on, old as they were, they were forced to look after a grandson whose father—the good-for-nothing—had taken to drink. The child had not been to school for a whole week because the fees had not been paid. They were only too aware of his—Dr Kawa's—responsibilities as the only man in his family and were deeply ashamed to add to them, but if he could find it in his heart—that heart which after all they had helped to nurture—if he could search in his pockets for a few shillings, they would continue to pray for him as they had always done. He obliged.

Only, for years the rain had come through the roof and the constant dampness accounted for their rheumatism. If he did not believe them he could go to see himself, and they took his hand. But Mr Y out of sheer kindness had offered to put the roof right for next to nothing, and if Dr Kawa could find it in . . .

All things considered, while his reputation during those first weeks at home expanded, his finances began to show a startling decline, and matters were not helped when his mother presented him with a bill for £60 at the end of his first fortnight, as part of his welcoming expenses.

Gradually he overcame his amusement and then his irritation at the demonstrative and inquisitive temperaments which swarmed around him and who considered every moment of his life as equally their own. Slowly he began to feel at home and relaxed, looking forward to the spiced meals, and no longer feeling embarrassed by the constant sweating. The leisurely meandering life of the tropics struck him as the right tempo for the human body and the endless gyrations of human pursuits in colder climates as artificial and contrary to the laws of nature.

These thoughts came to him usually in the evenings when he sat in the half-light of the porch by the window overlooking the street, and he felt tempted to accept this ultimate simplicity of life unquestioningly. He would sit back, resting his shoulders and his brain. Thus to revitalize his nerves and let the fat roll over his body proved a great temptation. At those moments he would sit suddenly upright in his chair and recall his noble ideas about progress in Africa, would ask himself whether the sunshine was more intoxicating even than the alcohol. Like an addict he would resolve his conflict with a quick squirt into his veins of the hormone for the preservation of Western Man—"feverish activity at all times"—and would go out for a walk down the boggy red earth trenches of Kroo Bay in the sweet stench of Slum Island, listening to the tuberculous chokings which poured out of the tin shacks. There he would watch the children with leg ulcers crack bloated lice between their finger-nails with the swift snap of horse-whips, while their mothers emptied dysentery pails into the uncomplaining waters of the bay. Along the back streets, through the nauseating din of flies and on to the main roads flanked by elegant air-conditioned houses, he would walk, asking himself what was responsible for that transformation from squalor and disease, ignorant superstition and degradation down by the bay, into the physical comforts of modern Freetown. If science—data and proof—had achieved this, then what did he dislike about it? about say, the motor-car?—nice comfortable shining timesaver. Was it its dehumanizing effect? The unsmiling dead hippopotamus look on the drivers' faces, the intolerable arrogance, the blindness and the greed? Once you had, for instance, a car, an endless line of scientific necessities stretched out and beckoned you into the distance. He remembered what a young barrister had told him: "Take me for instance: I got a car on credit the moment I got back; then a refrigerator. But you can't just keep eggs in the fridge, you need booze. But what's the good of it all if you can't show it off! So you have a few friends in. Heavens above, I haven't got a house! Let's see; I could borrow—everybody borrows nowadays, even the Government lives by credit. But if you borrow you have to pay interest to a chap who doesn't mind how he makes his money. I must have gone soft in the head—plain monkey mad. It's naïve to think you can build an honest house these days. They tell me everyone takes bribes these days; everyone, even bishops and judges. You can bribe your way to heaven as quickly as spit out a hot potato. Who am I to try to carry the social conscience on my back anyway? One day some great social pioneer will turn up and straighten things out. He's bound to turn up sooner or later—things can't just go to the dogs. As for me I'm human and I'm only concerned with making my cell nice and padded any way I can. Another thing; when I get my new house I must find a nice progressive woman."

That was it: squeeze out a man's personality like an orange pip and leave a whole lot of moving carcasses in splendid fall-out shelters.

Depressed by his attempt to isolate the links which so skillfully bound physical squalor to fertility of soil on the one hand, and the elegant shrouds of prosperity to barrenness on the other, he would find himself at the hospital. His nostrils dilated; he sniffed the air in search of that comfort which he hoped to find in the true harmony of science with human consciousness and fertility. Alas! they had not heard of science at the hospital. Medicine was still a hit or miss game with tons of luck thrown in, and any revolutionary upstart was merely heading for an early grave. The witch-doctor had been at it since the days of the cannibal and was thought quite adequate for most African needs.

Faced with frustrations, Dr Kawa wondered whether stagnation in any field that seemed potentially valuable was a reflection of the British genius for making their colonial peoples march no nearer than a century behind them, so that when frock coats and bowlers were being frowned on and discarded at Westminster, they had become the height of fashion in the tropical heat; or whether it was a cunning device of science to check its own overgrowth? Probably it was nothing more than a manifestation in social change of what biologists described as "The ontology retracing the phylogeny."

But his dispiriting thoughts did not then drive him to the depths of despair and depression which were to follow. Those were the painful days of readjustment, and, leaning against the once infallible pillar of reason, he continued to snarl out his questions. Where was the reconstruction to begin? What man could copy those ingenious wasps by thrusting his sting into the nerve centre of confusion without poisoning the entire system and say: "That is where sickness begins; these are the very earliest beginnings of decay—this cloudy swelling" without being subjected to the humiliation of being put away safely, Christlike, on a shelf? But the body needed a certain minimum of organs to survive, and Jung had warned against stealing from people, even their neuroses, unless one had something better to put in their place. But sickness was one thing, a moral epidemic quite another.

One evening as he walked home from one of his impulsive walks with bowed head, his hands behind his back, he felt breathtakingly elated because he thought he had found the answer to some of his questions.

It was an answer that would need a lot of pruning and reshaping and explaining, but an answer nevertheless—a starting point. He became overwhelmingly convinced that the trouble with the society into which he was snuggling like a roosting hen, was its weightlessness. Not light enough to take wings and soar but at the same time not heavy enough to settle on a firm foundation. A people at the middle way; the turning point. Hovering like evil ghosts and restless enough to be confused. He saw with an intuitive comprehension through the smiling faces and the rantings of the politicians the one collective visage of a frightened people. Frightened as if they had suddenly found themselves on the moon. People were always frightened. Frightened of pain, disease, love and death, but most of all frightened of emptiness, not knowing what they were about. So frightened in fact that they gave up trying to put things right and pretended nothing was the matter. Again the woman philosopher raised her intuitive head with shouts of "If we are to die, then let's die screaming."

Europe was frightened because she too was at the middle way and could not see round the corner. The whole world was frightened. Not so much of science or of nuclear bombs. The fear was deep inside the spirit of Man. If Mephistophelean science should win the wager, then his soul was gone—and there was only deluge, chaos, worse than chaos. So the blind had finally abandoned the blind—each for himself. The problem was not unique to Africa; it was only in a different shade of black. What was different was that Africa had a chance to stem it. Perhaps a last chance to banish the fear.

His mind turned to the origin of this fear. Was it conceit? Was it that man no longer felt the need to keep his feet warm in the milky bosom of the earth? Was it in his isolation from the harmony that held the earth to the sun and yet prevented the moon crashing into it? Here was a great event—the crystallization of vast energies into a mind, a perception able to understand and perhaps to throw back some little influence into the expanding whole. An organism which in a relatively short space of time had attained a position of dominance over the psychic impulse. What enormous opportunities opened to man and the universe for a happy remarriage between these opposing aspects of a fundamental reality. But rather like the centriole in the nucleus of a living cell at the moment of its dividing, at the very moment of its creation of new life through a process of sharing, they had positioned themselves at opposite poles and were held together precariously only by the flimsy threads of the artefactual spindle.

Worse still; time, which had appeared to be a fixed corridor along which we might hurry into a distant nothingness, had suddenly shown itself to be indecently elusive. Since it was not running out on us, we had to put up with our own nasty work—not a pleasant thought. What a dilemma! Knowledge against self-disintegration. With luck we might bounce on to the next stage of evolution without memory of the past, not as men, but as morons perhaps. Something capable of living by the dictates of machines. *Progress!*

from The Beautyful [sic] Ones Are Not Yet Born

■ Ayi Kwei Armah (Ghana)

Outside, the sight of the street itself raised thoughts of the reproach of loved ones, coming in silent sounds that ate into the mind in wiry spirals and stayed there circling in tightening rings, never letting go. There was no hurry. At the other end there was only home, the land of the loved ones, and there it was only the heroes of the gleam who did not feel that they were strangers. And he had not the kind of hardness that the gleam required. Walking with the slowness of those whose desire has nowhere to go, the man moved up the road, past the lines of evening people under the waning lamps selling green and yellow oranges and bloated bread polished with leftover oil, and little tins and packets ot things no one was in any hurry to buy. Under a dying lamp a child is disturbed by a long cough coming from somewhere deep in the center of the infant body. At the end of it his mother calmly puts her mouth to the wet congested nostrils and sucks them free. The mess she lets fall gently by the roadside and with her bare foot she rubs it softly into the earth. Up at the top a bus arrives and makes the turn for the journey back. The man does not hurry. Let it go. From the other side of the road there is the indiscreet hiss of a nightwalker also suffering through her Passion Week. At other times the hiss is meant only for the heroes, but now it comes clearly over. In the space between weak lamps opposite can be seen the fragile shine of some ornament on her. There are many of the walking dead, many so much worse off. The shine disappears then comes again, closer, somewhere near the middle of the road. Incredible. In a moment the air is filled with the sharp sweetness of armpit powder hot and moist, and the keenness of perfume trapped in creases of prematurely tired skin. At rapid intervals comes the vapor of a well-used wig. Horse or human?

"Sssssss." The appeal is not directed anywnere beyond the man. The incredible comes true at times like this. The man looks up and sees beneath the mass of the wig the bright circle of an earring. The walker does not see, or chooses not to see, the lukewarm apologetic smile.

"Five." The voice is not a used one. It is almost like a shy child's. The man shakes his head. How anyhow at a time like this?

"Three." Abrupt drop, this. So many desperate needs.

"Sister, I have nothing at all." No response. Light glinting on swirled earring. The walker steps back into the ambiguous shadow between the lights, waiting with a strange voice for strange faces in the dark. More sellers under more faint lights, selling more of the same inconsequential things. From the rise ahead an object made of power and darkness and gleaming light comes shimmering in a potent moving stream, and it stops in front of a half-asleep seller close to the man. Above the cool murmur of the engine the voice of a female rises from within, thin as long wire stabbing into open eyes.

"Driver, get some oranges."

"How much, Auntie?"

"Oh, two dozen."

The driver steps out and swings the door shut with the satisfied thud of newness. The wire voice within seems to wail something more, and from the back seat of the limousine a man dressed in a black suit comes out and makes straight for a little covered box with bread in it. The young girl behind the box hurries to open it and to hold out a large wrapped loaf. The man takes it and says, "One more."

The girl pulls out another. Glint of a fifty-pesewa coin. The man turns and walks confidently back to the car. The girl runs after him with his change, but he does not want it and the girl returns to her box. Next to the girl another, older seller wakes to her missed chance and begins to call out, "Big man, I have fine bread."

"I have bought some already." The voice of the suited man had something unexpected about it, like a fisherman's voice with the sand and the salt hoarsening it forcing itself into unaccustomed English rhythms. Why was this necessary? A very Ghanaian voice.

"My lord," comes the woman again, "my big lord, this bread is real bread."

Inside the big car the pointed female voice springs and coils around, complaining of fridges too full to contain anything more and of too much bread already bought. Outside, the seller sweetens her tones.

"My own lord, my master, oh, my white man, come. Come and take my bread. It is all yours, my white man, all yours."

The car door opens and the suited man emerges and strides slowly toward the praise-singing seller. The sharp voice inside the car makes one more sound of impatience, then subsides, waiting. The suit stops in front of the seller, and the voice that comes out of it is playful, patronizing.

"Mammy, I can't eat all of that."

"So buy for your wife," the seller sings back.

"She has enough."

"Your girl friends. Young, beautiful girls, no?"

"I have no girl friends."

"Ho, my white man, don't make me laugh. Have you ever seen a big man without girls? Even the old ones," the seller laughs, "even the old men."

"Mammy, I am different." The suited man pays the seller. She takes the money and holds on to the man's hand, looking intently into his face now.

"You are a politician," she says at last, "a big man."

"Who told you?"

"It's true, is it not?" she asks. "I have seen your picture somewhere."

"I see." The suited man looks around him. Even in the faint light his smile is easy to see. It forms a strange pattern of pale light with the material of his shirt, which in the space between the darknesses of his suit seems designed to point down somewhere between the invisible thighs.

"Hello-low," says the smile to the invisible man of the shadows, "what are you doing here? I almost didn't see you."

"Going home from work. At first I wasn't sure."

A pale cuff flashes, and the suited man looks at his watch and just murmurs something to himself, very low. "By the way," he says, "we'll be over to see you soon, Estie and myself."

"Hmmm."

"No. This time I mean it. Let's see. Today is Wednesday. Let's make it Satur . . . no, Sunday evening."

"What time?"

"Nine I'll be free, I think."

The car horn splits the air with its new, irritated sound, and the suited man spins instinctively around, then recovers and says, "Estie is in the car. Come and greet her."

The man walks behind the suit up to the car. The voice within starts scolding in an abrasive tone, but the suit cuts it short. "Estie, I found a stranger."

The woman's wire voice changes a little in tone. "Aaaa, ei look. I didn't see anybody." Out through the window she holds out a hand and something glitters in the night light. The man takes the hand. Moist like lubricated flesh. It is withdrawn as quickly as if contact were a well-known calamity, and the woman inside seems plainly to have forgotten about the man outside. Another sound of a door softly closing. "Well, Sunday, then. Nine."

"Fine."

A voice from the car, an afterthought as the engine turns impatiently. "Oh, by the way, we are not going back. Atlantic-Caprice, and we are late. Otherwise . . . ."

"Don't worry your soul," the man hollers after the fluid movement of the limousine. "Don't worry your soul . . ." he repeats the words in a whisper to himself, and turns his look away from the gleam above the hill.

The waiting period is a time of comforting emptiness. Thoughts that do not necessarily have to have anything to do with the sickness of despair come and go leaving nothing painful behind them. How many hands passing over the long bar of the bench at the bus stop since it was first put there? What do three lit windows mean in the dark dark Post Office at night? What have the others waiting been doing? With a wholly unnecessary burst of noise a bus comes and stops with its entrance door a yard beyond the bus stop opening. The waiting people slide toward it, but the conductor walks away down the road. In a few moments the waiters can hear the sound of his urine hitting the clean-your-city can. He must be aiming high. Everyone relaxes visibly. The poor are rich in patience. The driver in his turn jumps down and follows the conductor to the heap. His sound is much more feeble. For a long time they stand by the heap laughing and talking. Joking about what has just been going on? Comparing what? The driver wanders back, climbs in and goes to sleep over the wheel. The conductor is aiming to go down in the direction of the sellers. A few, fed up with waiting, climb in anyhow and put their heads to rest against the remaining panes. Someone coughs, but the noise gives place to an abrupt silence. Those still waiting outside drape their bodies over the long rails of the bus stop shelter, and the lights of passing vehicles play upon their shapes in strange, desolate patterns. When the conductor returns he is eating a shiny loaf of bread by hollowing it out, and the food handled in this way in the darkness looks intermittently like something resentful and alive. With a full mouth the conductor shouts at those who have climbed inside; a morsel shoots out from his jaws and drops in a pale arc by the bus.

"Get down! Get down! Have you paid and are you sitting inside?"

As if they have been expecting this all along, the people inside climb meekly down and hold out their money to the conductor. He is too angry to accept it, and sends them back to the end of the line. Nothing serious. The line is not long. The conductor mumbles insults aimed at no particular person as he snaps out the tickets. No one seems to need change, so things go rapidly, except when the conductor takes his time to say aloud some deeply felt insult.

The man gets in, choosing a seat by a window. The window turns out to have no pane in it. No matter. It is hardly a cold night. When the bus starts the air that rushes in comes like a soft wave of lukewarm water. The man leans back against his seat and fingers recoil behind his head. He does not look back. It is possible, after so much time up and down the same way, it is possible to close the eyes and lay back the head and yet to know very clearly that one is at this moment passing by that particular place or the other one, because the air brings these places to the open nose. Even at night there is something hot and dusty about the wind that comes blowing over the grease of the loco yard, so that the combination raises in the mind pictures of thick short men in overalls thickened with grease that never will come off; blunt rusty bits of iron mixed up with filings in the sand; old water that has stopped flowing and confused itself with decaying oil from broken-down boilers; even the dead smell of carbide lamps and electric cutters. After the wall of the loco yard, the breeze blowing freely in from the sea, fresh in a special organic way that has in it traces of living things from their beginnings to their endings. Over the iron bridge the bus moves slowly. In gusts the heat rises from the market abandoned to the night and to the homeless, dust and perpetual mud covered over with crushed tomatoes and rotten vegetables, eddies from the open end of some fish head on a dump of refuse and curled-up scales with the hardening corpses of the afternoon's flies around. Another stretch of free sea line. More than halfway now, the world around the central rubbish heap is entered, and smells hit the senses like a strong wall, and even the eyes have something to register. It is so old it has become more than mere rubbish, that is why. It has fused with the earth underneath. In one or two places the eye that chooses to remain open can see the weird patterns made by thrown wrecks of upended bicycles and a prewar roller. Sounds arise and kill all smells as the bus pulls into the dormitory town. Past the big public lavatory the stench claws inward to the throat. Sometimes it is understandable that people spit so much, when all around decaying things push inward and mix all the body's juices with the taste of rot. Sometimes it is understandable, the doomed attempt to purify the self by adding to the disease outside. Hot smell of caked shit split by afternoon's baking sun, now touched by still evaporating dew. The nostrils, incredibly, are joined in a way that is most horrifyingly direct to the throat itself and to the entrails right through to their end. Across the aisle on the seat opposite, an old man is sleeping and his mouth is open to the air rushing in the night with how many particles of what? So why should he play the fool and hold his breath? Sounds of moist fish frying in open pans of dark perennial oil so close to the public lavatory. It is very easy to get used to what is terrible. A different thing; the public bath, made for a purification that is not offensive. Here there is only the stale soapsuds merging in grainy rotten dirt from everybody's scum, a reminder of armpits full of yellowed hair dripping sweat down arms raised casually in places of public intimacy. The bus whines up a hill and the journey is almost over. Here are waves of spice from late pots of familiar homes, spices to cover what strong meats?

The man gets down and his hands find their own way deep into his pockets. The air around the spine at the base of his neck grows unaccountably cold. The puddle at the end of the gutter is widening so that it takes some effort to leap over it now. And it seems such a tiring thing to do, climbing up the four little stairs onto the veranda. There is light in the kitchen still, but everything is very quiet. Is that strange at this time of night? It does not matter, really. Why should there not be silence, after all, why not?

Silence. No voices, no sounds in the night, just silence. The man walks into the hall, meeting the eyes of his waiting wife. These eyes are flat, the eyes of a person who has come to a decision not to say anything; eyes totally accepting and unquestioning in the way only a thing from which nothing is ever expected can be accepted and not questioned. And it is true that because these eyes are there the air is filled with accusation, but for even that the man feels a certain tired gratitude; he is thankful there are no words to lance the tension of the silence. The children begin to come out of the room within. They are not asleep, not even the third little one. It seems their eyes also are learning this flat look that is a defense against hope, as if their mother's message needs their confirmation. It comes across very well. So well it fills the hall with an unbearable heaviness which must be broken at all costs. The table has food on it. The man moves forward and sits at it with his back to his guilt, resolving to break the heavy quiet.

"I saw Koomson on my way home," he says. The wife is slow about showing any interest.

"And Estella was with him, I suppose?" she asks at last.

"Uh-huh," he nods, turning to look at her. He sees instead the eyes of his children. O you loved ones, spare your beloved the silent agony of your eyes.

"Mmmmmmmmm." The sound she makes should mean approval or at the least acceptance, but it does not. Now it is a low cry full of resentment and disappointment. Then, "She has married well . . ." The man wishes he had learned to bear the weight of the silence before, but now going back is impossible.

"They were going to the Atlantic-Caprice." He raised the spoon to his mouth, and as he did so he caught the scent of perfume still on his hand. "I shook hands with his wife, and I can smell her still. Her hand was wet with the stuff."

"Mmmmmm." This long sound again. "Life has treated her well."

"Koomson says he wants to come and see us. Sunday, nine."

"Mmmmmmmm."

"That probably means your mother, not us. We should remember to tell her when she comes."

The woman paused before answering. "It is not only for my mother that Koomson will come."

"What do you mean?" asked the man. His spoon drops and he ignores it.

"I mean if things go well, they will go well for all of us."

"Do you think so?" The man looks worriedly at his wife. She is irritated.

"Why are you trying to cut yourself apart from what goes for all of us?"

"I did not know," the man says very slowly, "I did not know that I had agreed to join anything."

"But you will be eating it with us when it is ripe?" The woman's defensive little smile does nothing to remove the sharp edge of the question. The man rises from the table and goes toward his wife. She is about to shrink back from him, but he is smiling sadly down at her and she relaxes.

"Where is Koomson getting all the money for this boat?" he asks.

"He is getting it." Flat finality.

"All right," says the man. "Let us say I am not in it."

The woman stares unbelieving at her husband, then whispers softly, "Chichidodooooo."

Knock on the door. Answer from the woman, and an old woman with her breasts barely covered by her cloth comes in holding a little chipped enamel bowl at the tips of her fingers.

"Good evening," she says. "Here I am again. Sugar. Would you be pleased to lend me a little sugar? Just for the children."

The wife answers, "We have just finished our last packet ourselves."

On the old woman's face appears a smile halfway between scepticism and triumphant belief. As she disappears through the doorway she looks back at the couple within and says, "Ah, this life!"

The man looks at his wife and finds her eyes fixed on his face. "What were you saying?" he asked.

"Nothing," she says. He grows silent.

"Somebody offered me a bribe today," he says after a while.

"Mmmmmmmm!"

"One of those timber contractors."

"Mmmmmmm. To do what?"

"To get him an allocation."

"And like an Onward Christian Soldier you refused?"

The sudden vehemence of the question takes the man completely by surprise. "Like a what?"

"On-ward Chris-tian Soooooooldier!
Maaarching as to Waaaaaaaaar
With the Cross of Jeeeeeeesus
Goooing on be-foooooore!"

The man took a long look at his wife's face. Then he said, "It wasn't even necessary."

"What were you afraid of then?" the woman asked.

"But why should I take it?"

"And why not? When you shook Estella Koomson's hand, was not the perfume that stayed on yours a pleasing thing? Maybe you like this crawling that we do, but I am tired of it. I would like to have someone drive me where I want to go."

"Like Estella Koomson?"

"Yes, like Estella. And why not? Is she more than I?"

"We don't know how she got what she has," the man said.

"And we don't care." The woman's voice had lost its excitement and reverted to its flatness. With a silent gesture she sent the children back inside. "We don't care. Why pretend? Everybody is swimming toward what he wants. Who wants to remain on the beach asking the wind, 'How . . . How . . . How?' "

"Is that the way you see things now?" he asked her.

"Have you found some other way?"

"No."

"Would you refuse Koomson's car if it got given free to you?"

"No. It would depend . . ."

"Is there anything wrong with some entertainment now and then?"

"Of course not."

"Then why not?"

"Why not what?" he asked.

The woman's mouth opened, but she let it close again. Then she said, "It is nice. It is clean, the life Estella is getting."

The man shrugged his shoulders. When he spoke, it was with deliberate laziness. "Some of that kind of cleanness has more rottenness in it than the slime at the bottom of a garbage dump."

"Mmmmmmm . . ." the woman almost sang. The sound might have been taken as a murmur of contentment. "You are the chichidodo itself."

"Now what do you mean by that?" The man's voice was not angry, just intrigued. Very calmly, the woman gave him her reply.

"Ah, you know, the chichidodo is a bird. The chichidodo hates excrement with all its soul. But the chichidodo only feeds on maggots, and you know the maggots grow best inside the lavatory. This is the chichidodo."

The woman was smiling.

from The River Between

■ James Ngugi (Kenya)

Chapter Twenty-four

One evening a few days later Kinuthia burst into Waiyaki's hut. He looked worried and glanced back over his shoulder as if expecting some people to follow him.

"Waiyaki," he breathed out.

"What is it, Kinuthia?" Waiyaki asked. He felt frightened. He had never seen Kinuthia like this before.

"What have they done?"

"Who?"

"The Kiama!"

"What?"

"They are spreading rumours that you are no longer a teacher."

"Oh!"

There was a little silence. Waiyaki recovered from the momentary shock and said with a forced calmness. "Please sit down. Where did you hear this?"

"It is being whispered. You know how news spreads. Kamau told me the Kiama removed you from your job. You were in league with the white man."

Waiyaki felt bitter that the elders for whom he had struggled should turn against him so.

"And how do the people take it?" he asked.

"I don't know. I think not all the people have heard. When did they do this to you?"

Waiyaki felt a sharp pain at the last question. He felt as if Kinuthia was one of the conspirators.

"To me? They cannot remove me from the job. It is not their responsibility. It is only the Schools' Committee who can do it. I really know nothing about this."

Then he described to Kinuthia the events of the night he had been called to Makuyu.

"Perhaps I was wrong to let anger and passion get the better of me. The girl does not even love me."

"This is all Kabonyi's doing. He hates you. Oh, you don't know how. Look Waiyaki, I think something is happening tonight. Kamau hinted something about going to Joshua's household tonight. I don't know, but the young men might do something bad. They think it is Nyambura who has corrupted you."

"Wait! What do they want to do?"

"I don't know. But I think it might be something rough. And they will not stop at that. They may come to you. For they say you have broken the oath. You have given away the secrets. So you must flee the land. Fly to Nairobi. I tell you again: Kabonyi is after you and he will get you. He has a new influence with the elders. They cannot resist his power. The man has no roots anywhere and he talks of an ancient prophecy about a saviour. He is that saviour, he says. . . ."

Waiyaki rose. He remembered that Chege had told him that it was only Kabonyi who knew of the ancient prophecy. Perhaps that was why Kabonyi hated him. But now he knew there was no time to lose. His mind was made up. He had to go and warn Joshua.

"Thank you, Kinuthia. But I must go."

"Where?"

"To Makuyu. I must warn Joshua. Violence must not break out among the people. Oh, not now."

"No, Teacher."

"I must go."

"But you cannot. They will have an excuse to try you as a traitor if they get to know of this."

"Kinuthia."

"Yes?"

"You remember you and I have grown up together."

"Yes." Kinuthia could remember more than Waiyaki could guess.

"Then do not stop me." Waiyaki's voice was calm. "Do not think that I am not grateful. I value your concern so much. You are the only man I can now trust. But we cannot allow this to happen. The ridges will collapse if we allow anything to happen to Joshua through the madness of one person. Maybe I have not done all that I should have done for the tribe. I do not want to bring you into this. Don't come with me. If you stay here I'll come back and we shall talk. I will tell you of my plans."

Kinuthia did not argue. He could detect a firmness behind the calmness of Waiyaki. Yet he could still see that there was an agitation in the eyes of the teacher. He let Waiyaki go. But he did not remain in the hut. He too went out and followed the teacher up to Honia river.

Waiyaki climbed up the slopes, hoping fearfully that he might be in time to warn them. He tried to run up the ridge towards Joshua's house. He had never been there before. Even from afar, he could hear them singing.

> Maikarite thi Utuku
> Ariithi a Mburi
> Murekio wa Ngai niokire
> Nake akimera o uu.

> While shepherds watched their flocks by night
> All seated on the ground
> The angel of the Lord came down
> And glory shone around.

Indeed, Christmas was near. The Christians were keeping their watch by night like those shepherds of old.

When Waiyaki entered, breathless, everyone stopped and looked at him. To them he was a strange apparition. For a few minutes there was silence as Waiyaki tried to recover his breath. But he now felt foolish. What had he come to warn them against? What was he to tell these men of Joshua who sat around the table singing to heaven, waiting for a Christ?

"I am sorry for interrupting your meeting . . . but . . . but I think you are in danger. They may want to do something to you, tonight or another day."

"Who?" several voices asked.

"Kabonyi and his men. The Kiama. I don't know what you can do but——"

"Do not tell us what we can do," Joshua roared. He stood up and glared at Waiyaki. "This is all lies." The two men faced each other for the first time. The others watched, fascinated, fearing, wondering. "Go! Go! Out of my house! So you would come back to entice the only daughter that is left to me. I have never forgotten what you did to Muthoni."

It was the first time that Joshua had publicly mentioned her death.

Waiyaki felt hurt, as if this rejection of his well-meant warning had suddenly brought home to him the depth of the barrier between him and Joshua. Perhaps nothing would ever remove it. In that moment, too, he understood why Nyambura had refused him. Yet he felt himself ridiculed and humiliated before these people, before the girl he loved. He had seen Nyambura sitting beside Miriamu.

"Ni wega. I have done my duty. I was only trying to save you from danger." His voice carried a slight tremor.

"Save yourself first. Save yourself from the Wrath to come. What do you, who have always worked against the people of God, want in my house?"

Waiyaki suddenly turned his back on them and opened the door to go out. The light from the house shone on him—a lone figure facing the darkness outside.

As Kamau and his four men, lurking in the outer darkness, saw him, they gasped with fear and unbelief. Kamau did not know that Waiyaki had gone so far in his betrayal of the people, and he became convinced that Waiyaki was the greatest enemy to the tribe. He could not now go to capture Nyambura as the Kiama had ordered them. No. He would go back and report this to the Kiama. This was no longer a personal battle, but a war between the tribe and Waiyaki.

Nyambura had seen Waiyaki's entrance. She read sorrow and agitation in his face. Her heart jumped with excitement. There stood her man. There stood Waiyaki, the Teacher, her black Messiah, sent from heaven after Muthoni's death to come and rescue her from disintegration. And she knew the man loved her. She had heard it from his own lips. Since then she had thought about him day and night. It did not matter if her father forbade her standing with him. Joshua could control her body, but he could not control her heart. And so, day by day, she walked with him, touching him and holding him to herself in her own way. She lived in a dream. She was always with Waiyaki. Yet sometimes the separation pained

her. It hurt her and at times made her cry. For she too yearned for him
and wanted him to be near her all the time. She cried: "Waiyaki, you are
mine. Come back to me." But he did not come. Her duty to her parents
stood between him and her. A religion of love and forgiveness stood between them. No! It could never be a religion of love. Never, never. The
religion of love was in the heart. The other was Joshua's own religion,
which ran counter to her spirit and violated love. If the faith of Joshua
and Livingstone came to separate, why, it was not good. If it came to stand
between a father and his daughter so that her death did not move him,
then it was inhuman. She wanted the other. The other that held together,
the other that united. The voice that long ago said "Come unto me all ye
that labour and are heavy laden, and I will give you rest" soothed her and
she wanted to hear it again and again, as she lay near the Honia river
and listened to the throb which echoed the secret beating of her heart.
And she remembered:

> The wolf also shall dwell with the lamb, and the leopard shall lie down
> with the kid; and the calf and the young lion and the fatling together;
> and a little child shall lead them. And the cow and the bear shall feed;
> their young ones shall lie down together: and the lion shall eat straw like
> the ox. And the suckling child shall play on the hole of the asp, and the
> weaned child shall put his hand on the cockatrice' den. They shall not
> destroy in all my holy mountain: for the earth shall be full of the
> knowledge of the Lord, as the waters cover the sea.

That was her religion. That was what she now wanted for her tribe. It
was the faith that would give life and peace to all. So she clung to this
now as she prayed that Waiyaki would come back to her.

He came. Not when she expected him. But she was ready for him and
she was glad. She, however, feared for him. Maybe that was why her heart
jumped. That was why something strange settled in her bowels, giving her
both pain and pleasure.

She looked at the two men standing face to face. She saw her Waiyaki
being humiliated. Her obedience to her father fought with her love for
Waiyaki. And at last, when he turned his back, rejected, she stood up. Her
voice was clear and almost commanding.

"Teacher!" Waiyaki stopped.

"Come back!"

Waiyaki obeyed. Yet it was all like a dream. Even Joshua was shocked
to silence. To think that she had actually called him the "Teacher."

"The teacher is not telling a lie."

"You! You! How can you know that, little rebel?"

"I know. Last week Kamau wanted me to marry him. I refused. He said
he would compel me or do something worse. He said I was in his power
and he was the only person who could save——"

Joshua fumed with fury. He would not let her finish. And Waiyaki was
still in a dream. But still he was hurt and a burning anger was urging
him to go out. Outside he heard a faint noise. At first it had seemed distant but now he could hear some words—Teacher . . . traitor. . . . A heavy
dejection came over Waiyaki. He knew now that he was not wanted by

them in spite of all he had done for the hills. And the words of his father came back to him. *But they rejected Mugo,* his thin boy's voice had queried. *Let them do what they like. A time will come when they shall cry for a saviour.*

Had the time come? Was Kabonyi the saviour they were crying for? And what would Kabonyi do? He would only destroy what Waiyaki had built. But no. He could not. Surely there was a soul, a heart where at least what Waiyaki had done had taken root. And the teachers who were coming! They would carry on the work. The voices singing death became louder and louder. He thought they were coming towards Joshua's house. He went back to the hut to make one more desperate appeal.

"Be careful. They may be coming here."

"Go, go out from here. Get thee behind me, Satan."

Joshua was fierce. He hated the young man with the hatred which a man of God has towards Satan. There was another murmur in the room. Then silence reigned as Nyambura walked across towards Waiyaki while all the eyes watched her. Waiyaki and Joshua must have both been struck by her grace and mature youthfulness. She held Waiyaki's hand and said what no other girl at that time would have dared to say, what she herself could not have done a few days before.

"You are brave and I love you."

Joshua woke up from his stupor. He would never have thought that this meek, quiet and obedient daughter could be capable of such an action. He rushed towards her and was about to lay his hands on her when he realized that this was another temptation brought to him by Satan. Christ in him must triumph at this hour of trial. Waiyaki and Nyambura were standing near the door.

"For me and my house we will serve the Lord," Joshua declared, pointing at Nyambura with the forefinger of his right hand. "You are not my daughter. Yet let me warn you," he continued, his voice changing from one of fiery anger to one of calm sorrow, "you will come to an untimely end. Go!"

As if in a dream, Waiyaki and Nyambura went out. Miriamu was weeping and saying, "Don't let her go. Don't," while the others remained silent, wondering what curse had befallen Joshua's house.

Darkness still blanketed the land. Above the stars had gone out except for one or two. Nyambura had never rebelled before; not with deliberation. This was her first act of rebellion and she now knew that she was beyond the grasp of Joshua. The call of the inner voice that urged her on, the call of the land beyond Joshua's confining hand, was too strong.

"Please, Nyambura. Go back to your father," Waiyaki pleaded as soon as they had gone a few yards from the house and they were swallowed by the darkness. But she would not. And the voices that denounced him as a traitor rang through the darkness. Waiyaki remembered what Kinuthia had told him. And then it came—at first a small urge, but then it became stronger and stronger so that there was a real struggle in Waiyaki's soul. The insistent voice inside him told him to run and go to Nairobi. You have now the object of your heart's desire, and they have rejected you. Run! Run to Nairobi and live there happily with Nyambura. And why not? Had he not brought light to the hills, awakening the sleeping lions so that now they could shout 'Traitor'? Then he felt ashamed of himself. He could not run away. His father's words again glowed before him: ". . . salvation shall come from the hills. A man must rise and save the people in their hour of need. He shall show them the way; he shall lead them. . . ."

Waiyaki and Nyambura now stood on a piece of raised ground overlooking Honia Valley. They were near Kabonyi's house and that was where the voices came from. He felt frightened and his resolution not to run away wavered. He turned to the girl beside him and in a subdued voice said, "Death awaits you there."

She took his hand pressed it slightly. Waiyaki's blood warmed and he felt as if he would be carried away by the waves of desire and emotion that shook his whole being.

"Oh, Teacher. I have always loved you. I'll go where you go. Don't leave me now."

Waiyaki held her against his breast. Then they slowly descended the Makuyu ridge till they came to their sacred ground.

"Let's sit down," he whispered. They lay on the grass and the Honia river went on with its throb. Waiyaki and Nyambura did not hear it, for a stronger throb, heart-rending, was sweeping away their bodies. Their souls joined into one stillness; so still that their breathing seemed to belong to another world, apart from them.

When they rose to go a new strength had come to Waiyaki. Even Kinuthia, who had gone back to wait for him in the hut, was surprised more at the brightness on their faces than at the fact of their being together. Indeed Waiyaki felt his yearning soul soothed by the healing presence of this girl. Yet he knew that he would be forced to make a choice, a choice between the girl and the tribe. Tonight he felt he had something to say to the people. But he did not know what. He wanted a rest; time to make a silent inquiry into his heart. His father's image came back to him vividly. He remembered that journey into the sacred grove. And he said loudly, "I shall go there tomorrow."

"Where?" Kinuthia asked.

Waiyaki was shaken into the present by that question. He felt he could not explain his journey even to Kinuthia. Yet just now he felt his father's presence everywhere in the room, in the darkness outside. This feeling was as real to him as the presence of Nyambura, who had fallen asleep on his bed. She was very exhausted but she felt at peace.

"To the hill south of Kameno. To the sacred grove."

"To the sacred grove?"

"Yes, it is a long story." And now he told Kinuthia about it all, the journey with his father, the ancient prophecy and his bewilderment at its meaning. And Kinuthia sat mouth open; a new veneration for Waiyaki grew upon him. It was as if Waiyaki was a revelation, a thing not of this earth.

"Look here, Kinuthia," Waiyaki said after a long silence. "Do something for me. Tomorrow I must speak to the people just before the sunset. Call a meeting at Honia river on the initiation ground. It is flat there. Get some people to help you spread the news. On every hill. I'll fight it out with Kabonyi in the open. For, Kinuthia, I cannot run away. New thoughts are coming into my mind. Things I might have done and said. Oh, there are so many things I did not know. I had not seen that the new awareness wanted expression at a political level. Education for an oppressed people is not all. But I must think. I must be alone."

Still they talked far into the night and Kinuthia listened to Waiyaki's plans and felt himself inspired to new efforts and transported to new heights.

"I will never leave you!" he cried. "Whatever the others do, I will be with you all the way."

"Thank you, Kinuthia. Let us wait until tomorrow."

Chapter Twenty-five

He felt a dull pain inside his heart. He was weary. The country was below him again, but it did not have so much power over him as when he had stood there, a child, with his father. The sun was up and he could not see Kerinyaga. And the sacred grove seemed to be no more than ordinary bush clustering around the fig tree. But there was something strange about the tree. It was still huge and there was a firmness about it that would for ever defy time; that indeed seemed to scorn changing weather. And Waiyaki wondered how many people before him had stood there, where he now was, how many had indeed come to pay homage to this tree, the symbol of a people's faith in a mysterious power ruling the universe and the destinies of men.

And now he felt that mystery gradually enveloping him. But for him now the mystery was that of darkness clouding his heart. That was where in his loneliness he struggled with strange forces, forces that seemed to be destroying him. He wondered why he had come here. He wondered what answers he had hoped to find to the unformulated questions in his mind. Even Nyambura had faded from the reality around him and was no longer a consolation. For the reality around him, around his heart, was one of despair because he was aware that he was fighting against forces that he himself did not understand; forces that he had felt in the air all over the country. And he was afraid. Perhaps he was running away from what he did not understand because he feared. What had he awakened in the hills? And he remembered Kinuthia telling him: Your name will be your ruin.

Waiyaki stared at the country below him as if he were seeing nothing. Below the calm of the hills were strange stirrings.

What had brought all this trouble? Waiyaki blamed himself. He felt that things had really begun to go wrong from the time of the great meeting, the time when they all declared him the Teacher. Since then the rifts between the various factions had widened and the attempt by the Kiama to burn people's houses and their threat to Joshua and his followers were all an expression of that widened gulf. Perhaps he should not have resigned from the Kiama, he told himself over and over again. What if he had made his stand clear at that meeting? That was now a lost opportunity and he had to reckon with the present. Still he wondered if he had not betrayed the tribe; the tribe he had meant to unite; the tribe he had wanted to save; the people he had wanted to educate, giving them all the benefits of the white man's coming.

For Waiyaki knew that not all the ways of the white man were bad. Even his religion was not essentially bad. Some good, some truth shone through it. But the religion, the faith, needed washing, cleaning away all the dirt, leaving only the eternal. And that eternal that was the truth had to be reconciled to the traditions of the people. A people's traditions could not be swept away overnight. That way lay disintegration. Such a tribe would have no roots, for a people's roots were in their traditions going back to the past, the very beginning, Gikuyu and Mumbi. A religion that took no count of people's way of life, a religion that did not recognize spots of beauty and truths in their way of life, was uesless. It would not satisfy. It would not be a living experience, a source of life and vitality. It would only maim a man's soul, making him fanatically cling to whatever promised security, otherwise he would be lost. Perhaps that was what was wrong with Joshua. He had clothed himself with a religion decorated and smeared with everything *white*. He renounced his past and cut himself away from those life-giving traditions of the tribe. And because he had nothing to rest upon, something rich and firm on which to stand and grow, he had to cling with his hands to whatever the missionaries taught him promised future.

Waiyaki wondered if he himself fitted anywhere. Did Kabonyi? Which of the two was the messiah, the man who was to bring hope in salvation to a troubled people? But how could a man be a saviour when he himself had already lost that contact with the past?

Muthoni had tried. Hers was a search for salvation for herself. She had the courage to attempt a reconciliation of the many forces that wanted to control her. She had realized her need, the need to have a wholesome and beautiful life that enriched you and made you grow. His father, too, had tried to reconcile the two ways, not in himself, but through his son. Waiyaki was a product of that attempt. Yes, in the quietness of the hill, Waiyaki had realized many things. Circumcision of women was not important as a physical operation. It was what it did inside a person. It could not be stopped overnight. Patience and, above all, education, was needed. If the white man's religion made you abandon a custom and then did not give you something else of equal value, you became lost. An attempt at resolution of the conflict would only kill you, as it did Muthoni.

Waiyaki now thought it was time to go. The sacred grove had not lit the way for him. He did not quite know where he was going or what he really wanted to tell his people. He was still in the dark. He remembered Nyambura and wondered how she was feeling, being in his hut. For a moment he was gripped by terror and hated himself for having left the hut. What if they had come and taken her by force? What if Joshua had gone to report him at the government post? He again wondered if he should not run away and, as he descended the hill, he cast his eyes beyond. He had a vision of many possibilities and opportunities there, away from the hills. Maybe one day he would go there. Maybe one day he would join forces with the men from Muranga, Kiambu and Nyeri and with one voice tell the white man 'Go!' And all at once Waiyaki realized what the ridges wanted. All at once he felt more forcefully than he had ever felt before the shame of a people's land being taken away, the shame of being forced to work on those same lands, the humiliation of paying taxes for a government that you knew nothing about.

Yes. The Kiama was right. People wanted action now. The stirrings in the hills were an awakening to the shame and humiliation of their condition. Their isolation had been violated. But what action was needed? What had he to do now? How could he organize people into a political organization when they were so torn with strife and disunity? Now he knew what he would preach if he ever got another chance: education for unity. Unity for political freedom. For a time this vision made his heart glow with expectation and new hope. He quickened his descent, wishing to come to the people and communicate this new vision. Education, Unity, Political Freedom. And then came the doubt. What if they should ask him to give up Nyambura? What if—he did not want to think about it. He would fight for unity and Nyambura was an integral part of that battle. If he lost Nyambura, he too would be lost. He was fighting for his salvation.

Many people had come to the meeting ground. There were women and children and old men who were bewildered by the urgent call they had received from Kinuthia's messengers. And they came because they wanted to hear what their Teacher had to say and because they had heard things which they could not believe. Most still clung to the vision of the Teacher they knew; the Teacher whom they trusted, in whom they believed, a man they could always follow, anywhere. How could they believe that he would betray them? How could they believe this story about his marrying an uncircumcised girl, a daughter of Joshua, the enemy of the people? Waiyaki had awakened them to new visions, new desires, new aspirations. He had restored to them their dignity as a tribe and he had given them the white man's education when the missionaries had wanted to deny them that wisdom. Waiyaki had been too clever for them. He had taken the oath of loyalty to the purity of the tribe. That had been an example to all. Could he then go against the oath, could he?

They waited patiently, the sun's heat on their bare heads; sweat rolled down their backs. And still they waited. And Kabonyi was there and the elders of the Kiama and the young men of the tribe. And all waited, waited for Waiyaki to come. They nursed their secret thoughts to their hearts and they looked forward to his arrival and they knew that this was the day of trial. Initiation day would be tomorrow on this very ground and tonight would be the night of singing and dancing. Joshua and his followers would sing tonight for their Christ was going to be born tonight. But at the meeting nobody sung, nobody danced. They waited to hear what their Teacher would say.

And Kabonyi and some of the elders sat in a group separately and trembled with their secret knowledge. Let the people wait. Kabonyi was determined to win or die. For he knew that his victory was the victory of the tribe; that tribe that was now threatened by Waiyaki. And he hated Waiyaki intensely and identified this hatred with the wrath of the tribe against impurity and betrayal. To him then, this was not a personal struggle. It was a continuation of that struggle that had always existed between Makuyu and Kameno. For leaders from Kameno had failed; they had only betrayed people. The ridges would now rise and cry vengeance. Kabonyi felt himself the instrument of that vengeance. He was the saviour for whom the people waited. Not that Kabonyi knew exactly where he would lead the people. For he too was grappling with forces awakened in the people. How could he understand that the people did not want to move backwards, that the ridges no longer desired their isolation? How could he know that the forces that drove people to yearn for a better day tomorrow, that now gave a new awareness to the people, were like demons, sweeping the whole country, as Mugo had said, from one horizon touching the sea to the other horizon touching the water?

The sun was going down and people stirred with impatience. Some people, among whom were a group of Joshua's followers, stood on the hill. They had not yet descended. Miriamu was there. She too thought something was going to happen and she wept for her daughter; and she wept too because she knew she was weak and she could not do anything. And suddenly the people who stood on the hills or up the slope saw big yellow flames emanated by the setting sun. The flames seemed near and far and the trees and the country were caught in the flames. They feared.

Kinuthia too feared and for a time he had a momentary glimpse of Waiyaki and Nyambura caught in those flames. And he cried and blamed himself because he had failed Waiyaki. Nyambura had been stolen from Waiyaki's hut and he knew that she was in the hands of Kabonyi and the Kiama. How could he communicate this to Waiyaki? How would Waiyaki take it? He decided to let Waiyaki face the crowd and fight the battle unhampered by his fear for Nyambura. Then from somewhere people began to sing: "He has gone—traitor." Kinuthia trembled and wondered if Waiyaki would not turn up. If he did not, then Kinuthia's life would be in danger, for the people's wrath would turn against him. He sweated with fear as the people cried "Seek him out." It was Kabonyi and his followers who were shouting "traitor."

The crowd was big and more people were coming. Then there was a whisper which made everybody rise in excitement: "The Teacher! The Teacher!" Then they sat down again and let Waiyaki pass, his head and broad shoulders indeed caught against the yellow beams that passed through the trees. And he looked powerful and beautiful and they were tense on both sides of the Honia river. Great hush fell over the land as he strode towards a raised piece of ground where the Kiama sat, where his destiny would be decided.

from Jagua Nana

■ Cyprian Ekwensi (Nigeria)

Chapter 5

The bus put him down at Skylark Avenue where he bought a loaf of bread and lingered for a while. At this time of night Skylark Avenue exploded into life in a manner to attract even those who lived on it. Above the noise he could identify the *High-life* rhythm gushing from a record-dealer's loudspeaker. On the opposite side of the street cars were gliding into the petrol-filling station where the girls in their spaceman cloaks lunged about like red dervishes charging one car after the other with power.

A hundred yards from his room he recognised Mike—Jagua's house boy —standing on the steps, wringing his hands.

"Sir! Tenk God you return! Madam, she say make you come quick."

"Madam? But ah lef' her in de Tropicana."

"No, sah. She sen' message from police station, sir. She say make you come bail am."

"Bail—what? Police station?"

"Dem fight in de Tropicana. She and Mama Nancy, dem broke all de table, them wound themself with bottle."

"Hold on! What you talkin'? Jagua fighting Mama Nancy?"

"Yes, sah! She say make you come and bail am. Dem arres' de two and lock dem up in de guard-room."

Freddie knitted his brows. No self-respecting teacher would like to be mixed up with Charge Offices, certainly not he. When he had changed he had a quick bath, and like a man running away from his own shadow, Freddie got into bed and switched off the light.

In the darkness he could see nothing at first, and then the accusing face of Jagua began staring at him. "So you treat me, Freddie?" There was a twisted smile on her face, cold, unforgiving. "When trouble meet you woman, you turn into de bed and sleep. You lef' her to suffer?" The face was so real that he could not stand the terrifying judgement contained in the eyes. He found himself getting quickly out of bed and switching on the light. He took a law book from the locker, put it under his arm and set out for the Charge Office.

At the counter he saw a sergeant making entries in a fat book.

"I wan' to see Jagua, Sergeant."

"You tink I playin'?" the sergeant said. He looked up and waved his pen at the others on the counter, "All of you, see dis man, who tink I come here for play. Man, go siddown till is you turn. Ha, ha! Dis be Charge Office, not school!"

A young woman in the corner of the smelly room seemed to be making a statement which Freddie had interrupted. She stood away from the counter which ran across the room and began bawling swear words at the young police constable, who ignored her and kept on writing steadily. Freddie observed at once that other constables were deriving some lecherous satisfaction from the young woman's behaviour. She had a defiant twinkle in her eye, her breath smelled of alcohol and her blouse—one arm of which had been torn in some scuffle—slouched over a naked young breast with a dare-devil abandon that could not but be comical. She seemed by her manner to be conscious of the power of her femaleness over the males in the khaki uniforms.

Freddie stared at this ragged woman who confronted him with the eternal struggle to live, so tragic in the lower reaches of Lagos life. She must be a "habitual," Freddie concluded from the brusque manner in which all the men mocked her. He was interrupted by the loud voice of the sergeant who took him to the back of the Charge Office where the cells were. The strong smell of human urine hit nostrils in the warm air. It seemed to hang in invisible walls of mist along the corridors.

By this time it was nearly midnight and some of the "prisoners" had already accepted their fate and were lying on the cold cement floor, no bed, no pillow and rolling in their own excrements. But Jagua was wide awake. Freddie saw her standing behind bars, and looking directly at him with an animal muteness not unlike the face he had just visualised in his own darkened room. This was his mistress, and this squalor all came along with the kind of life she had chosen. He felt a mixture of shame, grief and pity. He wished that no one would recognise or identify him. He could not say a word as the big key rattled in the lock and Jagua, subdued and silent, her head swathed in bandages, came out and walked away with him after all the papers had been signed and the undertakings given.

Freddie was downcast. Jagua would yet see him in even less reputable places. How often had they quarrelled over her madness at the Tropicana? Once there, she became transformed into a she-devil. What angered him now was that her face showed not even a glimmer of distress. She seemed ready for more.

"Why you fight, Jagua?" Freddie asked when they got back to her room. Jagua was taking off her clothes as if they were already contaminated. Even in his anger the sensual feeling was creeping in on Freddie. Her skin was silken and paler than her face, especially at the back of her neck and sloping down her back beneath the arms. There were no collar bones to be seen when she faced him, and when she turned her back at him, stepping out of her clothes, the voluptuousness of her big moulded hips seduced him and made his anger sharpen at his own weakness for her. "You no wan' to answer me? Why you fight?"

She was nonchalantly lighting a cigarette now, and Freddie watched her put it to her lips and draw in a deep one. "Why you sen' for me? I don' tell you make we lef' de Tropicana. Yes, I tell you make we lef' but you done see de Syrian man and you tink you kin get money from him. So you disgrace me. Instead you get money now, you goin' to pay fine or get into de white college for assault . . . you see?"

When she had had her bath and combed out her hair she came and took him to bed and whispered to him. She would not be bad any more. "True, Freddie, ah mean it dis time."

She cuddled him and kissed him, and mothered him, bubbling over with love as she always did whenever she knew she was in the wrong and wanted to be restored to his favour.

"I goin' to return proper to mah trade. Ah already arrange to speak wid de manager of de company. He goin' to open branch shop for me, where I kin sell Accra and velvet cloth and lace. When ah pay security, de shop will be under my control."

Freddie made a face to show her he was not convinced. Jagua had always promised to be good, to settle down, to open a retail shop and engage in petty trading, mainly cotton-wax prints. He knew she had already made some money in the cloth trade, selling Georgettes and Damasks, and sheer brilliant Manchester prints—the kind which girls like Nancy tied skirt-wise over blouses. Jagua knew the West Coast of Africa from Gambia to Lagos, with Ghana as a kind of Parisian centre of fashion. Before Freddie met her she used to travel regularly to Ghana and beyond, buying there and selling in Lagos. It was partly one reason why they called her Jagua. She had style. Whenever she put on anything it became the fashion in Lagos, and the girls and women came flocking to her and wanting to know where the article had come from. Then she would go into the room and produce the material and more women would hear about it and come too. During that time Jagua was well known to all the Customs men and the Border Police. What had happened to her Freddie could not say. Sometimes she talked of going to Onitsha by the Niger. There she hoped to become one of the Merchant Princesses who controlled tens of thousands of pounds. Freddie had an idea that she was capable of doing it, but she would not leave Lagos. Or while in Lagos she would not exert herself. It was three years now since she had been to Ghana. The Tropicana had sapped all her energy. She seemed to be one of those women who are always trying to prove to men that they are still young. And to do so, she must always remain focused in their sights. Going away from the social centre might make them forget her.

Freddie soon learnt what had happened in the Tropicana after he had left. Jagua told him that Mama Nancy had come in and had lured away the Syrian gentleman from her. He rightly belonged to her, but why should Mama Nancy come and claim him when—that night—he had decided to change over to Jagua. Freddie was so irritated with her story that he cut her short half-way through.

"You know somethin'?" Jagua confided now. "Freddie I sorry for wat happen. I shame too much. If I tell you I no shame, I tellin' you lie. So I begin tink, as I lay down in de cell. If to say ah get me own man!"

Freddie grunted. He was used to these fits of repentance.

"If to say ah get me own man like you, Freddie. I mean—not jus' lover, but man forever! Den people will point and say, 'Das Freddie Namme, husband of Jagwa.' Oh, my heart will full up with proud. I no go care anythin'."

"Why den, Jagwa? You keep findin' trouble. I already tol' you, le's leave de Tropicana. I tol' you I been tryin' to read de law, so I kin pass all de exam and become a man. You won' let me learn. Always findin' trouble for me. How I kin get peace of min'?"

"No worry, Freddie. I goin' to sen' you to England. If you don' find peace of min' dere, den. God don't say make you become lawyer. I goin' to send you to England so you kin read proper law in de inns of court!"

Freddie's smile was tolerant. "Nonsense! You jus' jokin', Jagwa. You not goin' to sen' me to England with you own money. You got odder things to do wid de money."

"Ah got odder thing to do, but sendin' you is de best of all. I goin' to send you to Englan'; and you goin' to return and marry your Jagwa. Yes, Freddie. I wan' me own man now. Dem insult me too much. But as you is only a poor teacher you no reach yet for marry Jagwa woman. You mus' go train yousself to be proper man . . . Den I kin born chil' for you. An' you kin look after me, in me old age."

"So you sendin' me to Englan' to return an' marry you?"

"Ah got anodder reason. I hear say Mama Nancy, she want to bluff me. She say she sendin' her own young man to Englan', so he too kin return an' marry her."

"Oh! . . ." Freddie turned in the bed and faced the wall. He really had no wish to marry Jagua. As a mistress she was brilliant, but he could not imagine her as a wife, when young ones like Nancy* were available.

Jagua pressed her lips against his ears, and her arms enfolded him in a soft embrace. "I goin' to sen' you to England, so you kin come back and marry me."

Freddie did not share the delight she felt in the underlying condition.

Chapter 6

As the weeks slipped by, Freddie began to see signs that Jagua meant every word. How she surmounted most of the hurdles the Government placed in the way of the private, ill-equipped but ambitious student he never could tell. The Nigerian Government regarded the student "adventuring to England" with the same dark frown that the French Government viewed the globe-trotting fool attempting to cross the Sahara on a pedal-bicycle.

Jagua revealed that she had some money saved up from her cloth trade in Ghana and this money she now drew liberally. She paid for Freddie's dinners at the Inns, transferred enough money to pay Freddie's rent for one year and clothe him and buy him books.

Life began to acquire a new meaning for Freddie when, after months and months of waiting for letters from the immigration and the shipping authorities, they told him he would be travelling on a Norwegian cargo boat. The journey would be slow and long, but the food would be a compensation, he was assured. The sailing date was not definite—they still had a lot of cargo to take on board; and for this reason, Freddie could not tear himself away from Lagos and journey to his native Bagana in the East to say good-bye to his friends and relatives. He particularly wanted to see his mother, and if Jagua also wanted to be introduced to his parents, what harm could that do?

But Jagua herself could not readily leave Lagos now. She was still on

* the teen-aged daughter of Mama Nancy.

bail, and when eventually her case came up Freddie saw her fined thirty shillings and warned to keep the peace. After that, not enough time was left for journeying to Bagana, and besides they had not been able to include the visit in their plans.

About a week to sailing time, the news leaked out among Freddie's friends, who pinned him down to a nightmare of farewell parties. He had even less time for anything else. Many were the nights when he put on his baggy velvet trousers and fez and in the warm humid air sat down and listened to speeches by his friends. He was, they said, a good example to Africa in thus "seeking the Golden Fleece of Knowledge and Leadership." Nigeria's future salvation depended on such trained people, they claimed. Looking at the speaker's eyes, Freddie knew he was speaking what he believed. In a way he knew that all his friends identified him with their own secret ambitions to study abroad. He did not like being fêted, but he bore it all with fortitude safe in the knowledge that he would soon be out of their reach.

What troubled him more at this time was that Jagua had become unbearably touchy and morose. Freddie noted how unfriendly she had become. She walked about with a long face and for the most trivial reasons she started yelling abuses at him. Could it be that she no longer wanted him away from her? At such times when he tried to reason with her and failed his spirits would sink and he would wish he could be with Nancy to soothe away the rough edges of his nerves.

One afternoon he ran across her in the Square. He was transported with delight. The smell of that warm night under the woods immediately filled his nostrils. In the midst of the confusion of pressing bodies and arms reaching out to grip the bus railings, he felt the silky-sweet touch of her hand. He noticed her because of the way she moved—hips fanned out by the georgette check in bold yellow and brown, the unconscious wiggle which drew him out to "follow me." She wore her hair short, and perhaps because she had been shopping in the sun it stood straight, without kinks, with beads of oil glistening in it. Her upper lip had gathered the crystal drops of perspiration, but she gave him a sweet smile and her eyes were keen. The greenish nylon blouse blended with the yellow georgette, and he could see the shadow of her pointed breasts with the dark nipples and soft pale sides that trembled.

They climbed into the bus with Freddie close behind her, his hand on her smooth cool arm. They sat down, intimately crushed in the seat. She mopped her brow with a soft cloth and soaked away the crystals of her lip.

"Freddie, I hear you almos' leavin' for England; and you don' care to come and see me. Is it good? And you say you love me?"

"Not so, Nancy. I try to come, but——"

She gave him an accusing look. "When ah come to Englan', we will meet dere."

"You jokin'?"

"I mean it, Freddie."

He searched her face and could make nothing of her eagerly gleaming eyes. She took out two oranges from her shopping and offered him one.

"My Mama tryin' to sen' her young man; but he grown conceited, so she askin' me whedder I wan't to go and qualify as secretary typist. De Syrian man will pay all de fee."

"You mean it? You really mean it?" He tried to keep back his delight.

"I coming to England and we will marry there." She waved the orange joyfully, and pressed it to her lips.

They were nearing their destination now and Nancy looked at him suddenly and whispered. "I goin' to be your Englan' lady, Freddie. You no glad? See how God use to do him own thing."

Freddie helped her down, and together they walked some of the way. As they entered the home street, he handed back her shopping bag and stood for a moment under the trees, well away from the other end of the street where Jagua lived. But Nancy succeeded in enticing him out of his hiding and step by step they moved up, until Freddie found himself near the end of the street.

He watched her walk away with the young upright shoulders, dainty steps and trembling bottom. When she had vanished beyond the mango tree by the foodseller he looked up, and there gazing down at him from the balcony was Jagua Nana. The smile on her face did not mask the greenish tinge of anger. She must have seen everything.

"Freddie, who dat I see with you?"

"You mean—with me?" He looked up the street. "Oh—is only Nancy Oll. She gone back to her modder. Is only Nancy——"

"Wat you mean, is only Nancy? Nancy not woman, yet? She no reach for sleep wit' you and born pickin'?"

"I comin' up to explain, Jagua. Have patience—is nothin'. Nothin' at all. I comin' up to explain."

from The Dark Child

■ Camara Laye (French Guinea)

I was fifteen when I left home for Conakry where I was sent for a course of technical study at the Ecole Georges Poiret, now known as the Technical College.

I was leaving my parents for the second time. The first had been immediately after I had passed my scholarship examination when I had acted as interpreter for an officer who had come to map the land in our district and in part of the neighboring Sudan. But on this second occasion I was to be away for a much longer time.

For a whole week my mother had been collecting provisions for me. Conakry is about four hundred miles from Kouroussa, and to my mother it was an unknown if not an unexplored land where God alone knew if I would get enough to eat. So she gathered *couscous*, meat, fish, yams, rice, and potatoes. The week before, she had gone to the most celebrated marabouts to consult them about my future and make sacrifices. She had offered up an ox in memory of her father and had invoked the spirits of her ancestors that good fortune might attend me on a venture which in her eyes was rather like going to live among savages. The fact that Conakry is the capital of Guinea only served to accentuate its strangeness.

On the eve of my departure all the marabouts and witch-doctors, friends and notables, and indeed anyone else who cared to cross our threshold attended a magnificent feast in our concession. For my mother believed that on this occasion no one should be turned away. Representatives of all classes of society must be present so that the blessing I was to take with me might be complete. Moreover, this was the reason the marabouts had requested such great quantities of food. And so each guest, after having eaten his fill, took me by the hand and blessed me, saying:

"May good fortune favor you! May your studies prosper! And may the Lord protect you!"

The marabouts used much lengthier phrases. They began by reciting a few quotations from the Koran which they adapted to the present occasion. Then they invoked the name of Allah. After that they blessed me.

I passed a wretched night. I was very much depressed, a little upset, and I woke up several times. I thought I heard groans. I guessed immediately that it was my mother. I got up and went to her hut. She was tossing on her bed and moaning quietly. Perhaps I should have gone to her and tried to console her, but I did not know how she would take it. Maybe she would not have liked to think that she had been found weeping and wailing. I withdrew with a heavy heart. Was this what life was going to be like? Were tears a part of everything we did?

She woke me at dawn and I got up at once. I saw that her face was strained, but she was determined to keep control of herself and I said nothing. I pretended that her apparent calm had really convinced me. My luggage was piled up in the hut. Carefully wrapped and in a prominent position was a large bottle.

"What's in the bottle?" I asked.

"Do not break it."

"I'll look after it."

"Take great care of it. And every morning before you begin to study take a little sip."

"Is it supposed to be good for the brain?"

"It is indeed. It's the best thing there is. It comes from Kankan!"

I had already drunk some of this liquid. My teacher had forced me to when I was taking my scholarship examination. It is a magic potion possessing many qualities and particularly good for developing the brain. It is a curious mixture. Our marabouts have small boards on which they write prayers taken from the Koran. When they have written down the texts they erase them with water. The washing water is carefully collected and, when honey had been added to it, the resulting mixture is the essence of the elixir. If it had been bought—and bought at a very high price—in Kankan, a strongly Mohammedan town and the holiest of our native places, it must be a particularly potent drink. The evening before my father had given me a he-goat's horn containing talismans. I was to wear it always as a protection against evil spirits.

"Run and say your goodbyes now," said my mother.

I had to go and say farewell to the elders of our concession and to those of the concessions nearby. I went with a heavy heart. I had known these men and women since I was a baby. I had always known them. I had watched them living in this place and I had watched them disappear from it too. My father's mother had disappeared. Would I ever again see these people to whom I was now saying farewell? Overcome by doubts, I felt suddenly as if I were taking leave of the past itself. And wasn't that just what I was doing? Wasn't I leaving a part of my life behind me?

When I returned to my mother and saw her standing in tears beside my luggage I too began to weep. I threw myself into her arms. I begged her not to go with me to the station, for I thought that if she did I should never be able to tear myself away from her arms. She nodded consent. We embraced for the last time and I almost ran out of the hut. My sisters and brothers and the apprentices carried my luggage.

My father quickly caught up with me and took my hand as he had done when I was a little boy. I slowed down. I felt weak and cried as if my heart were broken.

"Father!"

"I am listening."

"Am I really going away?"

"What else can you do? You know that you must."

"Yes."

And I began to cry again.

"Come, little one! You're a big boy now, aren't you?"

But his very presence, his kindness—and even more the fact that he was holding my hand—destroyed the last vestige of courage. He understood.

"I shall not go any further," he said. "We shall say goodbye to each other here. It would not do if we burst into tears at the station in front of your friends. And I don't want to leave your mother alone just now. She is very much upset. I am too! So are we all. But we must be brave. You be brave, my son. My brothers will look after you. Work hard. Work as you worked here. We have made many sacrifices for you. They must not go for nothing. Do you hear me?"

"Yes."

He was silent a moment, then went on:

"You see, I had no father to look after me. At least not for a very long time. When I was twelve I became an orphan and had to make my own way in life. It wasn't easy. The uncles in whose care I was left treated me more like a slave than a nephew. Not that I was a burden to them for very long. They hired me out to the Syrians right away. I was simply a domestic drudge, and I had to hand over everything I earned to my uncles. But even so it did not lessen their cruelty and greed. I always had to keep my own counsel and work hard to make a name for myself. You. . . . But I have said enough. Make the most of your opportunity. And make me proud of you. I ask no more. Will you?"

"I will, Father."

"Good! . . . Well, be brave, son. Goodbye."

"Father!"

He held me close. He had never held me so close before.

"Goodbye, little one, goodbye."

Suddenly he let me go and walked away very fast. Perhaps he did not want me to see his tears. I went on along the road to the station. My eldest sister, my brothers, Sidafa and the younger apprentices went with me carrying my luggage. As we walked along we were joined by friends. Among them was Fanta. It was rather as if I were on my way to school again. All my companions were there. There had never been so many before. In fact, *wasn't* I on my way to school?

"Fanta, we're on the way to school."

The only answer was a faint smile. I was indeed on the way to school, but I was already alone. . . . There had never been so many of us, but I had never felt so alone. Although it was probably hardest for me we all shared the pain of parting. We spoke little. Soon we were standing on the station platform waiting for the train, but we had hardly said one word to one another. Weren't we all feeling everything that might have been said?

Several praise-singers had come to celebrate my departure. As soon as I reached the station they beset me with their flatteries. "Already thou art as wise as the White Man," they sang. "Verily thou art as wise as the White Man. In Conakry thou shalt take thy place even among the most illustrious." Such excessive praises dampened by vanity instead of inflaming it. After all, what *did* I know? I was still very far from "wise." The friends who were with me were as wise as I. I wanted to ask the praise-singers to stop or at least to moderate their flattery. But that would have been contrary to custom, so I kept silent. Perhaps their flatteries were not entirely useless. They made me determined to take my work seriously. It was true that I had always done so. But now I felt myself obliged to achieve, some day, everything they were chanting if I weren't to look like a fool when I came back.

Their flatteries had an additional effect. They kept me from thinking of the sadness I felt. They had made me smile before they began to embarrass me. Even though my companions had felt how ridiculous they were, and naturally they had, they didn't let it show. Perhaps we are so accustomed to the hyperboles of our praise-singers that we no longer take very much notice of them. But what about Fanta? No, she must have taken all those flatteries for truth. Fanta. . . . She never thought of smiling. Her eyes were filled with tears. Dear Fanta! . . . In despair I looked at my sister. She must surely know how I felt. She always felt as I did. But I saw she was tending to my luggage. She had already told me several times to keep an eye on it, and when our eyes met she told me so again.

"Don't worry. I will."

"You remember how many cases there are?"

"Yes."

"Good. Don't lose any. Remember you are staying the first night at Mamou. The train stops there for the night."

"You don't have to explain everything to me. I'm not a child."

"No, but you don't know what sort of people they'll be down there. Keep your luggage beside you and count it from time to time. You understand? Keep your eye on it."

"Yes."

"And be careful with strangers."

"Yes."

But I had stopped listening to her and smiling at the chants of the praise-singers. My sadness had returned. My little brothers had slipped their hands into mine and I kept thinking how warm and soft they were. I kept thinking too that the train would soon be here and that I should have to release those small hands. I began to feel afraid the train would come. I began to hope it would be late. Sometimes it was. Perhaps it would be, today. I looked at the clock. It was late! . . . But suddenly it appeared.

In the uproar of departure it seemed to me that I had eyes for my brothers alone. They were pushed about in the crowd; they were bewildered; but they always managed to be in front of the rest. My eyes kept returning to them. Did I care for them that much? I don't know. Often I had paid no attention to them. When I left for school in the morning they had usually been asleep or were being bathed. When I returned in the afternoon I never had much time to spend with them. But now they were all I could see. Was it the warmth of their hands which I still felt and which made me remember that my father had taken me by the hand just now? Perhaps. Perhaps this was the last bit of warmth from the hut where I had been born.

My luggage was handed to me through the window and I put it all on the seats. My sister gave me some last words of advice as useless as all the others. Everyone had something nice to say to me, Fanta and Sidafa especially. But in all the waving of hands and scarves that accompanied the departure of the train I really saw only my brothers who ran the length of the platform, the length of the train, shouting goodbye. Where the platform ended, my sister and Fanta joined them. I looked at my brothers waving their caps, at my sister and Fanta waving their handkerchiefs, and then suddenly they disappeared from sight, long before the first bend in the track, for a sudden mist enveloped them and tears blinded me. . . . For a long time I lay in a corner of my compartment with my luggage strewn all about me and before me that final image: my little brothers, my sister, Fanta. . . .

Toward midday the train reached Dabola. By this time I had sorted out my luggage and counted it. My interest in people and things was beginning to revive somewhat. I heard *Peul* spoken. Dabola is on the borders of the *Peul* country. The great plain where I had lived until now, that plain so rich, so poor, so sunburnt—yet so familiar and friendly—was giving way to the foothills of the Fouta-Djallon.

The train began its journey again toward Mamou. Soon the lofty cliffs of the mountains appeared. They blocked the horizon, and the train set out to conquer them. It was a very slow conquest, almost a hopeless one. So slow and hopeless, that sometimes the train went at barely more than a walking pace. This country, new to me, too new and too rugged, disturbed rather than enchanted me. I did not notice how beautiful it was.

I arrived at Mamou a little before nightfall. As the train does not go on from there until the next day, the passengers spend the night in a hotel or with friends. A former apprentice of my father's who had been told I was passing through, had offered me his hospitality. He gave me a most cordial welcome. Actually—but perhaps he had forgotten the difference in climate—he lodged me in a dark hut on top of a hill where I had sufficient leisure—more than I wanted—to feel the chill night and the keen air of the Fouta-Djallon. Mountains certainly did not agree with me!

The next day I continued my journey. But a complete change had taken place. Was I getting acclimated already? I do not know. But my feelings about mountains had changed, so much so that from Mamou to Kindia I did not leave the window for a moment. I was enchanted with the succussion of peaks and precipices, torrents and cascades of water, wooded slopes and deep valleys. Water gushed and flowed everywhere, animating everything. It was a wonderful spectacle. A little terrifying too, whenever the train seemed to go too close to the edge of a precipice. Because the air was extraordinarily pure, I could see everything in the minutest detail. It was a happy land; it seemed happy. There were innumerable flocks of sheep grazing, and the shepherds waved as we passed.

When we stopped at Kindia I no longer heard *Peul* being spoken. This time it was *Soussou,* the dialect of Conakry. I listened for a while but I understood little of what was being said.

Now we were descending toward the coast and Conakry. The train went on and on. Just as it had seemed to puff painfully up the mountains, now it rolled joyfully down. But the landscape was no longer what it had been between Mamou and Kindia. It was no longer so picturesque. There was less movement in it; it was less wild, more domesticated. Vast stretches of banana and palm trees, symmetrically laid out, followed each other. The heat was overpowering and increased as we approached the coast. The air was heavy, humid.

The brightly lit peninsula of Conakry appeared with evening. I saw it from afar, a huge shining flower floating on the sea, its stalk held to the mainland. The water shone softly, shone like the sky, but unlike the sky in its quivering animation. Almost immediately the flower began to expand and the water to recede. For a few moments more it extended on both sides of the stalk. Then it disappeared. We were rapidly approaching Conakry. When we arrived among the lights of the peninsula—the very heart of the flower—the train halted.

A tall, imposing man came up to me. I had never seen him before—or rather I had seen him too many years ago to remember—but from the way he looked at me I guessed he was my father's brother.

"Are you my Uncle Mamadou?" I asked.

"Yes. And you are my nephew Laye. I knew you at once. The living image of your mother. Really, I could not have missed you. How are your mother and father? . . . But come along. We'll have time to discuss that later. Now you must have something to eat and a good night's rest. Come one; you'll find dinner ready, and your room is in order."

That was the first night I had passed in a European-style house. Was it the unfamiliarity, or the humid heat of the town, or the fatigue of two days in the train that kept me from sleeping? Yet it was a very comfortable house: the room I slept in was large, and the bed soft, softer than any I had previously slept on. Also I had been welcomed as warmly as if I had been a son of the house. In spite of this, I missed Kouroussa. I missed my little hut. All my thoughts centered on Kouroussa. Once again I saw my mother and my father, my brothers and my sisters, my friends. I was in Conakry and yet I wasn't. I was really at Kouroussa. But, no—I was in both places. I was ambivalent. And I felt very lonely, despite the affectionate welcome.

"Well," said my uncle when I came down in the morning, "have you slept well?"

"Yes."

"No, you haven't. The change has been too abrupt. But you will soon get used to it here. You'll sleep better tonight. Don't you think so?"

"Yes."

"And what are you planning for today?"

"I don't know. Should I visit the school?"

"We'll do that tomorrow together. Have a look around town today. This is the last day of your holidays, after all."

I walked into town. It was very different from Kouroussa. The avenues were as straight as rulers and crossed each other at right angles. They were lined with mango trees which were also planted elsewhere in shady groups. Their thick shade was always welcome, for the heat was overpowering. Not that it was much worse than at Kouroussa—perhaps it was even less intense—but the humidity was greater. The houses were all embowered in flowers and foliage. Many looked submerged in all the greenery, drowned in a frantic proliferation. And then I saw the sea. . . .

Suddenly at the end of an avenue, I saw it. I stood a long time observing its vastness, watching the waves roll in, one after another, to break against the red rocks of the shore. In the distance, despite the mist around them, I saw some very green islands. It was the most astonishing spectacle that had ever confronted me. At night, from the train, I had only glimpsed the sea. I had formed no real idea of its size, nor even less of its movement, of the kind of fascination one feels toward its endless movement. Now that the whole spectacle lay before me I could scarcely come away.

"How did you like the town?" asked my uncle when I returned.

"Wonderful."

"Yes. But a bit hot, to judge from your clothes. You're perspiring. Go and change. You'll have to do that several times a day here. But be quick about it. Dinner is almost ready and your aunts want to serve it."

My uncle lived with his two wives, my aunts Awa and N'Gady, and a younger brother, my Uncle Sékou. Like my uncles, each of my aunts had her own room which she occupied with her own children.

My Uncle Mamadou was a little younger than my father. He was tall and strong, always very correctly dressed, calm and dignified. He was a man who made himself felt at once. Like my father he had been born in Kouroussa but had left it when he was very young. He had gone to school there, and then had come to Conakry to continue his studies at the École Normale de Goré. I believe he worked as a teacher for a short time, but went into business soon afterward. When I came to Conakry he was the chief accountant in a French establishment. I gradually became better acquainted with him, and the more I knew him the more I loved and respected him.

He was a Mohammedan—as we all are, I may add—but more orthodox than most of us. His observance of the Koran was scrupulously correct. He neither smoked nor drank and was absolutely honest. He wore European clothes only for work. As soon as he came home he undressed and put on a *boubou* which had to be immaculate, and said his prayers. On leaving the École Normale he had taken up the study of Arabic. He had learned it thoroughly by himself, using bilingual books and a dictionary. Now he could speak that language as well as French, though he never did so to create an impression. It was simply his desire for a deeper knowledge of religion that had persuaded him to learn the language of the Prophet. The Koran guided him in everything. I never saw him in a temper, nor quarreling with his wives. He was always greatly esteemed in Conakry, and I merely had to mention my relationship to him to share some of his prestige. I regarded him as a saintly personage.

When the holidays were over by Uncle Mamadou took me to my new school.

"Work hard," he said, "and the Lord will look out for you. You can tell me your first impressions on Sunday."

In the courtyard, where I was given my first instructions, and in the dormitory where I went to put away my clothes, I found other students who had come from Upper Guinea. We became friendly and I felt less lonely. A little later we entered our classroom. All of us, new and old students alike, assembled in the same vast room. I was attentive to everything, since I hoped to profit from some of the lessons given the older students while paying attention to whatever went on in my own class. But almost at once I saw that no great distinction was made between older and younger students. Instead, the teachers seemed prepared to repeat to the older students the lessons they had already crammed into them two or three times since the first year. "We'll see," I said to myself. But, all the same, I was disturbed. I thought such a method of teaching did not augur well.

To start us off, a very simple text was dictated. When the teacher marked the copies I could not understand how they contained so many errors. None of my friends in Kouroussa would have had any trouble with it. Afterwards we were given a problem to solve. Two of us got the right answer. I was stunned. Was this the school where I was to enjoy the advantages of higher education? I felt as if I were going back several years to the beginners' class in Kouroussa. And that is exactly how it was. On Sunday I complained loudly to my uncle.

"I've learned nothing. I already know everything they've taught us. Is it really worth while going to that school? I might as well go back to Kouroussa at once!"

"No," advised my uncle. "Wait a while!"

"There's nothing to wait for. I could see that immediately."

"Don't be so impatient. Are you always this way? Perhaps the school does operate on a low level so far as general subjects go, but it can give you practical training which you won't find anywhere else. Have you been in the workshops?"

I showed him my hands. They were covered with scratches and the tips of my fingers were scarred.

"But I don't want to be a laborer."

"Why not?"

"I don't want to be despised."

So far as general opinion went there was a tremendous difference between the students at our school and those at Camille Guy. We were looked upon simply as future laborers. It was certain that we would not become skilled workmen. At the most we might become foremen. Unlike the students at Camille Guy, we could never enter the colleges in Dakar.

"Listen to me carefully," said my uncle. "All the students who come from Kouroussa are scornful of the Technical School. They all dream of becoming clerks. Do you aspire to that sort of career? Clerks are thirteen to the dozen. If you really want to be a clerk, change your school. But remember this: if I were twenty years younger and had to go to school again I would not go to the École Normale. No! I would learn a good trade in a technical school. A good trade would have taken me a lot further."

"But I might as well never have left my father's forge."

"You needn't have. But, tell me, have you never had ambitions beyond the forge?"

Now I had ambitions. But I would never realize them by becoming a manual laborer. I had no more respect for manual laborers than most people have.

"But who said anything about manual labor? A technician is not necessarily a manual laborer. And, anyhow, there's more he can do. He's a man who directs others and knows how things should be done. He can turn his hand to anything should the need arise. Men who are in charge of businesses aren't always this versatile, and that will be to your advantage. Believe me, stay where you are. And I'm going to tell you something you don't know: your school is about to be reorganized. There will be great changes soon, and instruction in general subjects will equal that of Camille Guy."

Was I finally convinced by my uncle's arguments? Perhaps not altogether. But my Uncle Sékou, and even my aunts, argued as he did, so I stayed at the Technical School.

For four days out of six I was in the workshops filing bits of iron or planing boards under the direction of a monitor. It seemed to be easy and interesting. But it was not so easy as it looked at first sight. First of all I had had no practice, and in the second place the long hours of standing at a bench were a strain. I don't know how it happened—was it being too much on my feet or an infection from a splinter of metal or wool?—but my feet began to swell and I developed an ulcer. I believe that at Kouroussa such a growth would not have been malignant. It would not even have happened. But here in this burning, moisture-laden heat, in this climate to which my body had not had time to become adapted, the ulcer grew worse. I was hospitalized.

My spirits drooped. The more than Spartan fare which was given us in this otherwise magnificent hospital was not really intended to raise the spirits. But as soon as my aunts learned what had happened they brought my meals each day. My uncle visited me too and kept me company. Without them I should have been really miserable, lonely, in that city whose ways were foreign to me, whose climate was hostile, and whose dialect I could barely follow. All around me only *Soussou* was spoken. And I am a Malinké. Except for French the only language I speak is *Malinké*.

Then I began to think it was silly to lie there twiddling my thumbs, breathing sticky air, and sweating night and day. I began to think it was even sillier not to be at school instead of sweltering in such a suffocating atmosphere and in such useless immobility. What was I doing but wasting my time in a more unfortunate fashion? The ulcer wasn't getting any better. It wasn't getting any worse either. It just stayed the same. . . .

The school year passed slowly, very slowly. It seemed endless to me, as endless as the interminable rains that beat down for days and sometimes for weeks on the corrugated iron roofs. As endless as my interminable sickness. Then, by a strange coincidence which I can not explain, I got well just as the school year ended. It was high time. I was choking, bubbling over with impatience. . . . I set off for Kouroussa as if for the promised land

DRAMA

The Strong Breed

◼ Wole Soyinka (Nigeria)

Characters
EMAN a stranger
SUNMA Jaguna's daughter
IFADA an idiot
A GIRL
JAGUNA
OROGE
Attendant Stalwarts. The villagers

from Eman's past—

OLD MAN his father
OMAE his betrothed
TUTOR
PRIEST
Attendants. The villagers

The scenes are described briefly, but very often a darkened stage with lit areas will not only suffice but is necessary. Except for the one indicated place, there can be no break in the action. A distracting scene-change would be ruinous.

A mud house, with space in front of it. Eman, in light buba and trousers stands at the window, looking out. Inside, Sunma is clearing the table of what looks like a modest clinic, putting the things away in a cupboard. Another rough table in the room is piled with exercise books, two or three worn text-books, etc. Sunma appears agitated. Outside, just below the window crouches Ifada. He looks up with a shy smile from time to time, waiting for Eman to notice him.

SUNMA (*hesitant*): You will have to make up your mind soon Eman. The lorry leaves very shortly.

(*As EMAN does not answer, Sunma continues her work, more nervously. Two villagers, obvious travellers, pass hurriedly in front of the house, the man has a small raffia sack, the woman a cloth-covered basket, the man enters first, turns and urges the woman who is just emerging to hurry.*)

SUNMA (*seeing them, her tone is more intense*): Eman, are we going or aren't we? You will leave it till too late.
EMAN (*quietly*): There is still time—if you want to go.
SUNMA: If I want to go . . . and you?

(*Eman makes no reply.*)

SUNMA (*bitterly*): You don't really want to leave here. You never want to go away—even for a minute.

(*Ifada continues his antics.* EMAN *eventually pats him on the head and the boy grins happily. Leaps up suddenly and returns with a basket of oranges which he offers to* EMAN.)

EMAN: My gift for today's festival, enh?

(*Ifada nods, grinning.*)

EMAN: They look ripe—that's a change.

SUNMA (*She has gone inside the room. Looks round the door*): Did you call me?

EMAN: No. (*She goes back*) And what will you do tonight Ifada? Will you take part in the dancing? Or perhaps you will mount your own masquerade?

(*Ifada shakes his head, regretfully.*)

EMAN: You won't? So you haven't any? But you would like to own one.

(IFADA *nods eagerly.*)

EMAN: Then why don't you make your own?

(IFADA *stares, puzzled by this idea.*)

EMAN: Sunma will let you have some cloth you know. And bits of wool . . .

SUNMA (*coming out*): Who are you talking to, Eman?

EMAN: Ifada. I am trying to persuade him to join the young maskers.

SUNMA (*losing control*): What does he want here? Why is he hanging around us?

EMAN (*amazed*): What . . . ? I said Ifada. Ifada.

SUNMA: Just tell him to go away. Let him go and play somewhere else!

EMAN: What is this? Hasn't he always played here?

SUNMA: I don't want him here. (*Rushes to the window.*) Get away idiot. Don't bring your foolish face here any more, do you hear? Go on, go away from here . . .

EMAN (*restraining her*): Control yourself Sunma. What on earth has got into you?

(IFADA, *hurt and bewildered, backs slowly away.*)

SUNMA: He comes crawling round here like some horrible insect. I never want to lay my eyes on him again.

EMAN: I don't understand. It *is* Ifada you know. Ifada! The unfortunate one who runs errands for you and doesn't hurt a soul.

SUNMA: I cannot bear the sight of him.

EMAN: You can't do what? It can't be two days since he last fetched water for you.

SUNMA: What else can he do except that? He is useless. Just because we have been kind to him . . . Others would have put him in an asylum.

EMAN: You are not making sense. He is not a madman, he is just a little more unlucky than other children. (*Looks keenly at her.*) But what is the matter?

SUNMA: It's nothing. I only wish we had sent him off to one of those places for creatures like him.

EMAN: He is quite happy here. He doesn't bother anyone and he makes himself useful.

SUNMA: Useful! Is that one of any use to anybody? Boys of his age are already earning a living but all he can do is hang around and drool at the mouth.

EMAN: But he does work. You know he does a lot for you.

SUNMA: Does he? And what about the farm you started for him! Does he ever work on it? Or have you forgotten that it was really for Ifada you cleared that bush. Now you have to go and work it yourself. You spend all your time on it and you have no room for anything else.

EMAN: That wasn't his fault. I should first have asked him if he was fond of farming.

SUNMA: Oh, so he can choose? As if he shouldn't be thankful for being allowed to live.

EMAN: Sunma!

SUNMA: He does not like farming but he knows how to feast his dumb mouth on the fruits.

EMAN: But I want him to. I encourage him.

SUNMA: Well keep him. I don't want to see him any more.

EMAN (*after some moments*): But why? You cannot be telling all the truth. What has he done?

SUNMA: The sight of him fills me with revulsion.

EMAN (*goes to her and holds her*): What really is it?
(*Sunma avoids his eyes.*) It is almost as if you are forcing yourself to hate him. Why?

SUNMA: That is not true. Why should I?

EMAN: Then what is the secret? You've even played with him before.

SUNMA: I have always merely tolerated him. But I cannot any more. Suddenly my disgust won't take him any more. Perhaps . . . perhaps it is the new year. Yes, yes, it must be the new year.

EMAN: I don't believe that.

SUNMA: It must be. I am a woman, and these things matter. I don't want a mis-shape near me. Surely for one day in the year, I may demand some wholesomeness.

EMAN: I do not understand you.

(*Sunma is silent.*)

It was cruel of you. And to Ifada who is so helpless and alone. We are the only friends he has.

SUNMA: No, just you. I have told you, with me it has always been only an act of kindness. And now I haven't any pity left for him.

EMAN: No. He is not a wholesome being.

(*He turns back to looking through the window.*)

SUNMA (*half-pleading*): Ifada can rouse your pity. And yet if anything, I need more kindness from you. Every time my weakness betrays me, you close your mind against me . . . Eman . . . Eman . . .

(*A Girl comes in view, dragging an effigy by a rope attached to one of its legs. She stands for a while gazing at* EMAN. IFADA, *who has crept back shyly to his accustomed position, becomes somewhat excited when he sees the effigy. The girl is unsmiling. She possesses in fact, a kind of inscrutability which does not make her hard but is unsettling.*)

GIRL: Is the teacher in?

EMAN (*smiling*): No.

GIRL: Where is he gone?

EMAN: I don't really know. Shall I ask?

GIRL: Yes, do.

EMAN (*turning slightly*): Sunma, a girl outside wants to know . . .

(SUNMA *turns away, goes into the inside room.*)

EMAN: Oh. (*Returns to the girl, but his slight gaiety is lost*) There is no one at home who can tell me.

GIRL: Why are you not in?

EMAN: I don't really know. Maybe I went somewhere.

GIRL: All right. I will wait until you get back.

(*She pulls the effigy to her, sits down.*)

EMAN (*slowly regaining his amusement*): So you are all ready for the new year.

GIRL (*without turning around*): I am not going to the festival.

EMAN: Then why have you got that?

GIRL: Do you mean my carrier? I am unwell you know. My mothers says it will take away my sickness with the old year.

EMAN: Won't you share the carrier with your playmates?

GIRL: Oh, no. Don't you know I play alone? The other children won't come near me. Their mothers would beat them.

EMAN: But I have never seen you here. Why don't you come to the clinic?

GIRL: My mother said No.

(*Gets up, begins to move off.*)

EMAN: You are not going away?

GIRL: I must not stay talking to you. If my mother caught me . . .

EMAN: All right, tell me what you want before you go.

GIRL (*stops. For some moments she remains silent*): I must have some clothes for my carrier.

EMAN: Is that all? You wait a minute.

(*Sunma comes out as he takes down a buba from the wall. She goes to the window and glares almost with hatred at the girl. The girl retreats hastily, still impassive.*)

By the way Sunma, do you know who that girl is?

SUNMA: I hope you don't really mean to give her that.

EMAN: Why not? I hardly ever use it.

SUNMA: Just the same don't give it to her. She is not a child. She is as evil as the rest of them.

EMAN: What has got into you today?

SUNMA: All right, all right. Do what you wish.

(*She withdraws. Baffled, Eman returns to the window.*)

EMAN: Here . . . will this do? Come and look at it.

GIRL: Throw it.

EMAN: What is the matter? I am not going to eat you.

GIRL: No one lets me come near them.

EMAN: But I am not afraid of catching your disease.

GIRL: Throw it

(*Eman shrugs and tosses the buba. She takes it without a word and slips it on the effigy, completely absorbed in the task. Eman watches for a while, then joins Sunma in the inner room.*)

GIRL (*after a long, cool survey of Ifada*): You have a head like a spider's egg, and your mouth dribbles like a roof. But there is no one else. Would you like to play?

(IFADA *nods eagerly, quite excited.*)

GIRL: You will have to get a stick.

(IFADA *rushes around, finds a big stick and whirls it aloft, bearing down on the carrier.*)

GIRL: Wait. I don't want you to spoil it. If it gets torn I shall drive you away. Now, let me see how you are going to beat it.

(IFADA *hits it gently.*)

GIRL: You may hit harder than that. As long as there is something left to hang at the end.

(*She appraises him up and down.*)

You are not very tall . . . will you be able to hang it from a tree?

(IFADA *nods, grinning happily.*)

GIRL: You will hang it up and I will set fire to it. (*Then, with surprising venom.*) But just because you are helping me, don't think it is going to cure you. I am the one who will get well at midnight, do you understand? It is my carrier and it is for me alone.

(*She pulls at the rope to make sure that it is well attached to the leg.*)

Well don't stand there drooling. Let's go.

(*She begins to walk off, dragging the effigy in the dust. Ifada remains where he is for some moments, seemingly puzzled. Then his face breaks into a large grin and he leaps after the procession, belabouring the effigy with all his strength. The stage remains empty for some moments. Then the horn of a lorry is sounded and Sunma rushes out. The hooting continues for some time with a rhythmic pattern. Eman comes out.*)

EMAN: I am going to the village . . . I shan't be back before nightfall.
SUNMA (*blankly*): Yes.
EMAN (*hesitates*): Well what do you want me to do?
SUNMA: The lorry was hooting just now.
EMAN: I didn't hear it.
SUNMA: It will leave in a few minutes. And you did promise we could go away.
EMAN: I promised nothing. Will you go home by yourself or shall I come back for you?
SUNMA: You don't even want me here?
EMAN: But you have to go home haven't you?
SUNMA: I had hoped we would watch the new year together—in some other place.
EMAN: Why do you continue to distress yourself?
SUNMA: Because you will not listen to me. Why do you continue to stay where nobody wants you?
EMAN: That is not true.
SUNMA: It is. You are wasting your life on people who really want you out of their way.
EMAN: You don't know what you are saying.
SUNMA: You think they love you? Do you think they care at all for what you—or I—do for them?
EMAN: *Them?* These are your own people. Sometimes you talk as if you were a stranger too.

SUNMA: I wonder if I really sprang from here. I know they are evil and I am not. From the oldest to the smallest child, they are nourished in evil and unwholesomeness in which I have no part.

EMAN: You knew this when you returned?

SUNMA: You reproach me then for trying at all?

EMAN: I reproach you with nothing. But you must leave me out of your plans. I can have no part in them.

SUNMA (*nearly pleading*): Once I could have run away. I would have gone and never looked back.

EMAN: I cannot listen when you talk like that.

SUNMA: I swear to you, I do not mind what happens afterwards. But you must help me tear myself away from here. I can no longer do it by myself . . . It is only a little thing. And we have worked so hard this past year . . . surely we can go away for a week . . . even a few days would be enough.

EMAN: I have told you Sunma . . .

SUNMA (*desperately*): Two days Eman. Only two days.

EMAN (*distressed*): But I tell you I have no wish to go.

SUNMA (*suddenly angry*): Are you so afraid then?

EMAN: Me? Afraid of what?

SUNMA: You think you will not want to come back.

EMAN (*pitying*): You cannot dare me that way.

SUNMA: Then why won't you leave here, even for an hour? If you are so sure that your life is settled here, why are you afraid to do this thing for me? What is so wrong that you will not go into the next town for a day or two?

EMAN: I don't want to. I do not have to persuade you, or myself about anything. I simply have no desire to go away.

SUNMA (*his quiet confidence appears to incense her*): You are afraid. You accuse me of losing my sense of mission, but you are afraid to put yours to the test.

EMAN: You are wrong Sunma. I have no sense of mission. But I have found peace here and I am content with that.

SUNMA: I haven't. For a while I thought that too, but I found there could be no peace in the midst of so much cruelty. Eman, tonight at least, the last night of the old year . . .

EMAN: No Sunma. I find this too distressing; you should go home now.

SUNMA: It is the time for making changes in one's life Eman. Let's breathe in the new year away from here.

EMAN: You are hurting yourself.

SUNMA: Tonight. Only tonight. We will come back tomorrow, as early as you like. But let us go away for this one night. Don't let another year break on me in this place . . . you don't know how important it is to me, but I will tell you, I will tell you on the way .   but we must not be here today, Eman, do this one thing for me.

EMAN (*sadly*): I cannot.

SUNMA (*suddenly calm*): I was a fool to think it would be otherwise. The whole village may use you as they will but for me there is nothing.

Sometimes I think you believe that doing anything for me makes you unfaithful to some part of your life. If it was a woman then I pity her for what she must have suffered.

(EMAN *winces and hardens slowly.* SUNMA *notices nothing.*)

Keeping faith with so much is slowly making you inhuman.
(*Seeing the change in* EMAN.) Eman. Eman. What is it?
(*As she goes toward him,* EMAN *goes into the house.*)
SUNMA (*apprehensive, follows him*): What did I say? Eman, forgive me, forgive me please.

(EMAN *remains facing into the slow darkness of the room.* SUNMA, *distressed, cannot decide what to do.*)

I swear I didn't know . . . I would not have said it for all the world.

(*A lorry is heard taking off somewhere nearby. The sound comes up and slowly fades away into the distance.* SUNMA *starts visibly goes slowly to the window.*)

SUNMA (*as the sound dies off, to herself*): What happens now?
EMAN (*joining her at the window*): What did you say?
SUNMA: Nothing.
EMAN: Was that not the lorry going off?
SUNMA: It was.
EMAN: I am sorry I couldn't help you.

(SUNMA, *about to speak, changes her mind.*)

EMAN: I think you ought to go home now.
SUNMA: No, don't send me away. It's the least you can do for me. Let me stay here until all the noise is over.
EMAN: But are you not needed at home? You have a part in the festival.
SUNMA: I have renounced it; I am Jaguna's eldest daughter only in name.
EMAN: Renouncing one's self is not so easy—surely you know that.
SUNMA: I don't want to talk about it. Will you at least let us be together tonight?
EMAN: But . . .
SUNMA: Unless you are afraid my father will accuse you of harbouring me.
EMAN: All right, we will go out together.
SUNMA: Go out? I want us to stay here.
EMAN: When there is so much going on outside?
SUNMA: Some day you will wish that you went away when I tried to make you.
EMAN: Are we going back to that?
SUNMA: No. I promise you I will not recall it again. But you must know

that it was also for your sake that I tried to get us away.

EMAN: For me? How?

SUNMA: By yourself you can do nothing here. Have you not noticed how tightly we shut out strangers? Even if you lived here for a lifetime, you would remain a stranger.

EMAN: Perhaps that is what I like. There is peace in being a stranger.

SUNMA: For a while perhaps. But they would reject you in the end. I tell you it is only I who stand between you and contempt. And because of this you have earned their hatred. I don't know why I say this now, except that somehow, I feel that it no longer matters. It is only I who have stood between you and much humiliation.

EMAN: Think carefully before you say any more. I am incapable of feeling indebted to you. This will make no difference at all.

SUNMA: I ask for nothing. But you must know it all the same. It is true I hadn't the strength to go by myself. And I must confess this now, if you had come with me, I would have done everything to keep you from returning.

EMAN: I know that.

SUNMA: You see, I bare myself to you. For days I had thought it over, this was to be a new beginning for us. And I placed my fate wholly in your hands. Now the thought will not leave me, I have a feeling which will not be shaken off, that in some way, you have tonight totally destroyed my life.

EMAN: You are depressed, you don't know what you are saying.

SUNMA: Don't think I am accusing you. I say all this only because I cannot help it.

EMAN: We must not remain shut up here. Let us go and be part of the living.

SUNMA: No. Leave them alone.

EMAN: Surely you don't want to stay indoors when the whole town is alive with rejoicing.

SUNMA: Rejoicing! Is that what it seems to you? No, let us remain here. Whatever happens I must not go out until all this is over.

(There is silence. It has grown much darker.)

EMAN: I shall light the lamp.

SUNMA *(eager to do something)*: No, let me do it.

(She goes into the inner room. EMAN paces the room, stops by a shelf and toys with the seeds in an 'ayo' board, takes down the whole board and places it on a table, playing by himself.
The girl is now seen coming back, still dragging her 'carrier.'
IFADA *brings up the rear as before. As he comes round the corner of the house two men emerge from the shadows. A sack is thrown over* IFADA's *head, the rope is pulled tight rendering him instantly helpless. The girl has reached the front of the house before she turns round at the sound of scuffle. She is in time to see* IFADA *thrown over the shoulders and borne*

away. Her face betraying no emotion at all, the girl backs slowly away, turns and flees, leaving the 'carrier' behind.
SUNMA *enters, carrying two kerosene lamps. She hangs one up from the wall.)*

EMAN: One is enough.
SUNMA: I want to leave one outside.

(She goes out, hangs the lamp from a nail just above the door. As she turns she sees the effigy and gasps. EMAN *rushes out.)*

EMAN: What is it? Oh, is that what frightened you?
SUNMA: I thought . . . I didn't really see it properly.

*(*EMAN *goes towards the object, stoops to pick it up.)*

EMAN: It must belong to that sick girl.
SUNMA: Don't touch it.
EMAN: Let's keep it for her.
SUNMA: Leave it alone. Don't touch it Eman.
EMAN (*shrugs and goes back*): You are very nervous.
SUNMA: Let's go in.
EMAN: Wait. (*He detains her by the door, under the lamp.*) I know there is something more than you've told me. What are you afraid of tonight?
SUNMA: I was only scared by that thing. There is nothing else.
EMAN: I am not blind Sunma. It is true I would not run away when you wanted me to, but that doesn't mean I do not feel things. What does tonight really mean that it makes you so helpless?
SUNMA: It is only a mood. And your indifference to me . . . let's go in.

*(*EMAN *moves aside and she enters; he remains there for a moment and then follows.*
She fiddles with the lamp, looks vaguely round the room, then goes and shuts the door, bolting it. When she turns, it is to meet EMAN'S *eyes, questioning.)*

SUNMA: There is a cold wind coming in.

*(*EMAN *keeps his gaze on her.)*

SUNMA: It *was* getting cold.

(She moves guiltily to the table and stands by the 'ayo' board, rearranging the seeds. EMAN *remains where he is a few moments, then brings a stool and sits opposite her. She sits down also and they begin to play in silence.)*

SUNMA: What brought you here at all, Eman? And what makes you stay?

(There is another silence.)

SUNMA: I am not trying to share your life. I know you too well by now. But at least we have worked together since you came. Is there nothing at all I deserve to know?

EMAN: Let me continue a stranger—especially to you. Those who have much to give fulfil themselves only in total loneliness.

SUNMA: Then there is no love in what you do.

EMAN: There is. Love comes to me more easily with strangers.

SUNMA: That is unnatural.

EMAN: Not for me. I know I find consummation only when I have spent myself for a total stranger.

SUNMA: It seems unnatural to me. But then I am a woman. I have a woman's longings and weaknesses. And the ties of blood are very strong in me.

EMAN (*smiling*): You think I have cut loose from all these—ties of blood.

SUNMA: Sometimes you are so inhuman.

EMAN: I don't know what that means. But I am very much my father's son.

(*They play in silence. Suddenly* EMAN *pauses listening.*)

EMAN: Did you hear that?

SUNMA (*quickly*): I heard nothing . . . it's your turn.

EMAN: Perhaps some of the mummers are coming this way.

(EMAN *about to play, leaps up suddenly.*)

SUNMA: What is it? Don't you want to play any more?

(EMAN *moves to the door.*)

SUNMA: No. Don't go out Eman.

EMAN: If it's the dancers I want to ask them to stay. At least we won't have to miss everything.

SUNMA: No, no. Don't open the door. Let us keep out everyone tonight.

(*A terrified and disordered figure bursts suddenly round the corner, past the window and begins hammering at the door. It is* IFADA. *Desperate with terror, he pounds madly at the door, dumb-moaning all the while.*)

EMAN: Isn't that Ifada?

SUNMA: They are only fooling about. Don't pay any attention.

EMAN (*looks round the window*): That is Ifada. (*Begins to unbolt the door.*)

SUNMA (*pulling at his hands*): It is only a trick they are playing on you. Don't take any notice Eman.

EMAN: What are you saying? The boy is out of his senses with fear.

SUNMA: No, no. Don't interfere Eman. For God's sake don't interfere.

EMAN: Do you know something of this then?

SUNMA: You are a stranger here Eman. Just leave us alone and go your own way. There is nothing you can do.

EMAN (*he tries to push her out of the way but she clings fiercely to him*): Have you gone mad? I tell you the boy must come in.

SUNMA: Why won't you listen to me Eman? I tell you it's none of your business. For your own sake do as I say.

(EMAN *pushes her off, unbolts the door.* IFADA *rushes in, clasps* EMAN *round the knees, dumb-moaning against his legs.*)

EMAN (*manages to re-bolt the door*): What is it Ifada? What is the matter?

(*Shouts and voices are heard coming nearer the house.*)

SUNMA: Before it's too late, let him go. For once Eman, believe what I tell you. Don't harbour him or you will regret it all your life.

(EMAN *tries to calm* IFADA *who becomes more and more abject as the outside voices get nearer.*)

EMAN: What have they done to him? At least tell me that. What is going on Sunma?

SUNMA (*with sudden venom*): Monster! Could you not take yourself somewhere else?

EMAN: Stop talking like that.

SUNMA: He could have run into the bush couldn't he? Toad! Why must he follow us with his own disasters!

VOICES OUTSIDE: It's here . . . Round the back . . . Spread, spread . . . this way . . . no, head him off . . . use the bush path and head him off . . . get some more lights . . .

(EMAN *listens. Lifts* IFADA *bodily and carries him into the inner room. Returns at once, shutting the door behind him.*)

SUNMA (*slumps into a chair, resigned*): You always follow your own way.

JAGUNA (*comes round the corner followed by* OROGE *and three men, one bearing a torch*): I knew he would come here.

OROGE: I hope our friend won't make trouble.

JAGUNA: He had better not. You, recall all the men and tell them to surround the house.

OROGE: But he may not be in the house after all.

JAGUNA: I know he is here . . . (*to the men*) . . . go on, do as I say.

(*He bangs on the door.*)

Teacher, open your door . . . you two stay by the door. If I need you I will call you.

(EMAN *opens the door.*)

JAGUNA (*speaks as he enters*): We know he is here.
EMAN: Who?
JAGUNA: Don't let us waste time. We are grown men, teacher. You understand me and I understand you. But we must take back the boy.
EMAN: This is my house.
JAGUNA: Daughter, you'd better tell your friend. I don't think he quite knows our ways. Tell him why he must give up the boy.
SUNMA: Father, I . . .
JAGUNA: Are you going to tell him or aren't you?
SUNMA: Father, I beg you, leave us alone tonight . . .
JAGUNA: I thought you might be a hindrance. Go home then if you will not use your sense.
SUNMA: But there are other ways . . .
JAGUNA (*turning to the men*): See that she gets home. I no longer trust her. If she gives trouble carry her. And see that the women stay with her until all this is over.

(SUNMA *departs, accompanied by one of the men.*)

JAGUNA: Now, teacher . . .
OROGE (*restrains him*): You see, Mister Eman, it is like this. Right now, nobody knows that Ifada has taken refuge here. No one except us and our men—and they know how to keep their mouths shut. We don't want to have to burn down the house you see, but if the word gets around, we would have no choice.
JAGUNA: In fact, it may be too late already. A carrier should end up in the bush, not in a house. Anyone who doesn't guard his door when the carrier goes by has himself to blame. A contaminated house should be burnt down.
OROGE: But we are willing to let it pass. Only, you must bring him out quickly.
EMAN: All right. But at least you will let me ask you something.
JAGUNA: What is there to ask? Don't you understand what we have told you?
EMAN: Yes. But why did you pick on a helpless boy. Obviously he is not willing.
JAGUNA: What is the man talking about? Ifada is a godsend. Does he have to be willing?
EMAN: In my home, we believe that a man should be willing.
OROGE: Mister Eman, I don't think you quite understand. This is not a simple matter at all. I don't know what you do, but here, it is not a cheap task for anybody. No one in his senses would do such a job. Why do you think we give refuge to idiots like him? We don't know where he came from. One morning, he is simply there, just like that. From nowhere at all. You see, there is a purpose in that.
JAGUNA: We only waste time.
OROGE: Jaguna, be patient. After all, the man has been with us for some

time now and deserves to know. The evil of the old year is no light thing to load on any man's head.

EMAN: I know something about that.

OROGE: You do? (*Turns to* JAGUNA *who snorts impatiently.*) You see, I told you so didn't I? From the moment you came I saw you were one of the knowing ones.

JAGUNA: Then let him behave like a man and give back the boy.

EMAN: It is you who are not behaving like men.

JAGUNA (*advances aggressively*): That is a quick mouth you have . . .

OROGE: Patience Jaguna . . . if you want the new year to cushion the land there must be no deeds of anger. What did you mean my friend?

EMAN: It is a simple thing. A village which cannot produce its own carrier contains no men.

JAGUNA: Enough. Let there be no more talk or this business will be ruined by some rashness. You . . . come inside. Bring the boy out, he must be in the room there.

EMAN: Wait.

(*The men hesitate.*)

JAGUNA (*hitting the nearer one and propelling him forward*): Go on. Have you changed masters now that you listen to what he says?

OROGE (*sadly*): I am sorry you would not understand Mister Eman. But you ought to know that no carrier may return to the village. If he does, the people will stone him to death. It has happened before. Surely it is too much to ask a man to give up his own soil.

EMAN: I know others who have done more.

(IFADA *is brought out, abjectly dumb-moaning.*)

EMAN: You can see him with your own eyes. Does it really have meaning to use one as unwilling as that.

OROGE (*smiling*): He shall be willing. Not only willing but actually joyous. I am the one who prepares them all, and I have seen worse. This one escaped before I began to prepare him for the event. But you will see him later tonight, the most joyous creature in the festival. Then perhaps you will understand.

EMAN: Then it is only a deceit. Do you believe the spirit of a new year is so easily fooled?

JAGUNA: Take him out. (*The men carry out* IFADA.) You see, it is so easy to talk. You say there are no men in this village because they cannot provide a willing carrier. And yet I heard Oroge tell you we only use strangers. There is only one other stranger in the village, but I have not heard him offer himself (*spits*). It is so easy to talk is it not?

(*He turns his back on him.*
They go off, taking IFADA *with them, limp and silent. The only sign of life is that he strains his neck to keep his eyes on* EMAN *till the very moment that he disappears from sight.* EMAN *remains where they left him, staring after the group.*)

(*A black-out lasting no more than a minute. The lights come up slowly and* IFADA *is seen returning to the house. He stops at the window and looks in. Seeing no one, he bangs on the sill. Appears surprised that there is no response. He slithers down on his favourite spot, then sees the effigy still lying where the girl had dropped it in her flight. After some hesitation, he goes towards it, begins to strip it of the clothing. Just then the girl comes in.*)

GIRL: Hey, leave that alone. You know it's mine.

(IFADA *pauses, then speeds up his action.*)

GIRL: I said it is mine. Leave it where you found it.

(*She rushes at him and begins to struggle for possession of the carrier.*)

GIRL: Thief! Thief! Let it go, it is mine. Let it go. You animal, just because I let you play with it. Idiot! Idiot!

(*The struggle becomes quite violent. The girl is hanging to the effigy and* IFADA *lifts her with it, flinging her all about. The girl hangs on grimly.*)

GIRL: You are spoiling it . . . why don't you get your own? Thief! Let it
go you thief!

(SUNMA *comes in walking very fast, throwing apprehensive glances over her shoulder. Seeing the two children, she becomes immediately angry. Advances on them.*)

SUNMA: So you've made this place your playground. Get away you un-
trained pigs. Get out of here.

(IFADA *flees at once, the girl retreats also, retaining possession of the* "carrier."
SUNMA *goes to the door. She has her hand on the door when the signifi-cance of* IFADA'S *presence strikes her for the first time. She stands rooted to the spot, then turns slowly round.*)

SUNMA: Ifada! What are you doing here?

(IFADA *is bewildered.* SUNMA *turns suddenly and rushes into the house, flying into the inner room and out again.*)

Eman! Eman! Eman!

(*She rushes outside.*)

Where did he go? Where did they take him?

(IFADA *distressed, points.* SUNMA *seizes him by the arm, drags him off.*)

Take me there at once. God help you if we are too late.
You loathsome thing, if you have let him suffer . . .

(*Her voice fades into other shouts, running footsteps, banged tins, bells, dogs, etc., rising in volume.*)

(*It is a narrow passage-way between two mud-houses. At the far end one man after another is seen running across the entry, the noise dying off gradually.*
About half-way aown the passage, EMAN *is crouching against the wall, tense with apprehension. As the noise dies off, he seems to relax, but the alert hunted look is still in his eyes which are ringed in a reddish colour. The rest of his body has been whitened with a floury substance. He is naked down to the waist, wears a baggy pair of trousers, calf-length, and around both feet are bangles.*)

EMAN: I will simply stay here till dawn. I have done enough.

(*A window is thrown open and a woman empties some slop from a pail. With a startled cry* EMAN *leaps aside to avoid it and the woman puts out her head.*)

WOMAN: Oh, my head. What have I done! Forgive me neighbour. . . .
Eh, it's the carrier!

(*Very rapidly she clears her throat and spits on him, flings the pail at him and runs off, shouting.*)

He's here. The carrier is hiding in the passage. Quickly, I have found the carrier!

(*The cry is taken up and* EMAN *flees down the passage. Shortly afterwards his pursuers come pouring down the passage in full cry. After the last of them come* JAGUNA *and* OROGE.)

OROGE: Wait, wait. I cannot go so fast.
JAGUNA: We will rest a little then. We can do nothing anyway.
OROGE: If only he had let me prepare him.
JAGUNA: They are the ones who break first, these fools who think they were born to carry suffering like a hat. What are we to do now?
OROGE: When they catch him I must prepare him.
JAGUNA: He? It will be impossible now. There can be no joy left in that one.
OROGE: Still, it took him by surprise. He was not expecting what he met.
JAGUNA: Why then did he refuse to listen? Did he think he was coming to sit down to a feast? He had not even gone through one compound

before he bolted. Did he think he was taken round the people to be
blessed? A woman, that is all he is.

OROGE: No, no. He took the beating well enough. I think he is the kind
who would let himself be beaten from night till dawn and not utter a
sound. He would let himself be stoned until he dropped dead.

JAGUNA: Then what made him run like a coward?

OROGE: I don't know. I don't really know. It is a night of curses Jaguna.
It is not many unprepared minds will remain unhinged under the load.

JAGUNA: We must find him. It is a poor beginning for a year when our
own curses remain hovering over our homes because the carrier refused
to take them.

(*They go. The scene changes.* EMAN *is crouching beside some shrubs, torn
and bleeding.*)

EMAN: They are even guarding my house . . . as if I would go there, but
I need water . . . they could at least grant me that . . . I can be thirsty
too . . . (*he pricks his ears*) . . . there must be a stream nearby . . .
(*as he looks around him, his eyes widen at a scene he encounters.*)

(*An old man, short and vigorous looking is seated on a stool. He also is
wearing calf-length baggy trousers, white. On his head, a white cap. An
attendant is engaged in rubbing his body with oil. Round his eyes, two
white rings have already been marked.*)

OLD MAN: Have they prepared the boat?

ATTENDANT: They are making the last sacrifice.

OLD MAN: Good. Did you send for my son?

ATTENDANT: He's on his way.

OLD MAN: I have never met the carrying of the boat with such a heavy
heart. I hope nothing comes of it.

ATTENDANT: The gods will not desert us on that account.

OLD MAN: A man should be at his strongest when he takes the boat my
friend. To be weighed down inside and out is not a wise thing. I hope
when the moment comes I shall have found my strength.

(*Enter* EMAN, *a wrapper round his waist and a "danski" over it.*)

OLD MAN: I meant to wait until after my journey to the river, but my
mind is so burdened with my own grief and yours I could not delay it.
You know I must have all my strength. But I sit here, feeling it all eat
slowly away by my unspoken grief. It helps to say it out. It even helps
to cry sometimes.

(*He signals to the attendant to leave them.*)

Come nearer . . . we will never meet again son. Not on this side of the
flesh. What I do not know is whether you will return to take my place.

EMAN: I will never come back.

OLD MAN: Do you know what you are saying? Ours is a strong breed my son. It is only a strong breed that can take this boat to the river year after year and wax stronger on it. I have taken down each year's evils for over twenty years. I hoped you would follow me.

EMAN: My life here died with Omae.

OLD MAN: Omae died giving birth to your child and you think the world is ended. Eman, my pain did not begin when Omae died. Since you sent her to stay with me son, I lived with the burden of knowing that this child would die bearing your son.

EMAN: Father . . .

OLD MAN: Don't you know it was the same with you? And me? No woman survives the bearing of the strong ones. Son, it is not the mouth of the boaster that says he belongs to the strong breed. It is the tongue that is red with pain and black with sorrow. Twelve years you were away my son, and for those twelve years I knew the love of an old man for his daughter and the pain of a man helplessly awaiting his loss.

EMAN: I wish I had stayed away. I wish I never came back to meet her.

OLD MAN: It had to be. But you know now what slowly ate away my strength. I awaited your return with love and fear. Forgive me then if I say that your grief is light. It will pass. This grief may drive you now from home. But you must return.

EMAN: You do not understand. It is not grief alone.

OLD MAN: What is it then? Tell me, I can still learn.

EMAN: I was away twelve years. I changed much in that time.

OLD MAN: I am listening.

EMAN: I am unfitted for your work father. I wish to say no more. But I am totally unfitted for your call.

OLD MAN: It is only time you need son. Stay longer and you will answer the urge of your blood.

EMAN: That I stayed at all was because of Omae. I did not expect to find her waiting. I would have taken her away, but hard as you claim to be, it would have killed you. And I was a tired man. I needed peace. Because Omae was peace, I stayed. Now nothing holds me here.

OLD MAN: Other men would rot and die doing this task year after year. It is strong medicine which only we can take. Our blood is strong like no other. Anything you do in life must be less than this, son.

EMAN: That is not true father.

OLD MAN: I tell you it is true. Your own blood will betray you son, because you cannot hold it back. If you make it do less than this, it will rush to your head and burst it open. I say what I know my son.

EMAN: There are other tasks in life father. This one is not for me. There are even greater things you know nothing of.

OLD MAN: I am very sad. You only go to give to others what rightly belongs to us. You will use your strength among thieves. They are thieves because they take what is ours, they have no claim of blood to it. They will even lack the knowledge to use it wisely. Truth is my companion at this moment my son. I know everything I say will surely bring the sadness of truth.

EMAN: I am going father.

OLD MAN: Call my attendant. And be with me in your strength for this last journey. A-ah, did you hear that? It came out without my knowing it; this is indeed my last journey. But I am not afraid.

(EMAN *goes out. A few moments later, the attendant enters.*)

ATTENDANT: The boat is ready.

OLD MAN: So am I.

(*He sits perfectly still for several moments. Drumming begins somewhere in the distance, and the old man sways his head almost imperceptibly. Two men come in bearing a miniature boat, containing an indefinable mound. They rush it in and set it briskly down near the old man, and stand well back. The old man gets up slowly, the attendant watching him keenly. He signs to the men, who lift the boat quickly onto the old man's head. As soon as it touches his head, he holds it down with both hands and runs off, the men give him a start, then follow at a trot. As the last man disappears* OROGE *limps in and comes face to face with* EMAN—*as carrier—who is now seen still standing beside the shrubs, staring into the scene he has just witnessed.* OROGE, *struck by the look on* EMAN'S *face, looks anxiously behind him to see what has engaged* EMAN'S *attention.* EMAN *notices him then, and the pair stare at each other.* JAGUNA *enters, sees him and shouts, "Here he is," rushes at* EMAN *who is whipped back to the immediate and flees,* JAGUNA *in pursuit. Three or four others enter and follow them.* OROGE *remains where he is, thoughtful.*)

JAGUNA (*re-enters*): They have closed in on him now, we'll get him this time.

OROGE: It is nearly midnight.

JAGUNA: You were standing there looking at him as if he was some strange spirit. Why didn't you shout?

OROGE: You shouted didn't you? Did that catch him?

JAGUNA: Don't worry. We have him now. But things have taken a bad turn. It is no longer enough to drive him past every house. There is too much contamination about already.

OROGE (*not listening*): He saw something. Why may I not know what it was?

JAGUNA: What are you talking about?

OROGE: Hm. What is it?

JAGUNA: I said there is too much harm done already. The year will demand more from this carrier than we thought.

OROGE: What do you mean?

JAGUNA: Do we have to talk with the full mouth?

OROGE: S-sh . . . look!

(JAGUNA *turns just in time to see* SUNMA *fly at him, clawing at his face like a crazed tigress.*)

SUNMA: Murderer! What are doing to him. Murderer! Murderer!

(JAGUNA *finds himself struggling really hard to keep off his daughter, he succeeds in pushing her off and striking her so hard on the face that she falls to her knees. He moves on her to hit her again*).

OROGE (*comes between*): Think what you are doing Jaguna, she is your daughter.

JAGUNA: My daughter! Does this one look like my daughter? Let me cripple the harlot for life.

OROGE: That is a wicked thought Jaguna.

JAGUNA: Don't come between me and her.

OROGE: Nothing in anger—do you forget what tonight is?

JAGUNA: Can you blame me for forgetting?

(*Draws his hand across his cheek—it is covered with blood.*)

OROGE: This is an unhappy night for us all. I fear what is to come of it.

JAGUNA: Let's go. I cannot restrain myself in this creature's presence. My own daughter . . . and for a stranger . . .

(*They go off.* IFADA,*who came in with* SUNMA *and had stood apart, horror-stricken, comes shyly forward. He helps* SUNMA *up. They go off, he holding* SUNMA *bent and sobbing.*)

(*Enter* EMAN—*as carrier. He is physically present in the bounds of this next scene, a side of a round thatched hut. A young girl, about fourteen runs in, stops beside the hut. She looks carefully to see that she is not observed, puts her mouth to a little hole in the wall.*)

OMAE: Eman . . . Eman . . .

(EMAN—*as carrier—responds, as he does throughout the scene, but they are unaware of him.*)

EMAN (*from inside*): Who is it?

OMAE: It is me, Omae.

EMAN: How dare you come here!

(*Two hands appear at the hole and pushing outwards, create a much larger hole through which* EMAN *puts out his head. It is* EMAN *as a boy, the same age as the girl.*)

Go away at once. Are you trying to get me into trouble?

OMAE: What is the matter?

EMAN: You. Go away.

OMAE: But I came to see you.

EMAN: Are you deaf? I say I don't want to see you. Now go before my tutor catches you

OMAE: All right. Come out.

EMAN: Do what!

OMAE: Come out.

EMAN: You must be mad.

OMAE (*sits on the ground*): All right, if you don't come out I shall simply stay here until your tutor arrives.

EMAN (*about to explode, thinks better of it and the head disappears. A moment later he emerges from behind the hut*): What sort of a devil has got into you?

OMAE: None. I just wanted to see you.

EMAN (*his mimicry is nearly hysterical*): 'None. I just wanted to see you.' Do you think this place is the stream where you can go and molest innocent people?

OMAE (*coyly*): Aren't you glad to see me?

EMAN: I am not.

OMAE: Why?

EMAN: Why? Do you really ask me why? Because you are a woman and a most troublesome woman. Don't you know anything about this at all. We are not meant to see any woman. So go away before more harm is done.

OMAE (*flirtatious*): What is so secret about it anyway? What do they teach you.

EMAN: Nothing any woman can understand.

OMAE: Ha ha. You think we don't know eh? You've all come to be circumcised.

EMAN: Shut up. You don't know anything.

OMAE: Just think, all this time you haven't been circumcised, and you dared make eyes at us women.

EMAN: Thank you—woman. Now go.

OMAE: Do they give you enough to eat?

EMAN (*testily*). No. We are so hungry that when silly girls like you turn up, we eat them.

OMAE (*feigning tears*): Oh, oh, oh, now he's abusing me. He's abusing me.

EMAN (*alarmed*): Don't try that here. Go quickly if you are going to cry.

OMAE: All right, I won't cry.

EMAN: Cry or no cry, go away and leave me alone. What do you think will happen if my tutor turns up now.

OMAE: He won't.

EMAN (*mimicking*): 'He won't.' I suppose you are his wife and he tells you where he goes. In fact this is just the time he comes round to our huts. He could be at the next hut this very moment.

OMAE: Ha-ha. You're lying. I left him by the stream, pinching the girls' bottoms. Is that the sort of thing he teaches you?

EMAN: Don't say anything against him or I shall beat you. Isn't it you loose girls who tease him, wiggling your bottoms under his nose?

OMAE (*going tearful again*): A-ah, so I am one of the loose girls eh?

EMAN: Now don't start accusing me of things I didn't say.

OMAE: But you said it. You said it.

EMAN: I didn't. Look Omae, someone will hear you and I'll be in disgrace. Why don't you go before anything happens.

OMAE: It's all right. My friends have promised to hold your old rascal tutor till I get back.

EMAN: Then you go back right now. I have work to do. (*Going in.*)

OMAE (*runs after and tries to hold him. Eman leaps back, genuinely scared.*): What is the matter? I was not going to bite you.

EMAN: Do you know what you nearly did? You almost touched me!

OMAE: Well?

EMAN: Well! Isn't it enough that you let me set my eyes on you? Must you now totally pollute me with your touch? Don't you understand anything?

OMAE: Oh, that.

EMAN (*nearly screaming*): It is not 'oh that.' Do you think this is only a joke or a little visit like spending the night with your grandmother? This is an important period of my life. Look, these huts, we built them with our own hands. Every boy builds his own. We learn things, do you understand? And we spend much time just thinking. At least, I do. It is the first time I have had nothing to do except think. Don't you see, I am becoming a man. For the first time, I understand that I have a life to fulfil. Has that thought ever worried you?

OMAE: You are frightening me.

EMAN: There. That is all you can say. And what use will that be when a man finds himself alone—like that? (*Points to the hut.*) A man must go on his own, go where no one can help him, and test his strength. Because he may find himself one day sitting alone in a wall as round as that. In there, my mind could hold no other thought. I may never have such moments again to myself. Don't dare to come and steal any more of it.

OMAE (*this time, genuinely tearful*): Oh, I know you hate me. You only want to drive me away.

EMAN (*impatiently*): Yes, yes, I know I hate you—but go.

OMAE (*going, all tears. Wipes her eyes, suddenly all mischief.*) Eman.

EMAN: What now?

OMAE: I only want to ask one thing .. do you promise to tell me?

EMAN: Well, what is it?

OMAE (*gleefully*): Does it hurt?

(*She turns instantly and flees, landing straight into the arms of the returning tutor.*)

TUTOR: Te-he-he . . . what have we here? What little mouse leaps straight into the beak of the wise old owl eh?

(*OMAE struggles to free herself, flies to the opposite side, grimacing with distaste.*)

TUTOR: I suppose you merely came to pick some fruits eh? You did not sneak here to see any of my children.

OMAE: Yes, I came to steal your fruits.

TUTOR: Te-he-he . . . I thought so. And that dutiful son of mine over there. He saw you and came to chase you off my fruit trees didn't he? Te-he-he . . . I'm sure he did, isn't that so my young Eman?

EMAN: I was talking to her.

TUTOR: Indeed you were. Now be good enough to go into your hut until I decide your punishment. [*Eman withdraws.*] Te-he-he . . . now now my little daughter, you need not be afraid of me.

OMAE (*spiritedly*): I am not.

TUTOR: Good. Very good. We ought to be friendly. (*His voice becomes leering.*) Now this is nothing to worry you my daughter . . . a very small thing indeed. Although of course if I were to let it slip that your young Eman had broken a strong taboo, it might go hard on him you know. I am sure you would not like that to happen, would you?

OMAE: No.

TUTOR: Good. You are sensible my girl. Can you wash clothes?

OMAE: Yes.

TUTOR: Good. If you will come with me now to my hut, I shall give you some clothes to wash, and then we will forget all about this matter eh? Well, come on.

OMAE: I shall wait here. You go and bring the clothes.

TUTOR: Eh? What is that? Now now, don't make me angry. You should know better than to talk back at your elders. Come now.

(*He takes her by the arm, and tries to drag her off.*)

OMAE: No no, I won't come to your hut. Leave me. Leave me alone you shameless old man.

TUTOR: If you don't come I shall disgrace the whole family of Eman, and yours too

(EMAN *re-enters with a small bundle.*)

EMAN: Leave her alone. Let us go Omae.

TUTOR: And where do you think you are going?

EMAN: Home.

TUTOR: Te-he-he . . . As easy as that eh? You think you can leave here any time you please? Get right back inside that hut!

(EMAN *takes* OMAE *by the arm and begins to walk off.*)

TUTOR: Come back at once.

(*He goes after him and raises his stick.* EMAN *catches it, wrestles it from him and throws it away.*)

OMAE (*hopping delightedly*): Kill him. Beat him to death.

TUTOR: Help! Help! He is killing me! Help!

(*Alarmed,* EMAN *clamps his hand over his mouth.*)

EMAN: Old tutor, I don't mean you any harm, but you mustn't try to harm me either. (*He removes his hand.*)

TUTOR: You think you can get away with your crime. My report shall reach the elders before you ever get into town.

EMAN: You are afraid of what I will say about you? Don't worry. Only if you try to shame me, then I will speak. I am not going back to the village anyway. Just tell them I have gone, no more. If you say one word more than that I shall hear of it the same day and I shall come back.

TUTOR: You are telling me what to do? But don't think to come back next year because I will drive you away. Don't think to come back here even ten years from now. And don't send your children.

(*Goes off with threatening gestures.*)

EMAN: I won't come back.

OMAE: Smoked vulture! But Eman, he says you cannot return next year. What will you do?

EMAN: It is a small thing one can do in the big towns.

OMAE: I thought you were going to beat him that time. Why didn't you crack his dirty hide?

EMAN: Listen carefully Omae . . . I am going on a journey.

OMAE: Come on. Tell me about it on the way.

EMAN: No, I go that way. I cannot return to the village.

OMAE: Because of that wretched man? Anyway you will first talk to your father.

EMAN: Go and see him for me. Tell him I have gone away for some time. I think he will know.

OMAE: But Eman . . .

EMAN: I haven't finished. You will go and live with him till I get back. I have spoken to him about you. Look after him!

OMAE: But what is this journey? When will you come back?

EMAN: I don't know. But this is a good moment to go. Nothing ties me down.

OMAE: But Eman, you want to leave me.

EMAN: Don't forget all I said. I don't know how long I will be. Stay in my father's house as long as you remember me. When you become tired of waiting, you must do as you please. You understand? You must do as you please.

OMAE: I cannot understand anything Eman. I don't know where you are going or why. Suppose you never came back! Don't go Eman. Don't leave me by myself.

EMAN: I must go. Now let me see you on your way.

OMAE: I shall come with you.

EMAN: Come with me! And who will look after you? Me? You will only be in my way, you know that! You will hold me back and I shall desert you in a strange place. Go home and do as I say. Take care of my father and let him take care of you.

(*He starts going but* OMAE *clings to him.*)

OMAE: But Eman, stay the night at least. You will only lose your way. Your father Eman, what will he say? I won't remember what you said . . . come back to the village . . . I cannot return alone Eman . . . come with me as far as the crossroads.

(*His face set,* EMAN *strides off and* OMAE *loses balance as he increases his pace. Falling, she quickly wraps her arms around his ankle, but* EMAN *continues unchecked, dragging her along.*)

OMAE: Don't go Eman . . . Eman, don't leave me, don't leave me . . . don't leave your Omae . . . don't go Eman . . . don't leave your Omae . . .

(EMAN—*as carrier—makes a nervous move as if he intends to go after the vanished pair. He stops but continues to stare at the point where he last saw them. There is stillness for a while. Then the* GIRL *enters from the same place and remains looking at Eman. Startled,* EMAN *looks apprehensively round him. The* GIRL *goes nearer but keeps beyond arm's length.*)

GIRL: Are you the carrier?
EMAN: Yes. I am Eman.
GIRL: Why are you hiding?
EMAN: I really came for a drink of water . . . er . . . is there anyone in front of the house?
GIRL: No.
EMAN: But there might be people in the house. Did you hear voices?
GIRL: There is no one there.
EMAN: Good. Thank you. (*He is about to go, stops suddenly.*) Er . . . would you . . . you will find a cup on the table. Could you bring me the water out here? The water-pot is in a corner.

(*The* GIRL *goes. She enters the house, then, watching* EMAN *carefully, slips out and runs off.*)

EMAN (*sitting*): Perhaps they have all gone home. It will be good to rest. (*He hears voices and listens hard.*) Too late. (*Moves cautiously nearer the house.*) Quickly girl, I can hear people coming. Hurry up. (*Looks through the window.*) Where are you? Where is she? (*The truth dawns on him suddenly and he moves off, sadly.*)

(*Enter* JAGUNA *and* OROGE, *led by the* GIRL.)

GIRL (*pointing*): He was there.

JAGUNA: Ay, he's gone now. He is a sly one is your friend. But it won't save him for ever.

OROGE: What was he doing when you saw him?

GIRL: He asked me for a drink of water.

JAGUNA,
OROGE } : Ah! (*They look at each other.*)

OROGE: We should have thought of that.

JAGUNA: He is surely finished now. If only we had thought of it earlier.

OROGE: It is not too late. There is still an hour before midnight.

JAGUNA: We must call back all the men. Now we need only wait for him —in the right place.

OROGE: Everyone must be told. We don't want anyone heading him off again.

JAGUNA: And it works so well. This is surely the help of the gods themselves Oroge. Don't you know at once what is on the path to the stream?

OROGE: The sacred trees.

JAGUNA: I tell you it is the very hand of the gods. Let us go.

(*An overgrown part of the village.* EMAN *wanders in, aimlessly, seemingly uncaring of discovery. Beyond him, an area lights up, revealing a group of people clustered round a spot, all the heads are bowed. One figure stands away and separate from them. Even as* EMAN *looks, the group break up and the people disperse, coming down and past him. Only three people are left, a man (*EMAN*) whose back is turned, the village priest and the isolated one. They stand on opposite sides of the grave, the man on the mound of earth.*

The priest walks round to the man's side and lays a hand on his shoulder.)

PRIEST: Come.

EMAN: I will. Give me a few moments here alone.

PRIEST: Be comforted.

(*They fall silent.*)

EMAN: I was gone twelve years but she waited. She whom I thought had too much of the laughing child in her. Twelve years I was a pilgrim, seeking the vain shrine of secret strength. And all the time, strange knowledge, this silent strength of my child-woman.

PRIEST: We all saw it. It was a lesson to us; we did not know that such goodness could be found among us.

EMAN: Then why? Why the wasted years if she had to perish giving birth to my child? (*They are both silent.*) I do not really know for what great meaning I searched. When I returned, I could not be certain I had found it. Until I reached my home and I found her a full-grown woman, still a child at heart. When I grew to believe it, I thought, this, after all, is what I sought. It was here all the time. And I threw away my new-gained knowledge. I buried the part of me that was formed in strange places. I made a home in my birthplace.

PRIEST: That was as it should be.

EMAN: Any truth of that was killed in the cruelty of her brief happiness.

PRIEST: (*Looks up and sees the figure standing away from them, the child in his arms. He is totally still.*): Your father—he is over there.

EMAN: I knew he would come. Has he my son with him?

PRIEST: Yes.

EMAN: He will let no one take the child. Go and comfort him priest. He loved Omae like a daughter, and you all know how well she looked after him. You see how strong we really are. In his heart of hearts the old man's love really awaited a daughter. Go and comfort him. His grief is more than mine.

(*The priest goes. The old Man has stood well away from the burial group. His face is hard and his gaze unswerving from the grave. The priest goes to him, pauses, but sees that he can make no dent in the man's grief. Bowed, he goes on his way.*)

(EMAN, *as carrier, walking towards the graveside, the other* EMAN *having gone. His feet sink into the mound and he breaks slowly on to his knees, scooping up the sand in his hands and pouring it on to his head. The scene blacks out slowly.*)

(*Enter* JAGUNA *and* OROGE.)

OROGE: We have only a little time.

JAGUNA: He will come. All the wells are guarded. There is only the stream left him. The animal must come to drink.

OROGE: You are sure it will not fail—the trap I mean.

JAGUNA: When Jaguna sets the trap, even elephants pay homage—their trunks downwards and one leg up in the sky. When the carrier steps on the fallen twigs, it is up in the sacred trees with him.

OROGE: I shall breathe again when this long night is over.

(*They go out.*)

(*Enter* EMAN—*as carrier—from the same direction as the last two entered. In front of him is a still figure, the Old Man as he was, carrying the dwarf boat.*)

EMAN (*joyfully*): Father.

(*The figure does not turn round.*)

EMAN: It is your son. Eman. (*He moves nearer.*) Don't you want to look at me? It is I, Eman. (*He moves nearer still.*)

OLD MAN: You are coming too close. Don't you know what I carry on my head?

EMAN: But Father, I am your son.

OLD MAN: Then go back. We cannot give the two of us.

EMAN: Tell me first where you are going.

OLD MAN: Do *you* ask that? Where else but to the river?

EMAN (*visibly relieved*): I only wanted to be sure. My throat is burning. I have been looking for the stream all night.

OLD MAN: It is the other way.

EMAN: But you said . . .

OLD MAN: I take the longer way, you know how I must do this. It is quicker if you take the other way. Go now.

EMAN: No, I will only get lost again. I shall go with you.

OLD MAN: Go back my son. Go back.

EMAN: Why? Won't you even look at me?

OLD MAN: Listen to your father. Go back.

EMAN: But father!

(*He makes to hold him. Instantly the old man breaks into a rapid trot. EMAN hesitates, then follows, his strength nearly gone.*)

EMAN: Wait father. I am coming with you . . . wait . . . wait for me father . . .

(*There is a sound of twigs breaking, of a sudden trembling in the branches. Then silence.*)

(*The front of EMAN's house. The effigy is hanging from the sheaves. Enter SUNMA, still supported by IFADA, she stands transfixed as she sees the hanging figure. IFADA appears to go mad, rushes at the object and tears it down. SUNMA, her last bit of will gone, crumbles against the wall. Some distance away from them, partly hidden, stands the GIRL, impassively watching. IFADA hugs the effigy to him, stands above SUNMA. The GIRL remains where she is, observing.*
Almost at once, the villagers begin to return, subdued and guilty. They walk across the front, skirting the house as widely as they can. No word is exchanged. JAGUNA and OROGE eventually appear. JAGUNA who is leading, sees SUNMA as soon as he comes in view. He stops at once, retreating slightly.)

OROGE (*almost whispering*): What is it?

JAGUNA: The viper.

(*OROGE looks cautiously at the woman.*)

OROGE: I don't think she will even see you.

JAGUNA: Are you sure? I am in no frame of mind for another meeting with her.

OROGE: Let's go home.

JAGUNA: I am sick to the heart of the cowardice I have seen tonight.

OROGE: That is the nature of men.

JAGUNA: Then it is a sorry world to live in. We did it for them. It was all for their own common good. What did it benefit me whether the

man lived or died. But did you see them? One and all they looked up
at the man and words died in their throats.

OROGE: It was no common sight.

JAGUNA: Women could not have behaved so shamefully. One by one
they crept off like sick dogs. Not one could raise a curse.

OROGE: It was not only him they fled. Do you see how unattended we
are?

JAGUNA: There are those who will pay for this night's work!

OROGE: Ay, let us go home.

(*They go off.* SUNMA, IFADA, *and the* GIRL *remain as they are, the light
fading slowly on them.*)

THE END

from The Song of a Goat

■   John Pepper Clark (Nigeria)

Characters
ZIFA, a fisherman and part-time ship pilot at one of the Niger estuaries
TONYE, his younger brother and assistant
EBIERE, Zifa's wife
ORUKORERE, his half-possessed aunt
DODE, his child

Third Movement

Late afternoon. EBIERE *is bathing* DODE *on the verandah. A little away sits*
TONYE, *working on floats for nets and hooklines.*

EBIERE: A grown-up fellow like you strappling as
  A banana sucker, you still do not
  Know how to wash your body properly.
  There, steady! Let me bathe you. You have all
  The time only been rubbing the water on
  Your belly, and a big pot you have. Of course
  You can call for farina before the cock calls
  Forth the day. When dawn breaks, mouth opens and
  With you it stays so till dusk closes in.
  Now what are you yelling for? Anybody
  Would think you were being circumcised all
  Over again or that you have yaws on
  You. Take that! And that! Now you can holla

All day just as you please. I suppose your
Race can boast of that.
TONYE: What are you
Smacking the boy for, Ebiere?
EBIERE: Better be
About what you are doing. Don't splash
Me with water I told you, you scamp!
TONYE: That's enough; we don't allow our children
To be knocked on the head like that.
EBIERE: Don't you lecture me on how to beat my child.
What do you know of child-rearing anyway?
TONYE: Enough to know that knocking a child on
The head like that makes him prone
To attacks from small-pox. We simply forbid
It in the family. You may smack
Him on the backside if you please
But do not beat the boy on the head.
EBIERE: I can well see you people care for children
A great deal.
TONYE: Yes, we do. Here, Dode, come
This way and I will carve you a fine canoe out
Of this cork-wood and bamboo. I have enough
Floats already to fence off the bar.
DODE: Will I be able to go to sea like you
And father?
TONYE: Even so. Witches sail
In groundnut husks; and this boat I shall carve
You is many, many times fitter than any
(*She hisses.*)
Witch's craft. Why, what do you make that sound for?
EBIERE: Does it give you pain?
TONYE: From a snake such a sound is only to be
Expected; it is the signal of spite and
Sinister motives. But coming out of a woman
Like you with all the things a wife would want
· In the world I do not know what to make of it.
EBIERE: Poor, poor, father-of-my-marriage, what
Can you or anybody in this house do
About anything? At least, one has first to know
The roots to be able to gather the leaves.
TONYE: Ebiere, yes, I confess I do not know
Much. Both of you, you and Zifa, say very little.
But I do know that you have gradually
Become bitter over the months. Why, look
At how you cuffed the little boy just now.
Anybody seeing you would think you were his
Step-mother.
EBIERE: And he not my only child.
TONYE: I wasn't thinking of that.

EBIERE: You ought to have
 Been, yes, long before now, since you are
 So solicitous about my well-being.
TONYE: Everybody wants children of course.
EBIERE: Thus the elders pray: Only one seed
 The elephant brings forth at a time until
 The house is full, yes, until the house be
 Full even if this takes ten falls of the flood.
TONYE: Ebiere, you are bitter as bile. Lots
 Of people there are who want children but
 Have not been blessed with a fine one as you have.
EBIERE: That is bad, isn't it? Especially
 As custom dictates those who die childless
 Be cast out of the company of the fruitful whose
 Special grace is interment in the township.
TONYE: The Witch of Nine Plumes has your stomach
 For her cauldron.
EBIERE: She is a good cook, she
 Must be, to have boiled me dry of all content.
TONYE: I do not mean that, I mean you ought
 To be contented and not be so short
 Of temper with everyone. You cuff the child
 On the skull, and have taken to scolding and nagging
 All day. Have you cooked in time today for my
 Brother's home coming? Many times
 These past market days it has been so.
 Why, what is become of you? A man
 After long stay at sea deserves a proper and
 Regular dish when he arrives home. I wonder
 Zifa is so given to your new
 Irregular ways.
EBIERE: Don't talk to me about
 Your brother or about my irregular ways,
 I tell you, don't talk to me of them.
 Irregular ways! What do you know about
 Irregularities, anyway? If food was
 Not ready by noontide, that would be
 Irregular, wouldn't it? If I saw
 My period and stayed indoors and cooked
 For you and your big brother, that would
 Be irregular by all standards
 And practice, wouldn't it—you that are so correct
 And proper you know all these things?
TONYE: Don't you clap your hands in my face, woman!
 If my brother takes all this from you, I
 Certainly won't, do you hear me? I will
 Not have it.
EBIERE: You talk of your brother
 And of his patience as if patience were

His alone and he alone has suffered.
TONYE: Surely, he has suffered much abuse
From you lately.
Why, the whole village is talking.
EBIERE: Talking, are they? Like you are doing now
About his forbearance and his
Sufferings. What do they know about suffering and
Patience? And you, what do you know about them?
Of course, it is the woman who is in the wrong
Always—I who have suffered neglect and
Gathered mould like a thing of sacrifice
Left out in sun and rain at the cross-roads.
You talk to me of my short temper; what
Short temper have I when it is pulled and
Tugged at daily like a hook-line?
TONYE: You certainly are showing it today,
And nobody has baited you.
DODE: Mother, mother don't!
EBIERE: Stand aside, child. Flesh with thorn
In it must bud pus.
TONYE: Nobody stuck
Thorns in your flesh; why should you smart so.
EBIERE: You are a greater fool than the idiot
In the market-place to ask a question like that.
TONYE: I said, Ebiere, I'm not your husband.
EBIERE: Well, aren't you? Since you know his duties better
Than he does, why don't you take them up? If you
Don't, I should laugh your whole race to scorn.
TONYE: What you want is a good cry. Now will
You take your hands off me?
EBIERE: Do it, do it now
And show you are strong.
TONYE: I do not have to
With you to show I have one bone. Many who
Doubted have felt its weight in the wrestling pit.
EBIERE: Well, fell me down then; it would be so much
Easier for you to do, I being no cow.
TONYE: I say take your hands off me. Ebiere,
You certainly are desperate for danger.
See how like waters whipped by the wind you
Have run amok. Take your hands off.
EBIERE: No, no, show your powers, I say,
Floor me, march on me, strike me down as
You did Benikpanra the Bull to show
You are the strong man of the family.
TONYE: Why, Ebiere, you are mad, so gone far
Leaves-gathering, and you are hot all
Over, oh so shuddering, shuddering
So, you want to pull me down which is

A thing forbidden, now take that then, and that—Oh
   my father!
EBIERE: So I am crazed, completely gone leaves-plucking,
   And you? Aren't you shuddering too, Oh,
   So shuddering in your heat of manhood you
   Have thrown me? Now, hold me, do hold on and
   Fight, for it is a thing not forbidden!

(*Cock crows beyond.*)

DODE: Help, help! My mother, my mother! Tonye
   Is wrestling on
   The floor with my mother!
ORUKORERE: What is it, child, what is the matter? Can't
   I have a little sleep but one
   Of you in this house must kick me up?
DODE: There, there, look there, they have rolled
   And dragged each other over the doorstep,
   And now the door is slammed behind them.
ORUKORERE: Why, boy, these are no leopard and goat
   Interlocked between life and death, but
   Two dogs at play. Poor child, let me close the door.
DODE: Will you leave them to fight there? My
   Uncle is the strongest man in all
   The creeks. He will kill my mother.
ORUKORERE: He will not, my son, rather it is she
   Who may kill your uncle. Oh, my son,
   My son, I have seen a sight this dusk to make
   The eagle blind. I heard the cock crow
   As I woke up from sleep. That was sign
   Of omen enough but little did I know
   It was this great betrayal of our race.
DODE: You won't separate them then?
ORUKORERE: Only the gods and the dead may separate
   Them now, child. And what is your poor father
   To do should he hear the the liana has
   Entwined his tree of life? I said there was
   A serpent in the house but nobody as usual
   Will take me seriously. Yet the hiss of the creature
   Was up among the eaves, down under the
   Stool. Last night I cried it had coiled itself
   Into a pad to pillow my head but the house
   Was full of snoring sound and as usual
   Everybody snorted. Well, come on,
   Son, and I'll get you some snuff.

POETRY

■ Gabriel Okara (Nigeria)

Piano and Drums

When at break of day at a riverside
I hear jungle drums telegraphing
the mystic rhythm, urgent, raw
like bleeding flesh, speaking of
primal youth and the beginning,
I see the panther ready to pounce,
the leopard snarling about to leap
and the hunters crouch with spears poised;

And my blood ripples, turns torrent,
topples the years and at once I'm
in my mother's lap a suckling;
at once I'm walking simple
paths with no innovations,
rugged, fashioned with the naked
warmth of hurrying feet and groping hearts
in green leaves and wild flowers pulsing.

Then I hear a wailing piano
solo speaking of complex ways
in tear-furrowed concerto;
of faraway lands
and new horizons with
coaxing diminuendo, counterpoint,
crescendo. But lost in the labyrinth
of its complexities, it ends in the middle
of a phrase at a daggerpoint.

And I, lost in the morning mist
of an age at a riverside, keep
wandering in the mystic rhythm
of jungle drums and the concerto.

You Laughed and Laughed
and Laughed

In your ears my song
is motor car misfiring
stopping with a choking cough;
and you laughed and laughed and laughed.

In your eyes my ante-
natal walk was inhuman passing
your "omnivorous understanding"
and you laughed and laughed and laughed.

You laughed at my song
You laughed at my walk.

Then I danced my magic dance
to the rhythm of talking-
drums pleading, but you shut your
eyes and laughed and laughed and laughed.

And then I opened my mystic
inside wide like
the sky, instead you entered your
car and laughed and laughed and laughed.

You laughed at my dance
you laughed at my inside.

You laughed and laughed and laughed.
But your laughter was ice-block
laughter and it froze your inside froze
your voice froze your ears
froze your eyes and froze your tongue.

And now it's my turn to laugh;
but my laughter is not ice-block
ice-block laughter. For I
know not cars, know not ice-blocks.

My laughter is the fire
of the eye of the sky, the fire
of the earth, the fire of the air
the fire of the seas and the
rivers fishes animals trees
and it thawed your inside,
thawed your voice, thawed your
ears, thawed your eyes, and
thawed your tongue.

So a meek wonder held
your shadow and you whispered:
"Why so?"
And I answered:
"Because my fathers and I
are owned by the living
warmth of the earth
through our naked feet."

■   Abioseh Nicol

The Meaning of Africa

Africa, you were once just a name to me
But now you lie before me with sombre green challenge
To that loud faith for freedom (life more abundant)
Which we once professed shouting
Into the silent listening microphone
Or on an alien platform to a sea
Of white perplexed faces troubled
With secret Imperial guilt; shouting
Of you with a vision euphemistic
As you always appear
To your lonely sons on distant shores.

Then the cold sky and continent would disappear
In a grey mental mist.
And in its stead the hibiscus blooms in shameless scarlet
        and the bougainvillea in mauve passion
        entwines itself around strong branches;
        the palm trees stand like tall proud moral women
        shaking their plaited locks against the
        cool suggestive evening breeze;
        the short twilight passes;
        the white full moon turns its round gladness
        towards the swept open space
        between the trees; there will be
        dancing tonight; and in my brimming heart
        plenty of love and laughter.
        Oh, I got tired of the cold Northern sun
        Of white anxious ghost-like faces
        Of crouching over heatless fires
        In my lonely bedroom.
        The only thing I never tired of
        Was the persistent kindness
        Of you too few unafraid
        Of my grave dusky strangeness.

So I came back
Sailing down the Guinea Coast.
Loving the sophistication
Of your brave new cities:
Dakar, Accra, Cotonou,
Lagos, Bathurst and Bissau;
Liberia, Freetown, Libreville,
Freedom is really in the mind.

Go up-country, so they said,
To see the real Africa.
For whomsoever you may be,
That is where you come from.
Go for bush, inside the bush,
You will find your hidden heart.
Your mute ancestral spirit.
And so I went, dancing on my way.

Now you lie before me passive
With your unanswering green challenge.
Is this all you are?
This long uneven red road, this occasional succession
Of huddled heaps of four mud walls
And thatched, falling grass roofs
Sometimes ennobled by a thin layer
Of white plaster, and covered with thin
Slanting corrugated zinc.
These patient faces on weather-beaten bodies
Bowing under heavy market loads.
The pedalling cyclist wavers by
On the wrong side of the road,
As if uncertain of this new emancipation.
The squawking chickens, the pregnant she-goats
Lumber awkwardly with fear across the road.
Across the windscreen view of my four-cylinder kit car
An overladen lorry speeds madly towards me
Full of produce, passengers, with driver leaning
Out into the swirling dust to pilot his
Swinging obsessed vehicle along.
Beside him on the raised seat his first-class
Passenger, clutching and timid; but he drives on
At so, so many miles per hour, peering out with
Bloodshot eyes, unshaved face and dedicated look;
His motto painted on each side: *Sunshine Transport,*
We get you there quick, quick. The Lord is my Shepherd.

The red dust settles down on the green leaves.

I know you will not make me want, Lord,
Though I have reddened your green pastures
It is only because I have wanted so much
That I have always been found wanting.
From South and East, and from my West
The sandy desert holds the North.
We look across a vast Continent
And blindly call it ours.
You are not a Country, Africa,
You are a concept,
Fashioned in our minds, each to each,
To hide our separate fears,
To dream our separate dreams.
Only those within you who know
Their circumscribed Plot,
And till it well with steady plough
Can from that harvest then look up
To the vast blue inside
Of the enamelled bowl of sky
Which covers you and say
"This is my Africa" meaning
"I am content and happy.
I am fulfilled, within,
Without and roundabout.
I have gained the little longings
Of my hands, my loins, my heart,
And the soul following in my shadow."
I know now that is what you are, Africa:
Happiness, contentment, and fulfilment,
And a small bird singing on a mango tree.

ESSAYS

from The Myth of Non-Violence Versus the Right of Self-Defense

■ John Killens

The one thing most of the friends and all of the enemies of the American Negro have agreed upon is that black folk in the U.S.A. are by nature non-violent, and that they should forever remain as God and nature ordained them.

And so a new myth about the Negro is being perpetrated throughout the land. Along with the old myths of laziness and cunning, stupidity and irresponsibility, sexual prowess-and-obsession and all the others, tried and trusted, is being added the new myth of non-violence. In the middle of the twentieth century, when the disinherited all over the earth are on the move in affirmation of their manhood, the world is being sold a bill of goods, that America has evolved a new type of Homo sapiens, the Non-Violent Negro. In this era of automation and cybernetics, we should be highly suspicious of all such evolutionary claims. This new type, if he does indeed exist, might very well be the result of an immaculate conception, the absolute purity of which man and legend never imagined. He was most probably conceived by an impeccable computer, and has no relationship whatever to the order of the Primates.

As I have said elsewhere, one of the basic denials eternally experienced by the black man in America has been the suppression of his manhood. I believe one of the first songs I ever heard Harry Belafonte sing was one he wrote himself, "Recognition as a Man."

I was born on Virgin Street, at the edge of a white upper-middle-class neighborhood. On our way to school we black kids had to pass through this neighborhood, which consisted of great colonial mansions, two and three stories tall, and awesome, set in the midst of huge, majestic oak trees. Some of the grounds seemed more like college campuses. Each day on the way to *our* school and back we crossed paths with white children bound for *their* school.

One spring, which came quite early that year as it usually does in Georgia, an incident erupted at the crossroads. A white lad called a Negro boy that word, I mean the one white folk invented the better to castrate us black Americans.

Innocently enough he asked, "Hey, nigger, what you learn in school today?" Friendly-like.

"I learned your mother was a whore," the sassy black boy answered. We were all seven to eleven years old.

His black buddies laughed appreciatively, the white boy slapped his face, and that was how it started. Everybody got into the act. We fist-fought, we rock-battled, we laid on each other with sticks and baseball bats, and everything else that came to hand. Nobody won, and after a while it just sort of petered out. We black kids went home with cut lips and bloody noses, but we went home proud and happy, though we got our backsides whipped for tearing our school clothes. By the next day we had forgotten it.

But just before noon the school ground swarmed with police. They strode into classrooms without even a "Good morning" to the teachers and dragged out scared kids, many of them crying. They even dragged them out of the outhouses and snatched them as they tried to flee the school ground. They took some who had been in the "riot" and a number who'd never even heard about it. Somehow they missed yours truly. I felt left out and rejected, insulted even, especially since I was the bosom buddy of the kid who had started it.

Then frightened black mothers were brought down to the jailhouse to whip their children in front of the policemen to teach them not to fight white children. The alternative was the reformatory, though not a single white child was rounded up. Thus they drove the lesson home, the lesson that every black American must learn one way or another: that he has no inalienable right to defend himself from attack by Mister Charlie; that even though he can expect his own black person to be violated at any moment, he must remember better than anything else in this world that the white man's person is inviolable so far as he is concerned. The cruelest aspect of this story is how they used black mothers to drive this lesson home.

Notwithstanding all that has transpired in this country through the centuries, especially in the hospitable Southland down upon the Suwanee River, I am an advocate of non-violence as a tactic in the civil-rights struggle. It is practical and pragmatic; it has worked in many instances, most notably in Montgomery, Alabama. It has, moreover, placed the burden of the Black Man's Burden squarely before the nation and the entire world. It has rallied more Americans, black and white, to the cause of racial freedom than have been rallied since the days of Reconstruction. What then is the problem?

The problem is the tendency to take such a tactic and build it into a way of life, the growing tendency to invalidate all other tactics, as if the tactic of non-violence were the only road to freedom. But the truth of the matter is there are many highways and byways and depending on the circumstances every single one must be travelled.

The problem is the tendency to take such a tactic and build it into a way of life, the growing tendency to invalidate all other tactics, as if the tactic of non-violence were the only road to freedom. But the truth of the matter is there are many highways and byways and depending on the circumstances every single one must be travelled.

When non-violence evolves, as it has in this case, from a tactic into an ideology, and indeed into a way of life, it presupposes that one's opponent is a moral human being. But there is no evidence to support such a presumption. Every shred of evidence leads to the contrary.

Before leading the Negro people of Birmingham into a demonstration in that city, the Rev. Martin Luther King was reported to have said, "If blood is shed, let it be our blood!" But where is the morality that makes the white racist's blood more sacred than black children's? I cannot believe that Martin King meant these words, if indeed he ever uttered them. I can only believe that if he did he got carried away by the dramatics of the moment, the stresses and strains, the rhetoric. It has happened to other men.

The Rev. Martin King is one of the men whom I have met in this life for whom I have a very deep regard and hold in great esteem. We have been friends since 1957. Yet he loses me and many other Negroes when he calls upon us to love our abusers.

There is no dignity for me in allowing another man to spit on me with impunity. There is no dignity for him or me. There is only sickness, and it will beget an even greater sickness. It degrades me and brutalizes him. Moreover, it encourages him in his bestiality. I cannot love the murderers of the Birmingham children, the killers of Evers, Schwerner, Chaney, Goodman, and Moore. If we Negroes are so sick as to love those who practice genocide against us, we are in very bad shape indeed.

The racist murders in Birmingham and in Mississippi should have convinced us once and for all, if we still needed convincing, that we black folk must assert our right of self-defense. Who will defend the Negro if he refuses to defend himself? Certainly not the forces of law and order. They are, as often as not, the actual perpetrators of the violence. And the Federal government has indicated that it either cannot or will not defend the person of the black American.

The advocates of absolute non-violence have reckoned without the psychological needs of Black America. Let me state it plainly: there is in many Negroes a deep need to practice violence against their white tormentors. Frederick Douglass was aware of this a century ago when he called on black Americans to flock to the Union colors, even though they were unwanted, and would not receive equal pay. "There is something ennobling in the possession of arms," Douglass told his black brethren, "and we of all people in the world stand in need of their ennobling influence."

I saw the movie *Lydia Bailey* in downtown Manhattan and then once again in Harlem. The different reactions of the two audiences to one scene was highly indicative of this feeling. When William Marshall, tall, dark, and awesome, knocked a group of French soldiers into the harbor of Port-au-Prince, the Harlem audience burst into applause. It was entirely spontaneous. The applause was absent downtown.

Most Americans never understood why thousands of Negroes turned out in front of the Hotel Theresa on a cold rainy night to greet Castro. I was there and I saw the looks of anger and confusion on the faces of the white policemen as black voices screamed *"Viva Castro! Viva Fidel!"* It had nothing to do with Communism. I heard one black brother sum up the sentiment of most of that crowd: "Yeah, I dig Fidel the most. Any time a man kicks Whitey's ass, he's okay with me!"

Revenge? No, revenge is not the motivation. Racial hatred? No. Black chauvinism? Again, no, we are not Genêt's *Blacks,* waiting for the day we can assume the role the white man played for centuries. When white Americans witness black Americans affirming militantly their dignity and self-respect, they have nervous breakdowns and hurl charges of racial hatred. Just because I love myself, the black *me,* why do you think it means I have to hate *you,* the white American?

Actually, just the opposite is true. No man can love another unless he loves himself first. A man who does not love himself cannot love his wife or any other woman. When I despised myself, I didn't love you. I trembled in your presence. I was in awe of you. But awe and love are poles apart. At this juncture in our relationship, love is an irrelevance. Only equals can love with dignity. The slave cannot really love his master.

We black and white folk in America have to settle many things between us before the matter of love can even be discussed. What you want from me now is not love but worship, the fawning adoration of a dog for its master. But even a dog will bite his master if he kicks him. The point is, I don't, at this juncture, need to love you. Nor do I need to not love you. If you practice violence against me, I mean to give it back to you in kind. This is the frame of mind of most black men in this republic. Maybe this will help whip some sense into your head. Maybe there is no other way than this painful, violent road to mutual love and understanding. To encourage you in your sadistic ways is not love but abject masochism, and most black folk will no longer buy it. This is why millions of Negroes have not joined the non-violent movement.

Even most of you white liberals, who should know better, back away when I affirm my right to violence in the face of violence, which can only mean that you too deny my right of self-defense. Do you not realize how long you have been killing me? Are you not aware that atrocities against black people mount up into the hundreds of thousands? For any white man to raise the question of non-violence as a moral question with a black man is merely an indication of the depth of America's great insensitivity and degradation.

Let us speak plainly. The only reason black men have not long ago resorted to violence is that white men have the more powerful weapons and the greater numbers. We don't need to beg the question of morality; the burden of proof is on America. The ethics of the slave are always superior to those of his master.

The great fallacy of the whole non-violent ideology in America is that it is based on a set of circumstances and historical realities totally un-American. We black folk are captives in the land of our birth; but we are also in the land of our estrangement. The British in India were always foreigners, even though they ruled.

And lastly, the fact that we Americans are a nation of violence should give staunch advocates of non-violence pause for reflection. We have always been a nation of violence. Our, rather your, proud forefathers killed off an entire race whom they arrogantly called Indians, though they knew well enough they were not in India. And when John Fitzgerald Kennedy was assassinated little white children cheered in Dallas schools, and as at least one newspaper morbidly pointed out, in the comparatively short time of our existence as a nation we have assassinated more of our leaders than any nation in history. In classic Latin American coups, they at least put their rulers on airliners and give them a running start. We also dropped the most devastating bombs ever dropped in a military operation, and we dropped them on civilians—in Hiroshima and Nagasaki. Most colored people are convinced that those bombs were dropped there because the people we dropped them on were colored. There are a lot of colored people in this world, yet our ex-President apparently feels no deep remorse, a fact that possibly reflects the very low degree of sensitivity exhibited by most Americans toward a goodly share of the human race. It's mostly colored, you know.

I was an American soldier in the Philippines when the bombs were dropped. My outfit was preparing to form part of a task force that would have invaded the Japanese homeland. I remember the relief all of us felt when we heard the news and realized the war was nearly over, for many of us would have discolored the immaculate beaches of Japan with our patriotic blood. Yet after those first moments of rejoicing, there was a time of sober reflection.

I recall one of the men in my outfit saying in dead seriousness: "The thing they should do now is dump the rest of those fucking bombs in the middle of the Pacific, destroy the formula, then round up all the bloody scientists who know anything about that formula and blow their fucking brains out!"

Only the stars in the heavens could have kept track of the acts of violence perpetrated on the black American in his native land. If the Southern waters gave up their dead, if all that strange and bitter fruit hung from Southern trees again, what a sight for human eyes. What a retching of queasy stomachs. How long, America? How long, especially my friends of the liberal persuasion, how long, in the light of this violence against me, can you continue to speak to me of non-violence? The chasm widens steadily. Soon it will no longer be possible for me to hear you.

For your black brother *is* spoiling for a fight in affirmation of his manhood. This is the cold-blooded, Gospel truth. The more violence perpetrated against him, with pious impunity, the more he becomes convinced that this thing cannot resolve itself non-violently, that only blood will wash away the centuries of degradation. The burden is on White America to prove otherwise. But you had better get going in a hurry, for we are at the brink.

To All Black Women, From All Black Men

■ Eldridge Cleaver

Queen-Mother-Daughter of Africa
Sister of My Soul
Black Bride of My Passion
My Eternal Love

I greet you, my Queen, not in the obsequious whine of a cringing Slave to which you have become accustomed, neither do I greet you in the new voice, the unctuous supplications of the sleek Black Bourgeoise, nor the bullying bellow of the rude Free Slave—but in my own voice do I greet you, the voice of the Black Man. And although I greet you *anew,* my greeting is not *new,* but as old as the Sun, Moon, and Stars. And rather than mark a new beginning, my greeting signifies only my Return.

I have Returned from the dead. I speak to you now from the Here And Now. I was dead for four hundred years. For four hundred years you have been a woman alone, bereft of her man, a manless woman. For four hundred years I was neither your man nor my own man. The white man stood between us, over us, around us. The white man was your man and my man. Do not pass lightly over this truth, my Queen, for even though the fact of it has burned into the marrow of our bones and diluted our blood, we must bring it to the surface of the mind, into the realm of knowing, glue our gaze upon it and stare at it as at a coiled serpent in a baby's playpen or the fresh flowers on a mother's grave. It is to be pondered and realized in the heart, for the heel of the white man's boot is our point of departure, our point of Resolve and Return— the bloodstained pivot of our future. (But I would ask you to recall, that before we could come up from slavery, we had to be pulled down from our throne.)

Across the naked abyss of negated masculinity, of four hundred years minus my Balls, we face each other today, my Queen. I feel a deep, terrifying hurt, the pain of humiliation of the vanquished warrior. The shame of the fleet-footed sprinter who stumbles at the start of the race. I feel unjustified. I can't bear to look into your eyes. Don't you know (surely you must have noticed by now: four hundred years!) that for four hundred years I have been unable to look squarely into your eyes? I tremble inside each time you look at me. I can feel . . . in the ray of your eye, from a deep hiding place, a long-kept secret you harbor. That is the unadorned truth. Not that I would have felt justified, under the circumstances, in taking such liberties with you, but I want you to know that I feared to look into your eyes because I knew I would find reflected there a merciless Indictment of my impotence and a compelling challenge to redeem my conquered manhood.

My Queen, it is hard for me to tell you what is in my heart for you today—what is in the heart of all my black brothers for you and all your black sisters—and I fear I will fail unless you reach out to me, tune in on me with the antenna of your love, the sacred love in ultimate degree which you were unable to give me because I, being dead, was unworthy to receive it; that perfect, radical love of black on which our Fathers thrived. Let me drink from the river of your love at its sources, let the lines of force of your love seize my soul by its core and heal the wound of my Castration, let my convex exile end its haunted Odyssey in your concave essence which receives that it may give. Flower of Africa, it is only through the liberating power of your *re*-love that my manhood can be redeemed. For it is in your eyes, before you, that my need is to be justified, Only, only, only you and only you can condemn or set me free.

Be convinced, Sable Sister, that the past is no forbidden vista upon which we dare not look, out of a phantom fear of being, as the wife of Lot, turned into pillars of salt. Rather the past is an omniscient mirror: we gaze and see reflected there ourselves and each other—what we used to be, what we are today, how we got this way, and what we are becoming. To decline to look into the Mirror of Then, my heart, is to refuse to view the face of Now.

> *I have died the ninth death of the cat, have seen Satan face to face and turned my back on God, have dined in the Swine's Trough, and descended to the uttermost echelon of the Pit, have entered the Den and seized my Balls from the teeth of a roaring lion!*

Black Beauty, in impotent silence I listened, as if to a symphony of sorrows, to your screams for help, anguished pleas of terror that echo still throughout the Universe and through the mind, a million scattered screams across the painful years that merged into a single sound of pain to haunt and bleed the soul, a white-hot sound to char the brain and blow the fuse of thought, a sound of fangs and teeth sharp to eat the heart, a sound of moving fire, a sound of frozen heat, a sound of licking flames, a fiery-fiery sound, a sound of fire to burn the steel out of my Balls, a sound of Blue fire, a Bluesy sound, the sound of dying, the sound of my woman in pain, *the sound of my woman's pain,* THE SOUND OF MY WOMAN CALLING ME, ME, I HEARD HER CALL FOR HELP, I HEARD THAT MOURNFUL SOUND BUT HUNG MY HEAD AND FAILED TO HEED IT, I HEARD MY WOMAN'S CRY, I HEARD MY WOMAN'S SCREAM, I HEARD MY WOMAN BEG THE BEAST FOR MERCY, I HEARD HER BEG FOR ME, I HEARD MY WOMAN BEG THE BEAST FOR MERCY FOR ME, I HEARD MY WOMAN DIE, I HEARD THE SOUND OF HER DEATH, A SNAPPING SOUND, A BREAKING SOUND, A SOUND THAT SOUNDED FINAL, THE LAST SOUND, THE ULTIMATE SOUND, THE SOUND OF DEATH, ME, I HEARD, I HEAR IT EVERY DAY, I HEAR HER NOW . . . I HEAR YOU NOW . . . I HEAR YOU. . . . I heard you then . . . your scream came like a searing bolt of lightning that blazed a white streak down my black back. In a cowardly stupor, with a palpitating heart and quivering knees, I watched the Slaver's lash of death slash through the opposing air and bite with teeth of fire into your delicate flesh, the black and tender flesh of African Motherhood, forcing the startled Life untimely from your torn and outraged womb, the sacred womb that cradled primal man, the womb that incubated Ethiopia and populated Nubia and gave forth Pharaohs unto Egypt, the womb that painted the Congo black and mothered Zulu, the womb of Mero, the womb of the Nile, of the Niger, the womb of Songhay, of Mali, of Ghana, the womb that felt the might of Chaka before he saw the Sun, the Holy Womb, the womb that knew the future form of Jomo Kenyatta, the womb of Mau Mau, the womb of the blacks, the womb that nurtured Toussaint L'Ouverture, that warmed Nat Turner, and Gabriel Prosser, and Denmark Vesey, the black womb that surrendered up in tears that nameless and endless chain of Africa's Cream, the Black Cream of the Earth, that nameless and endless black chain that sank in heavy groans into oblivion in the great abyss, the womb that received and nourished and held firm the seed and gave back Sojourner Truth, and Sister Tubman, and Rosa Parks, and Bird, and Richard Wright, and your other works of art who wore and wear such names as Marcus Garvey and DuBois and Kwame Nkrumah and Paul Robeson and Malcolm X and Robert Williams, and the one you bore in pain and called Elijah Muhammad, but most of all that nameless one they tore out of your womb in a flood of murdered blood that splashed upon and seeped into the mud. And Patrice Lumumba, and Emmett Till, and Mack Parker.

O, My Soul! I became a sniveling craven, a funky punk, a vile, groveling bootlicker, with my will to oppose petrified by a cosmic fear of the Slavemaster. Instead of inciting the Slaves to rebellion with eloquent oratory, I soothed their hurt and eloquently sang the Blues! Instead of hurling my life with contempt into the face of my Tormentor, *I shed your precious blood!* When Nat Turner sought to free me from my Fear, my Fear delivered him up unto the Butcher—a martyred monument to my Emasculation. My spirit was unwilling and my flesh was weak. Ah, eternal ignominy!

I, the Black Eunuch, divested of my Balls, walked the earth with my mind locked in Cold Storage. I would kill a black man or woman quicker than I'd smash a fly, while for the white man I would pick a thousand pounds of cotton a day. What profit is there in the blind, frenzied efforts of the (Guilty!) Black Eunuchs (Justifiers!) who hide their wounds and scorn the truth to mitigate their culpability through the pallid sophistry of postulating a Universal Democracy of Cowards, pointing out that in history no one can hide, that if not at one time then surely at another the iron heel of the Conqueror has ground into the mud the Balls of Everyman? Memories of yesterday will not assuage the torrents of blood that flow today from my crotch. Yes, History could pass for a scarlet text, its jot and tittle graven red in human blood. More armies than shown in the books have planted flags on foreign soil leaving Castration in their wake. But no Slave should die a natural death. There is a point where Caution ends and Cowardice begins. Give me a bullet through the brain from the gun of the beleaguered oppressor on the night of seige. Why is there dancing and singing in the Slave Quarters? A Slave who dies of natural causes cannot balance two dead flies in the Scales of Eternity. Such a one deserves rather to be pitied than mourned.

Black woman, without asking how, just say that we survived our forced march and travail through the Valley of Slavery, Suffering, and Death— there, that Valley there beneath us hidden by that drifting mist. Ah, what sights and sounds and pain lie beneath that mist. And we had thought that our hard climb out of that cruel valley led to some cool, green and peaceful, sunlit place—but it's all jungle here, a wild and savage wilderness that's overrun with ruins.

But put on your crown, my Queen, and we will build a New City on these ruins.

Role of the Negro Intellectual— Survey of the Dialogue Deferred

■   Harold Cruse

The peculiarities of the American social structure, and the position of the intellectual class within it, make the functional role of the Negro intellectual a special one. The Negro intellectual must deal intimately with the white power structure and cultural apparatus, and the inner realities of the black world at one and the same time. But in order to function successfully in this role, he has to be acutely aware of the nature of the American social dynamic and how it monitors the ingredients of class stratifications in American society. The American people, aside from the handful of power wielders in the upper levels, have very little social control over the economic, class, and political forces of the American capitalistic dynamic. They are, in fact, manipulated by them. Therefore the Negro intellectual must learn how one might control and channel such forces.

Since the dynamics of American society create only one integrated class stratum, "the social world or worlds of 'the intellectual' and the creative and performing artist, whether literary, musical, theatrical, or visual,"[1] the Negro intellectual has the option of gravitating toward this world, under the persuasions of the American social dynamic, and resting there on his laurels. However, although this world exists rather independently of the main ethnic worlds, it manages to reflect the social aspirations of the WASP, Catholic and Jewish groups above all others. Among these three there is intense competition for recognition and group status, which, for political and propaganda reasons, is called fighting discriminatory practices. As long as the WASPS rule the roost, charges of discrimination will never cease until Catholics or Jews achieve more power and privileges than any "minority" could ever hope for in Rome or Israel.

[1] Milton M. Gordon, op. cit., p. 58.

The Negro intellectual must not be allowed to forget that the integrated intellectual world is not representative of ethnic group aspirations with regard to the world of American Negro or Indian. The Indian world of the reservation exemplifies the fate awaiting the American Negro, who is left stranded and impoverished in the ghettoes, beyond the fringe of absorption. He will be pushed there through the compulsions of the American capitalistic dynamic if, as the most populous ethnic "out" group, the American Negro fails to galvanize his potential as a countervailing force. But the Negro group cannot act out this role by assuming the stance of separatism. The program of Afro-American Nationalism must activate a dynamism on all social fronts under the guidance and direction of the Negro intelligentsia. This already implies that Afro-American Nationalism be broken down into three parts: political nationalism; economic nationalism; and cultural nationalism; in other words, organizational specialization. Therefore the functional role of the Negro intellectual demands that he *cannot* be absolutely separated from either the black or white world.

Today, Afro-American Nationalism is not Garveyism; it poses an American problem growing out of a specific American historical condition—involving three racial stocks—the white, the black and the red. The problem will be solved under specifically American conditions or it will never be solved, for Afro-American Nationalism is basically a black reflection of the unsolved American nationality question. American culture is sick not just because it is discriminatory, but because it reflects a psychological malaise that grows out of the American identity problem. As long as the Negro intellectual is beset with his own cultural identity problem, his attacks on American culture, as discriminatory, become hollow: *Two cultural negatives cannot possibly add up to a cultural positive in society at large.* Every single American political, social and cultural trend has contributed its bit of illusion to the total Americanization fantasy. Insofar as the Negro intellectual has accommodated this grand myth, his acquiescence must be examined critically before one can dispel the myth. Then, one is on clear ground, the better to deal with the *realities* of America.

In the effort to clear this ground it has been necessary to review a whole gamut of thinking on various topics: ethnic community; multigroup America; the political leftwing; nationalism vs. integrationism; Negro creative artists as thinkers and spokesmen; aesthetics; Negroes and the theater; individual *vs.* group roles in society; white liberalism and Negro intellectuals; culture and integrationism; culture and nationalism; literary, dramatic and social criticism; the Negro writer as revolutionary, and so on.

Under the impetus of Negro activism, agitation has been reflected in different areas of the cultural front. The Rockefeller Report on the Performing Arts, and the White House conferences on cultural matters, are two examples. In New York, jazz magazines and critics' panel discussions are taking up such topics as "Jazz and Revolutionary Nationalism." Yet the cultural front and its relation to the Negro movement, while intuitively sensed in many critical quarters, is neither broadly understood nor admitted in any definitive way. It is the vaguest of all fronts, yet in many ways the most crucial. It is so little understood, even by Negro creative intellectuals, that its implications are absent in most of the dialogues Negroes carry on with white liberals and the intellectual establishment.

The tentative acceptance the Negro intellectual finds in the predominantly white intellectual world, allows him the illusion that integration is real—a functional reality for himself, and a possibility for *all* Negroes. Even if a Negro intellectual does not wholly believe this, he must give lip service to the aims of racial integration, if only to rationalize his own status in society.

This integrated status is not threatened or challenged; it is even championed, just so long as the black world is on the move in the struggle for integration. But when voices from the black world begin to raise doubts about the meaning, the aims, and the real possibilities of integration, the Negro intellectual is forced to question his own hard-won status. At the same time, those black Doubting Thomases begin to question the status of the Negro intellectual—"What is he doing out there?" "What is *his* function in relation to *us*?"

Such questions as these arise only because the social role of the Negro intellectual has never really been defined at all. For the most part, the Negro intellectual has been a rather free agent in the black and white scheme of things. Inasmuch as the support, patronage and prestige of the Negro intellectual come from the white world and its cultural apparatus, his creative and cultural achievements have been seen by the black world as *Ebony* magazine and *Jet* see them. That is to say, such Negroes have achieved something, they have "made it." They have scored in the white world and are now recognized. It is not necessary to consider *how* they managed to score, the important thing is that they *did*. In this way, the Negro creative intellectual has never really been held accountable to the black world for his social role. If he scores, well and good. If he doesn't, that's unfortunate, but it will pass unnoticed and no one will care. This tacit agreement between the Negro intellectual and the black world has prevailed because it is understood that the black world cannot and does not, support the Negro creative intellectual. The black bourgeoisie does not publish books, does not own and operate theaters or music halls. It plays no role to speak of in Negro music, and is remote from the living realities of the jazz musician who plays out his nights in the effete and soulless commercial jungles of American white middleclass café culture.

The special function of the Negro intellectual is a cultural one. He should take to the rostrum and assail the stultifying blight of the commercially depraved white middle-class who has poisoned the structural roots of the American ethos and transformed the American people into a nation of intellectual dolts. He should explain the economic and institutional causes of this American cultural depravity. He should tell black America how and why Negroes are trapped in this cultural degeneracy, and how it has dehumanized their essential identity, squeezed the life-blood of their inherited cultural ingredients out of them, and then relegated them to the cultural slums. They should tell this brainwashed white America, this "nation of sheep," this overfed, overdeveloped, overprivileged (but culturally pauperized) federation of unassimilated European remnants that their days of grace are numbered. This motley, supercilious collection of refugees from "Fatherland" poverty worships daily, and only, at the altar of white Anglo-Saxon Protestant superiority. Notwithstanding their alleged vows to contribute to the fashioning of an American nation worthy of the high esteem of the rest of the world, so far they have reneged. The job has hardly been begun. America is an unfinished nation—the product of a badly-bungled process of inter-group cultural fusion. America is a nation that lies to itself about who and what it is. It is a nation of minorities ruled by a minority of one—it thinks and acts as if it were a nation of white Anglo-Saxon Protestants. This white Anglo-Saxon ideal, this lofty dream of a minority at the summit of its economic and political power and the height of its historical self-delusions, has led this nation to the brink of self-destruction. And on its way, it has effectively dissuaded, crippled and smothered the cultivation of a democratic cultural pluralism in America.

The cultural mainstream of the nation is an empty street, full of bright lights that try to glamorize the cultural wreckage and flotsam of our times. Over this deranged, tormented cultural wasteland reigns a social stratum—a white cultural elite of America, the soured cream of our creative and aesthetic intelligentsia, that dominates nevertheless to the roar of prestigious acclaim. This elite has become intellectually bloated, dull, unoriginal, critically tongue-tied, smug (or downright scared), time-serving and societally dishonest. It came into existence during the 1920's, and by constantly renewing its ranks, has established and maintained its position as the supreme arbiter of American cultural styles. It has dominated the cultural arts, in all of their native trends, in every conceivable field. Even during its years of highest achievements, this elite was always, by outside standards, very second-rate and it has been steadily declining in creative virtuosity over the decades. And during all these years of gradual descent from its own Parnassus, it worshipped at the altar of the white Anglo-Saxon ideal. Thereby, it collaborated spiritually in spreading the pall of debased and unprocreative white middle-class cultural values that shroud America today.

In other words, the prognoses and prophecies about American cultural trends, written by Randolph Bourne in his critical essays of 1920, have been borne out in the forty-seven years since. Bourne warned against the stultifying and retarding effects that the idealization of the Anglo-Saxon tradition would have on the reality of American pluralism if that tradition became the main source of the "cultural makers of opinion." He argued truthfully and convincingly about the failures of the American melting-pot ideology and the presence in America of "diverse nationalistic feelings," of "vigorous nationalistic and cultural movements." He called English-American conservatism "our chief obstacle to social advance," and argued for the cultivation of a kind of culturally "federated ideal" as the main social hope of America.[2] But this cultural ideal has never taken form or even been approached in this country, making it necessary for sociologists such as Milton Gordon to survey the problem again with the advent of the Negro integration movement.

For American society, the most crucial requirement at this point is a complete democratization of the national cultural ethos. This requires a thorough, democratic overhauling of the social functions of the entire American cultural apparatus. First of all: For whom, and in whose interest, does the cultural apparatus exist in America? Does it exist for the social needs, the social edification, the spiritual uplift, the cultural development, solvency and morale of all the diverse minority groups in America? Or does it exist solely, and disproportionately, for the social supremacy, the group narcissism, and the idealization of the white Anglo-Saxon Protestant minority? Up to now, the latter has been true, just as it was in 1920 when Bourne, himself an Anglo-Saxon, decried the supremacy of the "Anglo-Saxon tradition which [they] unquestioningly label 'American.' "[3] However, the total schematic value of this Anglo-Saxon tradition is deeply entwined with the roots of the political, economic, and societal foundations of the American national structure; it, in turn, inspires ideologies of racial and ethnic exclusion, discrimination and exploitation. On this social level the Negro integration movement conducts its legal and activist struggles. Hence, through this strategy of struggle, the Negro movement challenges Anglo-Saxon Protestant social supremacy in economics, politics and social life, but only indirectly and in the name of true democratic Americanism between the races—an unconscious, ignorant tactical error.

American group reality demands a struggle for democracy among ethnic groups, rather than between two races. What is called a racial struggle over civil rights is, in reality, the contention in America among several different ethnic groups, of which Anglo-Saxon Protestants and American Negroes are only two. However, among all the groups in contention these two are the most crucial: The fate of all the others depends on how they resolve the undemocratic differences in American society. Moreover, since no other ethnic minority in America is so thoroughly committed to racial democratization, the Negro group's civil rights engagement is, plainly, the most active force for social change. However, it is evident that if the Negro leadership is hampered by deficient conceptualizing of American group reality, then the Negro movement will defeat itself in the long run. It will defeat itself by encouraging other unassimilated ethnic groups to turn against the Negro minority, in a pro-Anglo-Saxon Protestant "racial" coalition. It will defeat itself by utilizing mechanical, narrow-minded agitational tactics that will discourage other unassimilated ethnic groups from assuming a pro-Negro attitude in the

[2] See Randolph Bourne's *History of a Literary Radical and Other Essays* (New York: B.W. Huebsch, 1920); especially the essay, "Trans-National America," pp. 266–299.
[3] Ibid., p. 266.

furtherance of their own group cultural rights. The Congress of Racial Equality (CORE) has been most guilty of such tactics in the North, for example, where it indiscriminately carries demonstrations into ethnic neighborhoods without giving due consideration to local neighborhood sentiments. This approach, however, stems out of the dominant NAACP ideology which does not sanction the reality of neighborhood group sentiments. This is yet another reason why the tactics of civil righters cannot be the same in the North as in the South. For the South is, specifically, the main bastion of the efficacy of the dominant Anglo-Saxon ideal. There, its dominance, *vis-à-vis* the Negro, is most naked and persuasive. All of these factors, and more, demand that the Negro movement adjust its strategy to fit reality, which means deepening its understanding and broadening its scope at the same time. But such an eventuality requires much educational groundwork, for here, where the role of the Negro creative intellectual is most crucial, it is most conspicuous by its functional absence.

Around 1960, a significant debate sprang up among the white intellectuals of the non-Communist Left, concerning the current relevancy of practically every dogma the Communist-oriented Left had preached since the 1930's. This debate was high-level and thoroughgoing, and nothing comparable to it has yet taken place within Negro intellectual circles. The leading inspiration of this debate was the late C. Wright Mills, professor of sociology at Columbia University, who initiated a critical review of the entire Marxist revolutionary tradition of this century, especially in Europe and the United States. The grassroots impetus behind this rather spontaneous review of the Marxist tradition was, of course, the upsurge of student sit-ins in the new Negro movement, but only a few of the critics said so. The curious thing about this debate was that not a single Negro sociologist, historian, writer, spokesman, leader (ex-Communist, pro-Communist or anti-Communist), took part in it. This, despite the fact that the only movement active at that moment on the American scene with any pretensions of radical potential, was the Negro movement. Nothing could point up more graphically the fact that the Negro intellectual does not rate as a serious thinker in the intellectual establishment. As things turned out, this debate brought out two main antagonists among the whites—Mills and Professor Daniel Bell, also of Columbia.

As theoretical rationalizer for the decline and irrelevancy of the radical Left, Daniel Bell laid out his thinking in a lengthy tome entitled *The End of Ideology—Or the Exhaustion of Political Ideas in the Fifties*. He summed up his critique in his last chapter with the following observations:

> Today, [these] ideologies are exhausted. The events behind this important sociological change are complex and varied . . . such social changes as the modification of capitalism, the rise of the Welfare States [are causes]. This is not to say that such ideologies as communism in France and Italy do not have a political weight, or a driving momentum from other sources. But out of all this history one simple fact emerges for the radical intelligentsia, the old ideologies have lost their "truth" and their power to persuade.

Few serious minds believe any longer that one can set down "blueprints" and through "social engineering" bring about a new utopia of social harmony. . . . In the Western world, therefore, there is today a rough consensus among intellectuals on political issues: the acceptance of a Welfare State, the desirability of decentralized power; a system of mixed economy and of political pluralism. In that sense, too, the ideological age has ended.[4]

Given the premises—historical, sociological, and theoretical—on which he bases his conclusions, Bell is right. However, Bell's premises are invalidated because he does not base them on the complete objective picture. His book, including text and notes, amounts to 397 pages: There is not a single page devoted to any phase of the Negro movement, past or present. Negroes are mentioned four times, in very brief references to Negro voting habits, the class nature of race prejudice, Negro society, and crime waves. It seems almost incredible that in the face of a social movement of such dimensions that some people even call it a revolution, a sociologist could write such a book and not even mention the existence of this movement or its impact. What does one conclude from this? Evidently, Bell does not consider Negroes as an integral sociological quantity within Western society.

If at this stressful moment in American history, Professor Bell could write off the 1950's as the decade of "the end of ideology," the question naturally follows: Whose ideology? Bell was talking about his own, a radical ideology that came out of the Western tradition. Since for Bell there is not the slightest possibility that anything could replace this "exhausted" ideology, the black social movement is not even worth mentioning inasmuch as the welfare state will ultimately subdue it. Or could it be that Bell was frightened and nonplussed by the implications of a movement whose ends *his* ideology cannot accommodate?

However, C. Wright Mills took serious issue with Daniel Bell and others of the "end-of-ideology" school of thought, which Mills discovered through his travels to exist not only in Columbia University, U.S.A., but in the NATO nations (as well as in the Soviet Union, which is not officially a NATO nation). Mills wrote:

> I neither want nor need to overstress the parallel, yet in a recent series of interviews in the Soviet Union concerning socialist realism [*N.B.*] I was very much struck by it. In Uzbekistan and Georgia as well as in Russia, I kept writing notes to myself, at the end of recorded interviews: "This man talks in a style just like Arthur Schlesinger, Jr." "Surely this fellow's the counterpart of Daniel Bell, except not so—what shall I say?—so gossipy." . . . The would-be enders of ideology, I kept thinking, "Are they not the self-coordinated, or better the fashion-coordinated, socialist realists of the NATO world?" And: "Check this carefully with the files of *Encounter* and *The Reporter*," I have now done so; it's the same kind of . . . thing.

[4] Bell, *The End of Ideology* . . . (Free Press of Glencoe, Illinois, 1960), p. 373. Used by permission of The Macmillan Company and Princeton University Press (for Dr. Bell's quote from *Socialism and American Life*, D. D. Egbert and S. Persons, eds., Princeton University Press, 1952).

Mills further observes:

> The end-of-ideology is very largely a mechanical reaction—not a creative response—to the ideology of Stalinism. As such it takes from its opponent something of its inner quality. What does it all mean? That these people have become aware of the uselessness of the liberal rhetoric.

Hence:

> The end-of-ideology is on the way out because it stands for the refusal to work out an explicit political philosophy.[5]

In this article, from which the above are salient quotations, Mills was addressing what was then called "the New Left." He continued:

> But enough. Where do *we* stand on . . . these . . . aspects of political philosophy? . . . As for the articulation of ideals: there I think your magazines [*New Left Review,* etc.] have done their best work so far. That is *your* meaning—is it not?—*of the emphasis on cultural affairs. As for ideological analysis, and the rhetoric with which to carry it out: I don't think any of us are nearly good enough but that will come with further advance on the two fronts where we are weakest: theories of society, history, human nature; and the major problem—ideas about the historical agencies of structural change* [italics added].

Here Mills effectively destroys the conceptual premises of Daniel Bell's end-of-ideology school, but with the social awareness that such a challenge presents formidable problems of new social methods. In pursuit of the creation and formulation of such methods, Mills emphasizes that to be Left (wherever Left stands, ideologically, to the "left" of Right) means: "To connect up cultural with political criticism, and both with demands and programmes."

For me, the emergence of C. Wright Mills, with his critique of the policies, dogmas and vanities of the old Marxist leftwing, was a landmark in American social theory. That Mills was a white man did not at all negate my own personal thesis that the American Negro was destined to become the vanguard social force in the revolutionizing of American society. On the contrary, the views of Mills served to corroborate a long-range strategic issue in the Negro movement, one that becomes more and more urgent as time passes. This issue involves the necessity of the Negro movement having white allies, as well as the aims, ideology and quality of such allies. It is to be noted, again, that when Mills ruled out the white laboring classes as having no radical potential, he theoretically eliminated the sole class basis on which Marxist Communism of all brands could maintain any effective links with the Negro movement.

---

[5] "The New Left," *Power, Politics and People: The Collected Essays of C. Wright Mills,* edited by Irving L. Horowitz (New York: Ballantine Books, 1963), pp. 247–259. (Published simultaneously in hardcovers by Oxford University Press, New York. Used by permission of Oxford University Press.)

This was the chief reason why the Marxist theorists could not agree with Mills' findings. But Mills was trying to deal with American social peculiarities as they really are, and although they cannot admit this to themselves, the Marxists' historical model is European society.

These American peculiarities pose acute problems for the Negro movement, particularly for the Afro-American Nationalists, whose strong anti-white stance tends to rule out any functional alliance with whites. Although this aversion to any white alliance is perfectly understandable, in view of the long-standing disabilities and disorientation imposed on Negroes by the institution of political interracialism, the Afro-American Nationalists cannot, in the long run, continue to oppose white alliances. The question will be—the specific type and quality of the alliances. The quality will depend on the quality of the goals, but it is the Negro movement itself that must select these goals. Without specified goals plotted on the political, economic, and cultural fronts, the nationalist wing will wither away in isolation to be swamped by the aggressive American capitalistic dynamic. But these goals must be stated unequivocally by the nationalist wing and controlled by it on its own behalf, inasmuch as no other faction—black or white—can do it for them. This is the imperative of the Negro social dynamic.

The C. Wright Mills thesis contained the seeds of a Negro-White alliance of a new type, to be anchored first around the structural question of the American cultural apparatus. But not a single one of the leading Negro intellectual spokesmen saw this implication. In view of the deeply-rooted American tradition of Anglo-Saxon anti-theoretical, anti-cultural, anti-aesthetic pragmatism and instrumentalism, C. Wright Mills was decidedly revolutionary, although isolated by the very conservative tradition that produced him. (He himself was Anglo-Saxon and a Southerner at that.) The problem here is that the nature of the American ethnic group composition—the white, black and red racial heritage—demands that each group produce for itself a *native* radical-intellectual trend, which trends should complement one another, so to speak. At least, the black and white groups must do this. Since the whites are divided into ethnic and religious subdivisions, with the Anglo-Saxons as the dominant and representative group, the Anglo-Saxon group must produce its representative radical-intellectual trend; or else social progress in America will be ethnically retarded, if not checkmated.

But the Anglo-Saxons and their Protestant ethic have failed in their creative and intellectual responsibilities to the internal American commonweal. Interested purely in materialistic pursuits—exploiting resources, the politics of profit and loss, ruling the world, waging war, and protecting a rather threadbare cultural heritage—the Anglo-Saxons have retrogressed in the cultural fields and the humanities. Into this intellectual vacuum have stepped the Jews, to dominate scholarship, history, social research, etc.[10] But Negro intellectuals function oblivious to the impact of these developments while protesting loudly about civil rights

[10] See "Zionist Influence on American Higher Education," *Issues*, Autumn, 1965, pp. 1–9

and freedom. In the face of new trends, new voices, new issues, the content of Negro intellectual opinion never varies, never changes. Negro intellectuals are moved by the world, but they hardly move *with* the world.

If the Negro intellectuals of the 1920's missed out on the debate between V. F. Calverton and the Communist Left on cultural compulsives, their spiritual progeny of the 1950's were also deaf to the debate between Mills, Bell and various leftwing diehards, on cultural radicalism. These two debates, although thirty years apart, are of course related historically, if only one would see it. And in the same way that Langston Hughes and company stood by during the Negro renaissance while the white Communist theoreticians beat down Calverton, the Negro creative intellectuals of the 1950's committed a breach of critical awareness.

No sooner had C. Wright Mills begun to emerge as a creative and original radical spokesman for the New Left, than the two main theoretical spokesmen of the official Marxist movement—Herbert Aptheker of the Communist Party and William F. Warde of the Socialist Workers' Party —took to the rostrum. Aptheker criticized Mills's findings in *The World of C. Wright Mills*[11] and Warde followed suit in an article entitled "A Marxist Analysis of C. Wright Mills."[12]

Herbert Aptheker, the Marxist-Communist historian, has played a very influential and specific role in the fashioning of the Communist Party's Negro intellectual and creative elite. The entire postwar generation of Communists of the 1940's and 1950's was educated on Negro history chiefly through his writings. He became *the* authority on what it meant to be Negro in America, both historically and contemporaneously. This situation raised some very serious and delicate questions concerning the problems of racial and ethnic identity and the historical ingredients that go into the formation of the Black American personality.

For over twenty-five years Aptheker thought he had all the answers about Negroes past and present, and turned out nine pamphlets and books on Negro history. But in 1965, he said to an Associated Press correspondent, concerning the Communist Party: "We are less naïve than in the past. We tended to minimize the difficulties of building socialism, of the problems of power and the approach to religion and nationalism . . . we have had to learn the perils of dogma, of not growing."[13]

Nationalism! How ironic . . . for here is a historian who simply refused to accept history at its face value, who rewrote it to suit his own preconceptions. This violates every methodological tenet of the historian —Marxist or otherwise. Thus, the scholar-on-high minimized what everyone among the rank and file knew. Yet he rushed to the fore to answer C. Wright Mills, on everything from politics, culture, economics to, of course, "The Negro."

[11] *Aptheker* (New York: Marzani and Munsell, 1960).
[12] Warde, *International Socialist Review*, Summer, 1962, pp. 67–75, 95.
[13] From a Saul Pett by-line, Associated Press correspondent, *Progress-Index*, Petersburg, Virginia, December 24, 1965, p. 10.

Although hardly any of the Negroes in the creative fields were aware that Mills had said anything of any import, Aptheker was sufficiently impressed to answer Mills by writing one of his longest pamphlets. *The World of C. Wright Mills* reveals Aptheker's appalling ignorance of the cultural facts of life in America, the very area in which Mills excels. Aptheker could not deal with Mills' ideas about the intellectuals and the cultural apparatus. Instead, he accused Mills of turning to what he, Aptheker, calls "unreal and utopian political devices—such as appeals confined to the intelligentsia." Trotskyist William F. Warde agreed with Aptheker that Mills was wrong on the intelligentsia: "He founds his hopes for peace, freedom and progress, not on the victory of the working masses over the plutocracy, but rather on the benign influences to be exerted by scholars, ministers, scientists and writers, the peripheral and not the central forces of our society."[14]

Both Aptheker and Warde were also critical of Mills' attitude toward the Negro struggle. Says Aptheker: "His blindspot concerning the whole matter of the Negro, which impairs his analysis generally, is especially glaring." Says Warde: "Mills seemed to look upon the Negro movement as something essentially separate from the general labor struggle."[15]

Neither Warde nor Aptheker understand that, in criticizing Mills's preoccupation with the intellectuals, they are ignoring the one great weakness of the Negro movement. The Negro movement is at an impasse precisely because it lacks a real functional corps of intellectuals able to confront and deal perceptively with American realities on a level that social conditions demand. But here the Marxists are simply bunching Negro intellectuals with white intellectuals, in general and as a class.

C. Wright Mills was well on the road to solving the dilemma for them —but from the white side of the intellectual class divide. He pretended not to see Negro intellectuals (which was not difficult since they were saying and doing little beside repeating civil rights slogans after the civil rights politicians). But they represented the missing elements in the class role that C. Wright Mills tried to project for the intellectuals in his aim "to connect up cultural with political criticism, and both with demands and programmes."

He was not sure how he would achieve this and admitted as much. But historically, the tasks of the intellectuals in America today resemble those of the young Marx's generation in Europe of the 1840's that had to fashion a new political philosophy for the European scene of their time. C. Wright Mills was simply saying that the young intellectuals of America have to do the same thing for their own country, and that *we* must help them do it. But the Marxists of today cannot admit that they are of nineteenth-century vintage and therefore, "old hat."

The arguments of C. Wright Mills on the cultural apparatus were incomplete and irresolute because the Negro creative intellectuals were not involved in the debate. They did not participate because they were not prepared to debate cultural issues on this level. It is a reflection of the

14 Warde, *International Socialist Review, op. cit.,* p. 73.
15 *Ibid.,* p. 74.

general intellectual backwardness of Negro thought that the Negro movement has failed, so far, to deal with structural problems pertaining to American society.

Even at this advanced stage in Negro history, the Negro intellectual is a retarded child whose thinking processes are still geared to piddling intellectual civil writism and racial integrationism. This is all he knows. In the meantime, he plays second and third fiddle to white intellectuals in all the establishments—Left, Center, and Right. The white intellectuals in these establishments do not recognize the Negro intellectual as a man who can speak both for himself and for the best interests of the nation, but only as someone who must be spoken for and on behalf of. But the present impasse of the Negro movement demands that the black and white dialogue must transcend this level of mere evasive debate if the Negro movement is to avoid defeat and racial stalemate in the United States. For the Negro creative intellectual, the watchword is this: There can be no real black revolution in the United States without cultural revolution as a corollary to the scheme of "agencies for social change." If, as Gilbert Seldes said, "the cultural institutions of a country belong to its inhabitants," the only inhabitants who will return those institutions to the people are those with the greatest conviction that this has to be done for the good of the nation and, therefore, have the most potential for carrying it out.

The Black Manifesto*

■ James Forman

To the White Christian Churches and the Synagogues in the United States of America and to All Other Racist Institutions:

Introduction: Total Control as the Only Solution
to the Economic Problems of Black People

Brothers and Sisters:

We have come from all over the country burning with anger and despair not only with the miserable economic plight of our people but fully aware that the racism on which the Western World was built dominates our lives. There can be no separation of the problems of racism from the problems of our economic, political, and cultural degradation. To any black man, this is clear.

* This document was presented by James Forman to the National Black Economic Development Conference in Detroit, Michigan, and adopted on April 26, 1969.

But there are still some of our people who are clinging to the rhetoric of the Negro, and we must separate ourselves from these Negroes who go around the country promoting all types of schemes for black capitalism.

Ironically, some of the most militant Black Nationalists, as they call themselves, have been the first to jump on the bandwagon of black capitalism. They are pimps; black power pimps and fraudulent leaders, and the people must be educated to understand that any black man or Negro who is advocating a perpetuation of capitalism inside the United States is in fact seeking not only his ultimate destruction and death but is contributing to the continuous exploitation of black people all around the world. For it is the power of the United States Government, this racist, imperialist government, that is choking the life of all people around the world.

We are an African people. We sit back and watch the Jews in this country make Israel a powerful conservative state in the Middle East, but we are not concerned actively about the plight of our brothers in Africa. We are the most advanced technological group of black people in the world, and there are many skills that could be offered to Africa. At the same time, it must be publicly stated that many African leaders are in disarray themselves, having been duped into following the lines as laid out by the western imperialist governments. Africans themselves succumbed to and are victims of the power of the United States. For instance, during the summer of 1967, as the representatives of SNCC, Howard Moore and I traveled extensively in Tanzania and Zambia. We talked to high, very high, government officials. We told them there were many black people in the United States who were willing to come and work in Africa. All these government officials, who were part of the leadership in their respective governments, said they wanted us to send as many skilled people as we could contact. But this program never came into fruition, and we do not know the exact reasons, for I assure you that we talked and were committed to making this a successful program. It is our guess that the United States put the squeeze on these countries, for such a program directed by SNCC would have been too dangerous to the international prestige of the United States. It is also possible that some of the wild statements by some black leader frightened the Africans.

In Africa today there is a great suspicion of Black people in this country. This is a correct suspicion since most of the Negroes who have left the States for work in Africa usually work for the Central Intelligence Agency (CIA) or the State Department. But the respect for us as a people continues to mount, and the day will come when we can return to our homeland as brothers and sisters. But we should not think of going back to Africa today, for we are located in a strategic position. We live inside the United States, which is the most barbaric country in the world, and we have a chance to help bring this government down.

Time is short, and we do not have much time and it is time we stop mincing words. Caution is fine, but no oppressed people ever gained their liberation until they were ready to fight, to use whatever means necessary, including the use of force and power of the gun to bring down the colonizer.

We have heard the rhetoric, but we have not heard the rhetoric which says that black people in this country must understand that we are the vanguard force. We shall liberate all the people in the United States, and we will be instrumental in the liberation of colored people the world around. We must understand this point very clearly so that we are not trapped into diversionary and reactionary movements. Any class analysis of the United States shows very clearly that black people are the most oppressed group of people inside the United States. We have suffered the most from racism and exploitation, cultural degradation and lack of political power. It follows from the laws of revolution that the most oppressed will make the revolution, but we are not talking about just making the revolution. All the parties on the left who consider themselves revolutionary will say that blacks are the vanguard, but we are saying that not only are we the vanguard, but we must assume leadership, total control, and we must exercise the humanity which is inherent in us. We are the most humane people within the United States. We have suffered and we understand suffering. Our hearts go out to the Vietnamese, for we know what it is to suffer under the domination of racist America. Our hearts, our soul and all the compassion we can mount go out to our brothers in Africa, Santa Domingo, Latin America and Asia who are being tricked by the power structure of the United States which is dominating the world today. These ruthless, barbaric men have systematically tried to kill all people and organizations opposed to its imperialism. We no longer can just get by with the use of the word capitalism to describe the United States, for it is an imperial power sending money, missionaries and the army throughout the world to protect this government and the few rich whites who control it. General Motors and all the major auto industries are operating in South Africa, yet the white dominated leadership of the United Auto Workers sees no relationship to the exploitation of the black people in South Africa and the exploitation of black people in the United States. If they understand it, they certainly do not put it into practice, which is the actual test. We as black people must be concerned with the total conditions of all black people in the world.

But while we talk of revolution, which will be an armed confrontation and long years of sustained guerilla warfare inside this country, we must also talk of the type of world we want to live in. We must commit ourselves to a society where the total means of production are taken from the rich and placed into the hands of the state for the welfare of all the people. This is what we mean when we say total control. And we mean that black people who have suffered the most from exploitation and racism must move to protect their black interest by assuming leadership inside of the United States of everything that exists. The time has ceased when we are second in command and the white boy stands on top. This is especially true of the welfare agencies in this country, but it is not enough to say that a black man is on top. He must be committed to building the new society, to taking the wealth away from the rich people, such as

General Motors, Ford, Chrysler, the DuPonts, the Rockefellers, the Mellons, and all the other rich white exploiters and racists who run this world.

Where do we begin? We have already started. We started the moment we were brought to this country. In fact, we started on the shores of Africa, for we have always resisted attempts to make us slaves, and now we must resist the attempts to make us capitalists. It is in the financial interest of the United States to make us capitalist, for this will be the same line as that of integration into the mainstream of American life. Therefore, brothers and sisters, there is no need to fall into the trap that we have to get an ideology. We HAVE an ideology. Our fight is against racism, capitalism and imperialism, and we are dedicated to building a socialist society inside the United States where the total means of production and distribution are in the hands of the State, and that must be led by black people, by revolutionary blacks who are concerned about the total humanity of this world. And, therefore, we obviously are different from some of those who seek a black nation in the United States, for there is no way for that nation to be viable if in fact the United States remains in the hands of white racists. Then too, let us deal with some arguments that we should share power with whites. We say that there must be a revolutionary black vanguard, and that white people in this country must be willing to accept black leadership, for this is the only protection that black people have to protect ourselves from racism rising again in this country.

Racism in the United States is so pervasive in the mentality of whites that only an armed, well-disciplined, black-controlled government can insure the stamping out of racism in this country. And that is why we plead with black people not to be talking about a few crumbs, a few thousand dollars for this cooperative, or a thousand dollars which splits black people into fighting over the dollar. That is the intention of the government. We say . . . think in terms of total control of the United States. Prepare ourselves to seize state power. Do not hedge, for time is short, and all around the world the forces of liberation are directing their attacks against the United States. It is a powerful country, but that power is not greater than that of black people. We work the chief industries in this country, and we could cripple the economy while the brothers fought guerilla warfare in the streets. This will take some long range planning, but whether it happens in a thousand years is of no consequence. It cannot happen unless we start. How then is all of this related to this conference?

First of all, this conference is called by a set of religious people, Christians, who have been involved in the exploitation and rape of black people since the country was founded. The missionary goes hand in hand with the power of the states. We must begin seizing power wherever we are, and we must say to the planners of this conference that you are no longer in charge. We the people who have assembled here thank you for getting us here, but we are going to assume power over the conference and determine from this moment on the direction which we want it to go. We are not saying that the conference was planned badly. The staff of the conference has worked hard and has done a magnificent job in bringing all of us together, and we must include them in the new membership which must surface from this point on. The conference is now the property of the people who are assembled here. This we proclaim as fact and not rhetoric, and there are demands that we are going to make and we insist that the planners of this conference help us implement them.

We maintain we have the revolutionary right to do this. We have the same rights, if you will, as the Christians had in going into Africa and raping our Motherland and bringing us away from our continent of peace and into this hostile and alien government where we have been living in perpetual warfare since 1619.

Our seizure of power at this conference is based on a program, and our program is contained in the following Manifesto:

Black Manifesto

We the black people assembled in Detroit, Michigan, for the National Black Economic Development Conference are fully aware that we have been forced to come together because racist white America has exploited our resources, our minds, our bodies, our labor. For centuries we have been forced to live as colonized people inside the United States, victimized by the most vicious, racist system in the world. We have helped to build the most industrialized country in the world.

We are therefore demanding of the white Christian churches and Jewish synagogues, which are part and parcel of the system of capitalism, that they begin to pay reparations to black people in this country. We are demanding $500,000,000 from the Christian white churches and the Jewish synagogues. This total comes to fifteen dollars per nigger. This is a low estimate, for we maintain there are probably more than 30,000,000 black people in this country. Fifteen dollars a nigger is not a large sum of money, and we know that the churches and synagogues have a tremendous wealth and its membership, white America, has profited and still exploits black people. We are also not unaware that the exploitation of colored peoples around the world is aided and abetted by the white Christian churches and synagogues. This demand for $500,000,000 is not an idle resolution or empty words. Fifteen dollars for every black brother and sister in the United States is only a beginning of the reparations due us as people who have been exploited and degraded, brutalized, killed and persecuted. Underneath all of this exploitation, the racism of this country has produced a psychological effect upon us that we are beginning to shake off. We are no longer afraid to demand our full rights as a people in this decadent society.

We are demanding $500,000,000 to be spent in the following way:

(1) We call for the establishment of a southern land bank to help our brothers and sisters who have to leave their land because of racist pressure, and for people who want to establish cooperative farms but who have no funds. We have seen too many farmers evicted from their homes because they have dared to defy the white racism of this country.

We need money for land. We must fight for massive sums of money for this southern land bank. We call for $200,000,000 to implement this program.

(2) We call for the establishment of four major publishing and printing industries in the United States to be funded with ten million dollars each. These publishing houses are to be located in Detroit, Atlanta, Los Angeles, and New York. They will help to generate capital for further cooperative investments in the black community, provide jobs and an alternative to the white-dominated and controlled printing field.

(3) We call for the establishment of four of the most advanced scientific and futuristic audio-visual networks to be located in Detroit, Chicago, Cleveland and Washington, D.C. These TV networks will provide an alternative to the racist propaganda that fills the current television networks. Each of these TV networks will be funded by ten million dollars each.

(4) We call for a research skills center which will provide research on the problems of black people. This center must be funded with no less than thirty million dollars.

(5) We call for the establishment of a training center for the teaching of skills in community organization, photography, movie making, television repair and all other skills needed in communication. This training center shall be funded with no less than ten million dollars.

(6) We recognize the role of the National Welfare Rights Organization, and we intend to work with them. We call for ten million dollars to assist in the organization of welfare recipients. We want to organize welfare workers in this country so that they may demand more money from the government and better administration of the welfare system of this country.

(7) We call for $20,000,000 to establish a National Black Labor Strike and Defense Fund. This is necessary for the protection of black workers and their families who are fighting racist working conditions in this country.

(8) We call for the establishment of the International Black Appeal (IBA). This International Black Appeal will be funded with no less than $20,000,000. The IBA is charged with producing more capital for the establishment of cooperative businesses in the United States and in Africa, our Motherland. The International Black Appeal is one of the most important demands that we are making, for we know that it can generate and raise funds throughout the United States and help our African brothers. The IBA is charged with three functions and shall be headed by James Forman:

(a) Raising money for the program of the National Black Economic Development Conference.
(b) The development of cooperatives in African countries and support of African liberation movements.
(c) Establishment of a Black Anti-Defamation League which will protect our African image.

(9) We call for the establishment of a black university to be founded with $130,000,000, to be located in the South. Negotiations are presently under way with a southern university.

(10) We demand that IFCO allocate all unused funds in the planning budget to implement the demands of this conference.

In order to win our demands, we are aware that we will have to have massive support, therefore:

(1) We call upon all the black people throughout the United States to consider themselves as members of the National Black Economic Development Conference and to act in unity to help force the racist white Christian churches and Jewish synagogues to implement these demands.

(2) We call upon all the concerned black people across the country to contact black workers, black women, black students and the black unemployed, community groups, welfare organizations, teachers' organizations, church leaders and organizations, explaining how these demands are vital to the black community of the United States. Pressure by whatever means necessary should be applied to the white power structure. All black people should act boldly in confronting our white oppressors and demanding this modest reparation of fifteen dollars per black man.

(3) Delegates and members of the National Black Economic Development Conference are urged to call press conferences in the cities and to attempt to get as many black organizations as possible to support the demands of the conference. The quick use of the press in the local areas will heighten the tension, and these demands must be attempted to be won in a short period of time, although we are prepared for protracted and long-range struggle.

(4) We call for the total disruption of selected church-sponsored agencies operating anywhere in the United States and the world. Black workers, black women, black students and the black unemployed are encouraged to seize the offices, telephones, and printing apparatus of all church-sponsored agencies and to hold these in trusteeship until our demands are met.

(5) We call upon all delegates and members of the National Black Economic Development Conference to stage sit-in demonstrations at selected black and white churches. This is not to be interpreted as a continuation of the sit-in movement of the early sixties, but we know that active confrontation inside white churches is possible and will strengthen the possibility of meeting our demands. Such confrontation can take the form of reading the Black Manifesto instead of a sermon, or passing it out to church members. The principle of self-defense should be applied if attacked.

(6) On May 4, 1969, or a date thereafter, depending upon local conditions, we call upon black people to commence the disruption of the racist churches and synagogues throughout the United States.

(7) We call upon IFCO to serve as a central staff to coordinate the mandate of the conference and to reproduce and distribute en masse literature, leaflets, news items, press releases and other material.

(8) We call upon all delegates to find within the white community those forces which will work under the leadership of blacks to implement these demands by whatever means necessary. By taking such actions, white Americans will demonstrate concretely that they are willing to fight the white skin privilege and the white supremacy and racism which has forced us as black people to make these demands.

(9) We call upon all white Christians and Jews to practice patience tolerance, understanding and nonviolence as they have been encouraged, advised and demanded that we as black people should do throughout our entire enforced slavery in the United States. The true test of their faith and belief in the Cross and the words of the prophets will certainly be put to a test as we seek legitimate and extremely modest reparations for our role in developing the industrial base of the western world through our slave labor. But we are no longer slaves, we are men and women, proud of our African heritage, determined to have our dignity.

(10) We are so proud of our African heritage and realize concretely that our struggle is not only to make revolution in the United States but to protect our brothers and sisters in Africa and to help them rid themselves of racism, capitalism and imperialism by whatever means necessary, including armed struggle. We are and must be willing to fight the defamation of our African image wherever it rears its ugly head. We are therefore charging the steering committee to create a black Anti-Defamation League to be founded by money raised from the International Black Appeal.

(11) We fully recognize that revolution in the United States and Africa, our Motherland, is more than a one dimensional operation. It will require the total integration of the political, economic and military components, and therefore we call upon all our brothers and sisters who have acquired training and expertise in the fields of engineering, electronics, research, community organization, physics, biology, chemistry, mathematics, medicine, military science and warfare to assist the National Black Economic Development Conference in the implementation of its program.

(12) To implement these demands we must have a fearless leadership. We must have a leadership which is willing to battle the church establishment to implement these demands. To win our demands we will have to declare war on the white Christian churches and synagogues, and this means we may have to fight the total government structure of this country. Let no one here think that these demands will be met by our mere stating them. For the sake of the churches and synagogues, we hope that they have the wisdom to understand that these demands are modest and reasonable. But if the white Christians and Jews are not willing to meet our demands through peace and goodwill, then we declare war, and we are prepared to fight by whatever means necessary. We are, therefore, proposing the election of the following steering committee: *

Lucius Walker   *Mark Comfort*
Renny Freeman   *Earl Allen*

* (This list was later revised; more Church representatives were added.)

Luke Tripp
Howard Fuller
James Forman
John Watson
Dan Aldridge
John Williams
Ken Cockrel
Chuck Wooten
Fannie Lou Hamer
Julian Bond

Robert Browne
Vincent Harding
Mike Hamlin
· Len Holt
Peter Bernard
Michael Wright
Muhammed Kenyatta
Mel Jackson
Howard Moore
Harold Holmes

Brothers and sisters, we are no longer shuffling our feet and scratching our heads. We are tall, black and proud.

And we say to the white Christian churches and Jewish synagogues, to the government of this country and to all the white racist imperialists who compose it, there is only one thing left that you can do to further degrade black people and that is to kill us. But we have been dying too long for this country. We have died in every war. We are dying in Vietnam today fighting the wrong enemy.

The new black man wants to live, and to live means that we must not become static or merely believe in self-defense. We must boldly go out and attack the white Western world at its power centers. The white Christian churches are another form of government in this country, and they are used by the government of this country to exploit the people of Latin America, Asia and Africa, but the day is soon coming to an end. Therefore, brothers and sisters, the demands we make upon the white Christian churches and the Jewish synagogues are small demands. They represent fifteen dollars per black person in these United States. We can legitimately demand this from the church power structure. We must demand more from the United States Government.

But to win our demands from the church, which is linked up with the United States Government, we must not forget that it will ultimately be by force and power that we will win.

We are not threatening the churches. We are saying that we know the churches came with the military might of the colonizers and have been sustained by the military might of the colonizers. Hence, if the churches in colonial territories were established by military might, we know deep within our hearts that we must be prepared to use force to get our demands. We are not saying that this is the road we want to take. It is not, but let us be very clear that we are not opposed to force and we are not opposed to violence. We were captured in Africa by violence. We were kept in bondage and political servitude and forced to work as slaves by the military machinery and the Christian Church working hand in hand.

We recognize that in issuing this Manifesto we must prepare for a long-range educational campaign in all communities of this country, but we know that the Christian churches have contributed to our oppression in white America. We do not intend to abuse our black brothers and sisters in black churches who have uncritically accepted Christianity. We want them to understand how the racist white Christian church with its hypocritical declarations and doctrines of brotherhood has abused our trust and faith. An attack on the religious beliefs of black people is not our major objective, even though we know that we were not Christians when we were brought to this country, but that Christianity was used to help enslave us. Our objective in issuing this Manifesto is to force the racist white Christian church to begin the payment of reparations which are due all black people, not only by the church but also by private business and the United States government. We see this focus on the Christian church as an effort around which all black people can unite.

Our demands are negotiable, but they cannot be minimized, they can only be increased, and the church is asked to come up with larger sums of money than we are asking. Our slogans are:

All Roads Must Lead to Revolution
Unite with Whomever You Can Unite
Neutralize Wherever Possible
Fight Our Enemies Relentlessly
Victory to the People
Life and Good Health to Mankind
Resistance to Domination by the White Christian Churches
and the Jewish Synagogues
Revolutionary Black Power
We Shall Win Without a Doubt

from The Nigger Bible

■ Robert H. DeCoy

DeCoy's Song of Genesis

It was a long time ago. Sometime, long before "The Pronouncement of Genesis" by God. When the Father elected to take Nature as his bridesmaid on a lovecouch, one of his planets named "Earth," for the conception of their children, called Mankind. Then, over this planet he conceded them dominion, by his will, to rule this garden as a paradise, to the perpetuation of his glory.

In a climate conducive to love, God lay back the shoulders of the virgin, Nature, then her legs he extended, wide apart.

Against the shores of an unnamed continent, He placed her virginal vagina and covered it gently with seaweed.

Her thighs and knees, he raised to rest on earthly mounds named mountains, which the children would come to call later the *Appalachians* or the mountains in the eastern portion, the *Rocky Mountains* in the West.

Her buttocks, he made to nestle on an ocean floor, the soft, sandy couch of a sea-gulf, to which, later, his children would also give title. For her trim waist, he molded a narrow strip of land, contoured to fit her proportions, serving as a link between two of God's major continents. The northernmost was to serve as a cushion for their bodies. The southernmost would serve as their pillow rest. Her head would settle in the "Tropic of Capricorn," that the "Equator" crossed the tips of her breasts. Where, upon orders from God, the sun was to bite them—kiss them, hard. To bruise, burn and darken them with his tongues, his lips and his teeth, kneading her into "the state of readiness."

In the meanwhile, the very spirit of God was busy. Forging. Shaping parts of his being to fashion and form his great organ of reproduction.

Yes, but for ages, more than eons of ages, the virgin Nature waited. While the sun still applied his treatment, licking, and sucking, biting and teasing the sensuous tips of her breasts.

Her body thrashed with impatience—twisted in throes of ecstatic torment. Her buttocks rose and fell with excitement, indenting the soft sand-couch of the sea floor.

The invigorating waters cooled and refreshed the lips of her burning vagina. The icy chill of the waters cooled her openings, condensing her body-fluids into pearls, crystallizing her pre-intercourse emissions into creatures, life-things.

Multicolored tropical fishes, large and small beasts of the forests, birds and insects of brilliant colors, magenta, emerald, and white, exploded, escaping from the mouth of Nature's vagina, to take possession of the earth, the sky and the waters—to make song to God's chosen bride.

Their songs were but simple echoes, imitated sounds, sighs and delightful cries of Nature, the restles virgin in heat.

But, their songs also served to stimulate God, that his organ became hardened in the process. The great sun, biding his time, did observe, so that he increased the application of his treatment. The sun was a master of persistence in making the virgin ready. He was all artistic, majestic, patient and tenderly cruel. The tips of her breasts became hardened, red turning to blue, as he rolled them between his hot teeth, tickling her tender bruises with his tongue, massaging them between his lips, that Nature cried out for mercy. And it was here that mercy had its beginning.

Nature cried, pleaded, whispered, whimpered, moaned and groaned— screamed alound for mercy. In wantonness and restless, helpless antici- pation.

(Oh, children of God's Mankind, have mercy. Hear me. And believe me. For this is how it all began and did happen. Believe when I say that God, too, became disappointed, that thereafter the quality of mercy would be- come strained.)

In his tender attempt to respond to her cries, God hurried to comply and fulfill her desire for his mercy. Thus, God himself, the Almighty, learned "shame" for having made the revelation of his own weakness. Haste. But, as all of Heaven and the Earth bore witness, despite his heavenly haste, as he lowered himself from the vast heavens, preparing for the initial thrust, he was slow And heavy. As God always has been, is and will be. Forever.

While lowering himself into the proper position, hovering above the body of the virgin, his toes dug in, jamming the ice and the snow solidly against the northernmost extreme of the world. But the pole held firm.

The mighty weight of his ponderous thighs and loins came down to hollow out valleys and fertile plains underneath him. And the soft earth welled up high on both sides of his great body to make sea-cliffs, swelling over the two great oceans.

But the waters rushed inland from the seas to fill his gigantic testicles, to form "five great pools," later named lakes, settling thereabouts for the purpose of cooling his fevers.

Then God pushed. And the load of his lumbering black penis slid forward, the throbbing head gouging a gap into his earth, which the raging waters rushed in to follow, trailing, foaming, fomenting to become "The Father of All Earthly Rivers." The prickhead developed a foreskin, a protection against bruises, as it glided forward in search, blindly seeking the entrance, solace and seclusion promised within, to blend, probing, to implant the prickhead into the pink-white infolds of Nature's tender belly, and fill her with this hardened, black crust of his being.

But, thus was the beginning intended my children, that the two extremes of God and Nature be fused by color, that all shades thereafter would range in between these two: Black and White be divinely joined in the beginning, that their glory and splendor might last and remain so, until the end.

Carefully, he had formed the cunt of the virgin in darkness, then tinted it with light, colored it with the rainbow of yellows, pinks, grays, purples and shades of red and white. Bleached it in the chemical solutions of chlorine, salt, sulphur, and the iodine of the seagulf waters. Protected it with a cover of seaweeds, till time for his divine intrusion. While placing her into the "position of readiness," he had used a similar seaweed beneath the pit of her arms, that the heat of his hot hands might not scorch her.

He had desired her in shades of immaculate white, for his majestic black to commune with. And that from this communion would come their offspring, the chosen creatures, called Mankind, arrayed in many shades, as their only contrasting feature.

The black-blue bruises of her breast-tips had been darkened by the hot tongue of the sun, while his blistering rays had splashed her body brown, yellow and red, for the Father had desired that the brightest of Nature's features remain untainted until her whiteness and his blackness could become joined as one.

Now, as God moved the great bulk of his body forward, pushing his prickhead toward the pouting lips of her belly, he moved all the things of the Earth before it into the tender recess of her being. All things before the path of his lumbering black penis went forth and in. Insects and beasts, fish and fowl. All of the Earth's elements: iron, copper, silver, gold and platinum. Salts, sulphurs and gasses. Oxygen, hydrogen, and nitrogen. Rocks of carbon, diamonds bright and black coal. Soft and hard went forth and in. Then, oil! Crude, hot black oil. For this black oil would be called "the sperm of God."

As he prodded and rammed, he packed these into the pulsating lips of her throbbing vagina; she screamed out so that panic, pain and agony became the first reality of hue-man experience. Even God held still and stiffened in spirit, in divine recognition of these three. Then, slowly, slowly, he pressed himself forward, down into her once more.

Her buttocks then gave, yielding to receive him, pressing back, down into the softness of the sea-floor. Hesitating, adjusting, then mustering her strength, Nature rose to meet him, receive him fully, then guide him further down into her that she might explore him and perceive him to fanthom entirely the totality of God's fullest extent.

Together, then they grooved—wrestled to discover the measure of each other; the depth, the height, the length and the width, both shifting, re-arranging to position their great torsos accordingly.

Together, as one, they rose and fell, creating harmony, that the rhythm of music was revealed. Tempo was felt, as they kept time in space, that centuries were jarred into measurement, called years. Up and down, their movement became seasons to mark off winter, spring, summer, & fall, division by degrees, making for periods of intensity, then rest. Their tremors slackened to trembling, keeping time, that hours might be counted by the minute, jarred slightly apart into passionate seconds for breath.

As they settled for breath the waters turned about them, churning into a million whirlpools, to make waves, colored red with her blood. For there-after, blood was the sign of the virgin. Her daughters, marked mothers, would suffer "the generosity of their blood."

The entire Earth pulsated with their rhythms, rolling and shaking the axis from its very foundations. Then rushing waterfalls appeared. Hot per-spiration from the great body of God, making the rains. Flowing down from the heat and the friction, melting, as it reached the inferno of her being, drenching and cascading, that the ice and snow foamed, pouring themselves into racing torrents of shrieking waters. Tributaries of fluid, all raging in course to join the mainstream, That mighty "Father of All Earthly Rivers," serving them as a slippery lubricant for the plunging black penis of the Master.

The virgin cavorted and screamed in delight upon receiving him. Filled with ecstasy, she gasped and grunted, giggled and moaned, sighed then groaned. She wrestled and wriggled her buttocks up from the bottom of the ocean floor, rising, determined to meet and match him, inviting the brunt of God's most powerful thrusts.

Her breathings became the "four winds of the world," her moans and groans became the cyclone, the hurricane and the monsoon. God's great breath became the typhoon, his grunts of satisfaction were the roars of the thunder. The lightnings flashed as they kissed!

Then, in time, he lunged downward, into her—plunging past the depth of her being. She screamed out, protesting in anguish, but God was unable to release her or to desist and withhold. For at last, this was her destiny. Nature had to be made to surrender, as all other things—compromised! To become as one with her God.

But, the virgin Nature fought back, like "the bitch that she is," she lifted her long legs skyward, then wrapped them about the centerfold of

God's spine, winding her great arms around him, she clutched him closer. And with her sharpened talons, she clawed furrows deep into the surface of his body, that God roared out his thunder of amazement, discovering of himself the meaning of pain. In anger and agony, he drove himself further, downward, dove deeper that his prickhead exploded past the pit, that darkened recess of her womb. The virgin grunted, ecstatic in response, then shuddered violently, surrendering. Tremors wracked her body, shook her into trembles, which shivered away into faint.

The great body of God jerked into spasm, that hot black oil emerged from the bottom of the sea and covered the surface of the waves. *God had come!*

As they both lay exhausted, the waters about them churned away their turbulence. The wild things slowed their screaming to a whisper. All became quiet. Observing in silence were the birds, beasts, fish, mammals and insects. Holding themselves in the state of transfixion, witnessing the initial lesson in procreation, the union manifest of God and Nature, that Mankind might come forth in their likeness.

Then, with a flutter of her eyes, awakened from the slumber of faint, the virgin was revived, became alive once again in her own brightness and glory. While God slept with such satisfaction that his great strength settled and was stilled, altogether spent. The sun turned the fierce face of his brightness away from the spectacle of God's exhaustion, ashamed that any others might observe the Father in his one moment of weakness. He turned away to make night, the absence of daylight, that this gloomy secret remain still unrevealed.

But, then the virgin was awake, alive in her glory, amidst this darkness. She would not altogether have it so willed. She raised her arms, waved her hands in signal for moonlight to illuminate the love scene. All the constellations of the heavens peeped and peered down through the darkness, winking, blinking in disbelief and bewilderment, seeking an answer to the question: "Had Nature conquered God? Was she really his equal, here in the gloom?"

She smiled "the smile of the bitch!" She would show them! And so that all her creatures might serve as witnesses to see, she turned on the full moon brighter. Then, with her tongue alive, licking, she kissed God. Awake! While gazing boldly her challenge up into his eyes and face, that his desire became re-aroused and re-enflamed. From his drowsy slumber, he summoned forth the reserve of his strength to resume. But, this time she, Nature, assumed the role of aggressor.

For this time, the virgin was ready, full blossomed and eager to meet him. As she intended, this time the honors would be equal. And they were. As all Heaven and Earth bore witness, observing the performance through the semi-darkness and moonlight. So, it is now believed and accepted by all, that Mankind was conceived in this "second round," redemption of the blessed re-communion, when Nature established to her own contentment, by God's eternal consent, that in moments of weariness, darkness and slumber, she could be and often was, the equal, if not the superior, of God.

So followed the first morning, when the sun returned to make day and to awaken them both. God lifted himself from atop her rapturous body to ascend to his heavens and leave her there, resting in the luxury of self-contentment, while awaiting the time for their offspring to come forth, ejected from her weed-covered orifice.

After a period, they spilled forth, pouring out in droves from the darkness of Mother Nature's womb. In all shapes and sizes, features and textures, colors and shades, they came forth, ranging and varied in hue, between the black and the white, two primaries, so joined divinely and fused from the communion between God and Nature, his bride.

The Children of Mankind were nursed there, in the garden, on a delta, where the "Mighty Father of All Rivers" still courses downstream, tracing the path of the "Black Father's penis," emptying its waters into the sea-gulf (called the Gulf of Mexico), just as in the Beginning that penis once surged forth, searching to spill its sperm into the opening of Nature's receptacle. That pale, pure, crystal clear, colorless cunt of the virgin.

But then, when the eyes of the children had been opened to see the beauties of the garden paradise about them, they turned rather to look and gaze upon each other, sensing their physical distinctions and differences as reflected upon the surfaces of the bright waters, worshipping their mortal outlines as mirrored back from the opaque depths of glittering stones and metals. Brilliant elements which they learned to extract from crusts of the earth.

As a result, the creatures called Children of God began to search more reflections in these physical surfaces, which illuminated only their own peculiar likenesses as to color, texture and features, in adoration of resemblances, emphasizing mortal, physical externals.

Thus was the "*original sin.*" For as a result they banded themselves into divisions called families, tribes, clans, races, and then into nations. They embattled and fought among each other. Accordingly, by custom, each claiming their individual group to be the sole inheritors by birthright, the divine rulers of the paradise.

So, God himself returned to the garden, alarmed to discover with displeasure, their folly. And in his anguish and anger, he drove them all from the paradise, scattering them in all the directions of the four winds, into undiscovered parts of the wilderness, confusing their tongues, clogging their ears, blinding their sight, till they would all stop and seek to hear and sing his original song of oneness and togetherness, which he and his bride had established prior to their mortal conception.

So, from then, until now, the original paradise was lost and denied unto the creatures who were designed to rule it. By decree of God Almighty, who scattered them in judgment, declaring: "They shall roam and wander, destroy and squander all of the wilderness and the garden, until I, Lord God of Heavenly Hosts, have elected to call them home again, before the end. As it was to be in the beginning!"

STORIES

A New Day

■ Charles Wright

"I'm caught. Between the devil and the deep blue sea." Lee Mosley laughed and made a V for victory sign and closed the front door against a potpourri of family voices, shouting good wishes and tokens of warning.

The late, sharp March air was refreshing and helped cool his nervous excitement but his large hands were tight fists in his raincoat pockets. All morning he had been socking one fist into the other, running around the crowded, small living room like an impatient man waiting for a train, and had even screamed at his mother, who had recoiled as if he had sliced her heart with a knife. Andy, his brother-in-law, with his whine of advice. "Consider . . . Brother . . ."

Consider your five stair-step children. Consider the sweet, brown babe switching down the subway steps ahead of me. What would he say? Lee wondered.

Of course, deep down in his heart, he wanted the job, wanted it desperately. The job seemed to hold so much promise, and really he was getting nowhere fast, not a God damn place in the year and seven weeks that he had been shipping clerk at French-American Hats. But that job, too, in the beginning had held such promise. He remembered how everyone had been proud of him.

Lee Moseley was a twenty-five-year-old Negro, whose greatest achievement had been the fact that he had graduated twenty-fourth in his high school class of one hundred and twenty-seven. This new job that he was applying for promised the world, at least as much of the world as he expected to get in one hustling lifetime. But he wouldn't wear his Ivy League suits and unloosen his tie at ten in the morning for coffee and doughnuts. He would have to wear a uniform, and mouth a grave Yes mam and No mam. What was worse, his future boss was a Southern white woman, and he had never said one word to a Southern white woman in his life, had never expected to either.

"It's honest work, ain't it?" his mother had said. 'Mrs. Davies ain't exactly a stranger. All our people down home worked for her people. They were mighty good to us and you should be proud to work for her. Why,

404

you'll even be going overseas and none of us ain't been overseas except Joe and that was during the big war. Lord knows, Mrs. Davies pays well."

Lee had seen her picture once in the *Daily News,* leaving the opera, furred and bejeweled, a waxen little woman with huge, gleaming eyes, who faced the camera with pouting lips as if she were on the verge of spitting. He had laughed because it seemed strange to see a society woman posing as if she were on her way to jail.

Remembering, he laughed now and rushed up the subway steps at Columbus Circle.

Mrs. Maude T. Davis had taken a suite in a hotel on Central Park South for the spring, a spring that might well be two weeks or a year. Lee's Aunt Ella in South Carolina had arranged the job, a very easy job. Morning and afternoon drives around Central Park. The hotel's room service would supply the meals, and Lee would personally serve them. The salary was one hundred fifty dollars a week, and it was understood that Lee could have the old, custom-built Packard on days off.

"Lord," Lee moaned audibly and sprinted into the servant's entrance of the hotel.

Before ringing the doorbell, he carefully wiped his face with a handkerchief that his mother had ironed last night and inspected his fingernails, cleared his throat, and stole a quick glance around the silent, silk-walled corridor.

He rang the doorbell, whispered "damnit," because the buzzing sound seemed as loud as the sea in his ears.

"Come in," a husky female voice shouted and Lee's heart exploded in his ears. His armpits began to drip.

But he opened the door manfully, and entered like a boy who was reluctant to accept a gift, his highly polished black shoes sinking into layers of apple-green carpet.

He raised his head slowly and saw Mrs. Davies sitting in a yellow satin wing chair, bundled in a mink coat and wearing white gloves. A flowered scarf was tied neatly around her small, oval head.

"I'm Lee Mosely. Sarah's boy. I came to see about a job."

Mrs. Davies looked at him coldly and then turned toward the bedroom.

"Muffie," she called, and then sat up stiffly, clasping her gloved hands. "You go down to the garage and get the car. Muffie and I will meet you in the lobby."

"Yes mam," Lee said, executing a nod that he prayed would serve as a polite bow. He turned smartly like a soldier and started for the door.

Muffie, a Yorkshire terrier bowed in yellow satin, trotted from the bedroom and darted between Lee's legs. His bark was like an old man coughing. Lee moaned, "Lord," and noiselessly closed the door.

He parked the beige Packard ever so carefully and hopped out of the car as Mrs. Davies emerged from the hotel lobby.

Extending his arm, he assisted Mrs. Davies from the curb.

"Thank you," she said sweetly. "Now, I expect you to open and close the car door but I'm no invalid. Do you understand?"

"Yes mam. I'm sorry."

"Drive me through the park."

Muffie barked. Lee closed the door and then they drove off as the sun skirted from behind dark clouds.

There were many people in the park and it was like a spring day except for the chilled air.

"We haven't had any snow in a long time," Lee said, making conversation. "Guess spring's just around the corner."

"I know that," Mrs. Davies said curtly.

And that was the end of their conversation until they returned to the hotel, twenty minutes later.

"Put the car away," Mrs. Davies commanded. "Don't linger in the garage. The waiter will bring up lunch shortly and you must receive him."

Would the waiter ever come? Lee wondered, pacing the yellow and white tiled serving pantry. Should he or Mrs. Davies phone down to the restaurant? The silence and waiting was unbearable. Even Muffie seemed to be barking impatiently.

The servant entrance bell rang and Mrs. Davies screamed, "Lee!" and he opened the door quickly and smiled at the pale, blue-veined waiter, who did not return the smile. He had eyes like a dead fish, Lee thought, rolling in the white covered tables. There was a hastily scrawled note which read: "Miss Davies food on top. Yours on bottom."

Grinning, Lee took his tray from under the bottom shelf, and was surprised to see two bottles of German beer. He set his tray on the pantry counter and took a quick peep at Mrs. Davies's tossed salad, one baby lamp chop. There was a split of champagne in a small iced bucket.

"Lord," he marveled, and rolled the white covered table into the living room.

"Where are you eating, mam?" Lee asked, pleased because his voice sounded so professional.

"Where?" Mrs. Davies boomed. "In this room, boy!"

"But don't you have a special place?" Lee asked, relieved to see a faint smile on the thin lips.

"Over by the window. I like the view. It's almost as pretty as South Carolina. Put the yellow wing over there too. I shall always dine by the window unless I decide otherwise. Understand?"

"Yes mam." Lee bowed and rolled the table in front of the floor-to-ceiling wall of windows. Then he rushed over and picked up the wing chair as if it were a loaf of bread

He seated Mrs. Davies and asked gravely: "Will that be all, mam?"

"Of course!"

Exiting quickly, Lee remembered what his uncle Joe had said about V-day. "Man. When they tell us the war is over, I just sat down in the foxhole and shook my head."

And Lee Mosely shook his head and entered the serving pantry, took a deep breath of relief which might well have been a prayer.

He pulled up a leather-covered fruitwood stool to the pantry counter and began eating his lunch of fried chicken, mashed potatoes, gravy and tossed salad. He marveled at the silver domes covering the hot, tasty food, amused at his distorted reflection in the domes. He thanked God for the food and the good job. True, Mrs. Davies was sharp-tongued, a little funny, but she was nothing like the Southern women he had seen in the movies and on television and had read about in magazines and newspapers. She was not a part of Negro legends, of plots, deeds, and mockery. She was a wealthy woman named Mrs. Maude T. Davies.

Yeah, that's it, Lee mused in the quiet and luxury and warmth of the serving pantry.

He bit into a succulent chicken leg and took a long drink of the rich, clear-tasting German beer.

And then he belched. Mrs. Maude T. Davies screamed: "Nigger!"

I still have half a chicken leg left, Lee thought. He continued eating, chewing very slowly, but it was difficult to swallow. The chicken seemed to set on the valley of his tongue like glue.

So there was not only the pain of digesting but the quicksand sense of rage and frustration, and something else, a nameless something that had always started ruefully at the top of his skull like a windmill.

He knew he had heard *that* word, although the second lever of his mind kept insisting loudly that he was mistaken.

So he continued eating with difficulty his good lunch.

"Nigger boy!" Mrs. Davies repeated, a shrill command, strangely hot and tingling like the telephone wire of the imagination, the words entering through the paneled pantry door like a human being.

Lee Mosely sweated very hard summer and winter. Now, he felt his blood congeal, freeze, although his anger, hot and dry came bubbling to the surface. Saliva doubled in his mouth and his eyes smarted. The soggy chicken was still wedged on his tongue and he couldn't swallow it nor spit it out. He had never cried since becoming a man and thought very little of men who cried. But for the love of God, what could he do to check his rage, helplessness?

"Nigger!" Mrs. Davies screamed again, and he knew that some evil, white trick had come at last to castrate him. He had lived with this feeling for a long time and it was only natural that his stomach and bowels grumbled as if in protest.

And then like the clammy fear that evaporates at the crack of day, Lee's trembling left hand picked up the bottle of beer and he brought it to his lips and drank. He sopped the bread in the cold gravy. He lit a cigarette and drank the other bottle of German beer.

A few minutes later, he got up and went into the living room.

Mrs. Davies was sitting very erect and elegant in the satin chair, and had that snotty *Daily News* photograph expression, Lee thought bitterly.

"Mrs. Davies," he said politely, clearly, "did you call me?"

"Yes," Mrs. Maude T. Davies replied, like a jaded, professional actress. Her smile was warm, pleased, amused. "Lee, you and I are going to get along very well together. I like people who think before they answer."

Sinner Man, Where You Gonna Run To?

■ Larry Neal

> *"Could there be a man in whose mind and consciousness
> all hopes and inhibitions of the last two thousand years
> have died? A man speaking our language, dressing and
> behaving as we do, and yet living on a completely dif-
> ferent plane? A man who would be the return of ancient
> man, pre-Christian man . . . ?"*
> RICHARD WRIGHT in *The Outsider*

No one sees the Appointed Ones on the David Susskind show. They do
not talk about how the "brothers will burn down 125th St." The Appointed
Ones are too busy taking care of business— t. c. b. baby; that's where it's
at. T. C. B. I mean the A. P. O's are together. And let me tell you something else: I discovered that when the Appointed Ones meet one another,
say on a subway, or in a crowd, at a party, anything, they always recognize
each other. It's kind of weird. They can feel each other's vibrations. If
they be in a crowded room, they can feel the vibrations—the force of that
person in the room. Inevitably, their eyes will meet. They will nod. And
that's all. And they go back to what they've been doing. And without looking to see, each can tell when the other has gone. They're the most beautiful guerrilla unit on the planet. Just the sheer force of their will and
soul-force, and things happen. These are the highest, most pure type. They
are total physically and spiritually; and they have worked themselves up
into the highest chambers of the white man's power, and are even now
working juju on him.

I mean, they be working juju on the "Man" so tough, they make him
fuck up his plans. He be jamming up his foreign policy, and his domestic
tranquillity, and he don't even know why. He be making the world hate
his ass. And he don't know why. At least, if he knows, he will not allow
himself to see it. For the chief weakness of these men are their illusions,
and their supreme arrogance before a world of black faces. Even when he
kills, and viciously so, he wants to be loved. So when the world spits at
his cardboard kindness, he begs to be loved, to be understood. Even as he
murders you, he pleads for understanding. And deadly children that they
are, they weep in confusion, because the world does not see that they are
kind and peace-loving children.

So, the A. P. O's, spiritually in league with Universal Black Brotherhood,
be working super juju on them—fuck up his thinking. Make them cause
chaos themselves. Make him harm his white self. And he be so dumb and
soulless he don't even see. That is why he continues to destroy the spiritual
world with one hand; and with the other, wipes his ass with a bloody olive
branch.

*The monster's eyes are watery colorless. With endless space beyond. The
thing inhabits the voids of reason. Its function was as a horrible nothing-*

ness. As absence of feeling of thought, of compassion. Out between the stars where life does not exist. This beast is the twisted thing a man would be alone . . . without his human soul.

"Sinner man where you gonna run to,
where you gonna run to judgment day?"

I left Reverend Worth and his deacons. And they were happy. I had done a good job on their legal papers. On the road, in the darkness, I thought about them. *Who* was their God? How did they see Him? What made them pray to Him so fervently? And for *what* were they praying? Was it for forgiveness? If so, what was the nature of their sins? Was it for understanding, as they stumbled through the white light of confusion?

Reverend G. K. Worth, smiling like Rex Ingram in *Green Pastures*, smiling benevolently like DE LAWD. Who would want to hurt such gentle people? It was a painful question. Because it is clear that there are many ready to crush them just for that gentleness. And for this reason, some of us have to descend into the Blackness and protect them by all the means at our disposal. So that that very gentleness would some day flower into bright sun-colors, blooming and singing in the universe. It is so awful—the pain. And the irony of it all is that the Appointed Ones will be the last ones to be loved. After chaos, someone will remember them as an afterthought. The last ones to be loved.

Even though we have acted out of love for them—for those who would or could not help themselves. Even though—even though we are nothing without them, and they without us—we would be vilified, scorned by our own for disturbing a false peace. And praying those kinds of dues is all part of the same tune.

The thick night and the swamp smell moved within me disturbing the argument. Occasionally something splashed in the darkness. The tree winds and the dog barks seemed linked somewhere in the distance. A narrow bumpy road, and there were no signs marking the way. Somehow, I had turned off the main highway. I stopped the car, and took out the road map. It was little help. I saw nothing that gave me direction. I could hear what sounded like whistling, way, way, off into the swamp, more, and then silence. The wind would rise out of the swamp, and it would be difficult to hear the whistling anyway. But when I did hear it, it was very distinct, lonely; it would rise; then fall into the womb of the darkness, beautiful and piercing. I looked down the road as far as I could see, and there was nothing there. Then I saw him standing at a kind of bend in the road; beyond him thick brushes, and a criss-crossing entanglement of trees and vines. And the whistling was clear now and rhythmic. I just sat there for awhile looking at him. He waved his hand.

"Hey man, hey! You know where the highway is?" No answer. "I say, brother, you know where the road is?" Still no answer. He walked to the car and motioned for me to follow. Instead of taking the bend, he turned into the trees and vines. He was about thirty yards in front of me; he seemed to fade in the darkness and appear again

"Hey man, this car can't get in there!" He stopped, turned around and came back.

"Get out the car, then."

"Just tell me where the highway is, man."

"I know you. And I know what you have done. And what you will do before it's over, nigger." Yeah, it was just that direct. That was when I first realized that the Appointed Ones recognized each other. But it frightened me then. I didn't want to understand it. I remembered the .38 in the glove compartment, but did not reach for it. He simply smiled.

"What are you talking about, man?"

"Nigger, don't pull that shit on me. I ain't dumb. I guards the roads. And I knows a lot—"

"Where *is* the main highway?" I wanted to change the subject.

"Oh that. Don't worry about that now. Don't worry. That can wait."

"What can wait?"

"*That.* Your business, nigger, can wait. There be more them than you can handle by yourself, anyway."

I knew that he did not know the plan. But he acted as if he knew it. I believed that only Carlton knew it. How would this country-looking black boy know it? And I am weak. Something ancient and sacred moved between me and him linking us together in a design of rhythm and night. The trees did their dance; and the whistling and dog barks commingled in the night—the rolling, undulating tug of history.

"Git out the car, brother." I obeyed. He began walking again deeper into the swamp, again the whistling. Then I heard something that sounded like hands clapping. It was rhythmical; and was beginning to augment itself to the whistling, which was becoming more and more shrill. The clapping. Suddenly, there was brightness as the lights from shacks were turned on. A large crowd, black men, women, and children, stood in a circle, in the center of which was a cross. But it was inverted. Around the cross was a kind of pit, raggedly cut out of the red earth.

The whistling was reaching an intense pitch; a kind of scream which blended into the clapping. Then the feet. Stomping against the ground. It was more of a shuffling than a stomping. It sent dust swirling in the night.

Then the Spirit began moving through it. Through the whistling, shuffling, and clapping. The first person it grabbed was a little girl, very thin, very black who danced around the edges of the circle, spinning and frenetically jerking herself like an epileptic. The others, her family, urged her on, shouting, intensifying the energy.

"Go on, child!"

"Have mercy, Spirit!"

"Owweee!"

"Feel the Spirit!"

"Yeeess, Sweet Spirit!"

"Owweee, Father!"

"Feel the Spirit, child! Feel the Spirit!!!"

"Oh, my baby, my baaaby!"

"Get it, child. Yes, God-Almighty so powerful!"

"God is good!"

"God is love!"

"God is pain!"

The child was dancing more powerfully now; the words seizing her body along with the energy of the rhythm, and throwing her with the force of hundreds of years of pain and death. She was dancing to the after-beat, the beat slightly behind or underneath the main one. Perfectly now. Precise. Spinning. Jerking. Somersaulting and occasionally rolling on the ground. Sometimes the child twisted in pain, a shout punching its way out of the frail body. No one moved to help her. Often, someone would slap his hands on the earth before her. But no one touched her. They just clapped and continued that stomping-foot-shuffle—the feet in one rhythm, the whistling and clapping in another, but total.

Then a young boy caught it. The Spirit riding him, throwing him into the air somersaulting, back flips, around the girl again and again. And fear rode my insides. And the rhythms rushed within me also. I moved with it—the Spirit of Obatala . . . Yemaya . . . Shango . . . Oshun . . . Allah . . . Siva . . . *Ba nla oka Yemowa! Orisha, wu mi ni 'budo ibi re l'orisha ka 'le!!!* The words pulled at my tongue, urging themselves up from the collective depths of my history. Visionary demons. Swirls of songs. Rivers. Streams. Old women peering over a baby near warm tropical springs where naked black women bathed. Drum nights. Fire nights. Ships flanking the shores. Chains. The smell of human flesh packed together. Song on song, song on song, singing off the layers of pale lies. Pulled at me. Pulled at the Word in my soul. *And would I ever live to reclaim my own?*

He appeared as if to calm us. Appeared in the midst of the most frightening moan I have ever heard. And I wept. And the moan rising into the rhythm, splintering somewhere in space and time; and in that moment, everything was everything that it could be; all that ever was existed in that moment, preserved within it were all of life's opposites; and everything danced with the night rolling, rolling through a cosmos of pain and suffering. How puny we are against the Gods within us. And He appeared among us as if to calm us, to begin the Act. The moan subsided as he spoke:

"Brothers and Sisters, we been brought across wide seas. We done seen children weepin' and moanin'. And the images of our Fathers broken and scattered to the Wind. Yes, I will tell it as I does every year. Seen the blood and heard the horror. No, my children, we are not strangers to blood. Yes, I will tell you. Seen them come tearin' and killin'. And yes, my children, we have prayed to their god; a god who has forgotten us. . . . Have seen things unspeakable before these children; but things they yet must know. Yes. And have believed, yes.

"For Nadi in the first year on the big boat . . . killed four white mens. . . . Was cut into pieces and eaten by the sharks and by the sea."

"Yes, we affirm, he is with us," they answered.

"For Baba Oyeluwa, great warrior who destroyed one of the big boats, escaped only to die by the hands of one his own."

"Yes, we affirm his presence."

"For Sekou who killed the Captain, and was himself caught and killed. May he be remembered."

"Yes, we remember."

"For Kwame, child of Saturday, wise priest, his head cut off defending his wives and children."

"Yes, we affirm he is with us."

"For Obafumi, great hunter, and a guardian of the tribes."

"Yes, we remember him."

"For Ezekiel Jones whose plan failed when he was betrayed by Mr. Jones's houseboy. May he be remembered."

"We will remember him, O Father."

"For Sarah Faulkner who refused Mister Faulkner and was split and pulled apart by two field horses. Her body dragged through the fields, and her guts spilling out of her vessel of creation."

"We remember her, and proclaim that she is with us."

"For all of the Nameless in the Motherland, and under the oceans; and those who died fightin' for the Spirit. For all of those by the devil and his children. For the wars upon wars, achin' bodies piled on the fields. For the Living and Dead, and for those about to be born. Let us remember them and affirm their eternal presence among us."

"We remember and affirm. Let the words make it so."

"Let us recall that we are the few remaining of the old; the bearers of a great secret; appointed by the Spirit to vindicate the Ancestors. I am merely your servant, elected by you to continue. . . . And I trust, yes trust, children, that I have served you well. . . .'"

"The words have been spoken. The deeds told. The Wind and Trees have heard them. And the Ancestors have made their presence known. You have served us well, Father."

He turned then in the direction of the inverted cross. As if it was a cue, several young men began drenching it in oil. The pit around it was filled with dry timbers. These were also drenched in oil. He was then given a large brass vase. He held it high above his head. Then the moan started up again, building, building slowly while he poured the libations. And the song . . . an old song . . . old and familiar poured out of him. The moan continued, screaming through the trees; and we whirled through time.

And then I saw them bringing him. He was young, strongly built. His hands were tied behind his back. And he struggled. They held. He screamed and squirmed as the horror leaped in his eyes: "NIGGERS! NIGGERS! NIGGERS! NIGGERS! NIGEEEERS!!!! WHAT ARE YOU NIGGERS DOING? LORD DON'T LET THEM DO IT! DON'T LET THEM KILL ME! PLEASE DON'T LET THEM, GOD! PLEASE DON'T LET THEM!

The fire made his face glow redly as the saliva hung from his lips. The trees danced in the wind. The moan stopped. Everything fell into silence. And the white man was silent also. It was much too large for him to understand. They dragged him to his cross, and stripped him naked. A young man came forth and whispered something to him, inaudible. And he seemed to relax a little. Just a little. The man was drained of everything now. He was ready to die. They tied him to his cross. Others came forth to help bind him. They poured the oil over him, again drenching the cross and the timbers in the pit. It was light. The flames exploded in the darkness, sucking at the wind which fed them. And he screamed, a white piercing scream of death; the swamp enveloped it, the darkness swallowing the scream and the light from the flames. We watched in silence. The stump burned. And then the fire died down, it was rekindled. It was so simple, yet so . . . yet so . . . .

Finally, nothing of him remained. Nothing. The Father carefully gathered up his ashes; and then very carefully scooped them into a black urn. The moan was continued, softly now. And they wept for him and his people. They wept for themselves. For the Act would vindicate only part of his sins. They were humble enough to realize this. They were humble enough to realize that they were dealing with unknowns.

The boy walked slowly toward me. Led me to the car. Walking through the swamp, neither of us spoke. When we reached my car, he gave me the directions I needed.

"You think you can find your way now?"

"Yeah, I think so."

"You on the right track now—straight ahead."

"Thank you, Brother. Thanks for the help."

"Anytime, Brother, anytime . . ."

NOVEL EXCERPTS

from The Free-Lance Pallbearers

■ Ishmael Reed

Part I. Da Hoodoo Is Put on Bukka Doopeyduk

I live in HARRY SAM. HARRY SAM is something else. A big not-to-be-believed out-of-sight, sometimes referred to as O-BOP-SHE-BANG or KLANG-A-LANG-A-DING-DONG. SAM has not been seen since the day thirty years ago when he disappeared into the John with a weird ravaging illness.

The John is located within an immense motel which stands on Sam's Island just off HARRY SAM.

A self-made Pole and former used-car salesman, SAM's father was busted for injecting hypos into the underbellies of bantam roosters. The old man rigged many an underground cockfight.

SAM's mother was a low-down, filthy hobo infected with hoof-and-mouth disease. A five-o'clock-shadowed junkie who died of diphtheria and an overdose of phenobarb. Laid out dead in an abandoned alley in thirty-degree-below snow. An evil lean snake with blue, blue lips and white tonsils. Dead as a doornail she died, mean and hard; cussing out her connection until the last yellow flame wisped from her wretched mouth.

But SAM's mother taught him everything he knows.

"Looka heah, SAM," his mother said before they lifted her into the basket and pulled the sheet over her empty pupils. "It's a cruel, cruel world and you gots to be swift. Your father is a big fat stupid kabalsa who is doin' one to five in Sing Sing for foolin' around with them blasted chickens. That is definitely not what's happening. If it hadn't been for those little pills, I would have gone out of my rat mind a long time ago. I have paid a lot of dues, son, and now I'm gonna pop off. But before I croak, I want to give you a little advice.

"Always be at the top of the heap. If you can't whup um with your fists, keek um. If you can't keek um, butt um. If you can't butt um, bite um and if you can't bite um, then gum the mothafukas to death. And one more thing, son," this purple-tongued gypsy said, taking a last swig of sterno and wiping her lips with a ragged sleeve. "Think twice before you speak 'cause the graveyard is full of peoples what talks too much."

414

SAM never forgot the advice of this woman whose face looked like five miles of unpaved road. He became top dog in the Harry Sam Motel and master of HIMSELF which he sees through binoculars each day across the bay. Visitors to his sprawling motel whisper of long twisting corridors and passageways descending to the very bowels of the earth.

High-pitched screams and cries going up-tempo are heard in the night. Going on until the wee wee hours of the morning when everything is OUT-OF-SIGHT. Going on until dirty-oranged dawn when the bootlegged roosters crow. Helicopters spin above the motel like clattering bugs as they inspect the constant stream of limousines moving to and fro, moving on up to the top of the mountain and discharging judges, generals, the Chiefs of Screws, and Nazarene Bishops. (The Nazarene Bishops are a bunch of drop-dead egalitarians crying into their billfolds, "We must love one another or die.")

These luminaries are followed by muscle-bound and swaggering attendants carrying hand-shaped bottles of colognes, mouthwash and enema solutions—hooded men with slits for eyes moving their shoulders in a seesaw fashion as they carry trays and towels and boxes of pink tissues—evil-smelling bodyguards who stagger and sway behind the celebrated waddle of penguins in their evening clothes.

At the foot of this anfractuous path which leads to the summit of Sam's Island lies the incredible Black Bay. Couched in the embankment are four statues of RUTHERFORD BIRCHARD HAYES. White papers, busted microphones and other wastes leak from the lips of this bearded bedrock and end up in the bay fouling it so that no swimmer has ever emerged from its waters alive. Beneath the surface of this dreadful pool is a subterranean side show replete with freakish fish, clutchy and extrasensory plants. (And believe you me, dem plants is hongry. Eat anything dey kin wrap dey stems around!!)

On the banks of HARRY SAM is a park. There the old men ball their fists and say paradoxes. They blow their noses with flags and kiss dead newsreels. Legend has it that when the fateful swimmer makes it from Sam's Island to HARRY SAM, these same old men will sneeze, swoop up their skiffles and rickety sticks, then lickety-split to rooms of widow executioners in black sneakers. It is at this time that the Free-Lance Pallbearers will take SAM.

I stood outside my dean's office at the Harry Sam College. I had flunked just about everything and had decided to call it quits and marry a chick I'd been shackin' up with for a few years. I would provide for her from earnings received from working at a hospital as an orderly and where I had been promoted frequently. ("Make-um-shit Doopeyduk," the admiring orderlies had nicknamed me.) U2 Polyglot, the dean, had been very nice to me so that I couldn't conceive of leaving the hallowed halls of Harry Sam without saying good-bye to him. Just as I opened the door to his office, a sharp object struck me in dead center of the forehead. It was a paper airplane which received its doom at the tip of my toes.

"O, forgive me," U2 said. "Are you hurt? Have a Bromo Seltzer," the dumpy redheaded man in clumsy tweeds and thick glasses fizzed.

"It's all right, U2 Polyglot. I just stopped by to tell you that I was leaving school."

"Leaving school? Why how can that be, Bukka?" (My name is Bukka Doopeyduk.) "You're one of the best Nazarene apprentices here. Why, you're on your way to becoming the first bacteriological warfare expert of the colored race."

"I know that and I appreciate everything you've done for me but I am flunking just about everything and plus I'm kinda restless. I want to get married and see what's out in the world. Got to go, Polyglot."

"Well, on the other hand, maybe dropping out and tuning in will turn you on, Bukka. Who knows? But whatever you decide, I wish you a lot of luck and I'm sure that we'll be running into each other from time to time."

U2 and I shook hands and I left him to a paper he was preparing for an English literary quarterly, entitled: "The Egyptian Dung Beetle in Kafka's 'Metamorphosis.'" He had dropped to his knees and begun to push a light ball of excrement about the room by the tip of his nose. He wanted to add an element of experience to his paper. You know, give it a little zip.

That night I called Fannie Mae's home to find out if she had made the final preparations for the wedding which would take place in the parish office of Rev. Eclair Porkchop, head of the Church of the Holy Mouth. A shrill tales-of-the-crypt voice answered the phone.

"May I speak to Fannie Mae?"

"She not home."

"What time will she be in?"

"No tellin' what time she be in. Is dis you, Bukka Doopeyduk, the boy what's gone marry my granchile?"

"That's me."

"Well, I don't have to tell you how fast dese youngins is today. She probably out whipping dope needles into her mouf or somethin' lak dat."

"When she returns, would you tell her that the wedding ceremony will take place tomorrow afternoon and shortly before I must present my application to the Harry Sam Housing Projects and—"

"Hold on, Dippydick. Dis ain't no IBM factory. I'm scribbling with a chewed-up pencil and considering the fact dat I'm a spindly ol woman with two bricks for breasts, it's awful admirable dat I'm even able to take my conjur lessons through the mail under the Mojo Retraining Act. So take it from the top and go real slow."

I repeated the instructions.

"Okay. I'll tell her Daffydink Dankeydim Doopeydank . . ."

"Doopeyduk."

"Whatever your name is, listen here. If you don't take good care of my granchile, I'm gonna put da hoodoo on you, and another thing . . ."

"What's that, ma'am?"

"Don't choo evah be callin' here at twelve o'clock when I'm puttin' da wolfbane on da do."

(CLICK!) She shut the phone down so hard my ears were seared. Well, that's show biz, Bukka Doopeyduk, I sighed, cakewalking my way back to the limbo of a furnished room.

We Would Need a Bigger Place

I picked up the booklet from the table in the housing project office. Above the table hung an oil portrait of SAM in a characteristic pose: zipping up the fly of butterfly-embroidered B.V.D.'s and wiping chili pepper sauce from his lips.

Next to the painting hung some employment ads:

"Passive sleep-in maid wanted."
"Apple-pickers 50¢ an hour. Must like discipline."

The cover of the booklet showed the housing manager holding the keys to an apartment. Color them gold. He smiles as he points to the Harry Sam Projects with the pose of an angel showing some looneybeard the paradise. On the next page, the typical family scene. Dad reading the papers, pipe in mouth. The little child seated on the floor busily derailing choo-choo trains, while with goo-goo eyes and smiles like half-moons, the appliances operate these five rooms of enveloping bliss. And after a long list of regulations a picture of the park area. All the little children having a ball. Fountains, baby carriages and waxen men tipping their hats to waxen women.

I sat in the section where the applicants were biding their time until a woman with a sweater draped over her shoulders called their names. They were interviewed by a roly-poly man in 90 per cent rayon Sears and Roebuck pants, mod tie and nineteen-cent ball-point pen sticking from the pocket of his short-sleeve shirt, and hush puppy shoes. (No shit. Da kat must have been pushing forty and he wore hush puppy shoes and a polka-dot mod tie. Why da man looked ridiculous!)

Some of the women had electronic devices plugged into their ears. They listened to the hunchbacked housewives phone in their hernias to the bugged benzedrined eyes who negotiated toy talk for a living.

Typical: "Hello Frank? Dis Frank? Been trying to get ya ever since you come on da air. Geez kids, it's Frank. Come and say hello to ya Uncle Frank. Hiya Frank. We sure like to hear toy talk out here in Queens and Brooklyn, which brings me to the point about what I wrung ya up. You see we tink dey got too much already, running around in da streets like monkies. Why can't dey behave demselves like da res of us 'mericans. And as far as bussing wit um goes—we don't tink it'ul 'mount to much for da very simple reason dat we don't tink it's too good. Dey should help themselves like we did when we come over on da manure dumps. Take my ol man for an instant. Worked hisself up and now he is a Screw. Killed fourteen hoods last week what was comin' at um with a knife. And my son jes shipped overseas to put down dem Yam riots what's gettin' ready to break loose. As you can see we are all doin' our part. Why can't *dey*?"

But occasionally this informative chitchat would be interrupted by a bulletin from radio UH-O:

UH-OOOOOOOOOOOOOOOOOOOOOOOOOOOOOOOOOOOOOOOOOOOOOOOOOOO

DEM CHINAMENS DONE GALLOPED INTO THE SUBURBS ON WEREWOLF SANDALS/KIDNAPING HEEL-KICKING HOUSEWIVES HANGING OUT DA WASH /BREAKING TV ANTENNAS OVER DERE KNEES DEY WAYLAID COMMUTER TRAINS AND SMASHED INK INTO THE FACES OF THE RIDERS WHO DOVE INTO THE HUDSON TRYING TO ESCAPE/

TONS OF CREDIT CARDS SALVAGED/BULLETPROOF RICKSHAWS SPOTTED IN NEW ROCHELLE/(AND SOME SINISTER-LOOKING JUNKS DONE SNEAKED INTO DA EAST RIVER TOO!) MAJOR CRISIS SHAPING UP/SAM TO DRESS HIMSELF AS SOON AS MAKEUP MAN ARRIVES AND THE URINALS ARE SCRUBBED.

Conorad: YAWL BETTER RUN!

"Bukka Doopeyduk," the social workers announced through his Rudy Vallee megaphone. Sitting down he officiously pinched his hooked nose.

On the desk were two round faces. One larger than the other. Smiling. Wife and girl child. In a box a row of half-chewed maraschino cherries resting in their wrappers. Gold trimmings on a get-well card which read: "We all miss you in unit X–followed by a list of stingy signatures. The Nazarene priest lifted his chubby face from the sheaf of papers he held in his hands. Rubbing his hands together he talked.

"Sorry I kept you waitin' so long, chum, but me and da missus were up late last night. Caught dat Sammy out at Forest Hills. Boy dat Sammy sure can blow the licoric stick and tickle da ivory. He was better 'n da time we caught him at da Eleanor Roosevelt birthday celebration. He was twirling his cane and kicking up wit da spats when suddenly a miracle happened. A helicopter landed right on da stage and out came da savior and hope of da world. He put his arm around Sammy and said, "Sammy is my ace boon koon so you guys treatum real good. Unnerstand?" Well, after dat somethin' happened dat'll just get you in da girth, I mean gird you in da pith, I mean dere was a dearth of boos and nothin' but stormy applause after an especially pithy ditty SAM done about how hard it was when he was back in rat pack p.s. Why pennies run outta da sky. You shoulda seenum. And den da dook come on. Dat dook. His band raised da roof beams off da joint."

"If you don't mind, your honor," I said, "I'm getting married this afternoon so if it's all right with you, I'd like to get on with the interview."

"Gettin' married! How wondaful. Here, have a piece of candy," he said, pressing the chocolate into my hand.

"I don't know what to say, sir. Gee, not only are you Nazarene priests in the Civil Service kind, but the candy melts in your mouth and not on your hands."

"Tink nothin' of it dere, Doopeyduk. Your name is Doopeyduk, ain't it? Where dat name come from, kiddo, da Bible or somethin'?"

"No, sir. It came from a second cousin of my mother who did time for strangling a social worker with custom-made voodoo gloves."

"I see. What do you do for a living, Mr. Doopeyduk?"

"I am a psychiatric technician."

"What precisely does that involve?"

"I empty utensils and move some of our senior citizens into a room where prongs are attached to their heads and they bounce up and down on a cart and giggle."

"That must be engaging work."

"Yes, it is. I'm learning about the relationship between the texture and color of feces and certain organic and/or psychological disturbances."

"Excellent! What do you intend to do in the future?"

"Well, my work has come along so well that I have been assigned to the preparatory surgery division of the hospital."

"What does that involve?"

"You see, when someone undergoes a hemorrhoidectomy, it's necessary that there are no hairs in the way. I'm sort of like a barber."

"Why do you want an apartment in the Harry Sam Projects?"

"I'm getting married this afternoon and as a Nazarene apprentice, it behooves me to start at the bottom and work my way up the ladder. Temperance, frugality, thrift–that kind of thing."

"Why, Mr. Doopeyduk," the priest exclaimed, removing his glasses. "I find that to be commendable! I didn't know that there were members of the faith among your people."

"There are millions, simply millions who wear the great commode buttons and believe in the teachings of Nancy Spellman, Chief Nazarene Bishop. Why, I wanted to become the first bacteriological warfare expert of the race. That was when my level of performance was lower than my level of aspiration. Now I'm just content to settle here on the home front. Wheel some of our senior citizens around, clean out the ear trumpets and empty the colostomy bags."

"The more I hear about you, the more impressed I am. You must come out and address my Kiwanis Club sometime, Doopeyduk. If there were more Negroes like you with tenacity, steadfastness, and stick-to-itiveness, there would be less of those tremors like the ones last summer, shaking SAM as if he had the palsy."

He gave me the keys to my apartment in the Harry Sam Projects and brought down the stamp of approval on my application.

That afternoon we sat in the front row of the Church of the Holy Mouth, a big Byzantine monstrosity that stood smack in the middle of Soulsville. Fannie Mae quietly chatted with her friend Georgia Nosetrouble. The two were inseparable so it seemed only natural that Georgia would be recruited as a witness.

We were waiting for Elijah Raven, a friend of mine who had consented to be best man, and of course Rev. Eclair Porkchop whose star was rising fast in SAM. Elijah was the first to arrive. He wore a dark conservative pin-stripped suit and colorful beaded hat. He was bearded.

"Flim Flam Alakazam! Brothers and sisters."

Wrinkling their noses at each other, Fannie Mae and Georgia smirked.

"Flim Flam what?" I asked Elijah.

"O, of course, you wouldn't know, would you? I mean—being the brainwashed Negro you are who believes in everything that SAM runs down. Your mind is probably in the attic with all the other dummies and hand-me-downs."

"But Elijah!" I persisted. "It was only a few weeks ago that you were saying familiar things like 'Hello' or 'Hya doin'' or 'What's happening, my man.' Sometimes even slapping the palm of your hand into mine."

"That was last week. I have rejuvenated myself by joining the Jackal-headed Front. We are going to expose SAM, remove some of these blond wigs from off our women's heads, and bring back rukus juice and chittlins. You'd better get on the right side, brother, because when the deal goes down, all the backsliding Uncle Toms are going to be mowed down. You hear? Every freakin', punkish Remus will get it in the neck, Doopeyduk."

Elijah scowled, moving his finger across his neck to stress the point and revealing cuff links the size of Brazil nuts on which were engraved: "To Elijah from Sargent Shriver." But before he could expound his separatist views, the door in the back of the church opened with a slow, labored creak. I felt a chill on my shoulders and the others indicated that they too were cold.

"Ain't dey got no kindlin' in dis place?" inquired Georgia Nosetrouble.

We fixed our attention upon the door. An outline hesitated in its well. A man wearing a cape and tall hat. Removing his gloves, he seemed to float down the aisle. Soon Rev. Eclair Porkchop stood before us, resplendent in tuxedo and walking cane. Clicking his heels together, he kissed Georgia and Fannie Mae's hands.

"Good eve-a-ning. Allow me to introduce myself. I am Eclair Porkchop, head of the Church of the Holy Mouth. I am sorry to detain you but I had to do some work downtown for SAM."

"I bet that ain't all you did, you faggot and enemy of the people. When the shit hits the fan, your life ain't gone be worth two cents."

Eclair Porkchop sneered at Elijah Raven. "O, if it isn't that silly little separatist! I thought you'd be wearing a bone through your nose by now. All of that talk about going back to Africa. What happened? They dispossess your stepladder and five-dollar public-speaking permit?"

"Now see here, cocksucker," Elijah said, moving closer to the preacher.

"Break it up. Break it up. Are Fannie Mae and I going to get married or are you two going to debate?"

I looked around for Fannie Mae and Georgia who had been seated in the pews. They were nowhere to be seen. Voices came from the direction of the outer hall.

"Excuse me, gentlemen, I'll get Fannie Mae and her friend so that we can begin."

Fannie Mae and Georgia were embracing in the shadows outside the door. Georgia was sobbing. "Oh baby, what will I do without you," she panted as she massaged Fannie Mae's thighs. Seeing me, Fannie Mae removed herself from Georgia's clutch.

"What you doin', spying on us or somethin'! Can't people be by demselves sometime without you snoopin' around!!!"

"O forgive me, dearest. I didn't mean to interrupt your departure from a lifelong friend and companion," I apologized sheepishly. "But Eclair Porkchop said he had to attend a meeting over there in the motel and I thought we'd better get on with the ceremony."

"Well, yawl jess have to wait a minute."

"Of course, dear. Certainly. No rush."

The wedding ceremony was performed in the pastor's study. Afterward I bade Elijah good-bye and accepted his and Eclair Porkchop's congratulations. Georgia sadly straggled off to her home.

"Why were you and Georgia giggling at Eclair Porkchop and Elijah Raven?" I asked my new bride as we walked down the steps of the Church of the Holy Mouth.

"Both da niggahs crazy," came her reply.

"Why do you say that, dearest poppy-stick and honey-pie sugar-bunch?"

"Well, to tell it like t-i-s, Porkchop got bubble gum in his brain. Wads and wads of it hunchin' all up ginst his skull walls. I 'member when he was runnin' da numbers and selling reefers to people. Now he goin' round heah talkin' all proper, tellin' folks he been called. Hee, hee, hee. Fool sound lak Count Dracula or some spook lak dat. And dat otha niggah talkin' bout he don't eat pork no mo. Shoot! Me and Georgia saw him back of da Soulfood Restaurant last night. And da niggah was wearing shades so nobody'd recognize him. Next thing we know he was rolling all 'round da floor with a big hog maw 'bout to choke him to death. Dey had to call da ambulance to get some oxygen, for da fool who by then was turnin' green and callin' on da lawd, his mama and 'bout six or seven prophets to save him. Well, when dey revived him, dey removed his shades and everybody recognized him as Elijah. 'I thought you didn't eat pork, Elijah,' somebody asked. You know what da niggah answered? What? Said dat he was doin' research on some beast name megamorphesis. And, if you ask me, da only beast in da place was dat hog maw which almost carried da fool on way from heah."

As I walked arm in arm toward our new home with my bride, an amazing thing occurred to me. Fannie Mae knew the inside dope on everybody in Soulsville. My sweet, innocent bride, who was fond of saying, "I loves to party and I know where I can find a party," was really together.

Fannie Mae and I stood near the amusement truck outside the Harry Sam Projects. The rides consisted of plastic and stainless steel drolls, giraffes and horses. The children were chitterwhimpering and higgledy-piggledy playing pickaback. A statue of HARRY SAM reigned over all, this time standing with his hands draped over two marvelous Victorian urinals. A black Screw sat at the entrance to the high-rise building that contained our apartment. (Screws are men armed with turkey muskets who patrol HARRY SAM.) At his feet was a victrola which played the jug music of a hot Memphis band. He wore a cracked cowbell around his neck marked Carnegie. (Elijah Raven and his gang had placed it there telling him that it was an award in recognition of his valor for preventing homicide by mediating a dispute over highjacked piecrust which involved several tenants. The bell provided an early warning system for the Jackal-headed

Front busily involved in some sinister pranks in the Harry Sam Projects.)

He slept while flies zoomed around his bean. Like the nasty little dive bombers they were, they dashed against his forehead. He jerked, one eyelid open and one shut, then went back to sleep.

Fannie Mae and I reached the door of our apartment and I put the key into the latch. Wheezing, I lifted Fannie Mae for the traditional threshold caper.

"Put me down, fool! You simple or somethin'?"

"But Fannie Mae, dearest. This is included in the marriage rite prescribed by the Nazarene manual."

"Aw dem white folks done fussed yo skull wit all dat crazy talk. Let's go inside like somebody's got some sense. You come on like some senile mailman with a case of dropsy."

Inside we examined the five empty rooms of our first apartment. Through the walls came the voices of our neighbors: "Who ate dat last piece of pie son of a bitch you ate it who ate it he ate it then what's the crust doin' in you greasy choppers if he ate it cause he snuck and ate it while you was sleepin' fool did you eat the pie yes I ate it woman you gone whup me about it aw woman don't whip da man let him res woman why don't you jess hush and let peoples res. . . ."

Outside the belching of foghorns. The interminable helicopters. The snow falling. EATS EATS EATS EATS.

The next morning my father-in-law called. A ninety-year-old punkish-looking mothball, he was devoted to thumb-sucking and living with the tales-of-the-crypt voice who decorated his house with crocheted pillows of Niagara Falls. He had been president of the colored Elks in 1928 and once kissed Calvin Coolidge's ass. He now sat about the house all day drinking Champale malt liquor and watching daytime melodramas on TV. Cobwebbed antlers rested upon his head.

He said, "Fannie Mae, dahlin'. I am spitting up dese colors, see, and I would like for you to come over and put some pink powder inbetween my toes for dey is crawlin' with what appears to be some kind of anamuls. Also, baby, as you know, I is real sceered of da dak. Dere are dese spooky shapes sitting atop my bedposts and dey won't go a-way, no matter how hard I huff and puff. Now baby, you know dat don't make no kind of sense. Yo daddy, as you will recall, was da head of da colored Elks in 1928 and I must send out correspondences. Granmama put some Uncle Jeeter's powder under da pillow and dat didn't seem to help a-tall. In fact, DEM SPECTERS DONE GOT BOLDER! Please come over and shoo dem away 'cause dey is makin' me wet the bed and scream and hollah fo Granmama whose tryin' to get her witchcraft doctorate and make somethin' out of herself. I will expect you fust ting in da morning and tings can be da way dey was 'fo you married dat boy what sticks prongs in people's heads and makes dem bounce up and down lak dey is some kinda acrobat. Dis is da Grand Exalted Ruler of da Elks signin' over to his daughter." (Click.)

"My father wants me to come over to his house and read old-timey pamphlets to him," Fannie Mae announced. "I'll be back in two weeks."

"Why can't his mother do that?"

"She's taking a course under the Mojo Power Retraining Act, dat's why. You so simple."

"Somebody ought to take a stick and bang the big sissy upside the head with it. Rusty dusty overgrown Mickey Mouse flapper afraid of the dark and calling for that ogress. Heh, heh, heh."

"Don't be thinkin' ugly 'bout my family. You're jess jealous 'cause he was da head of da colored Elks in 1928 and all you can do is take care of all dem screwballs skipping around what needs a shrink."

"Well, a kat who sits in the house all day wearing a moose headpiece got a whole lot of marbles to collect."

"Don't be laffin' at my daddy," Fannie Mae said, hurling a pan of lye at me. I ducked and the solution went through the window. Below, there was the sudden clang of a cowbell accompanied by a scream. Then many klang-a-langs in rapid succesion quietly dying in the distance.

"I was just jokin,' dearest. Don't get excited."

"You best be jokin.' Now I'm gone go over to Daddy's and take care of him. Dere is some week-old green chickens dat I bought at Gooseman's supermarket for seventy cents a pound. You can nibble on dat for a while."

She threw her garment about her and rushed from the apartment.

But she forgot something. I went to the closet and removed a plastic container from the shelf. I opened the window and yelled at Fannie Mae.

"YOU FORGOT SOMETHIN', SWEET PICKLE BUNCH."

"Whatchawont?"

"You forgot . . . the antler polish," I screamed.

The Job

■ Ben Caldwell

PERSONNEL INTERVIEWER, WHITE
APPLICANT #1, NEGRO WOMAN
APPLICANT #2, NEGRO MAN
APPLICANT #3, NEGRO MAN
APPLICANT #4, NEGRO WOMAN
APPLICANT #5, NEGRO MAN
APPLICANT #6, BLACK MAN
APPLICANT #7, NEGRO MAN (LATECOMER)

Scene 1. Bright lighted office interior. 8:45 A.M. is the time on the wall clock. A large white sign hangs from the light green wall, reading, "NEW

YORK OFFICE FOR N.O.," *in foot-high letters. Underneath, half the size, is "PROJECT NEGRO OPPORTUNITIES." A blond, blue-eyed male is seated at a grey steel desk. There is an unoccupied chair beside the desk. A tall file cabinet is close by. Six people stand in single file line. Pink filled-out application forms in their hands. First in line is a pretty dark-complex-ioned young lady. Straightened hair gleaming. She wears a blue imitation leather coat, a brown skirt, a pink blouse. Her facial expression is sad. Behind her, a young man of about 20. He has on a black leather coat, white shirt, dark tie, green corduroy trousers, brown suede shoes. He is trying so hard to give the impression that he's cool, unconcerned, that he looks tense. Like he's braced against a stiff wind. Behind him is a "cat" who would be considered "clean" in the slang sense. His processed hair sparkles electrically. He wears an olive green, continental cut, enter-tainer's suit. Black patent leather shoes. The cuffs of his clean yellow shirt hang far beneath his jacket sleeves. Large cuff links. Every now and then he hums the melody of a current popular R & B tune, ("Cool Jerk") and does a little step to relieve his boredom. Behind is a woman of about 35. She has on a fur collared black wool coat, a printed scarf is tied on her head. She looks bored, tired, disgusted. Behind her is a slumped negro man who looks tired from years of hard life and working. He has worked in the clothes he's wearing. Behind him is a tall black man. His hair long, bushy. His black sports coat is much too small. His much-washed khaki trousers are too short. He has dirty white sneakers on his big feet, he wears no sox. He carries a musical instrument case (saxophone). Maybe he just seems big because the clothes are not his. The line faces the blonde blue-eyed male. He examines and files some papers and cards from atop the desk. He then looks up, nods, signaling the first applicant to come forward. She walks to, and stands beside, the desk. The blonde stands to greet her, extending his hand.*

INTERVIEWER: Good-morning. Welcome to N.O. My name is Mr. Foster. Won't you sit down. *They both sit. She hands him her application.* Before we begin I'd like to ask you some questions, and tell you a little about N.O. Did the Welfare refer you to N.O.?

1, (*southern accent*): Yes.

INTERVIEWER: Good. Now Project N.O. is a government sponsored pro-gram designed to fill some of the gaps in our welfare programs. *Broad smile.* We realize that just to offer financial assistance does not solve or eliminate the problem. We realize that some of us have difficulty finding jobs because of educational limitations. The N.O. program tackles both problems. We offer assistance—financial—and training so that you may qualify for a better paying job. And with your newly acquired skills you also achieve job security. Would you give me your name, please?

1. May-ree Free-mun.

INTERVIEWER, *writing*. How old are you, Mary?

1. 20.

INTERVIEWER. Are you married, Mary?

1. No.

INTERVIEWER. Do you have any children, Mary?

1. *Slightly indignant.* No, I don't.

INTERVIEWER. Do you live alone or with your folks, Mary?

1. I live with my folks.

INTERVIEWER. How far did you go in school?

1. I graduated.

INTERVIEWER. You mean from high school?

1. Yes.

INTERVIEWER. Where was that—I mean where did you go to school?

1. In Georgia.

INTERVIEWER. What part of Georgia? And the name of the school?

1. Backwoods, Georgia. And I went to Freeman Gosden-Charles Corell High.

INTERVIEWER. Oh, yes, I understand that's a very good school. Did you like going to school, Mary?

1, *shrugging shyly.* It was all right.

INTERVIEWER. Well, did you take any special courses?

1. No.

INTERVIEWER. What are some of your interests, Mary?

1, *puzzled. No answer.*

INTERVIEWER. I mean is there something you like to do more than anything else?

1. I like to cook. And sew. I used to want to be a artist.

INTERVIEWER, *scribbling in his note pad.* Oh, that's nice. What kind of work have you done in the past?

1. Factory.

INTERVIEWER. Did you like working in a factory?

1, *shrugs. Indecisive.*

INTERVIEWER. Do you like to work, Mary?

1. Yes, but the jobs didn't pay much money—and they was always layin' off.

INTERVIEWER. I see. Now what we're going to try to do for you is, first, have you tested. Then we're going to see if we can send you to a school —to learn how to cook and sew—so you can get a good job cooking or sewing. Something that you like to do. How does that sound to you?

1. Well, I already can sew good enough to get a job, I just wan . . .

INTERVIEWER. Wait a minute. While you're going to school the government will pay you a salary until you graduate. Ah, you're smiling. I guess it makes you happy to know that things aren't so hopeless after all! *Big Smile.* Yes, N.O. is here to give hope to the hopeless. To give you a second chance for that chance you missed. *Pause.* Now, Mary, I want you to sign these two papers.

He waits while she signs. Meanwhile, on the line, the woman looks, impatiently, at her watch. Asks an unheard question of the man in front of her. The strange man on the end of the line (#6) drops a wrapped object, accidentally. It makes a loud metallic ring. He picks it up, unzips the instrument bag, and places the object inside.

INTERVIEWER. Now I want you to take this card and go to this address, tomorrow, 9 A.M., to be tested. Then you come back here to see me

Wednesday. I hope we've helped you on the way to an everlasting job.
Good luck!
1. Thank you.

She gets up to leave. Her disposition changed from the earlier gloom. The men turn to watch her walk out. One of the men makes a remark to her as she passes. She conspicuously ignores him. The INTERVIEWER *writes and files. Then signals the next applicant to come forward.*

Scene 2. The INTERVIEWER *is finishing with the next-to-last applicant. The wall clock states 11:40.*

INTERVIEWER. Now I'm sure that once you finish the training and get a good job—a good *steady* job—you and your wife won't fight, and she won't have to call the cops on you. Ha, ha, ha, ha, ha! Okay, Sam?
5. Ha, ha. Yeah, OK. Thank you fo' everything, Mr. Foster.
INTERVIEWER, *standing as the applicant does—extending his hand.* I want you to keep this job, Sam, so you can stay out of trouble. Okay?
5. Okay.
INTERVIEWER. Okay. Glad we could help you. Best of luck, Sam. SAM *nods his head and leaves.* INTERVIEWER *takes some papers to the file. Files them. Returns to desk to answer the phone.* Yes? Oh, hi Stan. No, not quite. So far only four or five. Got one more to go. Oh, you know, the usual. Yeh. What did you expect? Just another way of keeping them in line. Ha ha ha. Where're you having lunch? Oh, good, I'll meet you there in about 20 minutes. All right, bye.

He looks at the last applicant apprehensively, and motions him forward. He stands to greet him. Into the blonde's extended hand 6 shoves the application. They both sit.

INTERVIEWER. I'm sorry you had to wait so long, sir.
6. That's all right. We've waited so long a few more minutes don't matter.

The INTERVIEWER *looks puzzled at this reply, and more so when he looks at the application. He smiles a nervous smile. He gestures.*

INTERVIEWER. Sir, you haven't filled out your application.
6. I know.
INTERVIEWER. Why is that, sir?
6. There is no reason to fill it out.
INTERVIEWER. Aren't you looking for a job?
6. No. I have a job.
INTERVIEWER, *further puzzled and at a loss for words. The applicant's intense glare unnerves him even more. He makes a "conversation piece" of the instrument case.*
INTERVIEWER. You have a job? Oh! Are you a musician?
6. Yes.

INTERVIEWER, *trying to sound interested instead of uneasy.* Oh! What do you play?

6. I play the truth.

INTERVIEWER. The truth? Is that an instrument? I don't understand! . . What is this? Is this some sort of joke?

6. *just stares at him.*

We're here to help you. There's no information on this application and there's nothing I can do if . . .

6. *I* don't want you to do anything. Or I should say *"we."* I have a job. I'm doing what all my people should be doing.

INTERVIEWER. I don't understand you, but I have a job to do. What's your name, sir?

6. Just call me *BLACK NIGGER*—that's what you'd like to do, *WHITEY!*

INTERVIEWER, *excited.* I thought so! One of those "black nationalist" characters! Look here, I can understand your anger, and even your bitterness—and I sympathize—but what you're doing is unreasonable. You're doing nothing to help yourself or your people. We're here to help *you* people. We're doing all we can to change the shameful conditions that have existed for too long. People like you make things worse. Now if you came here for a job, good—if not . . .

6. *During the speech he places his instrument case on his lap and opens it. He places his hands on the instrument.* I told you I didn't come here to get a job. I have a job. I came to do a job. I feel like playing!

He rises, quickly, and swings the instrument, striking the INTERVIEWER *on the head, it makes a loud thump. The* INTERVIEWER *screams, loudly. Blood is running down his face, onto his white shirt. He runs to the file cabinet and frantically rummages through the cards.*

INTERVIEWER, *hysterical.* Wait! Wait! I know I can find you something! A good job! A good paying, steady, job! You don't have to do this!

6. Yeah! I feel like playing! Like swinging! How you like this JAZZ!? *The applicant swings again, striking him on the arms and hands. He sounds like a preacher preaching a sermon.* We should have done this long time ago! *All* niggers should be doing this! Instead of begging and being killed. Kiss your ass when they should be kicking your ass! And trying to be like you! Hoping you'd treat us as men. Hoping you'd stop killing us. Hoping you'd accept us! But all you offer us is jobs! We want our freedom and all you offer is jobs and integration! You've turned us wrongside out! You forced me into this role! Your clothes don't fit me! Your ways don't fit me! I'm not myself! I'm not a killer. *Whop!* I can't be myself till the world is free of you! *Whop! His blow knocks the* INTERVIEWER *to his knees.* I tried and I waited. But all you want is for us to be your slaves! That's all you want! I won't be your slave! *Whop!* I must save myself!

INTERVIEWER, *bubbling, babbling, gurgling, blood-choked sounds!* Oh, god, don't let them kill me! Don't let them kill me! Please don't kill me. *Trying to move away, on his knees.*

6. God ain't gon' answer you—your god is dead!

INTERVIEWER. AAaaaaaaaaaaaaaaaaaaalp! Please, god!

6. Understand how it feels to be beaten! *Whop!* Understand how it feels to beg! *Whop!* Understand how it feels to hope when there's no hope! *Whop!* So many of us died waiting and hoping! Placing faith in your lies and promises! So many of us never even had reason to hope! They shoulda been doing this! *Whop!* Understand how it feels to have your life taken from you! *WHAM!* There's no hope for you! There's no hope for you now!

He strikes again just as the phone rings. He pulls the desk in front of the apparently dead body. He puts his instrument back into the case. The phone continues to ring. He hurries to leave and bumps into a young man entering.

7. Oh! Excuse me! Is anybody here?

6. There's no one here! There's no one here!

7, *looking around.* Must be out to lunch! I guess I'll wait. I don't have anything to do. And I need a job, bad!

6 exits. 7 stands waiting.

Curtain.
Recorded music: Charlie Parker's "Now Is the Time."

The Monster

■ Ron Milner

A ONE-ACT PLAY

Characters:

ALI
JASON
RICK   } Young "black" students
MIKE
HELEN
DEAN: "Professional Negro"

Scene One

Day—probably afternoon, though there is no real sense of a time of day—light, darkness, etc.

Small, cave-like room, with the slanted beams of an attic, or a belfry. This is at the top of a seldom used building, or portion of a building, on the campus of a colored college. The one window is stage right (can be off-stage right) and on a rise; it is covered with black thick curtains. Entrance (and exit) is down stage left. The over-all sense is of a circle shaded and shaped to a triangle. The furniture is mainly boxes set around the room to enforce the triangle, with a large desk-table or maybe three boxes with a cover, rear-center; there are candles set in liquor bottles and a couple of ashtrays around. The incongruous pieces are: a once plush but now nearly ruined easy chair centerstage, and a dresser stage right.
As it begins ALI *and* RICK *are at desk listening to end of a tape—incoherent—on recorder.*

ALI,(*shutting off tape*): Damn. It's like you said all right. How'd you say you got it?

RICK: When this sister went to his place to interview him for the school paper she took a big recorder—for the interview. She also took along a little one—for us. Got his wife to show her around the house—and left it in a good spot.

ALI: Wife. What is a creature like that doing with a wife?

RICK: She's part of the thing, you know that. What I wanna' know is where do they find him?! I mean how do they make 'em, create 'em like that?! How can they keep coming off like that!?

ALI: You know how. If we had a few centuries of practice and all the machinery setup we could be turnin' 'em out like—like Mustangs and Coupe DeVille's just like they do!

RICK: I wouldn't want none in no world that I had anything to do with the shape of.

ALI: Well in a mess like this world, they can be used.

RICK: Yes.

ALI: And you don't know where they're coming from? Just look around you brother. On this campus right here they're doing their best to send out some every year. RICK *makes sound of agreement.* Young Frankensteins. *Assumes pose.* Striding around with their hands out-stretched. Ready to do whatever their masters command. Stumbling around being moved by somebody else's mind, heart and soul! Class A stars in a horror movie! And they don't even know it! Aw, man— damn! *Touches head.*

RICK: Keep runnin' it down brother. Don't let it run *you* down.

ALI, *sighing.* I'm all right. I'll be okay. It's just—just—*Looks to entrance as, supported by* JASON *and* MIKE *on each side, enters* THE DEAN *walking in fact like Frankenstein—his arms, held at the elbows by* JASON *and* MIKE, *wave before him like a stunned blindman's, his strides come too high, slow, and long to be normal. He wears suit, tie, etc.* JASON *and* MIKE *lead him to easychair and plunk him down.* ALI *turns away from the sight.* Aw man—damn!

JASON: Look what we done brung ya'!

MIKE: The dean of all us students!

JASON: Hey, yeh. Young up and coming future leader of the society!

RICK: All of a sudden on his way down.

MIKE: You tryin' to tell us somethin' 'bout our bossman? *Tries to force* DEAN's *glasses onto him; they slide off and fall into his lap.*

MIKE, JASON, *and* RICK *begin circling easy chair and adjoining table. Continue throughout "acceptance ritual."*

ALI (*studying* DEAN *thoughtfully*): I didn't know he wore glasses.

JASON: Oh, just at home. *Assuming jitterburg air.* You see, round campus he wears sunglasses, shades, you dig, like a cat should. You dig?

MIKE (*giving* JASON *five*): Don't I though? Don't I? And he don't walk like he just did around campus either!

JASON: He don't?!

MIKE: Aw, naw. Nonea' that straight-up zombie walkin', uh-uh. My man gets down wit' it. More of a, *Cattin'*, gritty-grit, groovin' dip to his bop! Youuunuhstan'?

JASON: Oh yeh! Definitely! But not too much of a dip you dig. Because he don't want to look like he is a jitterbug himself. Just want to look like he know where the jitter and the bug are coming from. In case he needs to wear that face too sometime.

MIKE (*stares at* JASON *as the joke wears out*): Yeh, I got you. Maybe we should give him just one real face to wear from now on.

They both move toward him and stand before him as if tempted to send fists into DEAN's *face.*

ALI: Cool it, man. Come on. Is he ready?

All the while DEAN *has been sitting staring straight ahead, mouth open.*

JASON (*stark tone change*): Ready as he can get.

MIKE: Yeh, we put the little truth needle to him. He can't sham now.

RICK: The serum works like the brother said huh?

JASON: Just like the brother said.

MIKE: Didn't take but a minute. And that stuff had him. And he was ready to finally be himself.

JASON: You can see the results.

ALI: What about Helen?

MIKE: She's in there getting it together.

RICK (*after he and* ALI *exchange glances*): Might as well try the key-words. Like the brother said.

All glance at each other and nod. ALI *joins the ritual circling now. And now it is more purposeful as after* RICK *gives the key-word the other three repeat it three times stepping in time to their shouts.*

RICK (*in solo whisper*): Prestige!

JASON (*same whisper*): Prestige!

MIKE: Prestige!

ALI: Prestige!

DEAN's *head snaps up at word. He begins to audibly sniff the air in all directions, an excited animation coming over him.*

ALI (*turning away*): Aw man—damn!
JASON: Dig it! Dig it!
MIKE: Look at him, man! Look at him!

All still moving.

RICK (*same whisper*): Status!

JASON, MIKE, *and* ALI *repeat word,* DEAN *becomes even more excited, looking and sounding very like a panting, hungry dog as he turns head in all directions.*

ALI: Damn! Damn! Damn!
RICK: Security!

JASON, MIKE, *and* ALI *repeat.*
DEAN *becomes near frantic; increasing animal sounds while bouncing in seat.*

ALI: Will you look at that shit, man? Just look at it!
RICK: Yeh, and we haven't even gotten to the big one yet.
ALI: Yeh we have, goddammit! Yeh, we have.

Leading them all to DEAN *in what becomes a shouted chant.*

ALL: ACCEPTANCE! WHITE ACCEPTANCE! ACCEPTANCE! WHITE ACCEPTANCE! ACCEPTANCE! WHITE ACCEPTANCE!! PRESTIGE—STATUS—SECURITY—ACCEPTANCE—WHITE ACCEPTANCE! PRESTIGE—STATUS—SECURITY—ACCEPTANCE—WHITE ACCEPTANCE! PRESTIGE—STATUS—SECURITY—ACCEPTANCE—WHITE ACCEPTANCE!

DEAN *begins to whimper and moan and squirm as a woman at the crest of lovemaking. They hide him from audience a moment. Then all suddenly turn from chair.*

JASON: Aw man!
MIKE: Damn!
RICK: O'oo wow. I guess that's the one all right.
ALI (*disgustedly*): Goddam! Look man, those words might have an effect on anybody! But— but they couldn't turn everybody into a—a—
JASON: Sick somethin'—
ALI: —a nothin'! Like—*Pointing without looking.* —like that!
RICK (*wiping face with handkerchief; same edge of disgust in tone*): Yeh. Well that's what and where he is. So are we going to do something with it or not!

JASON: Yeh. Do *something* with him!

MIKE: In a hurry!

ALI: Yeh. Helen! Helen!

HELEN (*off-stage*): I'm right here, Ali! I've got his drink! Ready when you get ready!

ALI: All right. (*Then to others*). Okay, looka' here.

Gathers them in a quasi-huddle, explaining idea, as lights intensify a blue haze around DEAN'S *area. They come out of huddle.* ALI *goes directly before* DEAN, *others surround and circle the chair.*

ALI: Mr. Dean, sir—

OTHERS: Prestige. Status. Security.

ALI: Our most reverent Mr. Dean Sir.

OTHERS: White acceptance is yours. Caucasian glory is yours.

ALI: This is a most beautiful home you have.

OTHERS: —White and beautiful—Beautiful and white—

ALI: This is a most elegant home.

OTHERS: —White and elegant—Elegant and white—

ALI: The most beautiful and elegant home around.

OTHERS: In all the snow around—

HELEN (*off-stage*): God!

ALI: Most reverent Mr. Dean, sir—

OTHERS: —Onto thee all manner of whiteness—

ALI: To you we say, yes-sur, yes-sur, yes-sur.

OTHERS (*bowing*): All white! All white! White all!

As they've performed, DEAN'S *head has come up and swayed as though listening to a classic mass. Then he's relaxed in an air of comfort and luxuriousness, and taken and lit a cigar from his breast pocket.*

JASON: He's ready now.

RICK: Definitely.

MIKE: Ain't he though.

DEAN *shows the effects of the flattery: caresses lapels, flicks ashes.*): Can we do anything for you before we leave? To show our appreciation? An ashtray, sir? (*Motions for one;* RICK *hands it.*) Here you are sir. (*Putting tray on arm of chair.*) Would you like your shoes removed? (DEAN *makes fluttery, false gesture of refusal—but is so thrilled and flattered he kicks his feet in air and leaves them there to be attended even while shaking head no.*) There you are sir. We're going now. We thank you for your time and consideration. Your wife—Your wife uh—(*Looks to others.*)

RICK: Jane.

JASON: Yeh. She Jane; him, Tarzan.

ALI: Ah yes, Jane.

DEAN (*clears throat*): Tarzan. Yes. One of my favorite fantasy figures.

Ape-like white lord of the black heathen jungle. Yes. Most interesting historical figure. Yes Burroughs. Written in—let me see—

MIKE: Wow. He's definitely ready.

JASON: Ain't he. Stripped right down.

ALI: Uh yes, I'm sure it's very interesting. But as I was about to say, your wife, Jane, is back from her trip. And she's on her way in with your drink, sir. So we have to be going now. Good-by. And thank you. Thank you. Thank you.

Backing off with others into shadows. JASON *and* MIKE *sit on opposite sides of stage. Halleluiah chorus from the Messiah blares forth near crescendo.* ALI *sits down.* HELEN—*Jane—enters to the music; wearing a mini-skirted jumper outfit, with long-sleeved highcollar tights, and go-go boots. The thing about the get-up is that it is divided right down to the boots with one side being all white, the other all black—excepting gloves which are both white. A black-white costume jewelry chain dangles from her waist. Her face is white rubber mask (lavender lipstick) including a ratty blond wig. Pointedly carying the tray she moves out in an exaggerated mince-step that is slowed down and set to the grand style of the music. After her initial moment, she breaks the feeling to give a little out-of-character shrug to the brothers, showing how ridiculous she feels; then resumes "role," posing with tray.*

HELEN: Dahling, I've brought your drink. My poo-poo.

JASON (*across to* MIKE): Her what, man?

MIKE: Her poo-poo.

JASON: Oh! That's what he is, huh?

ALI: Shhh. Dig.

DEAN: Oh, yes, Jane, my darling, Jane.

HELEN: Yes.

DEAN: Oh, my dear, dear Jane, you look so ravishingly white tonight!

HELEN: Do I dahling? Thank you. You took look quite white tonight, dear.

They both give silent-movie type cuddly laughs.

JASON: Aw, man! Turn the sound off. Or wake me up when they get to what's happening.

HELEN: Hasn't it all been just too wonderful tonight, dear? The music, the guests, and all?

DEAN: Yes, my dear. If you say so.

HELEN: Yes. And now I've brought you your drink. Dahling. (*Removes ashtray, puts tray on arm of chair and sits on other arm. Her white side turned to* DEAN *and audience.*)

DEAN (*rubbing his face on her white leg and arm, touching her face*): So beautifully, ravishingly, whitely white.

MIKE: Think I'm gonna' have to go to the toilet.

HELEN (*giving him a forced grin, then catching his hand as it disappears under her skirt*): Yes dahling. But your drink. Don't forget your drink. *As "real"* HELEN. Drink it!

DEAN (*stunned by her tone*): Huh?

ALI: Easy Helen, watch it.

HELEN (*correcting her tone*): Your drink, darling. Please. I made it a special one.

DEAN: Oh? Well. ("*Sips*" *from empty glass.*) Ummm. Uh, just what is it darling?

HELEN: Crushed snow.

DEAN: Oh, yes. Delight—What? What did you say dear?

ALI: Helen—

HELEN: crushed snow, darling. I thought you'd enjoy the chilling whiteness of its sliding slowly down your throat, numbing your insides.

DEAN: Ah, yes, yes. What would I do without you. (*Drinks from both glasses.*) Delicious. White-stuff. Yum-yum. White-stuff. (*His hands and face beginning to "devour" her white side.*) Marvelous, glorious whitestuff! Ummm. Fantastic! Fabulous! All this here white-stuff!

HELEN (*forcing grins, struggling*): Dahling. Darrr-linng! (*Forgetting role.*) Dammit—Uh, I mean, dear. Now dear.

JASON (*rising in background*): Don't worry, baby! Just tell 'im you accept him!

MIKE (*standing also*): Yeh! And he'll blow his whole thing right there in his pants!

JASON: Yeh! (*crossing to meet* MIKE *at center; gives him "five," "ten!"*)

MIKE: Yeh!

ALI: Cool it. Sit down. *They do, laughing.*

HELEN (*as* DEAN *drools and growls*): Come now, darling. Come now Come on, now, come, dear. (*Gets up, stands before him.*)

DEAN: What, dear? Darling you don't mean it? Is it Sunday night already? I had no idea! My dear! My darling! (*Rushes to embrace her.*)

HELEN *lifts her white leg and tries to wrap it around him.*

HELEN: What—Man what the hell you—

DEAN (*kissing and pawing as she struggles*): Mygloriouswhitestuff! Myyumyumwhitestuff! Goodwhitestuff! Marvelouswhitestuff!

ALI: Don't lose control now Helen. Lead him to it, now. Take him where you want him!

RICK (*grinning*): Yeh! Don't let him get you down, baby!

DEAN: Whitestuff! *etc. etc.* Whitestuff.

HELEN (*freeing herself, grabbing his cheeks, lips, with one hand, pointing her finger*): Yes, darling. But there is the other, dark, darker, black side of things. Remember? (*Rubs the black side of her dress.*)

DEAN (*touching head as though pained*): Dark? Darker? Black? How could you, dear? At a time like this? Whatever can you mean?

HELEN: What do I mean? Listen darling. Listen. (*Moving and pointing toward recorder in shadows.*)

RICK (*manipulates dials: The Impressions doing Curtis Mayfield's KEEP ON PUSHING, at the point where the voices go into the hummed, strained, yearning*): Hear it, dear?

DEAN (*clutching head*): Yes! Oh yes! They're at it again! Those black-power, black awareness students are gathering again!

HELEN: Yes. Talking of black courses.

JASON: And recourses!

MIKE: Of unifying.

RICK: And identifying.

DEAN: Oh, God! God! Won't they let me have any peace? Any peace at all!?

HELEN (*aside, smiling*): You definitely won't be getting any piece here.

ALI: Helen!

DEAN (*turning to look at her, his tone grim*): I suppose The Man has called for me.

HELEN: Yes, dear. He needs you. You're very important to him.

DEAN: Yes, I am. He needs me. Yes. (*Sighs, straightens shoulders.*) I suppose there's nothing to do but to go out and stop them.

HELEN: I suppose so dear.

DEAN: Yes, I must head them off and turn them back.

HELEN: Yes, dear.

DEAN: Come dear. I must prepare to meet them. (*Points to dresser.*)

HELEN (*goes to stand by it. Standing opposite dresser, he hands her his coat*): My ablution, dear.

JASON (*to* MIKE): His ab-what?

MIKE *points to* HELEN *opening top drawer.*

HELEN *takes out and sets bowl atop dresser, lays coat across it, and stands ready with towel.* DEAN *dips hands in, surgeon-like, and lets white liquid drain off.*

JASON: Milk! Aw shit!

Others shush him.

DEAN (*takes towel from* HELEN *and dries hands, then turns to audience and ceremoniously touches right finger-tips to forehead and each shoulder*): In the name of the white, the might, and the fright!

MIKE: What?—Well, I'll be—(*Others shush him.*)

DEAN, *facing audience, as he asks for tools holds left hand out to* HELEN *without looking at her.* Gloves! *She takes from drawer and hands him black-rubber surgeon gloves. He puts them on, flexes fingers.* Beard! *Takes and puts on so-called Van Dyke style mustache-beard; practices a grimace or two.* Natural! *She hands him very "high" Afro wig. He tries it; feels it; flings it away.* I've told you that one is too high, Jane! The smaller one! Quick!

HELEN (*wry face but straight tone*): Yes, dear. I'm sorry. (*Gives him shorter wig.*)

DEAN, *puts on wig.* Chest! *She hands and helps buckle onto him a virility-suggesting chestplate that reminds of both bullet-proof vest and something*

*for the Romans—it is ebony-colored, ana allows some of his tie and collar
to show.* Testicles!
HELEN: What dear? (*Looking.*)
DEAN: Balls, Jane! Balls!
HELEN: Oh, yes, of course. Of course. Well. (*Looking.*) I don't think you
have a pair left. Oh, yes, yes, here they are.
DEAN, *takes them; turns back to* HELEN *and audience and inserts them
inside pants. Stands; straight facing audience again takes deep pleased
sigh, smiles at* HELEN, *and moves down stage. Begins quick hard hand-
thrusting gestures—reminiscent of first Malcolm, the Stokely, then Rap.
It looks like a fencing lesson. As he carries it out further into Cagney-like
belt-lifts with the forearms, into dipping his knees and wiping his sweating
hands on his behind and his groin, it becomes like a dance; going even
into a J.B. thing complete with the sudden dynamic grunts; goes into a
kind of platform-speaker's Bugaloo.*
JASON (*giving* ALI *"ten"*) Aw get it Mr. D! He's really getting into it now,
ain't he?
ALI (*grinning*): Comin' outta' his soul bag brother!
MIKE: Jive motherfucker! Ain't he a bitch?

RICK *is bent with laughter.* HELEN *hides giggling face.*

DEAN (*finishes "exercises," turns to* HELEN *with wide grin*): I think I'm
about ready to face them now dear. I mean, Baby. (*Winks.*) Baby, I
mean. Have to get in character you know. (*Swaggering.*) Let me try one
of those numbers outta' that book, now.
HELEN (*staring amused and incredulous*): Huh?—Oh, yeh. I mean, yes,
dear, yes, certainly. (*Looking in dresser; comes out with white-covered,
official-looking book.*) Ummm, let's see now—
DEAN (*finger-poppin'*): Hurry, now, dear. Baby, I mean. Hurry. I'm hot
now. I'm ready. Sock it to me. Ummph!
HELEN (*character completely gone*): Yeh, all right, hot-shot, number
three.
DEAN: Number three. Yes. (*Moves around; then dynamically confronts
audience.*) Univer-sity! You dig? Understand? That's what all this is
about, learning to live on the universal level! Don't tell me about black
men's heads being split open, black men bleeding to death! When you
look at that blood don't say that's black man's blood. Say that is *Man*
bleeding there! Man's blood! When you bend down to see, don't just
look at the wound! Look there where the blood is seeping into the pores
of the all-accepting Earth! And think of all the countles plots of soil all
over this planet which for centuries upon centuries have been soaking
up, and gagging on, and sending back in the form of fresh flowers, the
blood of man! Lift your lucky heads and look at the clouds! At the
universal formations of—of—umm—uh—of—
HELEN (*disgustedly*) Shhitt!
DEAN: Huh—Uh, what dear?
HELEN: Oh. Uh—Nothing dear. I was just saying that that's enough of

that one. I mean, you have that one pretty well under control. I'm trying
to find another number for you.

The others all stare with cold hatred. JASON *gets up and starts toward*
DEAN *as if in a trance.* MIKE *grabs him pulls him back.*

DEAN: Yes, yes. But it did take me quite awhile to get away from the
point. Didn't it. Must brush up on that one.
JASON: Didn't it though! You motherfucker!!
MIKE: Come on, man. Don't let him bug you. Come on, now, Jason.
JASON (*really upset, wiping eyes*): Some damned clouds! Some fucking
pores of the earth! I'll stomp yo' brains out fucker. Yeh! Then let me see
you abstract and universalize that! Hear!
ALI (*coming over to help* MIKE *hold him*): Jace! Jace! Easy baby. You
gonna' blow it now, man.
JASON: Blow what?! We know where he's comin' from! Why we gotta'
listen to it all! Huh?!
DEAN (*vaguely aware of something being amiss*): Jane?—Jane?—are you
going to give me another number?
ALI: We have a plan, brother, remember? We have to draw it all out first.
Know the depth—
DEAN (*turning in little circles*): Jane? Jane? Are you going to give me
another?
JASON (*breaking away, going toward her and him*): You wanna' give him
a good number, sister? Huh? You already gave him a three, right? Well
now give him a six-nine, sixty-nine. Yeh! You ever—*to* DEAN—played
the numbers, sissy! Huh! You know what 369 plays for, punk?! Huh?!
Hell naw! You don't know nothin' like that! Well it's the Shit-row,
sucker! It plays for shit! And that's all you got in that book, your bag;
nothin' but a bunch of shit.
MIKE: Yeh, and we don't need to hear no more of it. Ain't gonna' hear no
more not from you we ain't.

All moving toward him now.

DEAN (*turning in half-circles*): Jane? Jane? A number from the book! A
number from the book.
ALI: Oh, we got a real hip number for you to dance to this time, man.
RICK: Yeh, you really gone execute some steps now.
JASON: Brand-new, bugaloo!
MIKE: Be socking it to you, Mister!
DEAN (*going to her demanding*): Jane! Jane! A number! A number!
HELEN (*snatching off wig to her own hair*): Helen, Dr. Doolittle! My
name is Helen!!
DEAN (*hands coming out like Frankenstein's again*): No, no— Jane—
Jane—(*wavering around in little half-circles*).
JASON: Dance-floor's this way, Mister. (*Pulling him toward chair, snatch-
ing off and throwing rear his Afro wig.*)
MIKE: Yeh. (*Affecting "Corliss Archer" tone.*) Don't be shy, guy! (*Pulling
off and throwing rear his beard.*)

RICK: You won't need your boobs, baby. (*Helping turn him around and unbuckle his "chest."*)

ALI: Down, Filthy McNasty. (*Pushing him into chair.*) Now.

HELEN (*standing aside with arms folded*): You're forgetting his other falsies.

RICK: Huh? Oh, yeh. (*They all grab him and pull him up at waist by his belt; start unzipping—then all come to same thought and make room for her.*) Would you like the honor?

HELEN: Hmmmm. I don't touch dead things.

They all shrug and lean over him, hiding him from audience. "Falsies" go flying rear.

ALI: Now.

All stand back looking.

HELEN *joins them in center. They suddenly all lean to him and begin shouted chant—which has* DEAN *in writhing, groaning agony unable to bend his straining Frankenstein hands to his ears.*

HELEN: Prestige!!
OTHERS: Black man's prestige!!

All clap hands.

HELEN: Status!!
OTHERS: Black men's Status!!

All clap hands.

HELEN: Security!!
OTHERS: Black men's security!!

All clap hands.

HELEN: Acceptance!!
OTHERS: Black men's acceptance!!

All clap hands. Men, Women, Children!

OTHERS: Black. (*Clap.*) Black. (*Clap.*) Black.
Clap. Prestige!! *Begins again with sense of drums, just as—Black Out.*

Scene Two

Same set; an hour or so later. RICK *winding the cord of the tape recorder.* HELEN, *now in her own clothes, is drinking coffee, sitting on a box; her "white" outfit rests folded near her feet by her bag.* JASON *sits on another box drinking coffee also.* ALI *and* MIKE *are up on other level, on box-steps, the top halves of their bodies hidden by the black curtains; they are looking out window.*

JASON: Yeh, he really blew my mind then. Talking about our blood like it's some water come trickling down off some mountain or something.

HELEN: That's the universal theory, Jace; objectivity, and all that good stuff.

RICK: Yeh, man, everything's just an artifact. Nothing's real. Blood is just color. Words are just sounds. Thoughts relative rationales. Don't you know that? Where you go to school, man?

JASON (*as all three exchange wry grins*): Yeh, well it's kinda hard being objective when you're the object; being the subject I'm very subjective. You dig? (RICK *and* HELEN *nod to him. He turns to* ALI *and* MIKE.) How's he comin'?

MIKE (*under curtain*): He just came out where we can see him. He's stumbling along pretty good.

ALI (*under curtain*): Carrying a real, honest message for once in his life.

HELEN: But are you really sure he's gonna' deliver it? I mean, how can we trust him?

JASON: I don't. And you all let me know when he gets to that bonfire, that meeting. I'm going to listen. And if he don't give that message, he won't give no more. (*Pats his back pocket.*)

ALI: It's a simple enough message.

RICK: And we handled him just like the brother said.

MIKE: And so far it's workin' all right.

ALI: Here comes the first real test, right here.

JASON: What's happening?

MIKE: Two of them little blond instructors just spoke to him, going the other way—Dig it, Ali! He's stopping, man!

All look.

ALI: I dig it. I see it.

MIKE: He's turnin' around, Ali!

ALI: I can see it, Mike! I can see it!

JASON: I knew it! (*Standing; slipping out 45 auto, and checking clip.*)

MIKE: Where's he at, Man!? What's he—these damned glasses ain't shit! —what's he doin' Ali?

ALI (*calmly*): He's looking around in the bushes.

JASON (*going to exit gun in hand*): For a gun? Is he getting a gun, man?

MIKE: I see him now. What's he doing? What's that he got?

ALI: He had some of his—his stuff hid out there. Beard. Natural.

MIKE: Yeh! The chestplate. He's puttin' it on. He's comin' back this way, man!!

JASON: He's comin' back here!? Here!?!

ALI: Yep.

MIKE: Yeh, that's what he's doin' all right. He's comin' back.

JASON (*checking gun again*): Well his chest-piece better be bullet-proof! And even if it is—Shame on his worthless ass! (*Starting out.*)

ALI (*coming from behind curtain and down box-steps; MIKE following him; binoculars dangling down their chests*): Wait Jace! Naw! There's not a whitie anywhere around who would kill him. And if he's found dead, some of us would be the first ones picked up! Now I don't know about you but I'm not out to be heroic! I'm out to get something done! All right!? (*As JASON pauses, waiting.*) All right. Now Rick, you go with him! And you two bring him back up here!

JASON: Alive, man?

ALI: Yeh. Bring it back alive. That's right. Okay?

JASON *shrugs and goes out; RICK goes with him, opening his sportcoat to check his shoulder-holster. ALI begins to pace.*

MIKE: What happen, man? We had all his buttons and gears turnin' for us. What went wrong?

HELEN: I told you you couldn't expect nothin' right from anybody as wrong as him!

ALI: We forgot something. Overlooked something.

MIKE: What? We ran it down just like the brother said.

ALI: Uh-huh, the brother missed it too.

HELEN: What Ali? Tell us what you're talkin' about?

ALI: Don't you dig it? A—A—thing! like this doesn't function, finally, to any—any words! Ideas! His deepest, utmost response, reaction, is to one thing! *Holds up finger.*

HELEN: Yeh, white skin.

ALI (*nodding*):White skin! And as soon as he ran into some of that, he shifted into reverse and started backsliding.

HELEN: Yeh.

MIKE: Yeh, I dig it now.

ALI: Ah-huh. Helen, you put that mask back on. This won't take but a minute. Looka' here, both of you.

Goes to bottom drawer of dresser. Begins to explain as HELEN puts on mask. Takes white rope from drawer, gives it to MIKE; points toward window, explains, MIKE nods, goes over, up box-steps and disappears behind curtain. The sound of others coming up the stairs. With JASON and RICK having an armpit apiece in clutch, DEAN comes back in; the chest-piece is buckled on backwards, beard and natural hang on one side of his face.

JASON: Yeh, man, just bring your ass on.

RICK: Yeh, we know, we know.

DEAN: Number six! Yes. Uh, the only way to match up to this man is to match him dollar for dollar. And that takes time! Takes planning! Means that one educates oneself according to the white man's needs! Yes, the white man's needs! Means that one makes himself a necessary part of the—the bowels of the white man's machinery, and bargains from there! Yes!

JASON: Yeh, we're hip, man, that is until he gets a real machine for that part of his bowels and decides to shit us out! Uh-huh!

RICK: Yeh, we know. We can't match him so we have to join him. Can't have our own machine so we have to be a wrench for his. We know. Come on, Mister.

MIKE (*on box-steps*): His needs! Yeh. We be holding down Civil Service while he's up on the moon—regulating the weather down there!

JASON: Civil-Servitude, you mean!

ALI: Cool it. Let Helen have him.

HELEN (*moving in, her white gloves caressing his face*): Dahling. Prestige, Dahling. Status, Dahling. Security, Dahling. Acceptance, Dahling. White Acceptance.

JASON: That shit again.

DEAN: Jane? Jane, dear. Number nine. (*On his fingers.*) The police! The National Guard! Coast Guard! Army! Paratroopers! Navy! Marines! Green Berets!

HELEN: Yes, dear. Yes, dear.

JASON: Uh-huh. So tote that barge and lift that bale, we know.

MIKE: Listen fool. You ever thought of all the non-white enemies with guns he's got all over the world!? Ever thought of him trying to fight down in his belly and outside his head and at both arms and feet all at the same time!? Here there and everywhere, at once?! Huh, sucker?!

JASON: Yeh, with his factories blowing up on him while he's at it.

DEAN: Jane—Jane—

ALI: Let her have him, man!

HELEN: Dahling, the man called.

DEAN: The man? (*Sniffing the air.*) The man?

HELEN: Yes, dear. (*Leading him over.*) He wants you to go up to the window there. He has a microphone there wired for the whole campus. He wants you to speak to them. Now, dear, right now.

DEAN (*trying to straighten his appearance*): The man. Yes. The man. Yes. (*Goes up steps; MIKE holds curtain back for him. He goes under it.*)

HELEN (*arms folded not looking*): Yes, dear. That's right. Now he said you are to put your head—your head—(*Falters.*)

ALI (*comes to look behind curtain which MIKE still holds*): Yes, Sir. Uh, we're the electricians, we did the wiring. That's it, Sir. Just put your head inside that—that white loop there. That's it. Make sure it's tight around your neck now. We want to be sure everyone hears you. Uh-huh. (*Wiping sweat.*) Is the end secure around that pipe above you, Sir? They're all waiting for you.

All but HELEN *come to steps.* MIKE *drops curtain.*

DEAN: Yes! The Army! The Marines! The Green Berets—(*They pull steps out from under him, he gives one grunt, then dangles silently.*)

HELEN *shudders. Others move away.*

HELEN: I can't stand being around dead things.

ALI (*sighing, wiping face and hands with handkerchief*): That's why we're trying to resurrect ourselves, baby. Wanna' wait downstairs? (*She shakes head no, goes to stand by door.*) All right, let's get it together and get out. Mike you wipe your prints off that rope? (MIKE *nods.*) Okay. Wipe everything we touched. Turn those steps over on their side, near where he could have kicked them. All right: ashtrays, candles, everything, but the chair and the dresser. (*They start getting it all together.* ALI *looks back at dangling legs, first one to do so.*) Yeh, they would believe that he'd kill himself. In a way that's all he's been doing all these years.

MIKE: Yeh, but it's still almost sad ain't it. I mean after a while he seemed almost human, you know?

JASON: Almost is right.

ALI: Yeh. We got everything now? Let's go. (*Starts for door.*)

DEAN (*suddenly grunts and shouts out*): THINK! THINK FOR YOUR OWN!! FEEL—FEEL FOR YOUR OWN!! WORK—WORK TOWARD YOUR OWN!! BE—BE—(*Falls silent again.*)

EVERYONE (*to audience*): BE FOR YOUR OWN!! THE OTHERS HAVE ALREADY DONE FOR THEIRS!! THEY CANNOT AND WILL NOT RESPECT YOU UNTIL YOU HAVE DONE FOR YOUR OWN!! THEN, AND ONLY THEN, WILL THEY ACKNOWLEDGE YOU WHOLLY!! AND MOVE OVER FOR YOU!! RELINQUISH SPACE TO OUR DIGNITY!! TO YOUR BEING!!

JASON (*after moment, staring at* DEAN): Damn, man— the message.

MIKE: Yeh, they say you see the light at the end.

ALI: Pick up the stuff you dropped, man. Come on, let's split.

JASON, MIKE, *and* RICK *all bend down to retrieve dropped goods.*

MIKE: Yeh, man, the message. But we left something out you know?

JASON: What, man? Come on.

MIKE: Uh, something like, look for your own, and it's gettin' harder and harder to tell who they are. You know? Like him with his beard, his natural, and all. You know what I mean?

ALI: It's not so hard, like that great book says, by their deeds you shall know them. Something like that.

JASON: Yeh, just add up his saids and his dids and you get his "is's" whoever he is. Whatever he is.

MIKE: Yeh, yeh, I dig. (*As they go out.*) But you know, man. Still, like I said, it's getting harder and harder, just like this cat who—

Important that it ends like there's a conversation going on down steps to—

CURTAIN

POETRY

from For Malcolm

■ LeRoi Jones

A Poem for Black Hearts

For Malcolm's eyes, when they broke
the face of some dumb white man. For
Malcolm's hands raised to bless us
all black and strong in his image
of ourselves, for Malcolm's words
fire darts, the victor's tireless
thrusts, words hung above the world
change as it may, he said it, and
for this he was killed, for saying,
and feeling, and being/ change, all
collected hot in his heart, For Malcolm's
heart, raising us above our filthy cities,
for his stride, and his beat, and his address
to the grey monsters of the world, For Malcolm's
pleas for your dignity, black men, for your life,
black men, for the filling of your minds
with righteousness, For all of him dead and
gone and vanished from us, and all of him which
clings to our speech black god of our time.
For all of him, and all of yourself, look up,
black man, quit stuttering and shuffling, look up,
black man, quite whining and stooping, for all of him,
For Great Malcolm a prince of the earth, let nothing in us rest
until we avenge ourselves for his death, stupid animals
that killed him, let us never breathe a pure breath if
we fail, and white men call us faggots till the end of
the earth.

from Black Arts

Black Art

Poems are bullshit unless they are
teeth or trees or lemons piled
on a step. Or black ladies dying
of men leaving nickel hearts
beating them down. Fuck poems
and they are useful, they shoot
come at you, love what you are,
breathe like wrestlers, or shudder
strangely after pissing. We want live
words of the hip world live flesh &
coursing blood. Hearts Brains
Souls splintering fire. We want poems
like fists beating niggers out of Jocks
or dagger poems in the slimy bellies
of the owner-jews. Black poems to
smear on girdlemamma mulatto bitches
whose brains are red jelly stuck
between 'lizebeth taylor's toes. Stinking
Whores! We want "poems that kill."
Assassin poems, Poems that shoot
guns. Poems that wrestle cops into alleys
and take their weapons leaving them dead
with tongues pulled out and sent to Ireland. Knockoff
poems for dope selling wops or slick halfwhite
politicians. Airplane poems. rrrrrrrrrrrrrrrrrr
rrrrrrrrrr. . . . tuhtuhtuhtuhtuhtuhtuhtuhtuh
. . . .rrrrrrrrrrrrrrr. . . Setting fire and death to
whities ass. Look at the Liberal
Spokesman for the jews clutch his throat
& puke himself into eternity. . . rrrrrrrrrr
There's a negroleader pinned to
a bar stool in Sardi's eyeballs melting
in hot flame. Another negroleader
on the steps of the white house one
kneeling between the sheriff's thighs
negotiating cooly for his people.
Aggh . . . stumbles across the room . . .
Put it on him, poem. Strip him naked
to the world! Another bad poem cracking
steel knuckles in a jewlady's mouth
Poem scream poison gas on beasts in green berets
Clean out the world for virtue and love,
Let there be no love poems written
until love can exist freely and

cleanly. Let Black People understand
that they are the lovers and the sons
of lovers and warriors and sons
of warriors Are poems & poets &
all the loveliness here in the world.

We want a black poem. And a
Black World.
Let the world be a Black Poem
And Let All Black People Speak This Poem
Silently

or LOUD

Black People: This Is Our Destiny

The road runs straight with no turning, the circle
runs complete as it is in the storm of peace, the all
embraced embracing in the circle complete turning road
straight like a burning straight with the circle complete
as in a peaceful storm, the elements, the niggers voices
harmonized with creation on a peak in the holy black man's
eyes that we rise, whose race is only direction up, where
we go to meet the realization of makers knowing who we are
and the war in our hearts but the purity of the holy world
that we long for, knowing how to live, and what life, is, and
who God is, and the many revolutions we must spin through in our
seven adventures in the endlessness of all existing feeling, all
existing forms of life, the gasses, the plants, the ghost minerals
the spirits the souls the light in the stillness where the storm
the glow the nothing in God is complete except there is nothing
to be incomplete the pulse and change of rhythm, blown flight
to be anything at all . . . vibration holy nuance beating against
itself, a rhythm a playing re-understood now by one of the 1st race
the primitives the first men who evolve again to civilize the
world

W.W.

Back home the black women are all beautiful,
and the white ones fall back, cutoff from 1000
years stacked booty, and Charles of The Ritz
where jooshladies turn into billy burke in
                    blueglass
kicks. With wings, and jungly-bew-teeful things.
The black women in Newark are fine. Even with
all that grease in their heads. I mean even

the ones where the wigs a
slide around, and they coming at you 75 degrees
                off course.
I could talk to them. Bring them around.
To something.
    Some kind of quick course, on the sidewalk,
            like Hey baby,
why don't you take that thing off yo' haid.
You look like
Miss Muffett in a runaway ugly machine.
I mean. Like that.

from Black Pride

■ Don L. Lee

The New Integrationist

    I
    seek
    integration
    of
    negroes
    with
    black
    people.

In the Interest of Black Salvation

    Whom can I confess to?
    The Catholics have some cat
    They call father,
                    mine cutout a long time ago—
    Like His did.
    I tried confessing to my girl,
    But she is not fast enough—except on hair styles,
                                clothes,
                                face care and
                                television.
    If ABC, CBS, and NBC were to become educational stations
    She would probably lose her cool,
                            and learn to read
    Comic Books.

My neighbor, 36-19-35 volunteered to listen but
I couldn't talk—
Her numbers kept getting in the way,
Choking me.

To a Buddhist friend I went,
Listened, he didn't—
Advise, he did,
        "pray, pray, pray and keep one eye open."
I didn't pray—kept both eyes open.
Visited three comrades at Fort Hood,
There are no Cassandra cries here,
No one would hear you anyway. They didn't.
Three tried to speak, "don't want to make war."
                                why???
When you could do countless other things like
Make life, this would be—
Useless too . . .

When I was 17,
I didn't have time to dream,
Dreams didn't exist—
Prayers did, as dreams.
I am now 17 & 8,
I still don't dream.
Father forgive us for we know what we do.
Jesus saves,
        Jesus saves,
                Jesus saves—S & H Green Stamps.

The Wall

> (43rd & Langley, Chicago, Ill.
> painted by the artists and photographers of OBAC 8/67)

    sending their negro
    toms into the ghetto
    at all hours of the day
    (disguised as black people)
    to dig
    the wall, (the weapon)
    the mighty black wall (we chase them out-kill if necessary)

    whi-te people can't stand
    the wall,
    killed their eyes, (they cry)
    black beauty hurts them—
    they thought black beauty was a horse—

stupid muthafuckas, they run from
the mighty black wall

brothers & sisters screaming,
"picasso ain't got shit on us.
  send him back to art school"
we got black artists
who paint black art
the mighty black wall

negroes from south shore &
hyde park coming to check out
a black creation
black art, of the people,
for the people,
art for people's sake
black people
the mighty black wall

black photographers
who take black pictures
can you dig,
              blackburn
              le roi,
              muslim sisters,
                    black on gray it's hip
they deal, black photographers deal blackness for
the mighty black wall

black artists paint,
              du bois/ garvey/ gwen brooks
              stokely/ rap/ james brown
              trane/ miracles/ ray charles
              baldwin/ killens/ muhammad ali
              alcindor/ blackness/ revolution
our heroes, we pick them, for the wall
the mighty black wall/ about our business, blackness
                                    can you dig?
if you can't you ain't black/ some other color
negro maybe??

the wall,
the mighty black wall,
"ain't the muthafucka layen there?"

The Traitor

he wore
a whi
te

shirt
&
bow tie,
a pretty
smile
&
the people called him
doctor.

    (honorary degrees from fisk,
    tenn. state a&i, morehouse &c.)

KA BOMMMM
KA BOMMMM
blood
splattered
his whi
te
shirt
his face
dis-
figured
by shot
gun
pellets
&
his head
fell
against
his
black
cadillac
&
bent
his
"clergy"
sign
toward the
black earth
&
somebody said,
"deal baby----------deal."

No More Marching

didn't i tell you
it would do no good

but you done gone
to school & read
all them books

now you is marchen
& singen

"we shall overcome"
getten hit &
looken dumb/ &
smilen

holden that whi
te girls hand pro
tecten her

this makes you
equal too??
wheres your mom?
whos protecten her?
          (protect the motherland
          not mother?)

is you a fool
fool
i guess you done
got what you wanted
          (setting next to her
          on a toilet continuing
          to eat whi-te shit)

my leaders? is you
mad
lead you to get
mo papers signed

world war 2
110,000 japs in
concentration camps
in home of slaves land of few

world war 3
ussr, england, france & u ass
          vs.
third world
30 million niggers in
uncle's concentration camps
          (formerly called public
          housing)

in whi-te a
mer i cause they
knew

you better wake up
wake up
before it's

too late

killed
marchen in gage
park chicago
ill

caught brick in
head while tryen
to protect whi
te

girl.

from Don't Cry, Scream

Blackwoman

blackwoman:
is an
in and out
rightsideup
action-image
of her man.. ....
in other
(blacker) words;
she's together,
if
he
bes.

A Message All Blackpeople Can Dig
(& a few negroes too)

we are going to do it.
US: blackpeople, beautiful people; the sons and daugh-
    ters of beautiful people.
bring it back to
US: the unimpossibility.

now is
the time, the test
while there is something to save (other than our lives).

we'll move together
hands on weapons & families
blending into the sun,
into each/other.
we'll love,
we've always loved.
just be cool & help one/another.
go ahead.
walk a righteous direction
under the moon,
in the night
bring new meanings to
the north star,
the blackness,
to US.

discover new stars:
street-light stars that will explode into evil-eyes,
light-bulb stars visible only to the realpeople,
clean stars, african & asian stars,
black aesthetic stars that will damage the whi-temind;
killer stars that will move against
the unpeople.

came
brothers/fathers/sisters/mothers/sons/daughters
dance as one
walk slow & hip.
hip to what life is
and can be.
& remember we are not hippies,
WE WERE BORN HIP.
walk on. smile a little
yeah, that's it beautiful people
move on in, take over. take over, take over take/over
        takeovertakeovertakeover
    takeovertakeover   overtakeovertakeovertake over/
        take over take, over take,
    over take, over take.
blackpeople
are moving, moving to return
        this earth into the hands of
human beings.

from 26 Ways of Looking at a Black Man

■ Raymond Patterson

At That Moment

When they shot Malcolm Little down
On the stage of the Audubon Ballroom,
When his life ran out through bullet holes
(Like the people running out when the murder began)
His blood soaked the floor
One drop found a crack through the stark
Pounding thunder—slipped under the stage and began
Its journey: burrowed through concrete into the cellar,
Dropped down darkness, exploding like quicksilver
Pellets of light, panicking rats, paralyzing cockroaches—
Tunneled through rubble and wrecks of foundations,
The rocks that buttress the bowels of the city, flowed
Into pipes and powerlines, the mains and cables of the city:
A thousand fiery seeds.
At that moment,
Those who drank water where he entered . . .
Those who cooked food where he passed . . .
Those who burned light while he listened . . .
Those who were talking as he went, knew he was water
Running out of faucets, gas running out of jets, power
Running out of sockets, meaning running along taut wires—
To the hungers of their living. It is said
Whole slums of clotted Harlem plumbing groaned
And sundered free that day, and disconnected gas and light
Went on and on and on . . .
They rushed his riddled body on a stretcher
To the hospital. But the police were too late.
It had already happened.

What We Know

There is enough
Grief—
Energy in
The blackness
Of the whitest Negro
To incinerate
America.

from "Riot Rimes U.S.A.," Section III

1

We are the same in our despair
Who now disturb your peace with riot—
The dark oppressed of yesteryear
Who swallowed grief and bled in quiet.

3

The cop said I threw a brick
Then he took his great big stick
And hit me six times quick.
But I didn't, but I might
If my poor head ever gets right.

19

They came with tanks
And marching feet.
They came with armoured cars.
And smoke and flame rose from our street
To blot out moon and stars
—And empty all the bars!

23

That crazy Uncle J.B.
Clean lost his wits.
Come home with all them groceries
And not one box of grits!

31

I thought both of them were dead
Instead of just the one.
They lay there in all that blood
Making both of them red—
Until the soldier shook his head
And got up and picked up his gun
He had just fallen down
From all the blood on the ground.

37

I said, Leroy,
You better come back
On this stoop and sit.
But Leroy gets up. He says,
Man, this is it!
I said, Leroy,
Put down that garbage can.
But Leroy says, Baby,
I'm going to meet the man.
I said, Leroy, cool it. They got the law
And they got the guns.
The best you can get is a busted head.
But Leroy says,
Ain't no way I can cool it no more.
All my life
I been playing dead.

40

I was surprised
When I looked into the eyes
Of my old army pal.
It broke down my morale
The way he held that bayonet
Against my chest, and pressed;
The way his eyes were set—
Like there had never been that other war,
Like he had never seen my face before
And somehow times-gone-by had lied
That had us friends and fighting side by side;
Like I had never been within the law.
But I was black and in the street
And he was armed and there to meet
Me—like a blind date someone planned;
And being late, I smiled and raised my hand.

85

If you want my views,
Well, I don't think
The Negro thinks he can win.
But then again
I don't think
The Negro thinks he can lose.

from Homecoming

■   Sonia Sanchez

nigger

nigger.
> that word
ain't shit to me
man.
> don't u know
where u at when
u call me nigger?
look.
> my man. I'll
say it slow for you.
>> N-I-G-G-E-R-
that word don't turn
me on man.
> i know i am
black.
> beautiful.
>> with meaning.
nigger.   u say.
> my man
you   way behind the set

to blk/record/buyers

don't play me no
righteous bros.
> white people
ain't rt bout nothing
no mo.
> don't tell me bout
foreign dudes
>> cuz no blk/
people are groovin on a
sunday afternoon.
>> they either
making out/
> signifying/
>> drinking/
making molotov cocktails/
>>> stealing
or rather more taking their goods

from the honky thieves who
ain't hung up
on no pacifist/ jesus/
cross/ but.
play blk/ songs
to drown out the
shit/ screams of honkies. AAAH.
AAAH. AAAAH. yeah. brothers.
andmanymoretogo.

from Paper Soul

■ Carolyn M. Rodgers

Written for Love of an Ascension—Coltrane

he tried to
climb a
ladder of light
veiled in mist/ incessantly
vacillating

he tried to
trap that
wheezy harmony that
solders quarter notes
on to our heads and

melts down minds like
molten lead, ejaculates
rhythm, curses, prayers, then
rings our ends like
shattering crystals

till a melody orgasm
explodes in our heads—
it's the sax, a
bladder splattering the
sky

gushing and exploding
to relieve itself with
notes that stalk and
split the clouds or that
rip the air into rifts of

whines for a jagged
crescendo, a man
a velvet willow suspended in air
with his roots
stretching to plant
themselves
                    in
                            any
star.

from Now See Here, Homes

■ Horace Mungin

White

What color
is heroin?
or the flames
of napalm?
            . . . not black.

What color
is the slave
master? . . . and
the Department
of War?
            . . . not black.

What color
are the sheets
of the K.K.K.? . . . and
the skins under them?
            . . . not black.

What color
is Law and Order?
or Integration?
            . . . not black.

Welfare

Why's Whitey
crying about one

out of every eight
New Yorkers
being on relief.

. . . Shit
He's the seven
that's working.

from Black Essence

■   Jewel Latimore (Johari Amini)

(For Nigareens)

my hair flows
long and straightly silken
conditioned to be so (i have
no naps at all which can be
seen

my complexion
is high and bright lightened
lightended lighter (than most
of my friends and all my
relatives

my fashions
are haigh/ British briefly
styled and show me to advantage
; indeed (i some/ time pass for
white

no one can
really know/see/everguess
who i am not even those People/
black and oddly proud who
smile
        while looking
        down
        in
        my
        direction . . .

To a Wite Boy (or an answer for a late question)

avoid blk (streets & women
avoid peddling us pettytrash on blood/cost credit
avoid making us offers of a pale & sterile groove
. . . we do not need you (business & fucking
Prey for your own

from Poems from Prison

■   Etheridge Knight

For Malcolm, A Year Later

Compose for Red a proper verse;
Adhere to foot and strict iamb;
Control the burst of angry words
Or they might boil and break the dam.
Or they might boil and overflow
And drench me, drown me, drive me mad.
So swear no oath, so shed no tear,
And sing no song blue Baptist sad.
Evoke no image, stir no flame,
And spin no yarn across the air.
Make empty anglo tea lace words—
Make them dead white and dry bone bare.

Compose a verse for Malcolm, man,
And make it rime and make it prim.
The verse will die—as all men do—
But not the memory of him!
Death might come singing sweet like C,
Or knocking like the old folks say,
The moon and stars may pass away,
But not the anger of that day.

It Was a Funky Deal

It was a funky deal.
The only thing real was red,
Red blood around his red, red beard.

It was a funky deal.

In the beginning was the word,
And in the end the deed.
Judas did it to Jesus
For the same Herd. Same Reason.
You made them mad, Malcolm. Same reason.

It was a funky deal.

You rocked too many boats, man.
Pulled too many coats, man.
Saw through the jive.
You reached the wild guys
Like me.   You and Bird.   (And that
Lil LeRoi cat.)

It was a funky deal.

from Solitudes Crowded With Loneliness

■   Bob Kaufman

Blues Note

Ray Charles is the black wind of Kilimanjaro.
Screaming up-and-down blues,
Moaning happy on all the elevators of my time.

Smiling into the camera, with an African symphony
Hidden in his throat, and (*I Got A Woman*) wails, too.

He burst from Bessie's crushed black skull
One cold night outside of Nashville, shouting,
And grows bluer from memory, growing bluer, still.

At certain times you can see the moon
Balanced on his head.

From his mouth he hurls chunks of raw soul.
He separated the sea of polluted sounds
And led the blues into the Promised Land.

Ray Charles is a dangerous man ('way cross town),
And I love him.

> *for Ray Charles's birthday*
> *N.Y.C./1961*

from Golden Sardine

Oct. 5th, 1963

Chronicle
Letters to the Editor
5th & Mission
San Francisco, Calif.
Gentlemen:
Arriving back in San Francisco to be greeted by a blacklist an
eviction, I am writing these lines to the responsible nonpeople. One
thing is certain I am not white. Thank God for that. It makes
everything else bearable.
The loneliness of the Long Distance Runner is due to the onliness
of the Long Distance Runner, that uniqueness that is the Long
Distance Runner's alone, and only his. This Loneliness of the Long
Distance Runner is the only reason for the Long Distance Runner's
existence. Short distance runners run, they finish neither first nor
last, they finish, that is all that can be said about them, nothing
can be said for them, an ordinariness that is their closest proximity
to the truly unique. Men die, as all men come to know, sooner or
later, at any rate either way, men die. On that all men can depend.
To answer that rarely asked question . . . Why are all blacklists
white? Perhaps because all light lists are black, the listing of all that
is listed is done by who is brown, the colors of an earthquake are
black, brown & beige, on the Ellington scale, such sweet thunder,
there is a silent beat in between the drums.
That silent beat makes the drumbeat, it makes the drum, it makes
the beat. Without it there is no drum, no beat. It is not the beat
played by who is beating the drum. His is a noisy loud one, the silent
beat is beaten by who is not beating on the drum, his silent beat
drowns out all the noise, it comes before and after every beat, you
hear it in between, its sound is
                                                    Bob Kaufman, Poet.

AFTERWORD

The Relation of AMSAC and the American Negro to Africa and Pan-Africanism

■ Jaja A. Wachuku
(Speaker, Nigerian House of Assembly)

I want to say first how grateful I am to be called upon to deliver the last address of this conference. It is of extraordinary coincidence that when we had the Pan-African conference in Manchester in 1945—attended by Dr. Du Bois, Kenyatta, Nkrumah, and the late Dr. Millard of British Guinea—it fell to my lot to deliver the last address. My subject then was "Where to Begin." I suggested to the conference that the two starting points of our Pan-African activities would be the Gold Coast and Nigeria. I remark on this now to point out that you can have your high ideals and philosophical speculations, but, really, they are nothing unless action is contemplated.

The year 1945 was the turning point from a period of speculative thinking to an era of practical action. Following the meeting of that year, we started what was then called the West African Secretariat in London. I went back to Dublin to manage the affairs of African students, and we left Nkrumah in London as editor of our paper, *The New African.* Of course, in some places when you begin to collect money to publish a paper and write seditious articles, the authorities clamp down on you. But in London we had freedom of expression; we said anything we pleased about imperialism and imperialists.

You will recall that this was not quite so easy in the case of Dr. Azikiwe when he was editor of the *African Morning Post* in the Gold Coast. The aim of his paper was independence in all things and neutrality in nothing that affected the destiny of Africa. Hence, when Wallace Johnson wrote an article, "The African and God," for the paper, Azikiwe landed in the warm embrace of the law. We who were then youngsters in Nigerian schools and colleges lapped up everything that was put in that paper, particularly the column "My Odyssey." We could recite the whole thing from memory. In 1937 those whom Azikiwe served conspired to get him into difficulties, and he had to leave the Gold Coast and return to Nigeria; there he started the *West African Pilot,* which still retains the maxim it had in that year: "Show the light and the people find the way." There were other leaders before him, but from 1934 to 1937 he was the moving spirit of African nationalism.

Therefore, when you are writing of Pan-Africanism or nationalism in Africa, if you have no page for Dr. Nnamdi Azikiwe, editor of the *African Morning Post,* your work is very incomplete. I mention this because in the papers presented at this conference there have been only passing references to him. Even persons who were inspired by him and who were encouraged by him to come to the United States did not give him the credit he deserves. I think that a lot of us who are younger people are here as a result of the fire he set in us. Some of us went to jail; some were restricted in other ways. (I can see here a good friend of mine who, as the result of youthful impetuosity and the challenging of established authority, landed himself in jail; but that did not stop him from being a nationalist. I refer to Anthony Enahoro.)

We all went through the mill, but we did not mind, because we believed that mere thinking—mere speculating, writing, living on a cloud—would do nothing until we actually planted the seed on African soil. Water the seed, the seed grows, and then—then the collective will of our people challenges the established authority, the imperial powers. And today we see what has happened on the continent of Africa. If in 1945 anybody had foretold what would happen, he wouldn't have been believed. How would you do it? Would you fight against the soldiers with bayonets and rifles and the like? What could you possibly fight them with? Well, our experiences in West Africa have shown that whatever the critics might say, the pen, the brain, human intelligence, human ingenuity are mightier than any soldier, mightier than any atom bomb. We have been able to do it by skillfully outmaneuvering the imperialist powers.

So you see, speculation is not enough. At this conference our subject has been African Unities and Pan-Africanism. AMSAC's executive director, Dr. Davis, has told us in his paper when speaking of the purposes of AMSAC: "Our aim has been to provide an understanding of the validity of African and Negro cultural contributions in order to provide a basis for mutual respect between Americans and Africans, and, indeed, between Africans and other citizens of the world." I must say that after listening to all that has been said,* I don't think this conference got down to the objectives of the organization given in Dr. Davis' statement.

Now, I would like to begin the main part of my discussion of African unities by asking you to make a choice between the viewpoints expressed in two quotations I am about to read concerning the American Negro.

I refer to an article written by one Leslie A. Fiedler, entitled "Negro and Jew Encounter in America." I think this was published in *Midstream* in the summer or autumn of 1956. To me, as an African, it seems that the article states the antithesis of the values of this organization and particularly of those Africans and descendants of Africans in the United States. If you have not already done so, I urge you to read it carefully. It says:

* See *Pan-Africanism Reconsidered* edited by Samuel W. Allen for The American Society of African Culture (Berkeley; 1962) *passim.*

"Whatever the shape of his own life, the Jew comes to America with a history, the memory of a world he cannot afford and does not want to deny. But the Negro arrives without a past, out of nowhere; that is to say, out of a world he is afraid to remember, perhaps could not even formulate to himself in the language he has been forced to learn. Before America there is for him simply nothing, and America itself—white America—scarcely exists until he is present." Further: "It is fashionable to forget this now, but salutary to remember that the Jew is the boast of the United States, as the Negroes are its shame. And it is across the barrier of this discrepancy that our two people comfort each other."

The same article continues: "The Jew is the father of Europe—irksome as that relationship may sometimes seem on both sides; the Negro, only an adopted child. If Christendom denies us [Jews], it diminishes itself; but if we reject the West, we reject not our legend, only a historical interpretation of it. We are what we always were—ourselves."

I have decided to cite this because, as I am sure my fellow Africans here will agree, it presents a challenge. That's how we are. We get these things, we read them, we let others know about them; we make up our minds about them. I am not embittered by this article; I say it is a challenge, that's all. My question is this: Sons and daughters of Africa, now nationals of the United States, what are your views on this matter? Do you accept these statements?

The circumstances of those earlier people who came here are known to us. Africa was not a barren place. Africa was a continent where kings were still building empires, a continent—like any other—where wars were going on. When one kingdom conquered another the tendency was to seize those who were conquered, those whom the victors feared would be detrimental to their vital interests. In those days it became very serious if one challenged the authority of the conquerors. They either finished him then and there, or they sold him into slavery. Sometimes youngsters were captured and sold; just children of circumstance. Also, women were often seized, their males segregated and rendered harmless. In short, slavery did not start in West Africa just for the fun of it. It started with the taking of prisoners of war—just as in the Roman Empire, whenever there was a triumphal return from battle, prisoners were taken along.

After the discovery of the Americas, the freebooters came over here and found themselves in a position—while extirpating the indigenous Indians—of being unable to cultivate the soil. They found the ubiquitous Negro was the only person capable of handling the environmental situation. He was brought here by force of circumstance. He arrived here and by his wit, toil, and tears he cultivated the soil and created the wealth that has made the Americas what they are today.

Now I ask you: Should such a history make the American Negro ashamed of his past? After all, even the descendants of criminals who were sent to Botany Bay, Australia, are proud of their ancestors; they pridefully trace them back to Europe—the same Europe that convicted those ancestors, deported them, threw them on alien shores. Today there are prime ministers and big businessmen who are proud of such despicable ancestry. Why, then, should the American Negro not be proud of his?

We can go to remotest antiquity to trace the deeds of the blacks. I am not a theologian, but surely American scholars know this. You must have read *The Dawn of Conscience* by Dr. Breasted. Almost certainly a lot of the writing of the Holy Writ came from the Africans. Some of the phraseology used in the Bible today was not of Hebraic origin at all; as Breasted has said, the Jews were only the conduit through which those things were transmitted to the Western world. The Phoenicians, in the graves of their kings, recorded that their civilization came to them from Egypt. We know, also, that circumcision was a universal practice among the blacks in Africa and had great significance for them in their religious traditions.

Moreover, the slave played an important role in the early development of Christianity. It was to the slave that Christianity was preached. It was through the slave that Christianity gained roots in Rome. Today the center of Christianity is in Rome, but don't forget the reason for that. Your scholars know these things. Do the masses of Negroes in the United States know them? Has any effort been made to bring this knowledge to them? Do they know that Western Europe owes its civilzation to their ancestors? Is it not extraordinary that Pliny could have written, "Ex Africa semper aliquid novi"—"From Africa there is always something new"?

Yet we are told that we have no history, we have no past. Obviously, this is not true. From remotest antiquity we were there, and to the end of the world we shall be there. This century is *our* century, as we shall see in the next quotation.

It was during the second [AMSAC] conference that the Honorable Charles C. Diggs, Jr., U.S. Representative from Michigan, made the following statement. My purpose in reading it here is to see how far this organization has gone in applying what he stated:

> The American Negro should have as much interest in the development of Africa as the American Jew has in the development of Israel. Not only will the renaissance of concern uncover the missing link between the American Negro and his African heritage, but it should further substantiate among other things the rich contributions Africans have made to the culture of the world: The resurgence of interest in Africa today presents a unique opportunity for American Negroes to forge an unbreakable chain with their African brethren. They should be inspired not only by great yesterdays in Africa, but even more motivated by great tomorrows. As was so aptly stated last December [1958] at the Accra conference: "Africa is a continent of the future."

I pose again the initial question: Which of the two passages I have quoted does this organization accept? I accept the second—and I believe those of you who have come from that old continent to this conference will agree. The other we reject, because we think it was written in abysmal ignorance. Apart from holding conferences and inviting us to come, I feel that AMSAC should devote itself not only to intellectual excursion but to practical education of the Negroes in America. Try to link them with their origin. They cannot be effective in the society in which they have found themselves unless, like searching roots, they reach deep into the rich soil of their birth to bring new strength and nourishment into the tree. This conference would be useless if we merely came all the way from Africa to talk to professors, lecturers, and eminent scholars. This organization must reach down to the twenty million American Negroes.

Thus, in dealing with Pan-Africanism and African unities, one of our primary concerns should be racial unity. I shall discuss others later, but here I want to point out that the reason people have been able to write as they have about the American Negro is that there is not, they claim, a strong and powerful African nation to which he can turn at any time. You mean to tell me, today—with Ghana there, Liberia there, with Nigeria soon to be there; with Sierra Leone there, Mali there, Guinea there, and the Congo this month, and the rest of them; and with the United Nations speaking on behalf of these sons and daughters of Africa—you mean to tell me you cannot lift up your head with pride, dignity, and self-respect? Can anyone dare to challenge your origin? Of course not, because there it is for all to see. You can see my color. This color—it is as they say in the Bible: The stone which the builders rejected will become the head of the corner. I am not a painter, but I know that if you use several colors and keep mixing and mixing and mixing them, the moment you add black it overwhelms the rest [*laughter and applause*]. It is very significant. I didn't bring it about; I merely observed it. It is black, the mythical, the unfathomable, the power that overwhelms. There is cause for pride.

Am I wrong in saying that when Perry went to the North Pole there was a Negro* with him? He was the least clad, but when the others perished was it not he who brought back the details in order that people would have a report of what the explorers did?

In the North Pole he survives; in the hot equatorial desert he survives; under the sea he survives; in the air he survives. Are you to tell me he has no destiny for which the Divine Creator made him? Today the African continent is the richest in the world! The power, the first uranium, for the atom bombs used at Hiroshima and Nagasaki came from Africa, from the Belgian Congo. In our soil there are latent forces embedded by the Divine Creator. In our soil there are the richest natural gases; in Nigeria there is virtually inexhaustible oil and iron. Over in Liberia there is a hill of iron—69 per cent pure iron; in Ghana you find bauxite, manganese. There is everything in Africa! During all the time our people were being subjected to all sorts of things, these discoveries were not complete. But now that the old continent has come to life again, you see these things. Am I to believe that all these resources are meant to be used for nothing?

We come here from that vivacious continent so brimming with life, abundant sun, abundant rain—abundant mosquitoes, abundant swamps! [*Laughter*] We have everything—good, bad, and indifferent. And the good Lord who put those things there must have known his purpose. Without the mosquitoes and the swamps we in Nigeria would have been suffering from the same ills that we see in South Africa, in Kenya, and in North Africa. But now that we are beyond the reach of these, we have means of

* Matthew A. Henson (1866–1955) a Maryland-born Negro explorer traveled seven trips with Robert Peary to the Arctic. On the 1908–1909 trip, he was the first man to set foot on the North Pole, where he planted the United States flag.

eradicating the swamps in order that our population may grow and our resources be developed to serve the African race and the human race.

Ours has been called the "dark continent." I don't know how they ever got that term. The sun rises most brilliantly there. The rain falls in buckets, not just in showers. The moon at night—very soothing and romantic. And yet they say it is the "dark continent." I just can't understand why. Perhaps because Nature closed the door, locked up everything, and refused to permit an alien eye to peer through the crevices. Perhaps it was deliberately made dark. But now, Africa is coming into her own.

We know that our continent is the richest at the moment, its natural resources the least exploited. Yet our human resources have been subjected to all sorts of things. The way I look at it is this: I think that it was for a purpose. Africa has gone through old barbaric processes. Civilization has gone from that continent right around through Asia Minor, to Western Europe, to the Americas; and now it is coming back to the roots where it started. And whereas others were not prepared to give credit to Africa for what she has contributed to humanity, the Africans now, in their own right, will have to make the world respect their knowledge, their experiences, and their contributions.

That is why such organizations as AMSAC have become so very important. Those who are responsible for running AMSAC must appreciate the importance of its role. It may be a weak organization now, but it can become an instrument of great good to this country, to Africa, and to the world. Consider, if you will, the extent of Pan-Africanism in geography alone. I purposely brought this map here. Look at the Americas; there are people of African descent in Brazil, the West Indies, and throughout the Americas. Here, in the United States, I think your latest census suggests that there are, in round figures, twenty million. All over here, all over there [indicating Africa and Americas]—that is ours. Here is Europe on our shoulders. When the Moors were in control, Spain was civilized by them. Europe could not have developed without the resources of our continent.

With the good will of the American Negroes and the people here, the combined forces of the Africans will bring stability to the world. So the twenty million American Negroes have a vital role to play. Join them with Nigeria's thirty-five to forty million; with Sudan, Egypt, the Congo, French Equatorial Africa, Ethiopia, Abyssinia, and the result will be a tremendous impact on the world by virtue of size, by virtue of population, by virtue of strategic position, by virtue of natural resources, by virtue of untapped intellectual capabilities. There are Dahomey, Togoland, Ghana, Ivory Coast, Mauritania [indicating these on map], and all the rest of them. Certainly you can't tell me that your country together with our countries in Africa cannot bring sanity to a world that has gone insane.

You have a very grave responsibility, but there appears to be a certain amount of diffidence on the part of the American Negroes, which I have noticed even though I have not been in the United States long. It is not good to be learned and allow your learning to rot. We have had similar experiences in Nigeria. There was a time when those early lawyers qualified, practiced, made money, and were quite comfortable. They were prepared to go to government functions and shake hands with all the big wheels. But they would not associate with the rank and file, the ordinary peasants, the society from which they had risen. As a result they were ineffective. But a new generation arose and withdrew from all the niceties of imperial society; we went back to the people, identified with them, transmitted our newly acquired knowledge to them and through them. So we created the ferment, became the catalyst in our society; and hence we see the transformation that has taken place.

Now if we have done it in Africa, I see no reason why you cannot do it here. Of course, you have to be loyal citizens of your state; nobody is asking you to divorce yourself from the place you built and the area to which you contributed so much effort to develop. I don't think any Nigerian or any Ghanaian or anybody from Africa would tell you that should reject what you have in you, in your system, in the blood running through your veins. That's not it. People of British descent have a claim in Canada; people of Dutch descent have a claim in the Americas, as do the Italians, Japanese, Chinese, Indians—this is indeed the melting pot. And if they have a claim to this place, how much more have you! With such a claim, you should certainly not cease to participate effectively. What we are saying is this: we are not happy with a situation where, numerically, you can have influence in politics, in business, in education, et cetera, but where you seem to have a kind of apathy, somehow.

I understand that there are about ten American Negro millionaires. What do they do with their millions? Can they not create the same type of industries as others are creating with their millions? Can they not also create employment for their people as others are doing elsewhere? Are they not interested in the question of development on the continent of Africa? Do they not want to make more money, as others are making it? Or are they contented? One thing I know: man is never satisfied, never contented—else he is dead!

After all, was it not the Irish-Americans who made it possible for the sovereign Ireland to have her independence? You could play a similar role on the African continent. Was it not the American Jews, the British Jews, and the Continental Jews who made it possible to wring the Balfour Declaration from Britain because of the discovery of TNT by (I think) Dr. Weizmann? Duplicity in politics made it possible. On the one hand you were giving assurances to the Arabs, and on the other a declaration to the Jews; they had a fight over it, and finally the Jews got a spot on earth. The financing and development of the desert and similar projects is being done by the Jews from abroad. If they can do it in Israel, why can't you do it in Africa?

Now, everybody need not pack up and come to the continent of Africa in order to develop a vital interest. We're not suggesting that. You already have a vital interest, and the American Negroes should recognize that the development of Africa is to their own advantage.

Similarly, if the United States believes—as I have seen from various writings—that Africa is going to have a decisive effect on the world situation, then the United States may have to reconsider a number of its economic and other policies that are not to our vital interest.

Although it is not for me to say what our attitude in Nigeria will be, I believe that with good will on both sides, with a stretching of friendly hands across the Atlantic Ocean, there is every possibility of a sound and friendly relationship between our two countries.

The United States never became a real world power until after the last war. Up to then, foreign policy and world opinion were determined in Europe. When the European countries met in Berlin in 1884 to divide the African territories among themselves, no Africans were there and the United States took a purely passive interest in the matter. It was after the last war, through the activities of President Roosevelt, that you came fully into the stream of world opinion and started being effective. All this time we were nowhere. Africa did not have a voice.

Now it is going to be different. The independent African countries are going to have a voice in the management of things through the United Nations. And I can assure you—though I'm not going to say what it is— that in the 1960's Africa is going to throw a bombshell into world affairs. New factors in international relationships will have to be considered; new standards will have to be introduced to satisfy the yearning ego of the African continent. And unless those standards are met, I don't think everything will be quite all right in this world of ours.

That's where the relationship between this country and those of Africa will become very, very vital. We don't believe in signing paper pacts, which may be broken any day. But there is something more lasting than paper pacts. The understanding between the United States and black Africa is written in blood. I would say that under normal circumstances we should consider the United States as our first cousin, because all of the American Negroes here are our kith and kin. On the other hand, I would describe Great Britain as our tutor: when I have learned my lessons and graduated, I shall simply go home. But as for America, never shall I turn by back on blood of my blood and flesh of my flesh. Thus, we have a strong relationship between our two lands facing each other across the sea. Its future will depend entirely on how Negro affairs progress.

This progress is going to depend a great deal on how we in Africa handle another kind of African unity—political unity. And in this matter I say that our first need is for *national* unity. If we have national unity in Liberia, in Ghana, in Nigeria, in Congo, in Sierra Leone, in all those other places, including the North African states, then I think we shall have a real start toward Pan-African unity. It will be only a question of time!

Do not mistake me: I believe in internationalism just as I believe in interracialism. But as for internationalism, there must be *nationalism* before you can have the "inter" between nations. Therefore, when you tell us—who are engaged in the practical politics of Africa—that we should not concentrate on nationalism and the building of a nation on the African continent, we answer forthrightly: We don't agree. You cannot have inter-racialism unless our racial stock is respected by the world. And we will gain this racial respect only after we have established strong and thriving nations in Africa, created mutual respect among these nations, and, con-sequently, gained the respect of other nations for Africa. Once we attain that respected status in the world community of nations, then there will be no black man anywhere who will be treated with lack of dignity.

So to tell us to think in terms of internationalism, while national unity and national stability are not assured, is not quite sound from a Nigerian's point of view. I am sure that people in Ghana, in Guinea, in Liberia, and in all the other African countries will agree. Yet people tell us, "But look what happened in Europe!" Let me tell you, we are not going by European standards!

We are scaling the centuries! What Europe did in hundreds of years, we intend to do in decades! We intend to learn from history; and I am sure that at the rate they are going now, the African states, with God's guidance, will be able to learn from the mistakes of others. It will be impossible for us, on a newly liberated continent, to wait to be united before we do things. We can't do that! Independence is not being given to all the states at the same time. When you do have independence you begin to make use of it until others join you, and tthen you keep on until you have sufficient numbers to be effective. After all, it has taken seventy years for the Americas to get just the Organization of American States! And only recently have they established a Bank for International Development and begun to think of highways and other such projects.

As an example of our aims and progress in Africa, let me tell you about some of our experiments in Nigeria. As usual, our imperial masters wanted to split our country into pieces before leaving, but we have been able to outmaneuver them and keep the whole thing together. Now, there are three things we must have in order to survive. First, we are going to have our political independence on the first of October; this we absolutely must have. Second, we must have our administrative independence. Aliens who have been controlling policy in our country and others must clear out and give opportunity to African nationals to control the policy-making posts. And third, we must have economic power in our hands. Once these prerequisites have been satisfied, we will be able to form the national unity and vitality that we desire as a prelude to interstate unity.

Any American who has gone to Nigeria, tell me: Where have you seen any place more democratic than Nigerian society? Move freely, go anywhere, associate with anybody. Eat where you like, go to a nightclub, etcetera. Nobody bothers you. And our papers are not afraid to tell you off if they disagree with you—no matter who you are. Freedom of expression!

I was in Washington recently when a motion was passed that the citizens [of the District of Columbia] there should have the right to vote for a Presidential candidate; it will take several years to get approval from enough of the states. What kind of approval is that? The Negroes in Washington, I am told, are 65 per cent of the population. And yet, unlike the citizens of Lagos, our own federal capital, those in Washington cannot vote on their own government!

In Nigeria we have three regions or states, and a Federal House, of which I am Speaker. We have taken care of our chiefs by giving them their place, where they can behave as chiefs; in the north and the west they are quite happy and contented. The younger, more virile element goes to the House of Assembly, where they can have a good fight—political war, there!—for the development of the country. We also have a Senate, composed of certain people we think can contribute in one form or another. We don't elect them as you elect senators here; they are appointed by the respective regional governments. They have a go, too, at legislation; but the most effective body is the House of Assembly. And there you can hear my friend Tony Enahoro (who is sitting here so mild and gentlemanly) lashing out on the opposition bench.

So you see, these are the kinds of things we are doing on the African continent. Some of you need to come and see for yourselves. It is when you see our institutions in operation that you realize the developments taking place.

And when our respective states have achieved national stability, they can begin taking steps toward Pan-African union. We will, for instance, be able to develop economic unity. We came to this conference by Pan-American Airways. In Africa at present we have Nigerian Airways, we have Liberian Airways, we have Ethiopian Airways. Of all of them, there's not one that begins to compare with Pan-American. But if we work toward economic unity the African states might decide: "Well, let's put our resources together and have Pan-African Airways!" And we wake up one day and find that instead of landing at Idlewild Airport on a Pan-American jet, we are arriving in a Boeing 707 of our own! After all, this is one of the unities you would like us to have!

Similarly, you might find us doing something with currency. Nigeria used to have a common currency with Ghana, Sierra Leone, and Gambia; but because of independence they broke away. They didn't want Colonial Office interference. And now that we are becoming independent they don't want to coöperate with us again. It's all right—we have a lion's share in the world and we're not bothered. We have our own money. I brought my own here; I have English money, I have the dollar. Nevertheless, we are quite willing to coöperate with everybody; after independence there's really no reason we should not have a currency arrangement. The African states should be able to get together and decide, "Why should a pound note have one value here and another there?" There may be an agreement for common currency; and our money will become one of the hard currencies of the world because we will have the resources to back it up.

Then too, we should be able to go from Nigeria through Dahomey, Togoland, to Ghana, to the Ivory Coast, right through to Mauretania, without customs barriers. We'll remove all those things so that you will be able to travel freely from there to the Congo and the rest.

The moment Africa is completely free, there will be no bone of contention. Every country will have to rely on what it is able to produce and by exchange to derive from others what it lacks. The old process of barter which our fathers practiced will, sooner or later, be reintroduced. You'll come with your ships and take my cocoa. With my ships I'll take your machinery. No money to pay; it's all in the paperwork. Isn't that barter? And yet some say that bartering is a process of savages! No, it is civilized, because now I come with a ship, whereas formerly I would have come on foot. But whether done by airplane, ship, or leg work—barter is barter!

You see, Nigeria thinks about Pan-Africanism realistically. We hope for political union to develop as if at the apex of a pyramid. Some people are suggesting that we should invert the pyramid, that we should build the base over the apex. You know that it could not bear the weight! We believe that we should start with sound economic, institutional, cultural, and other unities as a base. We will get to know ourselves, we will get used to each other, before joining in political union at the top.

Given her independence, Africa will work things out for herself. First, of course, we must make this independence a reality. We in Nigeria will not be satisfied with our independence on the first of October while much of Africa remains in slavery. We are not satisfied to see Portuguese Africa, South Africa, Southwest Africa, and others remain under alien domination.

And as for belonging to this camp or that camp—well, as Tony Enahoro has already said, we are not bound by foreign ideological speculations. We believe we can work out ideologies for ourselves. We are African first; anything else is secondary. When Marx wrote *Das Kapital* about the circumstances of Europe, Africa was not industrialized. When Lenin went to experiment with Marxism in Russia, we were not there. We are working out our own destiny, although we are prepared to learn about scientific processes from different people. After we have settled our affairs of state, then the question of ideological differences may arise. It will be a matter of intellectual speculation.

Here in the Americas it was made quite clear in Roosevelt's Good Neighbor Policy, coupled with the Monroe Doctrine, that American states can do virtually anything among themselves—fight each other, kill each other off—so long as no external force comes and interferes. We in Africa intend to follow the same policy. I state to all nations and parties concerned that you can strangle yourselves, for all we care; but once you are out of Africa, don't come back to interfere in our affairs. This policy has worked on the American continent because, as your "Big Brother" here knows, if any one of the American countries were to fall into alien hands, that would be a source of danger to him. We will learn from that same lesson. Nigeria is not going to be independent and allow any power—any puny, decadent power—to come in and undermine its future existence.

Of course, we appreciate the contributions of the Western world in the way of science and technology. But when you come to philosophy and religion and the arts, I don't think Africa has much to learn. Those who have studied the village community, the processes by which a balance of power is kept, the establishment of chieftaincy, the election of chiefs, and so forth, know that we have our own ways. Attempts have been made to undermine our culture by various forces, but we believe that—with the independence of the African states—we will be able to recapture the spirit of ancient Africa and produce a new civilization.

We Africans have gone to universities and have tried to learn of our past. When we realized that all that had belonged to us had been concealed, that an attempt had been made to undermine our culture, it was our duty, in spite of all we had learned about the Western world, to throw aside our learning from the West. For your law—or your philosophy, as the case may be—go back to your people. When I went back to Nigeria, I went back to my people. I am from a ruling house in my division. I served in the village council. I served in the district council. I served with the native authorities. In other words, I identified myself totally with my own people. And when you identify your interests with those of your people, they have confidence in you, they trust you completely; thus the changes we have been able to initiate on African soil.

The revolution that occurred in Nigeria and other places stems from the fact that the sons of the soil got into their past history through the archives of foreign universities. You discover your art, your culture; you see the terra cottas, the brass works from Benin. You unearth so many new things once you start to investigate matters for yourself.

And today it is possible to trace African culture as it extends up to South America, North America, and on over to Europe. Throughout the world the content of our culture has been studied in private and in public museums. Those who say we have "no culture" have the objects of our culture in their homes. In fact, our cultural artifacts have spread so far that we have to "repatriate" them by buying them, by doing everything we can to get them back. Yet we have "no culture"! I tell you, there is rich cultural content on that continent! The only problem is that American Negroes have lost their link with that culture, and it is necessary for them to reëstablish this link.

It isn't merely a matter of your saying, "Oh, you must teach us." That isn't enough. You need a more vital, unbreakable link, as Mr. Biggers said in the discussion on art. It is only through such a link that you will gain your self-respect on this continent.

And so we return again to the vital role of this organization in making Pan-Africanism a reality. The interests of twenty million American Negroes are entwined with those of two hundred million kith and kin in Africa. The American Negroes should appreciate that as long as our continent exists and thrives, as long as there are African states respected in the world community of nations, they themselves will have a full growth—which is what they require. Their full contribution will be appreciated, their role as human beings will be greater. That's all we want.

African Unity and Pan-Africanism: your African is an African, no matter where he is found.

Biographical Sketches

1. ACHEBE, CHINUA, was born in 1930 in Ogidi, Eastern Nigeria, and educated at Government College in Uhuahia and the University of Ibadan in Nigeria. Active in the administration of the B.B.C. radio, he has written short stories, including "The Sacrificial Egg" (1966), and several novels (*Things Fall Apart,* 1958; *No Longer at Ease,* 1960; *Arrow of God,* 1964; and *A Man of the People,* 1966). The first two have been translated into German, Italian, and Spanish. He has also published critical papers on modern African literature.
2. ARMAH, AYI KWEI is an American educated (Harvard and Columbia) Ghanaian who has written for *Jeune Afrique* in Paris and for *Okyeame* of Ghana and *New African of London.* Presently living in Massachusetts, he has just completed *Fragments* (1970), a second novel. *The Beautyful (sic) Ones Are Not Yet Born* (1968) was his first novel.
3. "Iceberg Slim" (BECK, ROBERT), according to his ostensible autobiography, *Pimp* (1967), was born in 1918 in Indianapolis with the makings of an I.Q. of 175. In Waupun State Prison he became aware of his desire to become a professional pimp, a desire that he realized for 25 years in Chicago and throughout the Midwest. His sensational *Pimp,* long a bestseller in black communities across the country, is similar to his *Trick Baby* (1967), a confessional autobiography of "White Folks," a fair-skinned con man, and *Mama Black Widow* (1969), another confessional autobiography whose main character is Otis Tilson, a homosexual.
4. BULLINS, ED, was born in Philadelphia in 1913 and grew up in Los Angeles. Widely respected for his exciting new drama, he is a resident playwright at Harlem's Lafayette Theatre and is also on the editorial staff of *Black Theatre Magazine.* His work has been published in most black publications, including *Negro Digest* and *Journal of Black Poetry.* He has edited *New Plays from the Black Theatre* (1969) and *Five Plays by Ed Bullins* (1968).
5. BROOKS, GWENDOLYN, was born in 1917 in Topeka, Kansas, but has lived in Chicago most of her life. She received her adult education at Wilson Junior College there. A distinguished poet and recently acclaimed Mother Superior of the National Diocese of New Black Poets, she has had her work published in Negro and white newspapers and magazines and has won several poetry prizes and awards from the American Academy of Arts and Letters. In 1946 she won a Guggenheim Fellowship; in 1950 she was awarded the Pulitzer Prize in poetry. In addition to a novel, *Maud Martha* (1953), she has published

many volumes of verse. Her latest works, *Riot* (1969), and *Family Pictures* (1971), were published by the Negro-owned Broadside Press of Detroit.

6. BROWN, H. "Rap," was born in 1943 in Baton Rouge, Louisiana, where he attended schools through a fitful period at Southern University. A dedicated Civil Rights worker, he was Alabama's Student Non-Violent Coordinating Committee (SNCC) director from 1966 to 1967, when he succeeded Stokely Carmichael as National Chairman of the organization. He was convicted of a gun-carrying charge, which he has appealed. Married to a former schoolteacher, Brown was working on a second book when he mysteriously disappeared from public notice just before he was to appear for a scheduled hearing in a Maryland courthouse in March, 1970.

7. CALDWELL, BEN, is a Harlem-based essayist-artist-playwright who has written almost a dozen short plays in the black idiom, including *"Riot Sale, Top Secret, Mission Accomplished,* and *Prayer Meeting or The First Militant Preacher.* He is also a contributing editor of *Black Theatre.*

8. CÉSAIRE, AIMÉ, born in 1913 on the island of Martinique, is one of the architects and exponents of the phenomenon of Negritude, along with Léopold Senghor and Leon Damas. In 1938, Césaire published his masterpiece, *Cahier d'un retour au pays natal,* in which the term *Negritude* first gained international popularity. Presently the Mayor of Fort de France, capital of his West Indian island homeland, Césaire has successfully conducted two careers as a politician and poet. His lectures are simultaneously genuinely eloquent and hard-headedly persuasive; for example, his famous *Letter to Maurice Thorez,* Secretary General of the French Communist Party in 1956. His poetry includes *Les Armes Miraculeuses* (1946), *Soleil cou-Coupé* (1946), *Ferrements* (1960), and *Cadastre* (1961). He has also written *La Tragedie du roi Christophe* (1963, translated into English in 1969), *Une Saison au Congo* (1967, translated into English in 1968), and other pieces.

9. CLARK, JOHN PEPPER, was born in 1935 in Nigeria and educated at Government College, Warri, and the University of Ibadan. He also studied at Princeton University in New Jersey. A versatile writer, he has collected three of his plays, *Song of a Goat, The Masquerade,* and *The Raft* (1964). *Ozidi,* a play, appeared in 1966. His verse volumes are *Poems* (1962) and *A Reed in the Tide* (1965). An account of his American experiences as a scholarship student at Princeton is recorded in his *America, Their America* (1964).

10. CLEAVER, ELDRIDGE, left his native Wabbeska, Arkansas, where he was born in 1935, and was reared and educated in the ghettoes of Los Angeles and in California state prisons at San Quentin and Soledad. The Minister of Information for the Black Panther Party, he is "a full-time revolutionary in the struggle for black liberation in America." Chosen as the presidential candidate by the Peace and Freedom Party in 1968, he despaired of fair treatment in a forthcoming trial and fled the country for Cuba and later Algeria. His essays have ap-

peared in *Esquire, Black Dialogue, Liberator, Mademoiselle,* and *Ramparts,* of which he was a senior editor.

11. CRUSE, HAROLD, was born in Petersburg, Virginia, and completed nigh school in New York City. After serving in World War II, he became a critic and writer, publishing articles in *Liberator, Negro Digest, New Leader, Presence Africaine.* He has also published two books, *The Crisis of the Negro Intellectual* (1967) and *Rebellion or Revolution* (1968), a collection of some of his earlier film reviews along with more recent essays.

12. DADIÉ, BERNARD BERTIN, was born in 1916 in Assinie, Ivory Coast. He attended Catholic schools through the Diplome de commis d'Administration. He served in Dakar, Senegal, for many years, and returned to the Ivory Coast to become a teacher and writer of verse. His verse collections include *Afrique debout* (1950) and *Le Ronde des jours* (1956). His novels are *Climbie* (1956) and *Un negre a Paris* (1959).

13 DECOY, ROBERT H., earned his M.F.A. degree from Yale in 1951 and has since undertaken several careers in Hollywood as actor-playwright-journalist, and radio and television personality. His books include the bestselling *Nigger Bible* (1967) and *The Big Black Fire* (1969), a so-called "black account" of Jack Johnson, the first black heavyweight champion of the world.

14. DIOP, DAVID (1927–1955), was born in Bordeaux, France, and raised in West Africa. A genuine revolutionary poet, he published one volume of verse, *Coups de Pilon* (1956), before he died in an air crash.

15. EKWENSI, CYPRIAN, was born in Minna, Northern Nigeria, in 1921 and educated at Achimota College, Ghana, and the School of Forestry in Ibadan. He has also studied pharmacy at London University, pointing out that "a writer must eat." A prolific writer, he has published much juvenilia, short stories including *Lokotown and Other Stories* (1966), but is perhaps best known as a novelist, the author of *People of the City* (1954), *Jagua Nana* (1961), *Burning Grass* (1962), *Beautiful Feathers* (1963), and *Iska* (1966). Several of his novels have been translated into foreign languages.

16. FANON, FRANTZ (1924–1961), was born on the island of Martinique, from which he went to France to study medicine, specializing in psychiatry. As a psychiatric physician on the staff of a hospital based outside rebellion-torn Algeria, he studied firsthand the ravages of French colonialism. He contracted leukemia and died in a Georgetown, D.C., hospital. The most brilliant theoretician of the universal black struggle against white domination, he wrote *Black Skins, White Masks* (1967, translated by Charles L. Markham), *The Wretched of the Earth* (1963, translated by Constance Farrington), *A Dying Colonialism* (1967, translated by Haakon Chevalier), and *Toward the African Revolution* (1967, translated by Haakon Chevalier).

17. FORMAN, JAMES, is director of international affairs for the Student Non-Violent Coordinating Committee (SNCC) and head of the Black Economic Development Conference. He has written *Sammy Younge, Jr.: The First Black College Student to Die in the Black Liberation Movement* (1968), and *Black Manifesto* (1969).

18. HAYDEN, ROBERT, was born in Detroit, Michigan, in 1913. He graduated from Wayne State University and received his M.A. at the University of Michigan where he taught English for two years before moving to a long and successful career of teaching at Fisk University in Nashville in 1946. He has won several fellowships and prizes, including the Hopwood Award from the University of Michigan in 1938 and again in 1942. His *Ballad of Remembrance* (1962) won the Grand Prize for Poetry at the First World Festival of Negro Arts held in Dakar, capitol of Senegal, in 1965. Other volumes include *Heart-shape in the Dust* (1940), *Selected Poems* (1966), and *Words in the Mourning Time* (1970). With Myron O'Higgins, he published The Lion and the Archer (1948). He has edited *Kaleidoscope* (1967) and remains active as the poetry editor of *World Order*, a magazine of the Bahai faith.

19. HEARD, NATHAN C., was born and raised in Newark, New Jersey, on and around the Howard Street of his novel by the same name. A self-described "unsuccessful criminal who took up writing," he has spent almost half of his thirty-three years of life in prisons, where he developed an interest in creative writing, and completed *To Reach a Dream* and wrote a first draft of *Howard Street*, the novel published with the help of his sympathetic lawyer, Joel Steinberg.

20. HUGHES, LANGSTON (1902–1967). Long the deservedly honored dean of American Negro professional writers, Hughes, who was born in Joplin, Missouri, was both a major participant and knowing commentator on the Harlem Renaissance of the 1920's and 1930's. He remained productive throughout his creative life as a ready friend to developing writers in America and Africa; as editor of several important anthologies, including *An African Treasury* (1961), *Poems from Black Africa* (1963), *New Negro Poets: U.S.A.* (1966), *Poetry of the Negro* (1949, with Arna Bontemps); as creator of an American folk hero, Jesse B. Simple; as a fiction writer of at least four published novels; as a dramatist of a dozen plays; as a biographer and popular historian of Negroes. But it is as a poet that the world remembers Hughes. Among his many volumes are *The Weary Blues* (1926), *The Dream Keeper* (1932), *Shakespeare in Harlem* (1961), and his final volume, *The Panther and the Lash* (1967). He has written in and translated from French and Spanish.

21. HUTCHINSON, ALFRED, was born in 1924 in Hectorspruit, South Africa. Fired from his schoolteaching position for association with a 1952 South African Defiance Campaign of coloureds and blacks to resist racial pressures, he became a member of another resistance organization, Africa National Congress, but was soon harried in exile to Ghana. In 1960 he left Ghana to live in England with his English wife. His writings include a play, *The Rain Killers* (1964), the autobiographical *Road to Ghana* (1962), and stories.

22. JONES, LEROI (Imamu Amiri Baraka), was born in Newark, New Jersey, in 1934. After attending local schools, he went to Howard, Rutgers, and Columbia Universities. He has moved from a career as a Negro writer to that of a widely acknowledged precursor of the present surge of

black literature. Versatile and unquestionably gifted, he was editor of *Yugen, Kulchur,* and *The Moderns* (1963), and *Four Young Lady Poets* (1964). He has published many plays, including *Dutchman* (1964), which received the Off Broadway (Obie) Award that year. *The Toilet* (1964) and *The Slave* (1964) are still performed by various Negro college groups. He has also written essays, *Blues People* (1963), *Home* (1966); short fiction, *Tales* (1967); a novel, *The System of Dante's Hell* (1966); and much poetry, including *Preface to a Twenty-Volume Suicide Note* (1961), *The Dead Lecturer* (1964), and *Black Arts* (1966, 1967). His work has appeared in such journals as *Black Orpheus, The Saturday Review, The Nation, Journal of Black Poetry,* and *Negro Digest.* With Larry Neal, he edited *Black Fire: An Anthology of Afro-American Writing* (1968).

23. KGOSITSILE, K. WILLIAM ("Willie"), is a South African-born (1938) writer who has been in chosen exile in America since 1960. He attended Lincoln University and the University of New Hampshire. His work has appeared in most black American publications. *Spirits Unchained* (1969) is his first volume. *For Melba* (1970) is his second volume, and *My Name is Afrika* (1971) is a third collection of poems. He also has an unpublished collection called *Mahube.*

24. KILLENS, JOHN OLIVER, was born in 1916 in Macon, Georgia. He has attended six colleges and won about as many literary awards. A longtime chairman of the Harlem Writers Guild Workshop, he also chaired the Writers Committee of the American Society of African Culture (AMSAC). He was writer-in-residence at Fisk University until he moved to a similar position at Columbia University in 1969. He has written for television and films—*Odds Against Tomorrow,* starring Harry Belafonte, and *Slaves* with Dionne Warwick and Ossie Davis. His novels are *Youngblood* (1954), *Sippi* (1967), *And Then We Heard the Thunder* (1968), and *Cotillion* (1971). *Black Man's Burden* (1965) is a successful collection of six provocative essays. *Trial Record of Denmark Vesey* (1970) makes available the trial transcript of the martyred black rebel who lived from 1767 (?) to 1822.

25. KNIGHT, ETHERIDGE, is from Corinth, Mississippi, where he was born in 1933. A wounded veteran of the Korean War, he has made the most of his term at Indiana State Prison by publishing stories and poems in various journals such as *Negro Digest, Journal of Black Poetry, Prison Magazine,* and others. He has collected his verse in *Poems from Prison* (1968), and has edited *Black Voices from Prison* (1970).

26. LAYE, CAMARA, was educated in Conakry, Guinea, but was born in Kouroussa, Upper Guinea, in 1924, of a father whose skills as a goldsmith and blacksmith were widely respected. His stories have appeared in *Black Orpheus* and other journals. He is more widely known for his novels, *L'Enfant noir* (1953, translated by James Kirkup and Ernest Jones as *The Dark Child,* 1955) and *Le Regard du roi* (1954, translated by James Kirkup as *The Radiance of the King,* 1956).

27. LEE, DON L., was born in Detroit in 1942. Lee is an essayist, but eminently a poet in the new black mode, which he is expanding with

his own works. He was black-poet-in-residence at Cornell University and later a lecturer in Afro-American literature and writer-in-residence at Northeastern Illinois State College in Chicago. He has lectured extensively at colleges and in black communities and has authored three volumes of poems, *Think Black* (1967), *Black Pride* (1968), and *Don't Cry, Scream* (1969). He has also completed an important book of criticism on black poets of the 1960's, *Dynamite Voices: Black Voices of the Sixties* (1971). His work has appeared in *Negro Digest, Journal of Black Poetry, Nommo, The New York Times, Evergreen Review,* and elsewhere.

28. LESTER, JULIUS, was born in 1939 in St. Louis, graduated from Fisk University in 1960, and struck out for a career as "a revolutionary journalist," publishing photographs and articles in *The Village Voice, The National Guardian, Escapade, Broadside, Sing Out, Liberator,* and *The Movement.* An active, prolific young man who was a field secretary for SNCC, and a provocative radio personality on station WBAI in New York, he has published *Look Out Whitey, Black Power's Gon' Get Your Mama* (1968), *To Be a Slave* (1968), *Revolutionary Notes* (1969), *Search for a New Land* (1969), and *Black Folk Tales* (1970), all essays and journalism. He lives with his wife and daughter in New York City.

29. Mc PHERSON, JAMES ALAN, was born in Savannah, Georgia, in 1943. He attended Morgan College and Morris Brown College in Atlanta before he graduated from the Harvard Law School in 1968. At Harvard he studied American Negro literature, which he teaches at the University of Iowa. He has written for the *Atlantic Monthly* and reported for the *Bay State Banner,* a community newspaper of the black Roxbury section of Boston. *Hue and Cry* (1969), a volume of short stories, is his first book.

30. MAJOR, CLARENCE, grew up in Chicago, but was born in Atlanta in 1939. He is a prolific writer who has published a novel, *All Night Visitors,* collections of poems, *Love Promises of a Black Man* (1964), *Human Juices* (1965), edited his own literary journal, *Coercion Review* (1958–61), and is a contributing editor to the *Journal of Black Poetry.* He also edited *The New Black Poetry* (1969). His work has appeared in many anthologies.

31. MILNER, RON, saw his play *Who's Got His Own* produced at The American Place Theatre to good reviews in 1966, and has since continued to write plays intended to dramatize the black experience in black dramatic terms. He was writer-in-residence at Lincoln University, Chester, Pennsylvania, and has written for *Negro Digest* and other journals. He has expressed a desire to "start a drama school in the black community."

32. MODISANE, WILLIAM "Bloke," was born in 1923 in the slums of Sophiatown, South Africa. He eventually escaped on foot without a passport to Tanganyika, and then to Europe. He lives in England and works as a free-lance writer of essays and short stories, earlier ones of which appeared in *Drum* and various black anthologies. His autobiographical

Blame Me on History was published in 1963 after selected parts had appeared in the *Atlantic Monthly.*

33. MPHAHLELE, EZEKIEL, was born in 1919 in South Africa where he attended secondary schools in Johannesburg and received a teacher's certificate at Adam's College in Natal. When he resisted governmental apartheid policies his teaching career was ended for him, prompting him into an exile that has taken him to Nigeria, Paris, Nairobi, and Zambia. He has cited anthologies of fiction by African writers, including *Modern African Stories* (1964, with Ellis A. Komey) and *African Writing Today* (1967). His autobiography, *Down Second Avenue* (1959) has been translated into German, Hungarian, Japanese, Czech, Serbo-Croatian, Bulgarian, Swedish, and French. Volumes of his own fiction include *Man Must Live* (1947), *The Living Dead and Other Stories* (1960), *In Corner B* (1961), and *The Wanderers* (1971), a novel. His critical essays have been collected as *The African Image* (1962).

34. MUNGIN, HORACE, has published *Dope Hustler Jazz* (1968) and *Now See Here, Homes* (1969), both volumes of verse. Chosen as the Negro Book Club's writer-of-the-month for March 1969, he has had the pleasure of having his works performed by the Lincoln Square Recital Group.

35. NEAL, LARRY P., was born in Atlanta in 1937 and reared in Philadelphia. He earned a B.A. at Lincoln University and did graduate work at the University of Pennsylvania. His poetry and criticism have appeared widely in *Freedomways, Liberator, Negro Digest, Soulbook, Black Dialogue, The New York Times,* and elsewhere. His selected and new poems comprise *Black Boogaloo* (1969). He edited *Black Fire* (1968) with Leroi Jones.

36. NGUGI, JAMES, was born in Limru, Kenya, in 1938 and was educated at Kenya's Makerere University College. Among the first generation of modern East African writers, he has published many stories for African and British journals. He also edited *Penpoint,* and has written drama including *The Black Hermit* (1968), and novels, *Weep Not, Child* (1965), *The River Between* (1965), and *A Grain of Wheat* (1967).

37. NKOSI, LEWIS, like many others from his homeland, chose exile from his native South Africa where he was born in 1935 and educated at Zululand public schools and the M. L. Sultan Technical College in Durban. A journalist for area newspapers, *Natal Sun, Drum,* and *Golden City Post,* he later accepted a Nieman Fellowship in journalism at Harvard University, 1961–62. Because of this, he was barred from returning in dignity to his native land. His essay, *Home and Exile* (1965), won a prize at the Dakar World Festival of Negro Art in 1965. Living in England as a free-lance critic, he has published short stories and a play, *Rhythm of Violence* (1964).

38. OKARA, GABRIEL I. O., was born in 1921 in Ijaw country of the Niger Delta, and was educated at Government College, Umuahia. He presently works for the Ministry of Information in Eastern Nigeria. One of Nigeria's leading poets, his poems and translations from Ijaw po-

etry have appeared in journals in Europe, America, and Africa. His first novel, *The Voice,* in which he experimented in using his background Ijaw dialect and English, appeared in 1966.

39. OYONO, FERDINAND, was born in 1929 in Cameroons, where he received his early Catholic education. He later studied in Paris at the Ecole Nationale d'Administration. After studying for the bar and returning to his homeland, he became a delegate to the United Nations and Ambassador in Monrovia. Writing in French, Oyono has published several works that satirize colonial administration and white and African missionary foibles, including *Chemin d'Europe* (1960), *Une Vie de Boy* (1950, translated as *Houseboy* by John Reed, 1966), and *Le Vieux Nègre et la Médaille* (1956, translated as *The Old Man and the Medal* by John Reed, 1966).

40. P'BITEK, OKOT, was born in 1931 in Gulu, Northern Uganda, of the Acholi (or Acoli) tribe. He was educated at Gulu High School and at King's College at Budu. An outstanding football player for Uganda, he read education at Bristol, law at Aberystwyth, and social anthropology at Oxford. He has lectured at Makerere. He has written two novels in the Luo dialect, essays on linguistics, and poetry that has appeared in several East African magazines. His *Song of Lawino* (1967), a book-length lyric confessional lament, is very popular in Afro-American communities and has prompted new editions. p'Bitek has completed another book-length poem, *Song of Ocol* (1971).

41. PATTERSON, RAYMOND, a New York-born poet (1929), graduated from Lincoln University and New York University. At Lincoln he won first prize in a nationwide intercollegiate poetry contest. His work has appeared in the English edition of *Sixes and Sevens,* and the bilingual anthology, *Ik Zag Hoe Zwart Ik Was* (*I Saw How Black I Was,* 1958). A former counselor of delinquents, he has organized a series of readings for new young Negro poets at the Market Place Gallery in New York City. He is presently working in the New York public schools and working on a novel. His first volume of verse is *26 Ways of Looking at a Black Man* (1969).

42. PETERS, LENRIE, was born in 1932 in Bathurst, Gambia, from which he moved to Sierra Leone when he was seventeen. He attended the Prince of Wales School in Freetown before going to Cambridge University where he read natural sciences at Trinity College. He has published two volumes of poetry, *Poems* (1964) and *Satellites* (1967), and a novel, *The Second Round* (1965).

43. POLITE, CARLENE HATCHER, was born in Detroit, Michigan. She has danced professionally for the Martha Graham Company, worked as a Civil Rights worker, and for a short time she was a Playboy Club Bunny. She lived in Paris where she finished her first novel, *The Flagellants* (1967). She has recently returned from Spain where she completed a second novel.

44. POOL, ROSEY (1905–   ), is a native of Amsterdam, Holland. She became interested in folk literature and music, which led her to discover Countee Cullen in 1925. Since that time she has been lecturing extensively on Negro poetry. During a tour of the American South in

1960, she visited and studied at 27 Negro colleges and universities. In 1961 she was a speaker at the inauguration of the Lagos Centre of the Society of African Culture, where she discussed her collection of Negro poets, published as *Beyond the Blues* (1962).

45. REED, ISHMAEL, was born in 1938 in Chattanooga, Tennessee. He was a correspondent for the *Buffalo Empire Star Weekly* while he attended the University of Buffalo. He has written poetry for the *Negro Digest* and *Liberator*, and has been widely anthologized. His two novels are *The Free-Lance Pallbearers* (1967) and *Yellow Back Radio Broke-Down* (1969). He has also edited the anthology, *19 Necromancers From Now* (1970).

46. RIVE, RICHARD, was born in 1931 and educated in Cape Town, South Africa, the son of an American Negro seaman father and a "Cape Coloured" mother. He graduated from the University of Cape Town where he excelled in track, and later taught English and Latin at a high school "for coloureds." Widely travelled, Rive has published short fiction in *Transition, Contrast, Presence Africaine*, and other journals. One of his collections is *African Songs* (1963). He has edited a volume of short fiction by fellow South Africans in *Quartet* (1963), and a collection of fiction from African writers from various parts of the continent, *Modern African Prose* (1964). His first novel, *Emergency*, was published in 1964.

47. RODGERS, CAROLYN, was born in 1942 and lives in Chicago. She has published *Paper Soul* (1968), *Two Love Raps* (1969), and *Songs of a Blackbird* (1969).

48. RUBADIRI, DAVID, was born in 1930 in what is now Malawi. He was educated at King's College, Budu, and Markerere, where he captained the university cricket team. He was imprisoned in 1959 for supporting the nationalist cause against Southern Rhodesia's racist policies. He was later released and became his country's first ambassador to the United States and the United Nations in 1964. His stories and poems have been widely anthologized. *No Bride Price* (1967) is his first novel.

49. SANCHEZ, SONIA, comes from Birmingham, Alabama, where she was born in 1935. She attended New York University and received her B.A. from Hunter College when she was 20 years old. Her black idiom poems have been widely published in such journals as the *New England Review, Liberator, Negro Digest*, and many others. She taught black literature at San Francisco State College and at the University of Pittsburgh. Active on the college lecture circuit, she is a mother, the producer of two one-act plays, and the author of two volumes of verse, *Homecoming* (1969) and *We a BaaddDDD People* (1970).

50. SCOTT, JOHNNY, was born in Cheyenne, Wyoming, in 1948 and taken by his father to what is now known as Watts, Los Angeles. There he grew up to become the first black from his community to be accepted at Harvard University. After a difficult year there he left to benefit from a scholarship to Stanford University where he studied writing. His essays and poems have appeared in several American periodicals, including *Harper's* and *Pageant*

51. SENGHOR, LÉOPOLD SÉDHAR, was born in 1906 in Joal, Senegal, where he was reared among the Serere farmers and fishermen whom he always remembered. Senghor went on to study at École Normale Supérieure in Paris, becoming the first black African to receive a French academic education on the highest level, the first to complete his agrégé (doctorate) at a French university. A prominent intellectual and statesman, he has been the President of the Republic of Senegal. A principal exponent of Negritude, he edited the important *Nouvelle Anthologie de la Poésie Nègre et Malgache de langue française* (1948), with an introduction by Jean-Paul Sartre. He has remained active, having published *Chants d'ombres* (*Song of Shadows*, 1945); *Hosties Noires* (*Black Victims*, 1948); *Chants pour Naëtt* (*Songs for Naëtt*, 1949); and *Éthiopiques* (1956), in addition to other poems and critical essays on black aesthetics, and a dramatic treatment of Chaka Zulu.

52. SOYINKA, WOLE, was born in 1934 in Isara, Ijebu Remo, in Western Nigeria, and was educated at the University of Ibadan and Leeds University. An outstanding and prolific writer—he had authored five plays and several important poems by the time he was thirty—he has also worked at the Royal Court, seeing his play, *The Lion and the Jewel*, through production there. He has produced several other of his plays in Nigeria and has traveled throughout the world, offering comments on emerging African literature, especially drama. Some of his work includes *Five Plays* (1964), *The Road* (1965), and *Kongi's Harvest* (1967), all plays, and *The Interpreters* (1965), a novel. In addition to producing a volume of poems, *Idanre and Other Poems* (1967), he has translated the Yoruba novel, *The Forest of a Thousand Daemons* (1968) by the late Chief D. O. Fagunwa.

53. SUTHERLAND, EFUA THEODORA, was born in 1924 in Ghana, and was educated at Cambridge, after which she taught at a school that she established in Transvolta. She has published two picture essays, *The Roadmakers* (1961) and *Playtime in Africa* (1962), several plays, and short stories that have been anthologized around the world.

54. TOLSON, MELVIN B. (1898–1966), was born in Moberly, Missouri. Tolson has led a crowded, rewarded life, always proud of his family of distinguished educators and professionals. He worked while attending Lincoln University and Columbia University with jobs as a bootblack, waiter, cook, and dishwasher. After a career as an English teacher and dramatics coach at Wiley College in Texas for twenty years, he also taught at Langston University and became mayor of Langston, Oklahoma. His *Dark Symphony* won the National Poetry contest and was later published in the *Atlantic Monthly*. In addition to a bulk of little-known work, he has also published in many important American magazines and has produced his own volumes, including *Rendezvous with America* (1944), the specially commissioned *Libretto for the Republic of Liberia* (1951, 1953), and *Harlem Gallery* (1965), book I of a planned trilogy.

55. THEMBA, CANADACE DANIEL, was born in 1923 in Pretoria, South Africa, and graduated with distinction in English from Fort Hare

University College. He has worked as an editor and reporter for Johannesburg publications, and his fiction has won several literary prizes.

56. VESEY, PAUL (Samuel W. Allen), was born in 1927 in Columbus, Ohio, and studied under James Weldon Johnson at Fisk University. He holds an L.L.B. degree from Harvard University and has also studied at the Sorbonne and the New School for Social Research in New York City. Once a professor of law at Southern University in Louisiana, he became an assistant General Counsel of the United States Information Agency. Presently he divides his time between duties as writer-in-residence at Tuskegee Institute in Alabama and as popular resource personality at Wesleyan University in Connecticut. While at the Sorbonne, he met Richard Wright who helped him to publish his first poems in *Presence Africaine* in Paris. His volume of poetry, *Ivory Tusks,* appeared in bilingual edition in Germany in 1956. He has written several penetrating pieces on Negritude and African and Afro-American aesthetics in both English and French. In addition to his translation of Jean-Paul Sartre's *Orphee Noir* and his preface to Senghor's *Anthologie of 1948,* Allen has edited *Pan-Africanism Reconsidered* for the American Society of African Culture (1962).

57. WRIGHT, CHARLES, was oorn in 1932 in Franklin, Missouri, and left high school during his sophomore year to hold various jobs while he studied and practiced writing. He has published fiction in various anthologies and has received the blessings of James Baldwin for his two novels, *The Messenger* (1963) and *The Wig* (1966).

58. WRIGHT, RICHARD (1908–1960), was the famous American Negro-born writer of international reputation based on his powerful stories, including *Uncle Tom's Children* (1936)), and novels, *Native Son* (1940) and *The Outsider* (1953), and essays, *Twelve Million Black Voices* (1941), *The God That Failed* (1949), *White Man, Listen* (1957), and other works

Bibliography

Even when confined to a selection of writers from the 1950's and the 1960's, the following bibliography is by no means exhaustive of modern African and Afro-American authors. To avoid excessive duplication, several references included in the introduction or among the biographical sketches are generally excluded here. Asterisks denote books which contain bibliographies. Unless otherwise noted, books are novels.

MODERN AFRO-AMERICAN LITERATURE

JOURNALS
Black Academy Review, 3296 Main Street, Buffalo, N.Y. (quarterly).
Black Dialogue, Box 1019, New York, N.Y. 10027 (quarterly).
The Black Scholar, Box 31245, San Francisco, Calif. 94131 (monthly except July and August).
Black Theatre, 200 West 135 Street, New York, N.Y. 10030 (six times a year).
Black World (formerly *Negro Digest*), 1820 S. Michigan Avenue, Chicago, Ill. 60610 (every 45 days).
College Language Journal, Morgan State College, Baltimore, Md. 21212 (Sept., Dec., and March).
The Cricket, Box 63, Newark, N.J.
The Crisis, 1790 Broadway, New York, N.Y. 10019 (monthly).
Encore, Department of Speech and Drama, Florida A & M University, Tallahassee, Fla. 32307 (monthly).
Freedomways, 799 Broadway, New York, N.Y. 10003 (quarterly).
Harvard Journal of Negro Affairs, Harvard College, Cambridge, Mass. 02138 (semiannually).
Journal of Black Poetry, 922 Haight Street, San Francisco, Calif. 94117 (quarterly).
Journal of Negro Education, Howard University, Washington, D.C. 20001 (quarterly).
Kenyatta, 1442 North Sedgwick Street, Chicago, Ill. 60610 (every 45 days).
Liberator, 244 East 46th Street, N.Y. 10017 (monthly).
Mojo, 514 West 125 Street, New York, N.Y. 10027.
Nkombo, Box 51536, New Orleans, La. 70150 (quarterly).
Nommo, 3806 S. Michigan Avenue, Chicago, Ill. 60653 (quarterly).
Phylon, Atlanta University, 223 Chestnut Street, S.W., Atlanta, Ga. 30314 (quarterly).
Soulbook, Box 10977, Berkeley, Calif. 94701 (quarterly).
Umoja, 144 N. Frazier Street, Philadelphia, Pa. 19131 (monthly).

BACKGROUND AND CRITICAL REFERENCES
Abramson, Dorothy, *Negro Playrights in the American Theatre: 1925–1959*, 1969.
Baldwin, James, *Notes of a Native Son*, 1955.
———, *Nobody Knows My Name*, 1961.
———, *The Fire Next Time*, 1963.
Bone, Robert A., *The Negro Novel in America*, 1958; revised 1966.*
Butcher, Margaret J., *The Negro in American Culture*, 1956.
Cayton, Horace, *Long Old Road*, 1965.
Cook, Mercer, and Stephen Henderson, *The Militant Black Writer in Africa and the United States*, 1969.
Dent, Thomas C., and Richard Schechner, *The Free Southern Theater by The Free Southern Theater*, 1969.
Ellison, Ralph, *Shadow and Act*, 1964.
Emanuel, James A., *Langston Hughes*, 1967.*
Ferguson, Blanche, *Countee Cullen and the Negro Renaissance*, 1966.
Gayle, Addison, *Black Expression: Essays by and About Black Americans in the Creative Arts*, 1969.*
———, *The Black Aesthetics*, 1971.
Gibson, Donald A., *Five Black Writers*, 1970.
Gloster, Hugh, *Negro Voices in American Fiction*, 1948.*
Gross, Seymour, and John E. Hardy (eds.), *Images of the Negro in American Literature*, 1966.*
Homer, Dorothy, and Ann Swartout, *Books on the Negro*, 1966.
Hughes, Carl M., *The Negro Novelist . . . 1940–50*, 1953.*
Jones, LeRoi, *Home: Essays Written Since 1960*, 1966.
———, *Raise, Race, Rays, Raise*, 1971.
Lee, Don L., *Dynamite Voices I*, 1971.
Littlejohn, David, *Black on White: A Critical Survey of Writings by American Negroes*, 1966.*
McCall, Dan. *The Example of Richard Wright*, 1969.
Margolies, Edward, *Native Sons*, 1968.*
———, *The Art of Richard Wright*, 1969.
Miller, Elizabeth W., *The Negro in America: A Bibliography*, 1966.
Mitchell, Loften, *Black Drama*, 1967.*
Murray, Albert, *The Omni-Americans*, 1970.
T.D.R. (Black Theatre issue), T-40, 1968.
Watkins, Mel (ed.), *The Black Review*, No. 1, 1971.
Webb, Constance, *Richard Wright*, 1968.*
Williams, John A., *The Most Native of Sons: A Biography of Richard Wright*, 1970.

ANTHOLOGIES
Adoff, Arnold, *I Am the Darker Brother*, 1968.
Alhamisi, Ahmed, and H.K. Wangara, *Black Arts*, 1969.
Barbour, Floyd, *The Black Power Revolt*, 1968.
———, *The Black Seventies*, 1970.
Cade, Toni, *The Black Woman*, 1970.
Brown, Patricia, Don L. Lee, and Francis Ward, *To Gwen with Love*, 1971.
Chapman, Abraham, *Black Voices*, 1968.*
Clarke, John, *American Negro Short Stories*, 1966.
———, *Harlem, U.S.A.*, 1964.

Coombs, Orde, *We Speak as Liberators: Young Black Poets*, 1970.
Couch, William, *New Black Playwrights*, 1968.
Emanuel, James, and Theodore Gross, *Dark Symphony*, 1968.*
Hill, Herbert, *Soon One Morning: New Writings by American Negroes, 1940–62,* 1963.
————, *Anger and Beyond*, 1966.
Hughes, Douglass A., *From a Black Perspective*, 1970.
Iman, Yusef, *Afro-Arts Anthology*, 1966.
Jones, Leroi, and Larry P. Neal, *Black Fire*, 1968.
Jordan, June, *Soul Script: Afro-American Poetry*, 1970.
Randall, Dudley, *Black Poetry*, 1969.
Shuman, H. Baird, *Nine Negro Poets*, 1968.
Smith, Arthur L., *Rhetoric of Black Revolution*, 1969.
Watkins, Mel and Jay David, *To Be a Black Woman*, 1970.
White, Edgar, *Underground: Four Plays*, 1970.
Williams, John A., *The Angry Black*, 1962.
————, and Charles F. Harris, *Amistad I*, 1970; II, 1971.
Wilentz, Tom, and Tom Weatherly, *Natural Process*, 1970.

INDIVIDUAL WORKS
Anderson, Alston, *Lover Man* (stories), 1959.
————, *All God's Children*, 1965.
Bontemps, Arna, *Hold Fast to Dreams* (poems), 1969.
Boles, Robert, *The People One Knows*, 1964.
————, *Curling*, 1969.
Brown, Frank London, *Trumbull Park*, 1958.
————, *The Myth-Maker*, 1970.
Brown, Lloyd, *Iron City*, 1951.
Bullins, Ed., *Five Plays*, 1969.
————, *New Plays from the Black Theatre*, 1969.
————, *The Duplex*, 1971.
Childress, Alice, *Trouble in Mind* (drama), 1959.
Cooper, Clarence, *The Scene* (1960).
————, *Weed* (1961).
————, *The Dark Messenger* (1962).
————, *Black! Two Short Novels* (1963).
————, *The Farm* (1967).
Cuney, Waring, *Puzzles* (poems), 1961.
Danner, Margaret, *Impressions of African Art Forms* (poems), 1960.
————, and Dudley Randall, *Poem Counterpoem*, 1966.
Dodson, Owen, *Powerful Long Ladder* (poems), 1946.
————, *Boy at the Window*, 1951.
————, *When Trees Were Green*, 1967.
Elder, Lonnie, *Charades on East Fourth Street* (drama), 1961.
————, *Ceremonies in Dark Old Men* (drama), 1965.
Ellison, Ralph, *Invisible Man*, 1952.
————, *Shadow and Act* (criticism), 1964.
Evans, Marie, *I Am a Black Woman*, 1970.
Fair, Ronald, *Many Thousand Gone*, 1965.
————, *Hog Butcher*, 1966.
Fabio, Sarah W., *A Mirror: A Two-part Volume of Poems*, 1969.
Gaines, Ernest, *Catherine Carmier*, 1964.
————, *Of Love and Dust*, 1967.
————, *Bloodline* (stories), 1968.

Gilbert, Herman, *The Uncertain Sound*, 1970.
Giovanni, Nikki, *Black Judgment*, 1968.
————, *Black Feeling: Black Talk*, 1968.
————, *Re: Creation*, 1970.
Gordone, Charles, *No Place To Be Somebody* (drama), 1969.
Hansberry, Lorraine, *A Raisin in the Sun* (drama), 1959.
————, *The Sign in Sidney Brustein's Window* (drama), 1964.
Henderson, David, *Felix of the Silent Forest* (poems), 1967.
Hunter, Kristin, *God Bless the Child*, 1964.
————, *The Landlord*, 1966.
————, *Soul Brothers and Sister Lou*, 1968.
Jackson, Mae, *Can I Poet with You?* (poems), 1969.
Johnson, Percy E., *Concerto for Girl and Convertible* (poems), 1960.
————, *Six Cylinder Olympus* (poems), 1964.
Jordan, June, *Some Changes* (poems), 1971.
Kaufman, Bob, *Solitudes Crowded with Loneliness* (poems), 1965.
————, *Golden Sardine* (poems), 1967.
Kelley, William Melvin, *A Different Drummer*, 1967.
————, *Dancers on the Shore* (stories), 1964.
————, *A Drop of Patience*, 1965.
————, *Dem*, 1967,
————, *Dunford's Travels Everywhere*, 1970.
Kennedy, Adrianne, *Funny House of a Negro*, (drama), 1962.
————, *The Owl Answers* (drama), 1963.
————, *A Lesson in Dead Language* (drama), 1964.
————, *A Rat's Mass* (drama), 1965.
————, *A Beast's Story* (drama), 1966.
Kgositsile, Keorspetse, *Spirits Unchained* (poems), 1969.
Knight, Etheridge, *Poems from Prison*, 1968.
Latimore, Jewel, *Images in Black* (poems), 1968.
————, *Black Essence* (poems), 1968.
Lockhart, Theodore, *In Search of Roots* (poems), 1969.
Lorde, Audre, *The First Cities* (poems), 1968.
Macbeth, Robert, *Black Ritual* (drama), 1969.
————, *The Resurrection of the Dead* (drama), 1969.
Macpherson, James A., *Hue and Cry* (stories), 1969.
Mahoney, William, *Black Jacob*, 1969.
Marshall, Paule, *Brown Girl, Brownstone*. 1959.
————, *Soul Clap Hands and Sing* (stories), 1961.
————, *The Chosen Place, The Timeless People*, 1969.
Marvin X, *The Son of Man* (proverbs), 1969.
————, *Fly to Allah* (poems), 1969.
————, *Black Man, Listen* (poems, aphorisms), 1969.
Meriweather, Louise, *Daddy Was A Number Runner*, 1971.
Mungin, Horace, *Dope, Hustler Jazz* (poems), 1968.
————, *Now See Here, Homes* (poems), 1969.
Nelson, David, *Die, Nigga!* (poems), 1968.
Nichols, James E., *Of Love* (poems), 1969.
Randall, Dudley, *Cities Burning* (poems), 1968.
Reed, Clarence, *Not Forever Tears* (poems), 1969.
Rivers, Conrad Kent, *Perchance to Dream, Othello* (poems), 1959.
————, *These Black Faces and This Sun-Burnt Face* (poems), 1962.
Rodgers, Carolyn, *Paper Soul* (poems), 1968.
————, *Two Love Raps* (poems), 1969.

————, *Songs of a Blackbird* (poems), 1969.
Sanchez, Sonia, *Homecoming* (poems), 1969.
————, *We A BaaddDDD People* (poems), 1970.
Shears, Carl L., *Among the Living Dead* (poems), 1969.
Smith, Daniel, *A Walk in the City*, 1971.
Spellman, A.B., *The Beautiful Days* (poems), 1965.
Stephany, *Moving Deep* (poems), 1969.
Taylor, Rockie D., *Drum Song* (poems), 1969.
Tucker, I.E., *From a Chocolate Inkwell* (poems), 1967.
Ward, Douglass Turner, *Happy Ending* (drama), 1966.
————, *Day of Absence* (drama), 1966.
Van Dyke, Henry, *Ladies with the Rachmaninoff Eyes*, 1965.
————, *Blood of Strawberries*, 1968.
Van Peebles, Melvin, *Sweet Sweetback's Baadassss Song* (Scenario), 1971.
Walker, Margaret, *Jubilee*, 1966.
Wideman, John E., *A Glance Away*, 1967.
Young, Al, *Dancing* (poems), 1969.

MODERN AFRICAN LITERATURE

SELECTED JOURNALS

Africa, 10-11 Fetter Lane, London EC4, England.
African Forum, 401 Broadway, New York, N.Y. 10013.
Africa Report, 505 Dupont Circle Building, Washington, D.C. 20036.
Afrique Nouvelle, B.P. 282, Dakar, Senegal.
Black Orpheus, Mbari, P.M.B. 5162, Ibadan, Nigeria.
Bulletin of the Association for African Literature in English, Department of English, Fourah Bay College, Freetown, Sierra Leone.
Busara, Department of English, University College, Nairobi, Kenya.
East Africa Journal, P.O. Box 30492, Nairobi, Kenya.
The Jewel of Africa, University of Gambia, P.O. Box 2379, Lusaka, Gambia.
Journal of Commonwealth Literature, 48 Charles Street, London W1, England.
Journal of New African Literature and the Arts, Box 4392, Stanford University, Palo Alto, Calif. 94305.
New African, 60 Paddington Street, London W1, England.
Nigeria Magazine, The Marina, Lagos, Nigeria.
Okyeame, P.O. Box M15, Accra, Ghana.
Penpoint, Department of English, Makerere University College, Kampala, Uganda.
Presence Africaine, 42 rue Descartes, Paris, France.
Transition, P.O. Box 20026, Kampala, Uganda.

BACKGROUND AND CRITICAL REFERENCES

Abrahams, William E., *The Mind of Africa*, 1962.
Abrash, Barbara, *Black African Literature in English Since 1952: Works and Criticism* (bibliography), 1967.
Beier, Ulli, *Introduction to African Literature*, 1967.*
Blyden, Wilmot E., *African Life and Customs*, 1908.
Bown, Lalag, and Michael Crowder, *First International Congress of Africanists*, 1964.
Brench, A.L., *The Novelists' Inheritance in French Africa*, 1967.*
Cameron, J.M., *Pan-Africanism and Negritude: A Bibliography*, 1964.
Cartey, Wilfred, *Whispers from a Continent*, 1969.

Cook, Mercer, *Five French Negro Authors*, 1943.
————, and Stephen Henderson, *The Militant Black Writer in Africa and the United States*, 1969.
Diop, Sheik Anta, *The Cultural Unity of Negro Africa*, trans. 1962.
East, N.B., *African Theatre*, 1970.
Gleason, Judith I., *This Africa: Novels by West Africans in English and French*, 1969.
Hughes, A.J., *East Africa*, 1969.
Jahn, Janheinz, *Muntu, the New African Culture*, 1961.
————, *Through African Doors*, 1962.
————, *A History of Neo-African Literature*, 1968.*
July, Robert, *The Origins of Modern African Thought*, 1967.
Kesteloot, Lilyan, *Les écrivans noirs de langue française: naissance d' une littérature*, 1963.
Killam, G.D., *The Novels of Chinua Achebe*, 1969.
Laurence, Margaret, *Long Drums and Cannons*, 1969.
Melone, T., *De la Négritude dans la littérature négro-francaise*, 1962.
Moore, Gerald, *Seven African Writers*, 1962.
Mphahlele, Ezekiel, *The African Image*, 1962.
Nicol, Davidson, *Africa: A Subjective View*, 1964.
Nkosi, Lewis, *Home and Exile*, 1965.
Nwoga, Donatus Ibe, *West African Verse*, 1967.
Osei, G.K., *The African, His Antecedents, His Genius, and His Destiny*, 1967.
Pieterse, Como, and Donald Munro (eds.), *Protest and Conflict in African Literature*, 1969.
Ramsaran, John A., *New Approaches to African Literature*, 1965.
Shelton, Austin J., *The African Assertion: A Critical Anthology of African Literature*, 1968.
Taiwo, Oladele, *An Introduction to West African Literature*, 1967.
Tempels, Placide, *Bantu Philosophy*, 1959; 1960.
Wastberg, Per (ed.), *The Writer in Modern Africa: African-Scandinavian Writers' Conference*, Stockholm, 1969.
Wauthier, Claude, *The Literature and Thought of Modern Africa: A Survey*, 1967.*

ANTHOLOGIES
Bassir, Olumbe, *An Anthology of West African Verse*, 1957.
Beier, Ulli, *Black Orpheus*, 1965.
————, *Three Nigerian Plays*, 1967.
Cook, David, *Origin East Africa: A Makerere Anthology*, 1965.
————, and Miles Lee, *Short East African Plays in English*, 1968.
Cartey, Wilfred, *Palaver: Modern African Writings*, 1970.
Dathorne, O.R., and Willfried Feuser, *Africa in Prose*, 1969.
Denny, Neville, *Pan African Short Stories*, 1965.
Drachler, Jacob, *African Heritage*, 1964.
Edwards, Paul, *West African Narrative*, 1963.
————, *Modern African Narrative*, 1966.
Hughes, Langston, *An African Treasury*, 1960.
————, and Christiane Reygnault, *Anthologie africaine et malgache*, 1962.
————, *Poems from Black Africa*, 1963.
Justin, Andree, *Anthologie Africaine*, 1962.
Kesteloot, Lilyan, *Anthologie Négro-Africaine*, 1967.
Komey, Ellis A., and Ezekiel Mphahlele, *Modern African Stories*, 1964.
Litto, Frederick M., *Plays from Black Africa*, 1968.

Moore, Gerald, and Ulli Beier, *Modern Poetry from Africa*, 1963.
Mphahlele, Ezekiel, *African Writing Today*, 1967.
Okpaku, Joseph, *New African Literature and the Arts*, I (1970); II (1971).
Pieterse, Como, *Ten One-Act Plays*, 1968.
Reed, John, and Clive Wake, *A Book of African Verse*, 1964.
Ridout, Ronald, and Eldred Jones, *Adjustments: An Anthology of African and Western Writing*, 1966.
Rive, Richard, *Quartet*, 1963.
————, *Modern African Prose*, 1964.
Rutherfoord, Peggy, *African Voices: An Anthology of Native African Writing*, 1960.
Senghor, Léopold S., *Nouvelle Anthologie de la Poésie Nègre et Malgache*, 1948.
Shore, Herbert L., and Megchelina Shore-Bos, *Come Back, Africa!*, 1968.
Swazy, Henry, *Voices of Ghana: Literary Contributions to the Ghana Broadcasting System, 1955–57*, 1958.
Tibble, Anne, *African English Literature*, 1965.
Whiteley, W.H., *A Selection of African Prose* (2 vols.), 1964.
Young, T. Cullen, *African New Writing: Short Stories by African Writers*, 1947.

WEST AFRICAN LITERATURE
Abruquah, Joseph, *The Catechist*, 1965.
————, *The Torrent*, 1967.
Aidoo, Christina Ama Ata, *The Dilemma of a Ghost* (drama), 1965.
————, *No Sweetness Here* (stories), 1969.
————, *Anowa* (drama), 1970.
Akpan, N.U., *The Wooden Gong*, 1965.
Aluko, T.M., *One Man, One Matchet*, 1965.
————, *One Man, One Wife*, 1967.
————, *Kinsman and Foreman*, 1967.
Amadi, Elechi, *The Concubine*, 1966.
Ananou, David, *Le Fils du Fetiche*, 1955.
Awoonor, Kofi, *This Earth, My Brother . . .* 1971.
Bediako, K.A., *A Husband for Esi Ellua*, 1967.
Beti, Mongo (Alexandre Biyidi), *Le Pauvre Christ de Bomba*, 1965.
————, *Ville Cruelle*, 1955.
————, *Mission Termineé*, 1957; translated by Peter Green as *Mission to Kala*, 1965.
————, *Le roi miraculé*, 1958; translated by Peter Green as *King Lazarus*, 1960.
Brew, Kwesi, *The Shadows of Laughter* (poems), 1968.
Clark, John P., *Poems*, 1962.
————, *America, Their America* (essays), 1964.
Conton, William F., *The African*, 1960.
Dadié, Bernard Bertin, *Afrique* (poems), 1950.
————, *Legendes Africaines* (stories), 1954.
————, *Le Pagne noir* (stories), 1955.
————, *La Ronde des jours* (poems), 1956.
————, *Legendes et poemes*, 1965.
Dei-Anang, Michael F., *Africa Speaks* (poems), 1959.
————, *Ghana Semi-Tones* (poems), 1962.
————, *Two Faces of Africa* (poems), 1965.
Diop, Birago Ismael, *Les contes d'Amadou Koumba* (stories), 1947.
————, *Les nouveaux contes d'Amadou Koumba*, 1958.
Dipoko, Mbella Sonne, *A Few Days and Nights*, 1966.
————, *Because of Women*, 1968

Djoleto, Amu, *The Strange Man*, 1968.
Easmon, R. Sarif, *Dear Parent and Ogre* (drama), 1964.
————, *The New Patriots* (drama), 1965.
————, *The Burnt-Out Marriage*, 1967.
Ijimere, Obotune, *The Imprisonment of Obatala and Other Plays*, 1966 in English adaptation by Ulli Beier.
Kane, Cheik Hamidou, *L'aventure ambigue*, 1961; translated by Katherine Woods as *The Ambiguous Adventure*, 1963.
Konadu, Asare, *Shadow of Wealth*, 1966.
————, *Come Back, Dora!*, 1966.
————, *Night Watchers at Korlebeu*, 1967.
————, *A Woman in Her Prime*, 1967.
————, *Ordained by the Oracle*, 1969.
Munonye, John, *The Only Son*, 1966.
————, *Obi*, 1969.
Nicol, Abioseh, *The Truly Married Woman and Other Stories*, 1965.
————, *Two African Tales*, 1965.
Nwapa, Flora, *Efuru*, 1966.
Nzekwu, Onuora, *Wand of Noble Wood*, 1961.
————, *Blade Among the Boys*, 1962.
————, *Highlife for Lizards*, 1965.
Okara, Gabriel, *The Voice*, 1964.
Okigbo, Christopher, *Heavensgate* (poems), 1962.
Ouologuem, Yambo, *Bound To Violence*, 1971.
————, *Limits and Other Poems*, 1964.
Ousmane, Sembène, *Le docker noir*, 1956.
————, *O pays, mon beau peuple!*, 1957.
————, *Les bouts de bois de Dieu*, 1961.
————, *Voltaïque* (stories), 1962.
————, *L'harmattan*, 1964.
Peters, Lenrie, *The Second Round*, 1966.
————, *Satellites* (poems), 1967.
Sadji, Abdoulaye, *Maïmouna*, 1958.
————, *Tounka, Nouvelle Africaine*, 1965.
Soce, Ousmane (O.S. Diop), *Karim*, 1948.
Tchicaya, U'Tamsi, Felix G., *Le mauvais sang* (poems), 1955.
————, *Feu de brousse* (poems), 1957; translated as *Bush Fire*, 1964.
————, *A triche-coeur* (poems), 1960.
————, *Epitomé* (poems), 1962.
————, *Le ventre* (poems), 1965.
————, *Légendes Africaines* (stories), 1968.
Uzodima, E.C.C., *Our Dead Speak*, 1967.

SOUTHERN AFRICAN LITERATURE
Abrahams, Peter, *Dark Testament* (stories), 1942.
————, *Song of the City*, 1945.
————, *Mine Boy*, 1946.
————, *The Path of Thunder*, 1948.
————, *Wild Conquest*, 1950.
————, *Tell Freedom: Memories of Africa* (autobiographical), 1954–1969.
————, *A Wreath for Udomo*, 1956.
————, *A Night of Their Own*, 1965.
Brutus, Dennis, *Sirens, Knuckles and Boots* (poems), 1963.
————, *Letters to Martha and Other Poems*, 1968.

Jabavu, Noni, *Drawn in Color* (autobiographical), 1960.
————, *The Ochre People* (autobiographical), 1963.
LaGuma, Alex, *A Walk in the Night*, 1962.
————, *And a Threefold Cord*, 1964.
————, *The Stone Country*, 1967.
Luthuli, Albert John, *Let My People Go* (autobiographical), 1962.
Matschikiza, Todd, *Chocolates for My Wife* (autobiographical), 1961.
Modisane, William "Bloke," *Blame Me on History* (autobiographical), 1963.
Mutwa, Credo V., *My People, My Africa* (autobiographical), 1964.
Samkange, Stanlake, *On Trial for My Country*, 1966.

EAST AND CENTRAL AFRICAN LITERATURE
Asalache, Khadambi, *A Calabash of Life*, 1967.
Asare, Bediako, *Rebel*, 1969.
Biebuyck, Daniel (ed.), and Kahombo C. Mateene (trans.), *The Mwindo Epic*, 1969.
Buruga, Joseph, *The Abandoned Hut* (poetry), 1969.
Gatheru, R. Mugo, *Child of Two Worlds: A Kikuyu's Story*, 1964.
Gicaru, Muga, *Land of Sunshine* (autobiographical), 1958.
Honwana, Luis B., *We Killed Mangy-Dog* (stories), 1969.
Itote, Waruhiu, *Mau Mau General* (autobiographical), 1967.
Kachwinge, Aubrey, *No Easy Task*, 1964.
Kayire, Legson, *I Will Try* (autobiographical), 1965.
————, *The Looming Shadow*, 1967.
Kibera, Leonard, and Samuel Kahiga, *Potent Ash* (stories), 1970
Kimenye, Barbara, *Kasalanda* (stories), 1965.
————, *Kasalanla Revisited* (stories), 1966.
Mbiti, John, *M and His Story* (stories), 1954.
Njau, Rebecca, *The Scar* (drama), 1965.
Oculi, Okello, *Orphan* (poetry), 1968.
————, *Prostitute*, 1968.
Ogot, Grace, *The Promised Land*, 1967.
————, *Land Without Thunder* (stories), 1968.
p'Bitek, Okot, *Song of Lawino* (poem), 1966.
————, *Song of Ocol* (poem), 1970.
Palangyo, Peter K., *Dying in the Sun*, 1969.
Rubadiri, David, *No Bride Price*, 1967.
Serumuga, Robert, *Return to the Shadows*, 1969.
Waciuma, Charity, *Daughter of Mumbi*, 1969.

About the Editor

Born and reared in Newport, Rhode Island, William H. Robinson is a veteran of World War II, and an English major graduate of New York University (B.A., 1951), Boston University (M.A., 1957), and Harvard University (Ph.D., 1964). He has lectured on and taught Black American literature for years at both Negro colleges (A & T State University, Greensboro, North Carolina; Howard University) and Northern universities (Harvard University Extension, Boston University, University of Massachusetts at Boston). Having studied with Pulitzer Prize winners Robert Lowell at Boston University and Walter J. Bates at Harvard, he is presently professor in English and Director of Black Studies at Rhode Island College, Providence. He has written for educational radio, stage, and television, published short stories and poems, and is the editor of *Early Black American Poets* (1969), and *Early Black American Prose* (1971).

Index